2

5

6

9

CAPTIONS FOR FRONT AND BACK MONTAGE

1. Von Braun at the podium during ceremonies on 24 February 1970 in downtown Huntsville shortly before his departure for NASA headquarters in Washington, D.C. Between him and his wife Maria stands Harry M. Rhett, Jr., leading businessman and banker.

2. A group of NASA officials observes the 25 May 1965 launch of the Saturn I SA-8 vehicle from Complex 37 at Cape Canaveral, Florida. Pointing at center is Dr. Kurt H. Debus, Kennedy Space Center director. To the right is Dr. Hans Gruene of Kennedy; Dr. Wernher von Braun, director of NASA-Marshall; and (leaning) Dr. Eberhard F. M. Rees. Directly above von Braun is Bob Moser, Kennedy launch director; and above Rees (standing) is Albert Zeiler.

3. Wernher von Braun and Maria von Quistorp marry at Landshut, Bavaria on 1 March 1947. Left to right Albrecht von Quistorp, Maria's brother; Sigismund von Braun, Wernher's brother; Wilhelm Edzard Prince of Innhausen and Knyphausen, Maria's uncle; Theda von Quistorp, Maria's mother; and Emmy and Magnus von Braun, Wernher's parents. *Illustrierte Bunte*/Burda GmbH, Germany/Von Braun Archives.

4. Dr. von Braun and his family gather at the Smithsonian Institution in Washington, D.C., on the occasion of his being awarded the Langley Medal on 4 June 1967. Young Peter holds the distinguished award for his father.

5. Formal photo-portrait of von Braun taken in celebration of his 50th birthday, March 1962. Courtesy Fabian Bachrach/Von Braun Archives.

6. Von Braun at 24 years old, in his Luftwaffe cadet uniform.

7. Maria and Wernher von Braun vacationing in Hawaii, 1959. Courtesy Hawaiian Airlines/Von Braun Archives.

8. Von Braun holds son Peter Constantine, who was born 2 June 1960 in Huntsville, Alabama.

9. The von Braun children as they appeared in 1960. Left to right: Iris Careen, born 1948; Margrit Cecile, born 1952; and Peter Constantine, born 1960.

10. Arthur Fiedler, conductor of the Boston Pops Orchestra, von Braun, and Mrs. Fiedler meet in von Braun's office on 23 March 1962.

11. Walt Disney, left, and von Braun, right, during production of the "Tomorrowland" television series on spaceflight, 1954.

12. In mid-November 1967, von Braun prepares for a dive at Marshall's neutral buoyancy tank.

13. President John F. Kennedy discusses the planned Apollo missions to the Moon with von Braun during a tour of the NASA-Marshall Space Flight Center on 11 September 1962.

14. Dr Martin Schilling, left; Stuhlinger, center; and von Braun, right, sign their U.S. citizenship papers in April 1955.

15. Rudolf Nebel, left, and 18-year-old Wernher von Braun carry Mirak rockets at the flight test field Raketenflugplatz in Berlin-Reinickendorf, 1930.

16. Von Braun relaxes moments after the Saturn V launch vehicle has lofted Apollo 11 and its three-man crew towards the Moon on 16 July 1969, Cape Canaveral, Florida.

17. Colonel Miles Chatfield, chief, Ordnance Guided Missile Laboratories; Army Ballistic Missile Agency commander Major General John B. Medaris; von Braun; Brigadier General Holger Toftoy, commander of Redstone Arsenal; and Colonel John R. Nickerson shortly after the creation of the new agency on 1 February 1956.

18. President Dwight D. Eisenhower confers the President's Award for Distinguished Federal Civilian Service on von Braun, 20 January 1959, accompanied by Secretary of the Army Wilbur Brucker.

A Biographical Memoir

Ernst Stuhlinger

Frederick I. Ordway III

KRIEGER PUBLISHING COMPANY

Malabar, Florida
1996

Original Edition 1994
Reissued 1996 with corrections

Printed and Published by
KRIEGER PUBLISHING COMPANY
KRIEGER DRIVE
MALABAR, FLORIDA   32950

Printed in the United States of America.

Library of Congress Cataloging-In-Publication Data

Stuhlinger, Ernst, 1913-
   Wernher von Braun, crusader for space : a biographical memoir /
Ernst Stuhlinger and Frederick I. Ordway III.
      p.   cm.
   Published simultaneously with Wernher von Braun, crusader for
space : an illustrated memoir.
   Includes index.
   ISBN 0-89464-969-8 (alk. paper)
   1. Von Braun, Wernher, 1912-1977. 2. Rocketry—Biography.
I. Ordway, Frederick Ira, 1927-   . II. Title.
TL781.85.V6S78   1994
621.43′56′092—dc20
[B]
                                                  93-10677
                                                    CIP

10   9   8   7   6   5   4   3   2

To all
who believe in mankind's future
in space

*"Dr. von Braun,
what is the most important
thing a man needs when he
wants to build a spaceship
and travel to the Moon?"*

"The will to do it!"

(von Braun gave this answer to a young space enthusiast after a presentation
on the Saturn-Apollo moon project in the fall of 1969.)

CONTENTS

Titles in quotation marks are verbatim von Braun quotes.

ACKNOWLEDGMENTS

Throughout the fourteen years of preparing and writing this book, the authors enjoyed help from a great number of individuals, institutes, companies, and organizations who were generous in offering their support in the form of discussions, memories, data, pictures, advice, and constructive critique. We wish to express our sincerest thanks for all this help.

The names of many of the individuals who granted us interviews or provided support in other ways are quoted in the text. Others who gave us their help include the following: Otto F. Cerny; David Christensen; Dr. Konrad K. Dannenberg; Frank E. Hall; H. Otto Hirschler; Dr. Helmut Hoelzer; Doris Hunter; Dr. Eduard Igenbergs; David Irving; James A. Michener; Dr. Harry O. Ruppe; Rudolf H. Schlidt; Betty Springge; H. Christoph Stuhlinger; Dr. Tilman Stuhlinger; Georg von Tiesenhausen; Henry M. Williams; John G. Zierdt; Helmut Zoike.

Our heartfelt and very special thanks go to our wives, Irmgard and Maruja, who gave us invaluable help through their encouragement, understanding, patience, writing and word processing assistance, proof reading, and spirited advice.

When the first draft of the manuscript of this book began to take shape and the authors tried to do justice to the unusually active and eventful life of von Braun, the book threatened to reach a length of 1,200 pages. A drastic reduction became necessary with the result that the names and achievements of many of von Braun's co-workers who deserved to be remembered in this book had to be left out. The authors wish to offer their sincere apology to all these unmentioned, but highly deserving members of the greater von Braun team.

Ernst Stuhlinger
Huntsville, Alabama

Frederick I. Ordway III
Arlington, Virginia

FOREWORD

Most of us sometimes dream of the future and what we would like to see happen. Few make such dreams come true. Young Wernher von Braun dreamed of man leaving the Earth and exploring the Moon and planets. In 1928, when he was sixteen, von Braun wrote: *"As soon as the art of [Earth] orbital flight is developed, mankind will quickly proceed to utilize this technical ability for practical applications."*

Throughout his life von Braun never lost this dream. Preparing himself academically, at an early age he was established as an engineer. When he was twenty, he was employed by the German Army as a civilian engineer. His task was to develop the necessary components for ballistic missiles. Simply stated, these components were reliable rocket propulsion, and guidance and control systems within a sound aerodynamic structure. Von Braun recognized that all of these elements were common to eventual achievement of the velocity necessary for spaceflight.

He understood that science and technology could be for both good and evil. In reply to critics, he once philosophized:

"Science, by itself, has no moral dimension. The drug which cures when taken in small doses may kill when taken in excess. The knife in the hands of a skilled surgeon may save a life, but it will kill when thrust just a few inches deeper. The nuclear energies that produce cheap electrical power when harnessed in a reactor may kill when abruptly released in a bomb. Thus, it does not make sense to ask a scientist whether his drug . . . or knife, or his nuclear energy is 'good' or 'bad' for mankind."

Von Braun was patriotic. His credo: *"In times of war, a man has to stand up for his country, whether as a combat soldier or as a scientist or engineer, regardless of whether or not he agrees with the policy his government is pursuing. "*

Despite the fact that during World War II he fully dedicated himself to the development of the long-range rocket as a weapon, he was arrested and imprisoned by the Gestapo, accused of really having spaceflight in mind.

Von Braun was a superb manager. In 1956, he wrote the following factors to be indispensable to guidance of a scientific and technical team:

"Maximum delegation of authority; efficient and continuous system of communications, from top to bottom and bottom to top; loyalty; honesty; justice."

His practice of these managerial techniques was evident in the enthusiasm and loyalty of his team members—in Germany and in the United States.

Over the twenty-six years that I knew von Braun, he occasionally exhibited justifiable pride in the accomplishments of his team, never arrogance. He once said, *"Fred, if our team in Huntsville has any more capability than others, it's because we've had thirteen more years of experience in making mistakes—and learning from most of them."*

Von Braun played a major role in bringing about public understanding of spaceflight. Throughout his life he exhibited the rare skill—in speech and prose—of explaining complex technical subjects in simple understandable terms. In the 1950s, von Braun led a group of experts in writing a series of articles for *Collier's* magazine, detailing the use of Earth satellites and manned flights to the Moon and Mars. Brilliantly illustrated by Chesley Bonestell et al., these articles gripped the imagination of many thousand young—and young minded.

It was during this period that I presented papers by von Braun at several annual international astronautical congresses. At the time, von Braun was working for the U.S. Army on security classified missile programs and was restricted from overseas travel.

Authors Stuhlinger and Ordway had long and close relationships—professional and personal—with von Braun. Ernst Stuhlinger was a senior and key member of the von Braun team in Germany, as well as in the United States, for thirty-three years. The son of a school teacher, Stuhlinger is widely respected, not only for his professional contributions but for his personal qualities as a gentleman. Fred Ordway worked closely with von Braun at Huntsville, Alabama for several years and collaborated with him on numerous books. Ordway is recognized internationally as a historian of rocketry and astronomy. In preparation for this book, he conducted nearly one hundred recorded interviews in the United States and Europe. Stuhlinger and Ordway relate how postwar rocket development of U.S. ballistic missiles paved the way for their use to achieve the first U.S. Earth satellite. This newly achieved plateau of technology, together with political, social, and economic factors that governed the *"race into space,"* culminated in landing men on the Moon.

For some thirty-five years I have known each of the authors—both as professional colleagues and warm friends. We share the feeling of privilege in having had a close association with von Braun, as well as the exhilaration of his accomplishments. Nevertheless, I was surprised—and fascinated—by many new insights into von Braun's life.

In my view, Wernher von Braun was a great man; a man who inspired millions to look to space as an expanding frontier. Future historians may well note this century (or millenium) as significant in that mankind took its first tentative steps into space. In accomplishing these steps to the Moon and beyond, Wernher von Braun was an eminent leader. He not only had a dream, but he made his dream come true for all of us.

A remarkable book about a truly remarkable man.

Frederick C. Durant III
Former president of the American Rocket Society
and the International Astronautical Federation
Chevy Chase, Maryland

PREFACE

"What kind of a person was Wernher von Braun?" That question, asked innumerable times of those who knew him well, set the present book in motion. Our intent was to answer this question.

While our book broadly maintains the historical sequence of events, particular features of von Braun's character, his ways of working and managing, of suggesting, arguing, dreaming, and planning, of seeking and obtaining support for his ideas, of spreading knowledge and enthusiasm for spaceflight, and of just plainly enjoying his life, often take precedence over simple chronology.

We chose this approach because we felt that it was the only way of portraying von Braun so that he would come to life in the imagination of the reader. A particular effort was made to round out our own picture of von Braun by reporting what his contemporaries had to say about him, his friends, co-workers, secretaries, colleagues, superiors, journalists, partners in projects, competitors in programs. Transcripts of interviews conducted for this book would easily fill a substantial volume; the present text contains as many excerpts as space permitted.

In planning the work with the publisher, we jointly decided that our purpose in researching and writing about the life of Wernher von Braun could best be served by the appearance of two volumes. This, the first of the two, would be descriptive and interpretative—the prose memoir, while the other would focus on the visual image—the illustrated memoir. The photographs, many never before published, supplement the written account presented in this volume and we hope will provide a more complete picture of the subject of our labors for more than a decade.

While the central theme in von Braun's life was the development of rockets and spacecraft, we do not dwell on the many technical details implicit in their description. Other books have already done this for us. Rather, we try to answer the simple question: What kind of man was Wernher von Braun? This biographical memoir is the first—and probably the last—written by authors who have been closely and personally associated with the man during a substantial part of his life—Ordway for twenty-five years and Stuhlinger for thirty-four years.

Numerous books in which von Braun, his team, and his work play a major role have been written during the past thirty-five years. Dornberger's book on the V-2 [1] is a splendid account of the program that created the V-2 in Peenemünde. David Irving's book, *The Mare's Nest* [2], with a wealth of documentary material, recounts how the Peenemünde story gradually unfolded for observers on the British Isles. Huzel's book, *Peenemünde to Canaveral* [3], describes in great detail life and work of the rocket people in Peenemünde, and later in the United States.

The book by Bernd Ruland, *Wernher von Braun, Mein Leben für die Raumfahrt* [4], is the result of a few days of interviews with von Braun, and of much study and dedication of an able journalist. Erik Bergaust, professional author and spaceflight enthusiast, wrote his book *Reaching for the Stars* [5] with deep affection and admiration for von Braun. Carsbie C. Adams, space enthusiast and frequent traveling companion of von Braun, gave a rather comprehensive overview of rocketry and spaceflight during the 1950s in his book *Space Flight* [6]. The story of von Braun's life and work was told briefly in a more colloquial style in John C. Goodrum's book *Wernher von Braun, Space Pioneer* [7]. Von Braun biographies were written by Heinz Gartmann [8], Helen B.

Walters [9], and Heather M. David [10]. The most detailed book about von Braun and his co-workers, covering more background studies, a wider span, and more facts than any of the other books, is *The Rocket Team* by F. I. Ordway and M. R. Sharpe [11].

Both of us authors of the present book had known von Braun very intimately. Stuhlinger was drafted into the Peenemünde Rocket Development Center as a young physicist (and Pfc.) early in 1943; twenty-five years later, he had come up through the ranks to be von Braun's chief scientist at the George C. Marshall Space Flight Center in Huntsville, Alabama. Ordway first heard of von Braun in 1947 through the American Rocket Society. The two of them met in 1952; they quickly became close friends. When von Braun left NASA in 1972 to join Fairchild Industries, both of us remained in contact with him until his life came to its end in 1977.

Systematic work on this book began in the late 1970s. A few years later, voices of criticism appeared in the news media, questioning von Braun's real motives behind his work in Peenemünde, and also the means by which he accomplished the development of the Peenemünde rocket.

Were von Braun alive today, he would not shy away from any effort to answer all questions posed to him in a most meticulous and honest way, as he did countless times over several years after the war when he was interrogated by teams from the Armed Forces, the Federal Bureau of Investigation (FBI), the Central Intelligence Agency (CIA), and the Department of Justice. Neither he nor many of his former superiors and co-workers are alive today to stand up and respond to those accusations.

We authors will not try to respond for von Braun. We do try to describe his life and work, his attitudes and reactions, his hopes and frustrations as conscientiously as we can in an attempt to convey a picture as true to life as possible. Many of the questions that have been raised recently will find their answers as von Braun's life story unfolds on the pages of this book.

Biographers writing about contemporaries whom they had known intimately for several decades face a peculiar problem. Many of the innumerable talks and discussions of their subjects that they wish to quote verbatim do not exist in recorded form. They can rely only upon their and other persons' memories, and they must try to reconstruct the words from these memories, using as a guide their close familiarity with their biographees' ways of thinking and talking.

This predicament of biographers is not new. It must have been even worse before the age of tape recorders. Thucydides, the brilliant Greek historian of the fifth century B.C., wrote in the introduction to his *History of the Peloponnesian War*:

". . . Concerning the speeches that . . . were given, I found it impossible, as a listener, to keep the exact words in my memory. Therefore, I had each individual speaker talk in a way that, in my feeling, would reflect the real circumstances as nearly as possible. In doing so, I stuck as closely as I could to the trains of thought expressed by the speaker . . ."

In this book, we could do no better than take the same approach in all quotes for which no printed references exist.

"I sure hope that nobody will ever have the crazy idea of erecting a monument for me. I don't belong on a pedestal. All I tried to do was to help others accomplish what they wanted to do anyway—reach out beyond the limits of our little Earth and travel toward the stars . . ."

Von Braun made this remark to some of his co-workers in 1970.

The present book does not try to erect a monument for him. It is an attempt to answer just one question: *"Wernher von Braun—what kind of man was he?"*

CHAPTER 1

ROCKETS IN WAR AND PEACE

1 PIONEERS OF ROCKETRY

Chinese warriors, we are told [1-1,1-2], left the first records of rocket-assisted lances and arrows in 1232. In the same century, Tartar armies applied rockets when they invaded Poland and Germany, Mongols launched rockets against Baghdad, China, and Japan, and the Moors used rockets in their conquest of Spain. French troops fired rockets against the British in 1429. It seems that all warfaring countries had rockets in their arsenals at those early times.

In 1529, army officer Konrad Haas in Romania proposed two- and three-stage rockets, exhaust nozzles, and fins for stabilization. During the eighteenth century, India developed military rockets and used them as barrage rockets against the British with considerable success. Further technical improvements of military rockets were made from 1800 on by Colonel (later, Sir) William Congreve in England. His rockets with ranges of more than two miles were used in the Napoleonic wars. Copenhagen burnt down after it was hit by 25,000 rockets in 1807. Rockets were launched in the War of 1812, and in numerous other conflicts during the nineteenth century. The *"rockets' red glare"* during the British siege of Fort McHenry near Baltimore in 1814 has been immortalized in the American national anthem. The city of Washington was set on fire by British rockets the same year.

Later in the 1800s, artillery weapons were greatly improved. As the importance of rockets as weapons diminished, ideas of using rockets for spaceflight took shape. Hermann Ganswindt in Germany, Konstantin E. Tsiolkovskii in Russia, Robert H. Goddard in the United States began to develop their thoughts of rocket flight through space before the end of the century; Hermann Oberth in Romania, Robert Esnault-Pelterie in France, Max Valier, Walter Hohmann, Willy Ley and Hermann Noordung in Germany, Guido von Pirquet in Austria, Nikolai Rynin in Russia, G. Edward Pendray in the United States followed. The theoretical basis for rocket flight was developed mostly by Tsiolkovskii (1895), Oberth (1910–1920), and Esnault-Pelterie (1912–1930). In 1925, thirteen-year-old Wernher von Braun in Berlin decided to devote his life's work to the goal of human travel into space. On 16 March 1926, Goddard successfully launched the first liquid-fueled rocket, an event that ushered in the age of modern rockets [1-3].

Societies for rockets and spaceflight sprang up in Germany (1927), the United States (1930), and England (1933). Military planners were slow in showing interest in rockets; World War I had demonstrated the superior capabilities of tanks, airplanes, and modern artillery. The German Army began rocket development work in 1929; in the mid-thirties, Frank Malina, Hsue-shen Tsien, Theodore von Kármán and others initiated a rocket program at the California Institute of Technology. Only few rocket weapons found direct-support field application in World War II: the bazooka by U.S. troops, Katyusha salvo rockets by Soviet troops, and Nebelwerfer by the German Army. All of them were short-range, unguided missiles. The first long-range precision rocket-powered missile, the A-4 (V-2), was developed by the German Army under von Braun's technical direction at Peenemünde. After the war, von Braun and a small number of his Peenemünde co-workers continued their rocket development work in the United States. From 1950 on, the Redstone and Jupiter rockets were built by the U.S. Army; the Atlas, Thor, Titan, and others by the U.S. Air Force; and the Polaris, Poseidon, Trident, and others by the U.S. Navy. In 1960, von Braun's work for the military ended. As a member of the newly formed National Aeronautics and Space Administration, he developed and built the Saturn V launch vehicle that propelled Apollo astronauts on their way to the Moon.

Beginning in 1946, a number of V-2 rockets from Peenemünde were launched at the White Sands Proving Ground in New Mexico under the auspices of the U.S. Army. Instead of a warhead, each carried scientific instruments to explore the upper atmosphere, the magnetosphere, cosmic rays, solar radiations, and other phenomena inaccessible from the ground. This flight program, which extended over a period of six years, formed the beginning of the modern era of scientific space exploration [1-4].

2   MODERN MILITARY ROCKETS

Under the World War I Treaty of Versailles, Germany was not permitted to develop artillery weapons of the conventional types. Charged with the duty of providing a defense capability for the country, the German Army decided in 1929 to revive the much-neglected rocket as a substitute for heavy artillery. Colonel (later Artillery General) Dr. Karl Becker, a highly talented and knowledgeable ballistic engineer, and a young captain, Walter Dornberger (later Major General), began rocket development at that time. Details of this program, and of the circumstances that brought young von Braun aboard and eventually led to the rocket development center at Peenemünde, are told in Chapters 2 and 3.

The V-2 rocket, developed between 1937 and 1945, represented a decisive step in the evolution of rocketry. Named A-4 (Aggregat #4) by its developers, it carried a payload of one metric ton (2,200 pounds) over a range of about 300 km (210 miles). Against a solid belief held by many experts worldwide, it demonstrated that large rockets can be built and flown that are not only equivalent, but superior to cannons as far as their combined performance in range, payload, and target accuracy is concerned. Even the rockets' reliability promised to become satisfactory.

After World War II, the Western Allies reduced their armies; they were reluctant to maintain strong military postures during the immediate postwar years. The outbreak of the Korean War in 1950 showed drastically the need to be militarily prepared for armed conflict. Von Braun in 1950 received the assignment from Army Ordnance to develop a rocket with a range of 200 miles (320 km) and a payload capacity of 8,000 pounds (3,200 kg). Three years later, that missile, the Redstone, was ready for flight testing. It was deployed as a defense weapon in European countries in 1958; on 31 January of that year, a modified Redstone rocket, designated Juno I, launched America's first satellite, Explorer 1. Three years later, another Redstone rocket took the first American astronaut, Alan B. Shepard, through a ballistic trajectory in a Mercury capsule.

That development marked the real beginning of the age of the long-range military rocket in the United States. The U.S. Army proceeded to develop further missiles, and so did the U.S. Air Force and the U.S. Navy. As these projects evolved, von Braun intensified his campaign for spaceflight, giving speeches and publishing papers on space rockets, satellites, orbiting stations, and travel to the Moon and Mars. He terminated his work on military rockets in 1960 when he and most of his team members were transferred from Army Ordnance to the newly founded National Aeronautics and Space Administration (NASA). With that transfer, the Saturn rocket program became official, about two years after the von Braun group had begun receiving funds from the Advanced Research Projects Agency (ARPA) to start the development of a rocket capable of launching astronauts on a round trip to the Moon.

Ever since the United States, a few years after the end of World War II, had begun a systematic effort to build powerful precision rockets, two parallel programs existed: a military program to develop weapons, and a civilian program to explore the upper atmosphere and outer space. President Dwight D. Eisenhower was determined to keep the two programs separate, although they were to support each other occasionally. Several civilian rockets were developed and used for programs of scientific exploration, such as Aerobee, Viking, Vanguard, Scout, and, later, the great Saturn family, but many scientific payloads were launched with military rockets, among them Redstone, Jupiter, Atlas, Thor, and Titan. Impressive discoveries were made by military rockets, such as the ultraviolet spectrum of the Sun, particle radiations and X rays from the Sun, the Earth's magnetosphere, and the Van Allen radiation belts. Pioneer, Ranger, and Surveyor probes to the Moon, the Mars landers Vikings 1 and 2, and the Voyager spacecraft to the planets Jupiter, Saturn, Uranus, and Neptune were launched with modified military missiles. More recently, the separation between civilian and military uses of launch vehicles has become increasingly difficult, as exemplified by the space shuttle used for both civilian and military payloads. No distinction between a *"civilian"* and *"military"* rocket or space project was ever made in the former Soviet Union.

3   WERNHER VON BRAUN BETWEEN SPACESHIPS AND WEAPONS OF WAR

Rockets for war and peace—the history of rocketry, particularly in this century, shows how intimately civilian and military projects can be intertwined. Rockets for most of the peaceful launches during the past half century would certainly not have existed if rockets had not been developed for military purposes. This is a very tragic fact indeed, a human dilemma that confronts not only those who are working on the development of rockets. There has scarcely been any great endeavor in the course of human evolution that was free from this deep-seated problem.

Von Braun's own work and life, on a compressed scale, reflect these two sides of rocket history. He began with the desire to travel to the Moon and to Mars, then worked on a military rocket at Peenemünde, then proposed to build rockets for space exploration and manned travel to the Moon and Mars, then developed guided missiles for the American Army, then launched the free world's first satellite, then brought his military work to an end, then built the Saturn rocket for the voyage to the Moon, then helped develop the space shuttle, then promoted and developed civilian uses of Earth satellites. He frequently talked about these two aspects of rockets, the brilliant tool for exploration and for human benefits on one side, and the deadly weapon on the other. This thought must have occupied his mind again and again. *"It is a fundamental and very tragic problem,"* he sometimes said, *"that human beings may never be able to solve. We have to learn to live with it."*

Celebrating the fiftieth anniversary of the first International Airshow in 1959, the city of Frankfurt on Main invited von Braun to give a keynote address with the title *"The Beginning of Space Flight"* [1-5]. Von Braun felt honored and happy by this invitation, but he began his speech by reminding his audience of the haunting dilemma into which almost any kind of creative work can lead: The same machine that can bring uncounted benefits to mankind may also be used for destruction and violent death.

While this decisive breakthrough toward space travel may give all spaceflight enthusiasts proud and happy feelings, he said, *"we must not overlook the depressing, although obvious fact that the same modern rockets that have opened the doors to the scientific exploration of space can also be equipped with atomic warheads and used as military weapons of horribly destructive power."*

Michelangelo, von Braun said, faced the same tragic conflict in 1529 when, at times of war and crises, Pope Clement VII ordered him to interrupt his artistic work and devote his talent to the design of fortresses and weapons of war. It is the same conflict that confronts the airplane designer when his beloved brainchild is used as a bomb carrier that causes destruction and death, and it is the same awesome conflict that haunts the nuclear physicist who appreciates capabilities of controlled energy-producing nuclear reactors for the benefit of mankind, but who also knows that with little modification the same nuclear chain reaction can be made to work as an all-destructive atomic explosion.

"There are simply no valid rules," von Braun told his audience, *"that can guide our decisions in this heartbreaking conflict which is a bitter and tragic reality for all those who are entangled in such situations,"* and he noted that even religious leaders, to whom we look up in great reverence when we search for guidelines in our ethical conduct, have never attempted to tell the engineers and scientists which activities in the wide fields of scientific-technical progress are permitted, and which areas must remain off limits because of the possibility of military misuse.

Indeed, where should such guidelines begin, where should they end? *"Should Dr. Einstein,"* von Braun asked, *"when he wrote down his famous formula for the relation between matter and energy, have dropped his pencil in despair because he had the vision of the release of unthinkably large amounts of atomic energy? Should Otto Lilienthal have discontinued his heroic glider flights because the possibility of a military misuse of the still unborn motorized airplane dawned on him? And should we rocket builders of today stop our efforts to open the universe to human exploration because rockets, just like airplanes, can be used also for military purposes?"* The most serious of these questions may be this: Can any nation allow its weapons to become obsolete as long as there is no guarantee that all the efforts of others to develop more modern and more destructive weapons will also be terminated?

"It is just unfair to ask of us scientists and engineers such questions to which even the wisest statesmen and church leaders do not find answers," von Braun said.

He ended his speech with a spark of hope: *"When all these superweapons of recent years, long-range bombers, atom bombs, and intercontinental rockets, have finally led to the obsolescence and abolishment of total war, then this terribly inhuman moral burden will be taken off the shoulders of the men and women who are working today in those areas which may prove to be the most promising for the welfare of mankind: Peaceful uses of atomic energy, and extension of human activities to our neighbor worlds in space . . ."*

Von Braun began building rockets when he was fourteen years old. At eighteen, he became an assistant to rocket pioneer Hermann Oberth in Berlin; at about the same time, he joined a group of young rocket enthusiasts in the Verein für Raumschiffahrt (Society for Space Travel). In 1932, when he was twenty, the German Army hired him for a program to develop rockets for defense, first in Kummersdorf near Berlin, and from 1937 on in Peenemünde.

Hitler first ignored, then ridiculed the Army's rocket development efforts. Only in

1943, long after the German Air Force had lost the Battle of Britain, did Hitler turn to the Peenemünde rocket as a last resort. Propaganda Minister Joseph Goebbels, trying to bolster the sagging spirits everywhere, dubbed the A-4 the *"Vergeltungswaffe 2"* (vengeance 2 weapon) or V-2. The buzz bomb, Fi-103, under development by the Air Force, was named V-1. General Dornberger, military commander of Peenemünde, and von Braun, its technical director, did not wish to release the V-2 for military deployment, with the truthful argument that more tests and improvements would be necessary before it could be deployed as a weapon. Subsequently, both men were accused by the SS of *"not sufficiently supporting the war effort."* On Reichsführer SS Heinrich Himmler's orders, Dornberger's authority was curtailed; von Braun and two of his associates were put in jail in Stettin. Reichsminister Albert Speer's personal intervention with Hitler resulted in von Braun's release after two weeks of imprisonment, but the SS assumed increasing control over V-2 production and deployment. SS General Hans Kammler was charged with this assignment in 1944, and Himmler assumed command over all V-weapons in the same year; V-2 rockets fell on Paris and London for the first time on 8 September 1944.

Against von Braun's fervent hope that this would not happen, German military forces launched more than thirteen hundred V-2s at targets in England, and more than sixteen hundred V-2s into Belgium and France, between September 1944 and March 1945. Their total effect with respect to damage and casualties, as horrible as it was, remained far behind the effect of aircraft bombings on both sides. All the V-2s together delivered less than 3,000 tons of explosives over France, England, and Belgium; but in single major bomber attacks, up to 10,000 tons of bombs were dropped within a few hours, and air raids went on for years. However, some people see in the V-2 bombardments, and not in the airplane raids, the most devastating horror of World War II. For them, that horror has become synonymous with just one person: von Braun.

How did von Braun's peers in other countries, and other persons in high positions, think of this conflict between developing rockets for spaceflight and building missiles for war which overshadowed von Braun's professional life?

Leonard J. Carter, one of the most active promoters of rockets and spaceflight in Great Britain, and executive secretary of the prestigious British Interplanetary Society (BIS) in London, recalls the circumstances surrounding the Society's invitation to von Braun to become an honorary member during the late 1940s. *"We did want to honor those who had contributed substantially to astronautics over the past decades, mainly the prewar period,"* he said in an interview in 1985 [1-6]. *"We spent some time discussing the different people who had made contributions. . . . and the name of von Braun, of course, came up head and shoulders above anyone else at that time."* However, this was an extremely sensitive area for the British in view of the V-2 rockets that had been used against London. *"In fact, von Braun himself was very, very conscious of this,"* Carter said. *"Anyway,"* he continued, *"the members . . . recognized that almost anything anyone does can be used for good or for evil, and in the case of von Braun, he was engaged in rocketry at the Verein für Raumschiffahrt (VfR) before the military became involved . . . in any event, many of us had been involved with weapons during the war just as he had—including some of our own people whom we were about to elect to honorary fellowship."*

The Council members overcame the emotion of the moment and asked that von Braun become an honorary fellow. *"He answered very graciously—I think he was very touched . . . Up to his death, he remained very sensitive on the issue . . . Leslie Shepherd and I went over to Cape Canaveral . . . to make a presentation to the Mercury Seven . . . Dr. von Braun went out of his way to receive us and show us around the installations . . ."*

There is yet another, quite different aspect to the military use of von Braun's rocket that found its expression during a visit of British rocket experts at NASA's George C. Marshall Space Flight Center in Huntsville during the 1960s. Von Braun related the story to his co-workers: *"Something really strange happened to me at the end of our presentation yesterday. After we had shown and described to them our Saturn project, they praised our technical work, and they were particularly appreciative of our very open discussions. When they were ready to depart, one of the visitors, a colonel, came to me and said: 'Dr. von Braun, I want to thank you most sincerely, not only for your splendid hospitality today, but for all the work you did in Peenemünde. This may sound strange to you, but if you had not concentrated thousands and thousands of expert engineers and scientists on your rocket project, these people would have built fighter planes and bombers, and the losses on both sides would have been far greater. Much more of the British Isles would have been destroyed, and, who knows, an atom bomb may even have been dropped on Germany. We really want to thank you!'"*

Winston Churchill expressed the same thought more tersely [1-7]: *"It was fortunate that the Germans devoted many of their efforts to rockets and not to bombers . . ."*

From the American perspective, the question of von Braun's V-2 project looks a little different. The United States was under no threat of a V-2 bombardment, as some technically uninformed people feared when they heard of paper studies for the A-10, a long-range, winged version of the V-2 that were made in Peenemünde toward the end of the war. Actually, these advanced planning studies were very futuristic; they concerned the possibility of intercontinental mail service by rockets, and also the return of future space vehicles by winged descent through the atmosphere. True, the A-10 might have been able to cover a range of about 8,000 kilometers (5,000 miles), but as a low-velocity, low-altitude glider, with a payload of less than 100 kg (220 pounds), and a target accuracy counting in the tens of kilometers (or miles), that vehicle would never have made an effective weapon. The fear that it would be capable of destroying New York was absurd in the extreme. On the other hand, regardless of an immediate threat to the homeland, America was involved in a world war, and von Braun stood and worked on the other side.

After the war in Europe had ended, the United States Government, mostly on the advice of Colonel (later Major General) Holger N. Toftoy, invited von Braun and some of his co-workers to come to America and to continue rocket development work under Army contract. For some Americans, von Braun's previous connection with military rockets made him unacceptable for life and work in the United States. Others took a more sober attitude. President Eisenhower was very definite in expressing his view. Dr. T. Keith Glennan, NASA's first administrator (1958-60) who worked very closely with the president while he established and organized the American space program, was asked during an interview in 1986 [1-8] whether there was ever any reservation in President Eisenhower's mind about having von Braun play such a prominent part in the country's missile and space program. *"No, none at all. The subject even never came up,"* was Glennan's answer.

Lieutenant General Bernard A. Schriever, who organized and masterminded the U.S. Air Force development of intermediate and intercontinental range ballistic missiles in the United States during the 1950s, and subsequently became commander of the Air Force Systems Command, was asked during an interview in 1988 [1-9] whether the idea of von Braun's wartime background disturbed him in working with von Braun. *"No, not at all,"* he replied. *"Being a German myself and having come from Germany under different circumstances, it didn't bother me because I figured that there was the war, and their military and scientific communities were doing exactly the same thing we were doing: trying to win the war. Now the fact that they had a s.o.b. like Hitler does not allow one to expect their people not to follow their government leadership. There was some dissension, as you know, within their armed forces; but the Germans are highly patriotic . . . Von Braun and I got together a number of times, formally and informally. Our meetings were usually associated with activities at the Cape or on the West Coast, or at some banquets . . . We had nothing but the best relationship."*

For von Braun, developing spaceships or Earth weapons was far more than a short question. It plagued him as an unsolved, and, in fact, unsolvable problem that never loosened its relentless grip on his conscious ever since he came to realize that his rocket may not be used for defense, as it had been conceived, but as a missile in a war of aggression that his own government had begun to wage.

He wanted to develop rockets for space exploration. In 1932, the desire of his country's army to be prepared for defense offered the financial means for this development. The following year, Hitler began to establish his dictatorship. At first, the Peenemünde people were left alone. Ten years later, against von Braun's will, and against his efforts and influence, his rocket was turned into a weapon of aggression. Could he have prevented this flow of events? Should he have totally desisted from developing rockets? Should he have laid down his hands in 1933? Withdrawing in 1943 would not have taken the V-2 out of the hands of the military. If he had never started building rocket motors back in 1931, how much of the cataclysm of the 1940s would have been avoided? What should he have done differently? There were questions without end . . .

Von Braun knew very well that others, in fact all of those who are driven by a creative spirit to develop new ideas in science and technology, sooner or later find themselves confronted with the same tragic dilemma. They come to a crossroad, but this crossroad does not leave room for a wilful choice—it heads off with irresistible force only in one fateful direction. Edward Teller, the nuclear physicist, remarked [1-10]: *"If a development is possible, it is out of our powers to prevent it."*

For Albert Einstein, Hiroshima and Nagasaki must have been a rude awakening. He vocally joined those scientists who wished that America had never dropped those atom bombs. However, he offered no guidance to those scientists who find themselves confronted with the dilemma of either working for weapons, or resisting the *"call of duty."* His own vacillating attitude during the war years reflects the contradicting convictions into which this dichotomy can lead. His only answer to the question what scientists should do in such a situation was the vague recommendation [1-11]: *"Frankly, I can only see the revolutionary way of non-cooperation in the sense of Gandhi's. Every intellectual . . . must be prepared for jail and economic ruin, in short, for the sacrifices of his personal welfare in the interests of the cultural welfare of his country . . ."*

When Einstein gave this advice, he may have overlooked a deeply human problem. Most intellectuals have families; could, and should they make the decision for economic ruin also for their wives and children, particularly under circumstances when their economic ruin would be certain, but when any tangible benefits for their country, or for mankind in general, accruing from their and their families' sacrifices would be extremely uncertain?

Should, and could the advice not to indulge in any work with potential military applications be given to all those who help build airplanes, helicopters, radar equipment, communication systems, high resolution telescopes, satellites for Earth observation, even telephones, automobiles, and railroads? What could be the criterion for an invention or a technological development that may lead—or will never lead—to military applications?

Two gigantic weapon systems came to life during World War II, the long-range rocket in Peenemünde, and the atom bomb in Los Alamos. After hostilities had subsided, the two converged into a superweapon, the intercontinental ballistic missile with a nuclear warhead. In the shadow of its threat, a period of solid peace between the great powers unfolded which has lasted now for almost half a century. During that time, the atomic nucleus became an impressive source of energy for peaceful purposes with a potential whose limits are even not yet in sight, and the powerful precision rocket has truly opened the doors to the universe for human exploration.

CHAPTER 2

BEGINNINGS

1   LIFE WITH FATHER AND MOTHER

Von Braun's family tree can be traced back to the year 1285. His ancestors lived in Silesia, an eastern province of Germany along the upper portion of the Oder river. At the end of World War II, in 1945, this land became a part of Poland. Among von Braun's forefathers were knights, landowners, governors, jurists, diplomats, generals, even rectors of religious schools, but no engineers or scientists.

Fortunately, Wernher did not have to pay for his abundance of technical talent with a lack of those abilities in which at least some of his forebears must have excelled. Again and again, he would impress colleagues and superiors alike by his diplomatic skill, by his adherence to very clean and orderly administrative procedures, by his deep-rooted understanding of military matters, by his fervent belief in professional honesty, and by his genuine love for the fine arts, particularly music and poetry.

Wernher's father, Baron Magnus von Braun, studied law and economics and chose the career of a government administrator. From the beginning to the end of his professional career, he always served in high-ranking positions, first as Landrat (approximately equivalent to a county commissioner) in the city of Wirsitz in Posen; then, during World War I, in several different positions in the German government in Berlin. After the war, he remained a member of the government of the new republic, occupying high positions in the ministries of economy and finance. Reichskanzler von Papen and then Reichskanzler Schleicher appointed him Reichsminister for Agriculture and Food Administration. When Hitler came to power in 1933, Magnus von Braun resigned from government service and retired to his estate in Silesia.

Fourteen years later, in 1947, Baron von Braun and his wife traveled to the United States to join their two sons, Wernher and Magnus, in Fort Bliss, Texas. They remained in the States for six and one half years, first in Texas, and then, from the summer of 1950 until 1953, in Huntsville, Alabama. The couple returned to Germany after father von Braun's government pension had been reactivated. The elder von Brauns wholeheartedly enjoyed their time in America. Baron von Braun even found there the leisure and inspiration to write his memoirs under the title *Von Ostpreussen bis Texas* (From East Prussia to Texas), a fascinating book about his unusually active life in the German government from 1902 to the end of the Weimar Republic in 1933, and then as a private citizen from 1933 until 1954 [2-1].

The book also provides a stirring insight into the political history of Germany before, during, and after World War I when the country first was transformed from a Kaiserreich into a democracy, and then into a ruthless dictatorship. It reveals the deep respect of its author for the stabilizing elements of society—tradition, duty, responsibility, sincerity, honesty. *"There was no bribery in the Administration,"* Baron von Braun writes of the times when he was a government official. *"There was no corruption."* Officials guilty of corruption *"not only would have been confronted with the criminal prosecutor, but with far stricter judges: social conscience, and society. Such persons would have found closed doors everywhere. The only way out would have been suicide or emigration."*

Asked about his early recollections of his son Wernher, the father answered with a twinkling in his eyes: *"What I remember most vividly from the years of his childhood is the absolute futility of all my attempts to apply a bit of parental guidance to him. His growth rate was exorbitant, and I often thought that I should channel his outbursts of activity toward the more civil goals that were the accepted standards of society. Determination, fatherly strictness, diplomacy—nothing worked. Any attempt to admonish him, or to convince him of the inappropriateness of a certain action, ran off not only like a drop of water, but like a drop of mercury, without leaving the faintest trace. I soon gave up—a reaction that really ran against my grain—and resigned myself to watching him grow, and to quietly paying the bills for broken windows, destroyed flower gardens, and other telltales that his early rocket experiments had left in the homes and yards of our neighbors. Looking back now over his life and mine, I am mighty glad that I took that stance; it was one of the best things I did in my life. As for his astounding talent for science and engineering, I can only play completely innocent. He certainly did not inherit this from me. I believe that he really got this from his mother who possessed an exceptional accumulation of talents. In fact, I am convinced that my sons had the best mother they could ever have wished to have."*

To those who knew Wernher's mother, Baroness Emmy von Braun, it was obvious that she must have been the source of a good portion of his innate gift for science and technology. However, her influence was by no means limited to the remarkable arrangement of his genes. Throughout Wernher's formative years, she was an inexhaustible wellspring of encouragement and stimulation, of straightforward knowledge, and of wise counsel.

Baroness von Braun, born von Quistorp, was a most impressive woman in many respects. She was the perfect *"grand lady"* with the unmistakable hallmark of a long line of aristocratic ancestors, but she had a genuine warmth of heart, a human immediacy that made everybody feel comfortable whose path crossed hers. She had a large household with many servants during the prewar years in Germany, but if one of them fell ill, she personally cared for her like a mother. Speaking six languages, she was at home in the most distinguished circles of society; but she conversed with equal ease and human interest with her gardener or coachman. Her great love of nature extended from flowers and animals all the way to the stars. In fact, she was an amateur ornithologist as well as an amateur astronomer.

Wernher was confirmed into the Lutheran Church at the age of thirteen. Confirmation in Germany is always a very festive event when the young boys and girls receive dignified presents from their parents, relatives, and friends. Wernher's mother, very typically, gave her son an astronomical telescope. *"This was a hit far beyond our expectations,"* his mother remembered in 1948. As von Braun would often remark in later years, this gift provided the spark that ignited an explosion in his course of life: it aroused in him a burning interest in our neighbors in space, particularly in the Moon and the planet Mars. It also started him dreaming of one day building machines that would enable man to leave the Earth and travel to other celestial bodies.

Baroness von Braun not only opened the gates to the world of science for Wernher, she also taught him to play piano. Teacher and student must have done quite well; in the early 1920s, when Wernher lived in Berlin with his parents, he was accepted for piano lessons by the great composer Paul Hindemith (1895–1963). Wernher even tried his hand at composing. At the age of fifteen, he wrote several short pieces for piano.

When Wernher transferred to the Hermann Lietz boarding school at Ettersburg Castle near Weimar in 1925, he started taking cello lessons. Soon afterwards, he became a member of the school's student orchestra. A life that was so full of activity as von Braun's certainly did not leave much time for practicing a musical instrument, and yet, he enjoyed making music so much that he occasionally played in a quartet during the prewar years in Peenemünde. His cello was accompanied by Rudolf Hermann's and Heinrich Ramm's violins, and by Gerhard Reisig's viola, when the four of them played works by Mozart, Haydn, and Schubert.

Many years later, von Braun visited the Mormon Tabernacle in Salt Lake City and admired the world-famous organ. When the organist learned of von Braun's great love of music, he invited him to play the precious instrument. Promptly, von Braun sat down and played "A Mighty Fortress Is Our God."

Wernher's relationship with his mother had a degree of intimacy, of human depth and warmheartedness that is rarely found. He might have said of her the same words that his father wrote about his own mother: *"My mother, in her warm-hearted and untiring love of all humans and all animals, and in her lively interest in almost everything, was for us children simply the center of the whole world."*

Long after Wernher had outgrown his childhood years, Baroness von Braun still happily remembered those times in Wirsitz and Berlin. *"It was exciting to have Wernher as a child,"* she would say. *"He was like a dry sponge, soaking up every bit of knowledge as eagerly as he could. There was no end to the questions he asked; he really could wear you out quickly!*

"I never succeeded in being cross with him," she continued. *"Whenever I tried to, he would put on his most cherubian smile and talk about something else. He had no problem learning good manners, and he usually practiced them. When he did not, it was just a brief spell of naughtiness, or simply his own way of expressing an exuberant joy of life.*

"Wernher has been an extremely active person from his early childhood on. There was always something that fully occupied his mind. He did much reading, but he also enjoyed greatly to be with friends. His inclination toward engineering and physics found its expression in an endless production line of vehicles, some small and powered by old clockworks, others larger and driven by rockets, often to the horror of our neighbors and to the dismay of his father who had to pay for the damaged flower beds and windows."

One of von Braun's young friends during the Berlin years was Rolf Engel, who in later years was to gain fame in his own right as a rocket expert and spaceflight pioneer. He reminisced about his first encounter with von Braun during an interview in 1986 [2-2]. *"The Verein für Raumschiffahrt (VfR) had a meeting in Berlin,"* he said. *"This must have been in 1928. Willy Ley was there, Max Valier, Johannes Winkler, all the people who at that time were concerned with rocketry, about twenty of them. And there were two sixteen-year-old schoolboys present, the one was me and the other Wernher . . . Johannes Winkler had sent us letters of invitation, we were both members of the VfR . . .*

"Wernher sometimes invited me to his home where we talked about rocket development, which at that time was very, very primitive . . . Later, in 1930, there was the test firing of Oberth's Kegeldüse [conical rocket motor] at the Reichsanstalt [an organization similar to the National Institute of Standards and Technology, formerly the National Bureau of Standards, in the U.S.]. Klaus Riedel and Rudolf Nebel made the preparation for the firings. Wernher and I made the electric connections and all that, and, as it sometimes happens, the test was good . . . [Chapter 2-4].

"We used to call Wernher 'sunny boy' . . . he was very good at mathematics and

physics, much more than the rest of us . . . I remember when his father became Minister of Agriculture . . . I was invited over by Wernher, and it was a terrific situation . . . there was a rule that every day the whole family spoke another language, French, Italian, English, Spanish, I think even Portuguese . . . I knew just a little French, and I always felt a little bit lost in the family . . . Wernher and I would go to his room, and we would sit on the floor and he would develop formulae of thermodynamics, combustion, and so on. I really learned thermodynamics from Wernher . . . He was fascinated with rocketry as the means of realizing spaceflight. I must say that Wernher was always very advanced in his education. I learned a lot from him . . ."

2   FASCINATION WITH ASTRONOMY

At the age of sixteen, young Wernher expressed his growing fascination with astronomy by composing an essay. Calling it *"Aus der Geschichte der Astronomie"* (Glimpses at the History of Astronomy), he covered a variety of topics of interest to him. His treatise reflects the enthusiasm, and also the insatiable quest for knowledge with which von Braun's youthful mind stormed into the fascinating world of astronomy, a world in which he would feel at home throughout his life.

The paper begins in a poetic vein: *"Camille Flammarion [1842–1925], the greatest of all French astronomers, once said: 'Astronomy is as old as mankind.' And he is right. Shouldn't even the most primitive aborigines, still devoid of any cultural inclinations, have raised their yearning eyes toward the stars which every night adorned the celestial dome above their heads? Shouldn't they have wondered why every winter is being followed by a summer, every night by a day? Shouldn't they have been deeply impressed when, during a total solar eclipse, the light of the sun suddenly darkened in the middle of the day, when flaming clouds protruded from behind the black disk that normally was the impeccably bright queen of the day, and when the stars began to blossom out in full splendor all over the firmament until, a few minutes later, the glaring light of the sun returned, and everything was again as before?"*

Von Braun then continues in a sober, down-to-Earth style. His essay illustrates some of his characteristic traits, even at that young age: His great love for astronomy and, in general, for natural sciences; his desire to understand scientific detail; his admirable skill in explaining scientific and technical facts; his great care in judging observations, even if they are made by experts; his astounding knowledge; and, last not least, his tenacious desire for further exploration.

After a brief recapitulation of the history of astronomy, he describes some of the astronomers' basic tools, such as spectroscopy, and the Doppler effect. Then, he talks about the planets, with particular emphasis on Mars. Percival Lowell's claim that the 'canali' on Mars, discovered by V. G. Schiaparelli, are artificial canals built by intelligent beings, provoked definite doubts in the mind of the young writer.

"This would mean," von Braun wrote after some theorizing about geological conditions on Mars, *"that in springtime, when the polar caps are melting, enormous masses of meltwater are flooding the lower portions of the land. Under this cosmic coercion, those of the intelligent beings who live in these areas had to resort to a remedy which, in its technical concept, would far exceed all technical accomplishments on this Earth . . ."*

At this point, the youthful essay ends abruptly. The reason is not known. Wernher's mind must have been full of ideas about Mars, realistic ones as well as dreams. After all, Mars, which he once called *"the most popular of all planets,"* became his personal favorite at the time of his first acquaintance with celestial objects. And it remained so to the very end of his life.

Von Braun may have terminated his essay simply because he became thoroughly engulfed in a real-life astronomy project that left no room for literary work. At the time when he wrote about astronomy, he was a student at the Hermann Lietz boarding school on the island of Spiekeroog in the North Sea. He had transferred to that school in the fall of 1928 after graduating from the Ettersburg school which he had attended from 1925 until early 1928.

At the Spiekeroog school, he persuaded his principal to buy a 5-inch refractor telescope. Wernher organized an *"Observatory Construction Team,"* and the sixteen-year-old boys built a complete observatory in their spare time, working as earth diggers, bricklayers, and carpenters. This was probably the first on von Braun's impressive list of projects. Each of them began with a dream that soon would evolve into a realistic plan. Then, his uncanny talent to find wealthy sponsors would come into play, together with an almost magical ability to form and lead a team. The end product of most of his projects would be complete success.

Some of those who try to judge von Braun's accomplishments say that he was just unbelievably lucky. His own view on this point was quite sober. In the middle of piles of working papers on his desk, there was a little card on which he had written the words: *"Luck is what happens when preparedness meets opportunity."*

Twenty-five years after the construction of the astronomical observatory at the boarding school on Spiekeroog Island, von Braun spearheaded another amateur observatory project. At that time, in 1953, he was technical director of the large Guided Missile Development Group at Redstone Arsenal in Huntsville, Alabama. One day, sixteen-year-old Sammy Pruitt and some of his high school friends asked him whether he could give them a few words of wisdom on how to start a local astronomical society.

Von Braun happily agreed and attended the next 'organization' meeting of the boys, together with some of their fathers who were von Braun's co-workers. The youngsters eagerly proceeded according to Robert's Rules of Order, naming a recording secretary, a parliamentarian, a historian, a membership chairman, a finance committee, a vice president, and finally a president. At that time, von Braun's patience had run out. *"My dear young friends,"* he said, *"didn't you say that you wanted to start an astronomy club? All these fine things you are talking about here will come on their own good time. What you need most of all, right at the beginning, is a telescope. I happen to know a chap in California who grinds and collects mirrors; I'll call him and ask whether he can spare one of them and ship it to us for an affordable price. Then we need money. I donate 100 dollars. How much do you give?"* he asked one after the other of the fathers and the colleagues. After about five minutes, he had pledges for 800 dollars.

"Now," he continued, *"we need an observatory building, something with a turn-able dome. Who would be able to build that?"*—*"The best man for this job would be Wilhelm,"* one of the colleagues said, referring to Wilhelm Angele, one of von Braun's guidance and control engineers, and an accomplished expert for all kinds of instruments, machinery, and special buildings. Von Braun called him by phone. It was late in the evening, and Angele was already asleep; his wife answered the phone. *"I have to talk to him,"* von Braun said, *"please let me talk to him."* And then: *"We need you. You should build for us an observatory with a turnable dome for a big telescope. Will you do it?"* *"Yes,"* a very sleepy voice replied. *"Good; put on your shirt and pants, and come right over."*

Von Braun returned to the table. *"Now, we need more money and building materials. Ernst, will you join me next Saturday for a fund-raising campaign among the wealthy business people in Huntsville?"* Stuhlinger agreed, of course. In the meantime, Angele had arrived. When he saw what kind of a project was in the making, all his sleepiness disappeared. Von Braun's spark ignited a fire in him for observatory buildings and telescopes and astronomy which was still burning thirty-five years later! He started planning and designing right away. On Saturday, von Braun and Stuhlinger went on their fund-raising spree; after two hours, they had $3,000 in cash, and more than $8,000 worth of cinder blocks, concrete, lumber, nails, paint, screws, plasterboard, electric wire, switches . . .

Then Stuhlinger rented a little Piper airplane and, together with his colleague and friend Theodor (Ted) Paludan, flew over the mountains around Huntsville in search of a suitable place for the observatory, close to an access road, but far away from buildings and from city lights. They found a proper location on Monte Sano, in a remote corner of the Monte Sano State Park. The Alabama State Park Administration gave the *"Rocket City Astronomical Association"* a 25-year lease on a 13.5-acre tract at the north end of Monte Sano for the sum of $1, renewable at the group's option.

Club members cut several hundred trees, leveled the terrain at a suitable place within the area, and started digging ditches for the sewage system and the foundations. Contractors poured the concrete and laid the cinder blocks. Angele, with a handful of volunteers, designed and built the dome. The commander of Redstone Arsenal, Brigadier General Holger N. Toftoy, and later the commander of the Army Ballistic Missile Agency, Brigadier General John Bruce Medaris, permitted the group to use an empty hangar in Redstone Arsenal for the construction and assembly of the dome. They also authorized the post engineers to transport the big structure, with a base diameter of thirty feet, on an Army truck to the observatory site on Monte Sano, accompanied by squad cars from the Huntsville police force, with sirens blaring and red lights flashing. An Army crane finally placed the dome on the observatory building.

Von Braun joined the construction groups at the site whenever time permitted him to do so, just working among the ditch diggers and the construction workers. When the building was completed, parts for a telescope with a 16½-inch mirror arrived from California. Some of the local companies helped with the structural elements for the mount, and the astronomy club soon could boast to possess the largest amateur telescope in the Southeast at that time. Observing with the instrument was a wonderful experience not only for the club members, but also for countless visitors who attended open nights at the observatory. Von Braun was a frequent user of the telescope after work, which for him meant mostly the hours between 1 and 3 A.M.

As the years went by, a planetarium with a Goto projector was added to the observatory, and a new telescope was built with a 21-inch mirror, ground by club member Clarence Ellis. Huntsville industrial firms very generously helped again with the mount. In later years, more instruments were added: a very fine 16-inch Celestron of professional quality, with substantial support from the George C. Marshall Space Flight Center and the University of Alabama in Huntsville; a 12-inch Newtonian reflector; a 6-inch refractor; a new Goto planetarium projector; and a 10-inch solar telescope which allows daytime visitors to observe sunspots, and to see prism and grating spectra of the Sun. The city government of Huntsville supports the astronomy club's activities with a yearly contribution. Over the years, more than 40,000 visitors and guests have enjoyed looking at the Sun, the Moon, the planets, and the stars.

On his sixtieth birthday in 1972, a group of friends gave von Braun a beautiful 8-inch Celestron telescope with a piggyback-mounted 6-inch Schmidt camera, complete with dome and photographic equipment. It was erected in the backyard of his home in Alexandria, Virginia where he had moved in 1970. The fine photographs of the

Moon, planets, star clusters, Andromeda galaxy, the Ring Nebula, the Pleiades, and his special favorite, Orion, which he soon began to show his friends, attested to his great and abiding love for our celestial neighbors.

3   ROAD TO ROCKETS AND SPACEFLIGHT

More than astronomy occupied young Wernher's over-active mind, and no one knew this better than his mother. Years later, during the 1950s in Texas, Stuhlinger recalled her reminiscing about her son. *"Learning always was easy for Wernher,"* she said. *"When he was ten, we decided to send him to the Französiches Gynnasium (*French Gymnasium*) in Berlin to give him a somewhat broader basis of education. Around that time, I asked him once what he would like to do later in life. 'I want to help turn the wheel of progress,' was his answer. At times, he may have tried to turn a little too fast. Besides school, he involved himself in numerous projects with his friends. The boys were constantly on the move; they built all kinds of rockets, and they collected pieces of old automobiles from junkyards and built a 'new' car which they tried out on vacant lots, with and without rocket propulsion. They certainly had a lot of fun, but as a side result Wernher flunked in mathematics and physics. His father decided that our son really needed more guidance and control than he was willing to accept from his parents. So we enrolled him, in 1925, in that [*Ettersburg] boarding school. He was allowed to take his telescope along, but not his jalopy, and not his rockets.*

"Wernher would have been the last person to be disheartened. He read the book The Rocket into Planetary Space *which Hermann Oberth [1894–1989], the great theorist of spaceflight, had published in 1923, and he immediately made two decisions: first, to really learn mathematics, and second, to become a space pioneer. After studying the laws of Johannes Kepler [1571–1630], he said: 'Kepler's ellipses are for me what automobile races on the Avus speedway in Berlin are for others!'"*

Throughout his life, von Braun loved to describe and explain to his friends at considerable length any interesting subject that attracted his attention. So, as a fourteen-year-old student at the Ettersburg boarding school, he was eager to share his newly acquired knowledge about rockets and spaceflight with his school mates. He wrote an essay about a journey to the Moon, published in the journal *Deutsche Jugendzeitung* (Journal for the German Youth) on 15 February 1927 under the title: *"Journey to the Moon: Its Astronomical and Technical Aspects."*

"An age-old dream of mankind—to travel to the stars—appears to approach fulfillment," he wrote, and he assured his readers that the time is close when man will begin to reach out for the stars.

He first talked about the tremendous distances with which spacefarers will have to cope, and then described the fundamentals of celestial mechanics which show that it is actually not the large distance between celestial bodies, but the gravitational field around each of these bodies that presents the prime challenge to space travel planners. Orbital velocity, escape velocity, transfer ellipses, ascent of minimum energy, as well as the principles of rocket propulsion were well known to the boy. He even described how the high velocity of a returning spacecraft can be slowed down effectively by utilizing the atmospheric drag during the vehicle's descent through the atmosphere, called *"aerobraking"* by modern spaceflight planners.

In 1927, while he was still at the Ettersburg boarding school, the boy wrote a letter to Professor Hermann Oberth, short and to the point: *"I know that you believe in the future of rockets. So do I. Hence, I take the liberty of sending you a brief paper on rockets that I wrote recently."* Oberth, with a fine instinct for real talent, answered the letter with these encouraging words: *"Keep going, young man! If you keep up your good work, you will certainly become a capable engineer!"* Wernher's teachers, likewise, must have been positively impressed by their young student. One of them wrote to his parents in 1927: *"Wernher is a genius. You will be proud of him! He will do great things!"*

"After finishing the Ettersburg school early in 1928," Wernher's mother recalled in 1953, *"and after staying with us in Berlin for some time, he enrolled in the Hermann Lietz boarding school on the island of Spiekeroog. This must have been a happy place and time for him. Not only did he build an astronomical observatory with his schoolmates; he became a passionate sailor, and the school taught the boys a number of practical skills. He once wrote us that his mathematics teacher had fallen ill, and that he had been chosen to substitute for the professor and teach the math class! And then, he was told that he could graduate one year earlier than the rest of his class because 'you have learned all we can teach you here,' as the teachers said. Well, what could we say? We just hoped for the best."*

It was still during the Spiekeroog days when Wernher joined the fledgling VfR (Society for Space Travel), stimulated by the books of Hermann Oberth and rocket expert and writer Willy Ley. He began writing an essay on *"The Theory of the Long-range Rocket"* in which he put his knowledge to the test and described the multistage rocket principle. Also, at the age of seventeen, he wrote a short story entitled *"Lunetta"* [Little Moon] which offered an early vision of a manned space station. Lunetta was published in the school magazine *Leben und Arbeit* [Life and Work] in 1930.

At a time when other boys of his age thought of automobiles and perhaps airplanes, he fixed his daydreams on a journey into orbit, thirty years before Sputniks and Explorers turned people's attention toward Earth-orbiting satellites. He described a dramatic rescue operation for stranded polar explorers via orbiting observing station, and although he took some poetic license with respect to a quick and easy descent from orbit to a high northern latitude, and an equally easy ascent back to the station, he showed a remarkably good understanding for the specific problems of life and work under weightlessness. In fact, the story has a surprisingly modern ring!

It is obvious that young von Braun's mind was dwelling in outer space during much of the very happy time he spent on Spiekeroog Island. When he returned to Berlin early in 1930, he began very systematically to make his dreams come true.

4   EVENTFUL 1930 AND 1931

Wernher enrolled for the spring semester at the Technische Hochschule (Technical University) of Berlin Charlottenburg as an engineering student, taking the usual courses in physics and mathematics as a prerequisite for an aeronautical curriculum. He must have been a devoted student. His notebook for a lecture course in mathematics [2-3] shows how seriously he took his assignments; all his entries are very carefully worded and beautifully written, their mathematical presentation flawless. His notebooks give eloquent testimony to the high quality of his work.

At about that time, young von Braun had his first personal contact with Hermann Oberth. This was in Berlin, where Oberth was putting together an experimental setup that would enable him to demonstrate and prove the proper operation of a liquid-fuel rocket motor. Oberth had designed a combustion chamber and a nozzle, called Kegeldüse (conical rocket motor), for a combination of gasoline and liquid oxygen, pressurized by compressed nitrogen. Von Braun helped Oberth in this work. It was probably his first encounter with practical rocket work that was carefully planned and executed on the basis of exacting theoretical studies. It marked also the beginning of a friendship between two geniuses that was to last for almost fifty years, until von Braun's death in 1977. Von Braun remembered those long-ago times many years later [1-4]:

"The Chemisch-Technische Reichsanstalt in Berlin [an organization akin to the U.S. National Institute of Standards and Technology, the former Bureau of Standards] had offered Oberth its test facilities to continue his static testing of rocket motors . . . I had eagerly kept track of Oberth's efforts through the journal of the Verein für Raumschiffahrt, and also the daily papers." Willy Ley, whose publications von Braun had devoured clandestinely during his Latin lessons at school, introduced the young von Braun to Professor Oberth in April 1930.

"I shall never forget these evenings at the Reichsanstalt. A bucket, filled with water and mounted on a grocery scale, surrounded the Kegeldüse, a cone-shaped rocket motor of steel; its tiny nozzle protruded from the water and pointed upward."

Oberth's and his co-workers' tireless efforts were finally rewarded with success. In August 1930, Dr. Alexander Ritter witnessed a static test of the Kegeldüse. It worked, and Dr. Ritter attested, complete with official seal, that the little motor had generated a thrust force of 7 kilograms for a period of 90 seconds, consuming 4.92 kilograms of gasoline and liquid oxygen. Thus, the liquid-propellant rocket motor joined the family of scientifically acknowledged and respected combustion engines in Germany.

Recognizing von Braun's unusual talent for public relations work, Oberth also asked him to be the speaker at an exhibit on rocketry that he, Oberth, had put together at a department store in Berlin. Von Braun happily accepted this assignment, describing future manned voyages to the planets in colorful detail, and promising his awe-struck listeners that during their lifetimes, they would witness the spectacle of space travelers walking on the surface of the Moon.

Following a common practice among engineering students in Germany at that time to spend half a year as apprentices in some factory between their first and second semesters in order to learn the basics of their future trade from the grass roots, von Braun joined the big Borsig locomotive factory in Berlin. His first job at the work bench—prescribed by a time-honored rule for student apprentices—was to file a perfect cube from an irregular piece of steel. *"He gave me a chunk of cast iron as big, and as curvacious, as the head of a baby,"* he would recall thirty-five years later. *"I filed and filed, and I began to doubt the fundamental theorems of Euclidean geometry. Do you know how many sides, edges, and corners a cube has? I am sure that mine had at least twice that many. I filed for weeks. Remember, each corner has three right angles, and in a perfect cube each angle has exactly ninety point zero zero zero degrees. Well, I finally made it. Do you want to know how large my masterpiece was? It had shrunk to the size of a walnut!"*

After that, von Braun worked at the lathe and the milling machine, and then in the foundry. Finally, he helped putting locomotives together. His apprenticeship completed, he took a brief vacation in the mountains of the Riesengebirge in Silesia and joined the gliding and soaring school of world-famous soaring champion Wolf Hirth. At the end of the course, he had acquired not only the license to fly a glider plane, but also the life-long friendship with another young soaring flight enthusiast, Hanna Reitsch. *"Hanna was by far the most courageous and fearless girl I met in my life,"* von Braun said forty years later. Not only did she become famous all over the world for her daring sailplane flights across the Alpine mountains; she was the first to fly a helicopter inside a building, the Deutschlandhalle in Berlin; she flew the all-rocket powered Me 163, and she even piloted a V-1 buzz bomb on test flights after it had been temporarily fitted with a cockpit. Willie Fiedler was another intrepid test pilot of the V-1.

Flying always held a great fascination for von Braun. He received his first pilot's license for motorized airplanes in 1933. Many years later, as a U.S. citizen, he would acquire one after the other of all the different pilot's licenses and ratings that can be obtained by nonprofessional civilian pilots, and that included multi-engine rating, instrument rating, commercial rating, and airline transport rating. This great passion for flying did not weaken with age. At sixty, he made the grade as a seaplane pilot, after two days of intensive training on Lake Hood near Anchorage in Alaska [2-3].

During the summer of 1930, Oberth and two of his rocket co-enthusiasts, Rudolf Nebel and Klaus Riedel (who had also been members of the VfR since its inception) had set up a rocket workshop and experiment station in a deserted government ammunition depot at Reinickendorf near Berlin. Von Braun worked with them in his spare time. Later that year, Oberth returned to his native Transylvania (now Romania); Nebel, as the senior member of the group, proudly baptized the place *"Raketenflugplatz Berlin"* (Rocket Proving Ground Berlin). He designed a first flight model of their liquid-propellant rocket, called Mirak for Minimum Rakete.

At about that time, von Braun wrote another paper on rocketry. Entitled *"Das Geheimnis der Flüssigkeitsrakete"* [The Secret of the Liquid-fuel Rocket], it was published in June 1932 in a popular science journal, *Die Umschau.*

"The twentieth century," he wrote, *"has made one of mankind's oldest dreams come true, flying. However, our technical evolution knows no standstill. It presses on; it wants to develop means to bridge far distances quickly and safely, undisturbed by wind and weather . . ."*

All of our present flight systems, he observed, need a surrounding atmosphere. If we want to fly higher, we have to resort to rocket propulsion.

"Modern industrial technology succeeded in developing powder rockets of high performance and reliability that are widely used for marine rescue work, illumination purposes, photographic projects, and as weather rockets. However, the performance of powder rockets of this type is quite limited . . ."

A new chapter in the history of rockets, he wrote, began when the first rocket with liquid propellants was built and successfully launched. Fuels such as alcohol and gasoline, burned with liquid oxygen, have a much greater energy content than even the best smokeless powders. On the other hand, the motor material must withstand temperatures of 2,500 degrees C on one side, and −183 degrees C of the liquid oxygen on the other side. He emphasized that rocket flights to high altitudes would be of great value to science. Not only could they explore the highest layers of the atmosphere; they would be ideal for weather observations, and they could take photographs of the Earth from far distances.

Talking about rockets to the Moon, von Braun felt, would be too early. *"Today,"* he wrote, *"we can only say that space travel is theoretically possible. Before it becomes reality, experimentation and engineering will have to cover much ground. Where it will finally take us, we have no way of telling today . . ."*

Young Wernher was not even twenty years old when he wrote these words. Less than forty years later, his Saturn V rockets launched twenty-one Apollo astronauts on their way to the Moon.

The year 1930 was a particularly active and eventful one for von Braun. Besides studying at the Technical University of Berlin, helping to assemble locomotives at Borsig, working with Oberth, learning how to fly sailplanes, and writing papers on rocketry, he spent all his remaining time at the Raketenflugplatz in Reinickendorf where the Mirak rocket began to take shape.

During the same time, but virtually unknown to the members of the VfR, a very active program of rocket development was underway in the United States by a lone genius, Dr. Robert H. Goddard. A firm believer in liquid propellants, he had succeeded in launching a rocket with a gasoline-oxygen motor near Worcester, Massachusetts, to an altitude of 12 meters (40 feet) on 16 March 1926. After conducting a large number of static tests with better and better rocket motors, a rocket model launched near Roswell in New Mexico reached an altitude of about 600 meters [2,000 feet] on 30 December 1930. Goddard worked incessantly on the improvement of his rockets. In a flight test on 28 March 1935, an altitude of 1,440 meters [4,800 feet] was reached. A record-setting flight of 2,700 meters [9,000 feet] occurred on 26 March 1937.

Goddard was an extremely active and brilliantly gifted man, but he was a loner, keeping his work program, his results, and his plans completely secret. Unfortunately, there was no Goddard team, no school, no followership, no publication with broad distribution, even no correspondence with colleagues. The importance of his many contributions to rocketry was not fully appreciated until after his death in 1945. Von Braun would not learn about Goddard's extensive work in rocketry until after World War II, when he had become a resident of the United States.

As the year 1930 drew to a close, the young rocketeers at the Raketenflugplatz Reinickendorf were busy designing and building their Mirak rocket. Von Braun, joining the work gang during his spare time while he went through the routine and rigors of his engineering education at the university, felt that he would like to see more of academic life, and of the world in general, than what the Technical University of Berlin had to offer.

For centuries, it has been a custom among students at European universities to spend one or two semesters at a university other than their chosen alma mater. This custom afforded the students the opportunity to meet a greater variety of professors and of other students, and to widen their intellectual horizons. In the spring of 1931, von Braun enrolled for the summer semester at the Eidgenössische Technische Hochschule [Federal Technical University] of Zurich in Switzerland.

He must have enjoyed that summer tremendously. It was a time filled with youthful exuberance and joy of life, but the dream of spaceflight never left him. His newly acquired friend, Constantine D. J. Generales, a student at the medical school, recalled [2-4] that young von Braun *"spoke ebulliantly about rockets and spaceships,"* and about *"traveling to the Moon. Wernher showed me a letter he had received from Albert Einstein, replete with formulae about rocket design and propulsion. . . ,"* which Generales did not understand. *"If you want to go to the Moon,"* Generales suggested that *"we had better send some mice first, and find out how they react to the accelerative forces expected during rocket launchings!"* They built a crude centrifuge from a bicycle wheel, put some white mice into little bags attached to the rim of the wheel, and whirled the luckless creatures around. Some of them survived, others did not. *"These were probably the first experiments ever of this kind,"* von Braun remarked later, and Generales said: *"It was actually the birth of the science of space medicine"* [2-4].— *"Our experiments came to an end sooner than we had expected,"* von Braun added. *"My landlady discovered mouse blood splattered on the wall of my room, so she gave me notice to either stop fooling around with mice on a centrifuge, or leave her premises. This terminated our high-acceleration experiments."* As von Braun later remarked, he was not unhappy about this turn of events. The inhumane mouse experiments never were to his liking, nor did he believe that they would influence man's reach for the stars after all.

During their summer vacation, von Braun and Generales made a trip to Greece, Constantine's native country. *"We traveled in my Opel roadster,"* he remembered [2-5]. *"When we reached Bolzano in Italy, we had a flat tire. We had a hand pump, but the rubber gasket for the nozzle was missing, so I wound some grass around it, and Wernher said: 'You really know how to do everything!' Later, the right front wheel dropped off. When we discovered that we needed a ball bearing, Wernher went back to Rome to see whether he could find one. But he was not successful, so . . . we left the car in a garage and went on to Brindisi by train and then to Korfu, Greece, by boat . . . Wernher was liked by everyone, he was very outgoing and very grateful for the hospitality given to him in Greece. There were no excesses. We were busy with so many things, but in those days there were no girls; if you went out with one you were expected to be planning to get married . . . We would get up and have breakfast after I had wakened him with my little trumpet . . . I do remember that he was very antagonistic to religion in the classic way . . . He later went through some kind of revelation and changed his views . . ."*

Von Braun returned to Berlin late in 1931, to the university as well as the Raketen-flugplatz Reinickendorf. The first flight tests of the Mirak rocket had just begun. After some initial failures, launchings eventually became quite successful. G. Edward Pen-dray, the famous American rocket pioneer and at that time president of the American Interplanetary Society, visited the Reinickendorf rocketeers in April 1931 [2-6]. He expressed great admiration for the fine work, and particularly for the enthusiastic dedication he saw at the Raketenflugplatz [2-7]. However, in spite of good engineering work and best intentions, all operations at Reinickendorf remained small-scale, mainly due to persistent money shortage. In 1986 Rolf Engel recalled the situation [2-2]: *"I must say that it was often difficult to . . . have something to eat. Klaus Riedel and I went over to Siemens* [the huge electric corporation] *to their cafeteria and brought food back to our group . . . At that time, none of us had any money. Later, we made some money by having rocket demonstrations . . . I convinced my mother to come over to the Raketenflugplatz and run our kitchen for us. She was called the* "rocket mother" *by everybody. Wernher's mother was very deeply interested and in favor, but his father was always very skeptical. He would not say anything against what Wernher was doing, but he always felt that the boys were just dreaming. Once, a lady from America—the girlfriend of Hearst, king of journalists in the United States—came with Wernher's mother to the Raketenflugplatz. Willy Ley, who spoke English better than the rest of us, made the presentation . . . One day* [in late 1931 or early 1932], *Wernher told me: 'Look, Rolf, we want to push this thing. And we have no money. The only way we can get the money, the assistance and all the means, is the Army.'"*

This very sober and simple assessment was the basis for the most consequential decision that von Braun ever made.

CHAPTER 3

ROCKET CENTER PEENEMÜNDE

1   THE ARMY STEPS IN

Dreams must be dreamed before they can come true. Von Braun dreamed for years of the big rocket to planetary spaces that he might help build, together with thousands of engineers, scientists, planners, designers, and rocket pilots, and with a plentiful supply of money. Toward the end of 1931, he had come to the conclusion that nothing short of a huge organization, such as the Army, could breathe life into a venture of that magnitude. Although the members of the VfR obtained most of the material and components for their rockets as donations, it proved very difficult, if not impossible, to keep the program going, simply because most of the co-workers could not afford to spend the necessary time on rocket work at the Raketenflugplatz without remuneration.

But how would a handful of young rocket amateurs, working during spare hours in a run-down shack at an old ammunition dump, and suffering from a total lack of operating funds, evolve into a 10,000-man Army development center, with the most modern machines and the best brains available at that time?

Well, the dream did come true. The history of Peenemünde has been the subject of numerous essays and reports for nearly fifty years. Although many of them, as von Braun remarked, are *"utterly nonsensical,"* they agree on one point: they state that early in 1932, the German Army took an interest in von Braun's work at Reinickendorf. However, the earlier phase of this development, when a stroke of fate was still more important than systematic planning, is difficult to reconstruct.

There are two stories that tell how the doings of the amateur group in Reinickendorf and the big ways of the Army began to converge during the 1931–32 period. The two stories are quite different. None of the main players who could shed the light of truth on the tales is alive today, but there are first-hand witnesses for both stories. The events they describe do not contradict each other; considering the credibility of the witnesses, both stories are probably correct.

The first story reflects the Army view. It is remembered by Doris Dornberger, widow of Major General Dornberger who began working for Army rocket projects as a young captain in 1930, and who later became commander of the Peenemünde Rocket Center [3-1].

"During the winter of 1931/32," so the story goes that Mrs. Dornberger had heard from her late husband, *"von Braun was a student of engineering at the Technical University of Berlin. During his spare time, he built and tested rockets with some friends at the Raketenflugplatz Reinickendorf. Like all nineteen-year-old students, he was in need of self-earned spending money, so he spent some hours every day working as a taxi driver in the city of Berlin. One day, his passengers were two Army officers. The two were engaged in a lively discussion of a rocket problem, obviously in connection with experiments they helped conduct as part of the Army's rocket development program. When they continued their discussion in the rear of the taxicab, young von Braun*

could not help overhearing their talk. After a while, he broke in: 'Excuse me, please, gentlemen,' he said, 'but I believe I can shed some light on that problem,' and he offered some suggestions. The two officers listened, not without considerable surprise, and when they departed, one of them said: 'Young man, why don't you come to my office in the Army High Command tomorrow, we want to discuss this further with you!'

"Von Braun went to the office the next day to meet with his two taxi passengers. They were Walter Dornberger and [Wolfram] Ritter von Horstig, central figures in the Army's fledgling rocket development program." Their talk on that day was to become the beginning of the long road whose milestones included Kummersdorf, Peenemünde, the United States, a large family of successful rockets, the first American satellite, the first American in space, the journey to the Moon, the first manned station in orbit.

The second story reflects a view from the von Braun side. Rolf Engel, a co-worker and close friend of von Braun since 1928, remembered the old Reinickendorf days during an interview in 1986 [2-2]. He is convinced that it was von Braun's father, at that time Reichsminister for Agriculture and Food Administration in the German government, who took the first step to bring his son's work and the interests of the Kriegsministerium [Department of Defense] together.

"He contacted von Blomberg," Engel said, *"who at that time was the head of the German Army.* [Field Marshal Werner von Blomberg later became secretary of defense, 1935–38.] *Then, Dr. [Karl] Becker was contacted who was the head of the Army Development Office. Becker was greatly interested because at that time he already had a small team led by Captain [Walter] Dornberger that was working with solid-propellant (black powder) rockets. Wernher and Dornberger met in the spring of 1932. Soon afterwards, Dornberger started to develop a facility to test rockets at Kummersdorf. A few months later . . . the Army made a contract with Wernher, who was still a student!"*

That first contact between Dornberger and von Braun, wherever it happened, must have left a positive impression on Dornberger. Typical for him, he followed up with a series of actions, among them a visit at Reinickendorf; intense technical discussions; suggestions for further work; constructive criticism of what he believed were wrong approaches; an admonition to concentrate on serious work, rather than on show-manship; and, finally, a proposal to von Braun to leave his amateurish tinkering and to accept a contract with the Army for some real rocket research and development work.

Von Braun described the events that followed this first contact, and that culminated in the Army Test Station Peenemünde, in his essay *"Reminiscences of German Rocketry,"* published in the *Journal of the British Interplanetary Society* (BIS) in 1956 [3-2]. That essay represents expanded *"Recollections"* prepared by von Braun following his initial interrogation in the United States in October 1945. Excerpts from *"Reminiscences"* are presented in the next chapters.

2   EARLY ROCKET WORK AT KUMMERSDORF PROVING GROUND

"In the spring of 1932," von Braun begins his story, *"three inconspicuous visitors in civilian clothes called on us young rocketeers at the Raketenflugplatz Reinickendorf."* They came from the Army Ordnance Department: Colonel (later General) Dr. Karl Becker, Chief of Ballistics and Ammunition; Major Wolfram Ritter von Horstig, his ammunition expert; and Captain Dr. Walter Dornberger, in charge of powder rockets for the Army. Von Braun's group included Willy Ley, an author as well as rocket and

spaceflight enthusiast; Rudolf Nebel, self-styled expert and promoter of rockets; and Klaus Riedel, an engineering genius.

It became obvious quickly, von Braun remembered, that the visitors knew much about rockets. They wanted to know how the thrust was measured during static firings, and they asked for thrust-time diagrams. Although there was not much they could be shown, they signed a contract for 1,000 marks, contingent upon a successful firing of a Mirak II rocket at the Army Proving Ground near Kummersdorf.

So, one morning in July 1932, the rocketeers loaded a silver-painted Mirak II with launcher, containers with gasoline and liquid oxygen, and some tools on their two automobiles and drove to Kummersdorf, some 60 miles (about 100 kilometers) south of Berlin. Captain Dornberger, who had been waiting for them, took them to an isolated spot on the artillery firing range. *"There,"* von Braun wrote, *"a formidable array of photo-theodolites, ballistic cameras, and chronographs had been set up—instruments of whose very existence we had been unaware heretofore . . ."*

Mirak II soared to an altitude of some 200 feet (60 meters). Then, however, its trajectory became erratic, and the rocket crashed before the parachute could open.

Naturally, the men from Ordnance were not impressed; they hesitated to continue with their support. Finally, von Braun decided to take all available data to Colonel Becker, and to discuss the situation with him. He was quite successful; *"despite his uniform,"* von Braun told his friends, *"Becker seemed to be broadminded, warm-hearted, and a scientist through and through."*

"We are greatly interested in rocketry," von Braun quoted Becker, *"but there are a number of defects in the manner in which your organization is going about its development work. For our purposes, there is far too much showmanship. You would do better concentrating on scientific data, rather than firing toy rockets."*

Von Braun answered that he would be glad, and, in fact, eager to provide technical and scientific data if he only could afford to buy the necessary measuring equipment. Becker, accepting von Braun's argument, offered some financial support, provided that the group would be willing to continue its work in the closed quarters of an Army establishment.

"When I returned to the Raketenflugplatz I found Nebel anything but enthusiastic about again submitting to the rigors of military control. He'd had enough of that during his service years. His fear of 'ignorant people who would hinder the free development of our brain-child' caused long and bitter arguments between us."

Klaus Riedel did not want to accept the Army's offer either. He felt that private enterprise should provide the necessary finances for such a worthy objective as spaceflight. *"Exactly how he proposed to bridge the gap between our small, sputtering rocket and a huge, passenger-carrying spaceship wasn't quite clear to me, nor, it may be supposed, to him,"* von Braun said.

It was easy to see that the toy-like Mirak II, even if and when it performed properly, was indeed a far cry from the precision rocket needed for spaceflight. A host of well-working components would have to be developed: an efficient and reliable rocket motor, a gyro control system, jet vanes, servo-controlled actuators, a cut-off system, electromagnetic valves, pumps for the propellants, a control and guidance system, and many more. The little group of rocket enthusiasts at Reinickendorf would never be able to conduct such a program. *"It became obvious,"* von Braun wrote, *"that the funds and facilities of the Army would be the only practical approach to space travel."*

At that time, none of the young rocketeers thought of their rocket as a potential horror weapon in the hands of a Nazi regime. *"There is not a word of truth in the . . . rumor that the Raketenflugplatz sold out to the Nazis. For us, Hitler was still only a* *pompous fool . . .", von Braun wrote. The situation of the young rocketeers was similar to that of the aviation pioneers when the airplane could only be developed because of military support.

Reluctantly, Nebel and Riedel agreed that Colonel Becker's offer could not be ignored. So, von Braun departed Reinickendorf and became a member of the Army's rocket section in November 1932. *"Little did we imagine,"* von Braun remembered, *"that a mere five years later most of us would be working together again at the great rocket center of Peenemünde . . ."*

Even more unthinkable would have been the idea, in the fall of 1932, that a mere ten years later Hitler and some of his accomplices would wrench von Braun's rocket out of his hands and enforce its production and deployment as a weapon.

"My laboratory at Kummersdorf," von Braun wrote, *"was one half of a concrete pit with a sliding roof, the other half being devoted to solid-propellant rockets."* His staff consisted of a single mechanic, and his work orders disappeared in an artillery shop jammed with jobs of higher priority. *"Not until January 1933 was the first small water-cooled motor ready for static firing . . . It developed a thrust of 140 kilograms (308 pounds) for 60 seconds in its first test. After that, trouble began. Explosions upon ignition, frozen valves, fires in cable ducts, and numerous other malfunctions beset the work, and we were often hard put to find their cures."*

Remedies were found. The young rocket pioneers used the *"yellow pages"* in the telephone book and called in professional welders, instrument makers, valve manufacturers, and pyrotechnicians, and *"with their assistance,"* von Braun wrote, *"a regeneratively-cooled motor of 300 kilograms (660 pounds) thrust, fueled by liquid oxygen and alcohol, was tested in preparation for flight in the A-1 rocket that had been under construction for 6 months."* Half a second after the start signal the motor burst into fragments. Delayed ignition detonated an explosive mixture that had accumulated in the combustion chamber.

Besides this motor problem, the A-1 was plagued by other shortcomings. It was replaced by a redesigned A-2 with better motor, better mass distribution, and better stability. Two years after the beginnings at Kummersdorf, in December 1934, the group had a fine success. Two A-2 rockets, called Max and Moritz after two well-known German comic figures, were launched simultaneously from the island of Borkum in the North Sea. Both reached altitudes of about 2.5 kilometers (1.5 miles); the launchings were considered a complete success.

The flights of the A-2 Max and Moritz twins were a decisive factor in the history of rocket development. *"This caused a loosening of the official purse strings,"* von Braun wrote, *"and considerable elation among the rocketeers who immediately proceeded to make plans for the A-3, an instrumented rocket of advanced design."*

The A-3 was to have a three-axis gyro control system and jet rudders. It had to lift a considerable load of recording instruments. Among the innovations crammed into the A-3 were a liquid nitrogen pressurization system, together with a vaporizer, to replace the thick-walled nitrogen tank of the A-2. Novel alcohol and oxygen valves, operating pneumatically, were similar to the valves used later in the A-4 rocket, particularly the two-stage flow feature that practically eliminated the hazard of ignition explosions.

Unfortunately, the A-3 rockets did not function as planned. Their takeoffs were satisfactory, but they failed shortly thereafter. Was the gyro control system inadequate? Did excessive wind forces throw the vehicle out of balance? Were the jet rudders too slow in responding to the rocket's angular movements? A number of factors came under suspicion; finally, it was decided to incorporate several changes and modifications in a new design, called the A-5.

Originally, it was hoped that the A-3 could lead directly to the much larger A-4, an ambitious project that would meet Army requirements for a missile with a metric-ton payload and a 250 kilometer (160 mile) range. However, the unsatisfactory flight results of the A-3 made an intermediate step necessary to straighten out stability and guidance problems. This is why the A-5 became the precurser of the A-4.

Von Braun and his co-workers had been aware of the need for comprehensive analytical and experimental work concerning rocket stability almost from the beginning of their rocket experiments. During those early years of rocket development, little was known of supersonic aerodynamics. Mechanical and electric simulators did not even exist, and their powerful descendents, high-speed computers, were still totally unknown. Trying to calculate the motions of a guided rocket under the influences of aerodynamic, gravitational, and control forces was not only extremely cumbersome and time consuming; it was also mostly groping in the dark. The best approach during the mid-thirties was still to build a rocket, equip it with instruments and a primitive telemetering system, fly it, and hope to obtain enough flight data so that an analysis could be made of the rocket's behavior in flight. Even the step-by-step calculation of a simple trajectory, taking into account varying thrust, mass, angle of attack, and atmospheric density, was a major task. Groups of mathematicians had to make do with rattling alleys of desk-top calculators; a single trajectory took several weeks of computation.

Decisive support in the study of aerodynamic stability problems came from the Technical University in Aachen where a young assistant professor, Dr. Rudolf Hermann, working under the guidance of Professor Carl Wieselsberger, had developed, built, and operated a supersonic wind tunnel of the blowdown type with a 10 by 10 centimeter (4 by 4 inch) cross section and a flow velocity of up to Mach number 3.3. Adolf Busemann, working at the institute of the famous aerodynamicist Ludwig Prandtl (1875–1953) in Göttingen, had built and operated the very first supersonic wind tunnel with a 6 by 6 centimeter (2.5 by 2.5 inch) cross section the previous year.

On 6 January 1936 von Braun took the drawing of a pointed, slender body with fins to the aerodynamicists at the university in Aachen, and asked that a model of this design be tested for drag and stability. Hermann's measurements on various rocket models not only revealed the inherent instability of the first A-3 designs, but also produced a new model that was aerodynamically stable through the entire velocity range from subsonic speeds up to Mach 3.3. That model became the starting point for the A-5 and following designs.

A few months after the success with Max and Moritz, the Kummersdorf team was visited by Major Wolfram von Richthofen, in charge of aircraft development for the Luftwaffe. He was a cousin of the great ace of World War I, Baron Manfred von Richthofen, the *"Red Baron."* The major's objective at Kummersdorf was to investigate the possibilities of using liquid-propellant rockets to power aircraft. This was to be tested initially in a conventional aircraft, and then applied to a specially designed all-rocket plane.

Von Braun and his co-workers were quite surprised to see an Air Force officer request an Army installation to develop an aircraft power plant for the Air Force. Even more to their surprise, the Army accepted the request on behalf of the rocketeers.

Within a week, engineers from the famous Heinkel factory arrived to help install the rocket drive in a Heinkel 112 airplane. The first static tests were carried out during the summer of 1935. *"They were observed by a group of Luftwaffe officers,"* von Braun remembered, *"who were first incredulous, and then amazed."*

Major von Richthofen was surprised and impressed when he saw how quickly his desires had been met, and he wanted to start working on the all-rocket fighter at once.

He also asked for the development of a jet-assisted takeoff device for heavy bombers. The Kummersdorf facilities then comprised about eighty people and a small experimental station between two Kummersdorf ranges. Von Richthofen's demands could not be carried out in such cramped quarters. The major promptly offered five million marks to build expanded facilities elsewhere.

This offer, no doubt, constituted a breach of the military etiquette which usually was observed strictly between branches of the Wehrmacht. *"My immediate superior, Colonel von Horstig,"* von Braun remembered, *"solemnly took me into the office of General Becker who, in the meantime, had become chief of Army Ordnance. The general was wrathfully indignant at the impertinence of the Junior Service."*

"Just like that upstart Luftwaffe," Becker growled, *"no sooner do we come up with a promising development than they try to pinch it! But they will find that they are the junior partners in the rocket business!"*

"Do you mean," asked Colonel Horstig in astonishment, *"that you propose to spend more than five million on rocketry?"*

"Exactly that," retorted Becker, *"I intend to appropriate six million on top of von Richthofen's five!"*

Von Braun's yearly budget at Kummersdorf had never exceeded 80,000 marks. This unexpected windfall of funds brought the dreams of the big rocket a large step closer to reality, but it also meant that the facilities at Kummersdorf would be hopelessly too small for the work that lay ahead. The rocketeers began to make plans for a development and test site that would allow the launching and monitoring of their rockets over ranges up to about 320 kilometers (200 miles), possibly over water parallel to the coast that would permit the placement of optical and electric observing instruments along the trajectory, but would not endanger any human settlements along the entire range.

As these plans progressed, the rocket test site Kummersdorf faded into history, giving way to a dramatic new chapter in the development of rocketry: Peenemünde . . .

3   PEENEMÜNDE

During the autumn of 1935, the search began for a suitable place that would offer a firing lane along a seacoast and, at the same time, a clandestine and secure environment for a large technical installation. Von Braun's mother remembered that her husband had been duck hunting on the little island of Usedom in the Baltic Sea, near a tiny fishing village called Peenemünde. Von Braun paid an inconspicuous visit to the place in December. He later wrote [3-2]:

"The neighborhood of the Baltic village of Peenemünde offered exactly what we needed, and four weeks after Christmas, in January 1936, a Luftwaffe civil engineer was in residence there, preparing for construction with the eleven million marks assigned to our project by General Becker and Major von Richthofen."

Unknown to most people in Germany, the little hamlet of Peenemünde at the northern tip of the island Usedom, 180 kilometers (115 miles) north of Berlin, had been of interest only to local fisherfolk and occasional duck hunters. Then, in the mid-1930s, the placid landscape underwent a breathtaking metamorphosis: Legions of mainlanders rushed in, among them surveyors, road builders, construction workers, engineers, technicians, military people, support personnel, and scientists. Trees, shrubs, and sand dunes gave way to modern structures, many of them of huge and bizarre design. Barriers were erected to keep the inquisitive out of sight. Nothing less than the cradle of the modern, long-range, high-precision guided rocket was to emerge from those frantic activities.

"Construction of the basic installations at Peenemünde took about two years," von Braun wrote. *"In April 1937 our rocketeers moved to the Baltic and seemed almost lost in the tremendous plant. Increasing numbers of personnel were needed . . ."* This brought several of von Braun's former co-workers from Reinickendorf back into the rocket team, among them Klaus Riedel, Hans Hüter, Kurt Heinisch and Helmuth Zoike. Rudolf Nebel started a business of his own. *"It may be doubted whether his genius at salesmanship would have found a place in an organization such as Peenemünde. Whatever salesmanship within the Government was needed—and it was very considerable—would be provided by General Dornberger's consummate skill,"* von Braun said.

Beginning in the summer of 1938, successful launchings of A-5s were made, at first without the new guidance system which the failures of A-3 had shown to be necessary, and from the autumn of 1939 on with that system. It worked perfectly. Von Braun described one memorable A-5 launching:

"After weeks of waiting for clear weather on the Greifswalder Oie, a small island not far from Peenemünde, it was decided to launch the first controlled A-5 . . . The slim missile rose steadily . . . and, without the slightest oscillation, disappeared vertically into the clouds . . . Some five minutes later, the island resounded from cries of joy, for the missile reappeared, suspended by its parachute, and slowly sank into the Baltic . . . It was quickly hauled aboard a salvage boat, and it could have been relaunched immediately, except for the sea water with which it was drenched."

About two dozen A-5s were launched during the next two years, some of them several times. Three different types of control systems were tested; all of them worked very well. Experiments with radio guidebeams were also made. In contrast to its predecessor A-3, the A-5 was considered a full success. It cleared the way to the much larger A-4.

In reply to accusations that the A-4 was originally planned as a weapon against the city of London, von Braun declared emphatically [3-2]: *"There is not a shred of truth in any statement that the A-4 (or V-2, as it was called later) was originally conceived as a weapon with which to devastate London . . ."*

At that time, many refused to believe in the imminence of a major war, let alone one against England. For the people in Peenemünde, the development of rockets was a technical enterprise that could provide a defense weapon, but at the same time would lead to a new means of transportation, including transportation into space. Like many other major technical developments, it became possible by the support of the armed forces. The similarity to the airplane's development history is obvious.

The basic layout of the A-4 evolved during 1936 and '37. After the successful launchings of A-5 rockets, systematic work on the A-4 began in 1939. It was decided that the motor of the A-4 would be pump-fed. Various types of turbine-driven pumps were discussed with manufacturers, and testing equipment was installed in the Peenemünde works. In the summer of 1940, a turbo-driven pump for the alcohol and oxygen of the A-4 was ready for production.

Steam for the turbine was generated from hydrogen peroxide and permanganate, a method that had been developed at the Walter Company in Kiel for a submarine drive project. The first peroxide steam generator was ready for an A-4 in 1941.

The rocket motor was a more difficult problem. That development was in the hands of Walter Thiel who succeeded in reducing the original size and weight of the motor substantially, at the same time increasing its combustion efficiency to better than

95 percent. Instead of one large propellant injector plate, a number of small, well-proven injection units proved to be more efficient, and to provide a more stable combustion. Later, a single injector disk was developed which proved superior to the old design, but it was never used in a flight unit.

Hermann's measurements in the supersonic wind tunnel at the Technical University of Aachen had shown how decisive, even indispensable a large, supersonic, high-Mach-number wind tunnel would be for the successful development of large precision-guided rockets. Von Braun, seeing this need very clearly, succeeded in convincing Dornberger of the necessity to build a large supersonic wind tunnel. On 1 April 1937, Hermann joined the rocket center in Peenemünde. Two and one half years later, his huge wind tunnel was in operation with a working cross section of 40 by 40 centimeters (16 by 16 inches) and Mach numbers up to 5.3. During the ensuing years, Hermann and his staff solved countless intricate aerodynamic problems of the A-5 and A-4, and also of the surface-to-air missile Wasserfall, of the A-9, and of winged cannon-launched missiles with which the Army experimented.

Guidance and control of the A-4 was another virgin territory for the rocketeers. The systems used in A-3 and A-5, which had been supplied by industrial firms, were simple as compared to the system needed for the A-4. What stability range would be required? What angular velocity of the jet vanes to maintain a well-damped flight path? What optimum tilt program for the trajectory? To answer such questions, a flight mechanics office was established in 1939 under Dr. Hermann Steuding.

Analog computers and electronic simulators did not yet exist at that time, but they were needed to help solve Steuding's problems. One of his friends, Ernst Steinhoff, assistant professor ('docent') of electric engineering at the Engineering School at Bad Frankenhausen, was brought in to head an electronics laboratory that Gerhard Reisig had built up at Peenemünde during previous years. Steinhoff and his co-workers developed their own complex guidance and control systems, depending on industry mainly for components such as gyros, inverters, and servomotors.

The outbreak of war in the fall of 1939 brought no changes in the work assignments at Peenemünde. The political leaders did not believe that anything of military value could be produced in time to be useful. Some of the most experienced members of the Peenemünde work force were even drafted into the armed fores, and the remaining ones were held under tight administrative control. Rocket development drifted in the doldrums until Field Marshal Walther von Brauchitsch, then supreme commander of the Army, decided to intervene. He wanted the Army's rocket program to continue; and, having much confidence in Dornberger, he assigned to Peenemünde some 3,500 officers and men from the Army. Nominally stationed there *"to be trained,"* they were actually employed as technicians, engineers, and scientists to support and expedite the development.

Recalling those times of need during the early 1940s, von Braun wrote: *"Supplementing this addition to our labor force, we held a 'wisdom day' by inviting 36 university professors of engineering, mathematics, physics, and chemistry to Peenemünde with the objective of enlisting their interest and cooperation."*

Members of universities, like everybody else at that time, suffered severely from the relentless military draft. Therefore, the professors were quite eager to participate in a novel scientific effort that, besides being professionally stimulating and attractive, would also give their academic co-workers, and themselves, a chance to evade the draft board. Among the projects assigned to universities were integrating accelerometers, improvement of pump impellers, trajectory tracking by Doppler radio, gyroscope bearings, research on wave propagation, antenna patterns, new measuring methods for

Peenemünde's supersonic wind tunnel, computing machines for flight mechanics, trajectory calculations, and many others.

"*Cooperation with the professors was extremely pleasant as well as constructive,*" von Braun recalled. Contracts were set up in very broad terms to allow the institutions a wide latitude of approach. As a rule, the universities developed and tested prototypes of their instruments or systems; engineers from Peenemünde would then undertake some "*ruggedization*" (flight hardening) and flight testing, while scientists and engineers would jointly help set up production at an industrial firm.

"*This arrangement with the professors,*" von Braun wrote, "*withstood a later attempt by the Nazis to 'organize' all research in Germany. When loud-mouthed and heavy-handed Party men presented lists and forms to be filled out by the universities, those working for Peenemünde would politely decline to follow instructions, pointing out that they were totally busy with Peenemünde work.*"

The first A-4 was ready for a test launch in the spring of 1942. While the motor ignited with the expected terrifying roar, and the missile began to rise majestically, the launch was not successful. After about one second, the fuel feed system malfunctioned; the heavy rocket, losing its propulsive power, fell back upon its tail fins. The fins crumpled; the missile toppled over and quickly disintegrated in a great explosion.

Four weeks later, the second A-4 was launched. It passed through the dreaded sonic barrier without incident, although some aerodynamicists had predicted that "*transonic phenomena*" would destroy the rocket at this point. However, after 45 seconds of flight, oscillations could be seen; white steam emerged, and the big rocket broke apart. Obviously, the hull was not strong enough near the instrument compartment. It was reinforced for the next launching on 3 October 1942.

That rocket performed as expected. *Brennschluss* (burning cutoff) after 63 seconds was clearly visible. Radio tracking by Doppler indicated that the on-board transmitter operated for more than five minutes. Doppler tracking also recorded the location of impact in the Baltic, and a reconnaissance plane spotted a wide green area caused by a dye marker. This A-4 rocket had reached an altitude of 85 kilometers (53 miles), and a range of 190 kilometers (118 miles).

Dornberger, like all Peenemünders, was jubilant over this success. Von Braun quotes his boss with these words of exuberance and, at the same time, sober assessment: "*Do you realize what we accomplished today? Today the spaceship has been born! But I warn you: our headaches are by no means over—they are just beginning!*"

Dornberger, recounting the events of that memorable day in his book on Peenemünde [3-3], quotes his address to his co-workers: "*We have proven that rocket propulsion can be used for space flight . . . This 3 October 1943 is the first day of a new era of travel, the era of space travel! . . . As long as there is war, our most urgent task can only be the completion of the rocket as a weapon. The development of possibilities that cannot even be foreseen today is a task for peace times . . .*" These were words of the professional soldier, spoken in 1943. In his book, he expressed his conviction that "*. . . The military situation by mid-1943 was far beyond the point when the firing of 900 V-2s per month with one-ton warheads over 250 kilometers (155 miles) could have brought a war of those gigantic dimensions to its end.*"—What would have happened if the V-2 had been available two years earlier? "*It is a futile exercise to speculate about such 'ifs',*" Dornberger wrote. "*We have opened the gates, and we have shown the way to the future.*"

The truth of Dornberger's warning about the headaches was to become evident almost immediately. Hitherto, only few Nazi officials had shared Dornberger's and von Braun's faith in rocketry. "*Hitler himself,*" von Braun wrote, "*had gone so far as to predict failure on the basis of revelations in one of his 'infallible' dreams. His sycophants, of course, had followed his lead, and most of the Nazi hierarchy had begun to regard rocketeers as heretical."*

After this success of the third A-4, Hitler forgot his dreams and became an enthusiastic supporter of rocketry, and soon his followers began demanding mass production of A-4s. Even the more sensible men around Hitler looked now to rockets because the Luftwaffe had lost its air superiority.

A special A-4 Committee was created within the Ministry of Armaments and Munitions under the chairmanship of *"Locomotive Czar"* Gerhard Degenkolb. It developed a formidable bureaucracy, issued high-handed directives, and tried to set up a mighty production organization. Composed of men with little technical or scientific expertise, but with vast energy, this committee was very troublesome to the Peenemünders.

Speer was Reichsminister [approximately equivalent to *"secretary"* in the U.S. Government] of Armaments and Munitions until 2 September 1943, when Hitler made him Reichsminister of Armaments and War Production, with sweeping powers over all facets of German industry. Speer told of his life and work under Hitler in two books. The manuscript of the first, *Erinnerungen*, was written during his long imprisonment; the second, *Der Sklavenstaat*, about thirty years after the end of the war. Both books were translated into English under the titles *Inside the Third Reich* [3-4], and *Infiltration* [3-5]. *"Ever since the winter of 1939,"* Speer wrote in his first book, *"I had been closely associated with the Peenemünde development center, although at first all I was doing was meeting its construction needs. I liked mingling with this circle of non-political young scientists and inventors headed by Wernher von Braun—twenty-seven years old, purposeful, a man realistically at home in the future . . . The work, mere glimmerings of which were being sketched out in 1939, also exerted a strange fascination upon me. It was like the planning of a miracle. I was impressed anew by these technicians with their fantastic visions, these mathematical romantics. Whenever I visited Peenemünde, I also felt, quite spontaneously, somehow akin to them. My sympathy stood them in good stead when, in the fall of 1939, Hitler crossed the rocket project off his list of urgent undertakings, and thus automatically cut off its labor and materials. By tacit agreement with the Army Ordnance Office, I continued to build the Peenemünde installations without his approval—a liberty that probably no one but myself could have taken."*

In June 1942, Speer and several high-ranking officers flew to Peenemünde to witness the launching of an A-4 rocket. The launching was a failure. Speer later wrote: *"I knew what hopes the young inventor was placing on this experiment. For him and his team, this was not the development of a weapon, but a step into the future of technology."*

Under the increasing pressure of war, Speer later tried to help enforce quantity production of the still immature A-4 missile by establishing Degenkolb's A-4 committee. After the war had ended, Speer said in retrospect that supporting the A-4 project as a weapon system was probably one of his most serious mistakes. These long-range rockets, he wrote, *"proved to be, when they were at last ready for use in the autumn of 1944, an almost total failure . . . Those rockets, which were our pride and for a time my most favorite armaments project, proved to be nothing but a mistaken investment . . ."*

From late 1942 on, technical work at Peenemünde was often hampered by visits and demands of members of the A-4 committee. And yet, there was progress; from launching to launching, the A-4 gradually improved in accuracy and reliability. Degenkolb increased his pressure for early production. Several plants for component manufacturing and for missile assembly were built south of Peenemünde, and also near Berlin, near Vienna, and in the huge Zeppelin hangars near Friedrichshafen on the Lake of Constance. Dornberger was ordered to organize and train special units of the armed forces for the deployment and launching of A-4s in the field.

During the night of 17 August 1943, the Royal Air Force raided Peenemünde with some 600 four-engine Lancaster bombers, escorted by 45 scouts and night fighters. For three hours, bombs rained down on the relatively small area. When the smoke had cleared away and the fires were extinguished, it was learned that about 800 casualties had occurred, half of them Russian prisoners of war engaged in technical and road building work. Among the other victims were many engineers and craftsmen and their families, also Walter Thiel, responsible for rocket engine development. The model shops were badly damaged, and the housing area was devastated. However, not one of the 11 elaborate test stands was hit, nor was Hermann's wind tunnel, or Steinhoff's guidance and control laboratory.

Following the Peenemünde raid, Hitler ordered the entire rocket production underground. This became Heinrich Himmler's responsibility; SS General Hans Kammler was to carry out the order. Kammler was in charge of several concentration camps and therefore had a ready supply of labor. By relentlessly driving the unfortunate prisoners, he converted an abandoned mine southeast of the Harz mountains into Germany's largest underground factory, *"Mittelwerk,"* for the manufacturing of aircraft engines, fighter planes, buzz bombs, A-4s, submarine parts, and other military equipment. Construction of Mittelwerk facilities had begun during the spring of 1943. Manufacturing started later, and the first A-4s were assembled in December 1943. Most of the initial output was used in Dornberger's training program; the rest was assigned to Peenemünde for the testing of modifications. From the fall of 1944 on, part of the A-4 rockets produced at Mittelwerk were shipped directly to the western front for military deployment.

At Peenemünde, work on the A-4 was by far the major activity during the war years. However, the early assignments of Air Force projects which had led, back in 1937, to the birth of the Peenemünde rocket center, were still modestly alive in the form of some work for rocket-powered airplanes, jet-assisted takeoff units for airplanes, and rocket-driven ground-to-air guided missiles. Part of this program was carried out in a joint effort between *"Peenemünde East,"* the Army's establishment under Dornberger and von Braun, and the neighboring *"Peenemünde West"* under Air Force management.

"During the winter of 1942–43, when most of the basic development of the A-4 had been completed, work on ground-to-air missiles began," von Braun wrote. A radio-controlled, supersonic rocket of this type, *"Wasserfall,"* was developed under Ludwig Roth, assisted by engineers from the Air Force. Wasserfall rockets made two or three dozen flights, most of them successful. The missile could be maneuvered from the ground by means of a joy stick; a fully automatic guidance system with a Doppler tracking dish was under development. Actually, Wasserfall was the first true supersonic guided missile. It did not reach deployment status before the end of the war.

As the A-4's reliability and accuracy gradually improved, and as military planners showed growing interest in the rocket project, the A-4 began to enter into intimate Nazi party politics. Von Braun successfully eluded being drawn into any political web until the end of 1943, because Dornberger, pleading the need for absolute secrecy, energetically and skillfully prevented political interference at Peenemünde.

Later in 1943, von Braun wrote, *"SS General Kammler began to conceive that he was a rocketeer because he had used the inmates of his concentration camps to excavate the underground halls of Mittelwerk."* Kammler opened an offensive against Leo Zanssen, commanding general of Peenemünde at that time. Zanssen, a professional officer of the old school, had successfully blocked all efforts of the Nazi Party to gain influence over operations at Peenemünde. The Gestapo now informed Dornberger, Zanssen's superior, that they had a record of the latter, clearly indicating that he was a security risk. This was accompanied by an order for Zanssen's replacement. Dornberger cleverly complied with this order by appointing Zanssen as his deputy in charge of the A-4 program in Berlin, while Dornberger himself took over the top command at Peenemünde. He thus put himself in the position of reporting to his own deputy! Kammler, who needed Dornberger's cooperation to reach his goal, accepted that solution.

The second target of Kammler's penetration was to be von Braun. In February 1944, he received a telephone call ordering him to report to the headquarters of Reichsführer Heinrich Himmler. *"I entered his office with considerable trepidation,"* von Braun recalled. *"It must be said though that he was as mild-mannered a villain as ever cut a throat, for he was quite polite, and he rather resembled a country school teacher* (Himmler's profession before he joined Hitler*)."*

"I hope you realize," Himmler began, *"that your A-4 rocket has ceased to be a toy; the whole German nation eagerly awaits the mystery weapon . . . As for you, I can imagine that you've been immensely handicapped by Army red tape. Why not join my staff? I'm sure you know that no one has such ready access to the Führer, and I promise you vastly more effective support than you can get from those hide-bound generals . . ."*

"Herr Reichsführer," von Braun replied, *"I couldn't ask for a better chief than General Dornberger. Such delays as we are still experiencing are due to technical problems, but not to red tape. You see, the A-4 is rather like a little flower. In order to flourish, it needs sunshine, a well-proportioned quantity of fertilizer, and a gentle gardener. What I fear you are planning is a big gush of liquid manure! That really would kill our little flower!"*

As von Braun reported, Himmler smiled sardonically and changed the subject. *"Some few minutes later, he dismissed me with what I felt was entirely feigned politeness . . . Then, at 2 o'clock one morning, I was awakened by three Gestapo men who hauled me and two of my co-workers off to their jail in Stettin. There I languished for two solid weeks without the slightest information . . . as to why I had been arrested."*

Finally, a court of SS officers charged von Braun that he did not intend the A-4 to be a weapon of war, that he had only space travel in mind while he developed the A-4, and that he regretted its military use. They also accused him of keeping an airplane in readiness to fly to England with important rocket data! How could he prove that he had no traitorous intentions?

Just as this mock trial was in progress, Dornberger stepped into the room with a document, obviously from a high government office. As soon as the presiding officer had read it, von Braun's immediate release was ordered, and he was allowed to depart with Dornberger. What had happened?

When Dornberger learned of von Braun's arrest, he lost no time trying to have him released—only to find out that this would not be so easy. He described his courageous and eventually successful efforts in his book *V-2* [1].

Dornberger first asked Field Marshall Keitel to help obtain von Braun's release, but without any success. Keitel simply said that this matter was in the hands of the SS, and that he would have absolutely no influence on Himmler. Dornberger tried to see Himmler, but the Reichsführer only told him to see SS General Hans Kaltenbrunner, head of the SS Security Office. Kaltenbrunner was not available, so Dornberger met with SS General Heinrich Müller, chief of the Gestapo. After endless arguing and negotiating, during which Dornberger continued to assure Müller that von Braun was absolutely indispensable for the A-4 program, von Braun was *"released provisionally for a duration of 3 months."* At the end of this 3-month period, his release was extended by another 3 months; before that period ended, there was the assassination attempt on Hitler of 20 July 1944, after which the whole von Braun matter was forgotten.

Two factors contributed to the release of von Braun and his co-workers: First, the SS and other Party officials had stated publicly again and again that secret weapons (meaning the A-4) were being developed that would assure final victory. If von Braun and two of his top engineers were imprisoned, how could the wonder weapon be completed? Second, Albert Speer had made a personal plea to Hitler to release von Braun immediately, and to allow him to continue his work for the A-4 [3-4]. Hitler gave in—albeit grudgingly—as Speer remembered.

Kammler held back with his nefarious aspirations on Peenemünde until after 20 July when the SS gained influence. At that time, the A-4 was close to military deployment. Kammler reduced Dornberger's role to supervising the preparation and training of troops; beyond that, Dornberger lost all control over the military units that he had organized and trained.

Beginning on 8 September 1944, A-4s were launched against Paris and London, without any previous announcement to the German public.

What was the truth behind the rumors of a mysterious *"America Rocket,"* the A-10, that von Braun and his team allegedly were building in Peenemünde? Adolf K. Thiel, one of von Braun's early co-workers, reminisced many years later [3-6] about those studies. *"The A-9 and A-10 stories circulating after World War II were pretty much fairy tales . . .",* he explained. *"We did investigate how the range of ballistic rockets (like the A-4) could be increased by glider wings . . . in fact, I wrote a PhD thesis dealing with that study in 1944 . . ."*

The A-4b, a single stager with wings, could have covered 450 kilometers (280 miles); an enlarged two-stage combination, called A-9/A-10, would have been capable of 3,000 kilometer (1,900 mile) ranges. Those studies, which referred strictly to spaceflight and not to weapons, dealt only with aerodynamic aspects; no work was done on propulsion, structures, guidance systems, or thermal design. The studies showed that multistage rockets would permit the establishment of Earth-orbiting space stations, and that glide rockets would be able to land safely on the surface of the Earth after returning from orbit.

Von Braun, in his essay of 1945, elaborated on those early studies of his planning group in Peenemünde. *"During the 1944–45 winter,"* he noted, *"two A-9 rockets were test-launched. While the first was unsuccessful, the second was probably the first winged guided missile to penetrate the sonic barrier."* However, after a successful ascent, as Gerhard Reisig [3-7] recalled, the rocket went into a steep dive, and the wings broke off.

"Our design drawings for the A-9," von Braun continued, *"showed a pressurized cockpit instead of the warhead, and also a landing gear! While we kept these drawings hidden from Army Ordnance visitors, we calculated that the A-9 would be capable of carrying a pilot over a distance of 400 miles (640 kilometers) in 17 minutes."*

Quietly, planning for the future continued, although on a very modest scale. If the A-9 were mounted as the second stage on top of a powerful booster stage such as an A-10, it would be a passenger-carrying supersonic rocket plane capable of crossing the Atlantic. Beyond the A-10, an imaginary A-11 could serve as the first stage of a three-stage spaceship. *"That combination,"* von Braun predicted, *"could launch a pilot with his A-9 into a permanent satellite orbit around the Earth! Only one further step from this concept leads to that of a permanent satellite station in space . . ."*

One of the proposals that Oberth described in his book concerned a huge mirror in a satellite orbit. He wrote that such a mirror could be used for changing terrestrial climates, and even for burning up war ships and cities—ideas that would certainly exceed the limits of reality. For reasons unknown, this space mirror was portrayed in some quarters as the ultimate goal of the men in Peenemünde. Shortly after the war, artists' conceptions of engineers in the act of ruling the globe by the space mirror's threat appeared in the press—definitely a case of artistic and journalistic imagination racing far beyond the limits of reason, fact, and logic.

"We who gave life to Peenemünde," von Braun wrote in his essay of 1945 [3-2], *"deplore as much as anyone that developments like aviation, atomic energy, or rockets are applied to destructive purposes rather than for human benefit . . . We desire to open the planetary world to mankind."* For more than thirty years after the end of the war, he often spoke of Peenemünde; it was a tremendous source of experience for him, a time of the most intense learning. The amount of technical detail that he remembered was amazing, and he made the best use of the profound knowledge he had acquired during those eight years in Peenemünde for all his projects that followed the A-4. There were not only problems in technology and science that had to be solved; in fact, he sometimes said that technical problems always presented a pleasant challenge to him while the *"human engineering"* aspects that confront the leader of a program of that magnitude and complexity really make life tough.

Peenemünde was more than a technical venture. It was a phase in history, not only in the history of Germany during the war years, but also in the history of mankind's technical evolution.

4   LIVING AND WORKING AT PEENEMÜNDE

Work at Peenemünde began with a few hundred people; during the first years, their number grew to a few thousand. A major increase occurred from the fall of 1942 on. By the end of the war, more than 10,000 people worked at and for Peenemünde. This rapid growth went parallel with a rather drastic change in the life-style of the Peenemünders.

The pace of work had always been fast and intense. However, as Rudolf Hermann, the aerodynamicist who joined Peenemünde in April 1937, remembered in 1983 [3-8], *"there was even time for nonprofessional activities, such as swimming in the beautiful Baltic Sea, bicycle trips over the island, and colorful parties with neighbors and friends. Wernher von Braun had a sailboat, and I remember many joyful sailing weekends. He was a bachelor, but it was rumored that he had never yet been alone on his boat. Wernher also had a cello, which he played with much verve and ardor . . ."*

During those early times, did you also talk about rocket flights to outer space?" Hermann was asked.

"Always," was his brief and convincing answer. *"We talked about spaceflight all the time. Wernher was full of ideas about flights to the Moon, orbiting satellites with telescopes and radio transmitters, a huge space station, and a manned expedition to Mars. For him, the A-4 was just the first step toward the space rocket of the future . . . I also remember that in 1937 and '38 von Braun and I made frequent trips to Army Headquarters in Berlin to talk about our project. After a day of meetings, we often attended one of the classical concerts for which Berlin was famous at that time. After the concert, we sometimes had a drink in a bar on Kurfürstendamm. Minimum age to enter these bars was twenty-one. One evening, the bar maid at the entrance door asked von Braun: 'Are you twenty-one? That is the law. May I see your I.D. card?' Even with the*

card under her eyes, she would not believe that von Braun was twenty-five. He looked like eighteen with his blond hair, rosy cheeks, and boyish smile."

"Did you also talk about the possibility of a war at that time?" he was asked.

"Never," Hermann replied. *In 1937 and '38, we did not think of war, and we would not have believed that it could happen . . ."*

Years later, when the war began to extend its iron grip over most of Europe, work and life in Peenemünde changed. Many young men were drafted into service, and those who remained in Peenemünde had to accept higher and higher workloads. Helmut Horn, a physicist from the Technical University in Darmstadt who joined the Peenemünde project in 1939, remembered that *"our work week had about 60 hours; when we planned a firing test . . . , we used to spend 70 to 80 hours per week on the test stand. There were cots on which we could catch a few hours of sleep between tests. Swimming in the ocean? Well, the beach was only some 500 yards from where I lived; I managed to have a few hours of swimming in 1939, but not thereafter. There simply was no time. The same goes for my little sailboat; no sailing from 1940 on."*

In the memories of those who worked there, Peenemünde stands out as a dream, remote and shining, almost eerie. But while it happened, particularly after 1940, it was different. Each day and night rolled off with relentless realism. It was working and sleeping and working and eating and working and traveling and working and standing in line. It was a simultaneous existence in a multilayered world; the layers of work were predominant, but they were interspersed with spells of desperation under the heavy clouds of a meaningless, hopeless, destructive, and gruesome war, and with the struggle of sheer survival in bomb-shattered, emaciated Germany. It was *"The Project"* that still gave this life structure and stability, and even a meaning. For those who worked at Peenemünde, The Project reached far beyond the fragility of the present with its anxieties and grief, its hunger and cold, its destruction and death.

During 1940 and 1941, Peenemünders did not think of imminent mass production, let alone of military deployment of their rocket. They were totally engulfed in the problems of development, testing, and continuous improvement of the machine they were about to invent. They would never have believed that Germany would be able to withstand the counteroffensive of the Allies for so long. What did people believe at that time? Hitler and his sycophants, of course, believed only in the grand victory. Others, assessing reality in a more sober fashion, did not believe that, in view of the enormous resources of the Allies, Germany would ever have a chance to win that war. With a logic that certainly was not free from wishful thinking, they hoped that fate would take a turn that would free Germany from its dictator, and would give the country an opportunity to build a new democracy that could live peacefully among other democracies. It was an open secret that there were heroic minds at work that tried to help fate take such a course. In a book published in 1981 [3-9], Will Berthold described forty-two attempts on Hitler's life between 1933 and 1945—all of them failed.

The Army decided in 1942 to increase the work force at Peenemünde by calling a number of soldiers with engineering or science degrees back from the battlefronts. One of them, Stuhlinger—a young Pfc.-PhD.—later wrote an essay about his arrival and first impression at Peenemünde [3-10]. *"When I arrived at Peenemünde in the spring of 1943,"* he wrote, *"I was immediately overwhelmed by the gigantic effort that had been underway here for several years, unknown to the average citizens in Germany. Particularly impressive was the devotion of the Peenemünders to their task. I learned that there was a young director, Wernher von Braun, but several weeks passed before I saw him for the first time. However, his spirit, his remarkable leadership, his powerful thrust were so perceptible everywhere that I soon felt that I knew him quite well. His message was simple: 'We have a job to do, let's go to work!' This message came from a man who combined with his persistent drive for action a variety of outstanding human qualities: Brilliant intelligence, sharp wit, warmhearted compassion, power of persuasion, technical talent, a highly creative mind, skillful diplomacy, a gift for inspiration, the capability to make others eager to work for him, a fantastic talent to get along with his co-workers and his superiors alike, a seemingly unlimited capacity for hard work, contagious optimism, and, above all, a burning desire to develop rockets for interplanetary flight."*

The first encounter of the newly employed Pfc. with von Braun illuminates several of von Braun's characteristic features. *"I had been assigned to the laboratory for accelerometer development under Dr. Walter Schwidetzky,"* the essay goes, *"who also wore the uniform of a Pfc. Our laboratory had many visitors who brought in or picked up electronic equipment and wanted to discuss test data. One day, a young man came in who was quite different from all the other visitors. "Good afternoon, Doctor," he said to Schwidetzky, "how do you do?" While I barely noticed the many people who came through our laboratory every day, I was immediately struck by fascination when I saw and heard this man. He certainly was an impressive human being, tall, blond, and of strong build. He talked and moved with greatest ease, but his eyes and face, in fact his entire body, expressed an utmost alertness, a total involvement in the thoughts he tried to convey. And yet, he was in no way overbearing. His questions were precise and to the point, but they stimulated creative thought; they brought out the best in the person he asked. They were the questions of a partner and colleague, not of a boss.*

As the young man asked Schwidetzky how the accelerometer tests had gone the day before, I noticed that he was fully familiar with the work we were doing in this laboratory. While he talked, he sat down on a wooden box in the corner, discarding the chair offered to him. 'We ran through a whole gamut of vibration frequencies, but the system held up quite well, thanks to some recent modifications,' Schwidetzky said.— 'Did you find any strong resonances?'— 'There were some, but obviously without any adverse effects.'— 'Did you use sinusoidal vibrations only?'— 'Yes, sir.'— 'I wonder', the young man said, 'whether you could not record on a magnetic wire recorder the real noise of a rocket engine during one of our next captive firing tests. Then, you could play this recorded noise through a power amplifier and feed it directly into the coil of your vibration table. That would give you a more realistic test than the pure sine waves. Would you think that this could be done?'— 'I imagine so,' Schwidetzky said. 'I'll try it immediately.'— 'Keep me posted, please,' was the brief reply, and the young man left as quickly as he had come in.

For a while, I was under a strange spell, then I enquired who that man was. In an almost solemn voice, Schwidetzky said: 'This was Professor von Braun.'— 'How old is he?' I wondered. 'Thirty-one.'— 'And he is the director of this huge establishment?'— 'He has been its director from the beginning, for six years already. In fact', Schwidetzky added, 'I doubt whether he has ever been anything else but the director, wherever he was!'"

Most of those who had the good fortune of being close to von Braun during his lifetime would agree that the magic spell that radiated from his personality never came to an end. When he entered a room or joined a group of people, he was immediately the center, the force that attracted attention and interest from everyone. When he talked, everybody listened. (It must be said, though, that he sometimes started speaking before the other person had finished!) The population density in a crowd was always greatest where he stood, laughing and talking, and obviously relishing the fact that so many were eager to see him and listen to him.

His true passion, however, was undoubtedly the technical debate with his co-workers. There he would listen with fullest attention and great patience, absorbing every detail, correlating the new information with the countless bits stored in his fast-access memory, jumping in with a quick question or a stimulating remark, and at frequent intervals summing up the situation in characteristic von Braun fashion with the most lucid words and cogent logic that would make sure that everybody around understood the problem in the way he believed it should be understood.

Meetings with von Braun—he held several every day—were stimulating and informative, and they always brought progress in the solution of the problems under discussion. Regardless of what the subject was—combustion instability, pump failures, design problems, control theory, supersonic aerodynamics, gyroscopes, accelerometers, ballistic trajectories, thermal problems—von Braun was always fully knowledgeable of the basic subject and of the status of the work. He quickly grasped the problem, and he formulated it so that everyone understood it clearly. If he had difficulties with a presentation, he simply said: *"You must explain this again. I'm too dumb to get it the first time."* All those meetings ended on a positive note. Solutions came within reach; ways to solve the difficulties were found. Something could really be done, and would be done, to assure continuing progress.

Test launchings of A-4s from Test Stand P-7 in Peenemünde always caused great excitement, not only for those who were directly involved in test and launch procedures, but for almost everybody. Word of an imminent launching was spread by telephone. Those who had the opportunity watched from the roofs of assembly hangars or other tall buildings; others walked over to the woods that surrounded the test area; still others went out on the street to see the rocket rise over the tree tops at a distance of some kilometers.

The best vantage point was on top of the big hangar at P-7, not more than 150 meters away from the rocket. Here stood this mighty machine, filled with the most advanced technology of the time, and with a tremendous amount of energy waiting to be released, ready to show the way to our neighbors in outer space. In a few minutes, the launch signal would be given, superheated steam would drive a turbine with 460 horsepower; two centrifugal pumps, mounted on the same shaft, would force 120 kilograms of alcohol and liquid oxygen per second into the combustion chamber. The rocket thrust, 25 tons of force, would lift the rocket and, in a minute's time, accelerate it to a speed of 2,000 meters per second (4,500 miles per hour), faster than any rocket had flown before.

For the Peenemünders, launching of a test rocket became an almost common sight during 1943 and 1944. *"...3...2...1...0...ignition...prestage...mainstage... lift-off"* the loudspeaker would announce. A cloud of steam and smoke would burst out of the nozzle, a yellow beam of fire would follow, and a moment later the rear end of the rocket would be engulfed in a most violent turbulence of fire and smoke. Moments later, the sound waves would reach the spectators. The sound would begin with a tremendous bang, but it would be a bang that continued with unbroken strength as a thunderous howling. Everything in the neighborhood would vibrate; the skin of the entire body would act as a membrane that transmitted the sound to the sensory system. It would be quite painful, but who would think of pain at such a moment? Almost miraculously, the upper portion of the rocket, protruding from the cauldron of fire, would remain completely immobile, standing there in supreme tranquility for about three seconds. Then, the thunder and turmoil would increase, and the rocket would begin to move very, very slowly, with unbelievable steadiness, totally undisturbed by the wild maelstrom at its rear end which by now would have swallowed up all the structures at and near the launch table. The exhaust beam, becoming visible as the rocket gained altitude, would look like a giant blow torch, and the spectators would feel the tremendous heat radiated from it on their faces. Accelerating more and more, the rocket would turn into an easterly direction, parallel to the coast line of the Baltic Sea from where ground stations would observe and track it during flight.

Among the frequent observers of rocket launchings was Professor Hermann Oberth, at that time a consultant at the Peenemünde rocket development center. One day, a young rocket engineer addressed him after a successful launching: *"Professor Oberth, it must give you a feeling of great satisfaction to see that your early work has led to such a beautiful success!"* Typically for Oberth, he paused a while before he answered: *"I have the greatest respect for those who built that rocket. For them, this flight certainly is a great success. However, it has been known for a long time that large rockets can be built, and that they will reach high supersonic speeds, if only the engineering is done right. What we have seen is just the very first beginning. We should not forget over this fine success that the real goal of the modern rocket is not on this Earth. It is far out there, on the Moon, and among the planets."* Surely, many of those who worked at Peenemünde shared Oberth's thoughts, and they combined them with a silent hope that the war would come to an end before this awesome machine could be turned into an active weapon.

5   BLACK CLOUDS OVER PEENEMÜNDE

A memorable event occurred in the summer of 1943. Reichsführer SS Heinrich Himmler, certainly the most influential, most enigmatic, most vicious, most cruel, and most dreaded man under Hitler in Germany at that time, announced his visit to Peenemünde and his desire to see an A-4 test launching. For Dornberger and von Braun, that visit was a matter of great concern because they knew that Himmler wanted to take the A-4 project out of the Army's hands and put it under his own command and control. For the rank and file Peenemünders, Himmler's visit meant that they must be particularly careful in all their work. They sensed the tension of their leaders, and they all hoped that the visit would have no adverse consequences.

The A-4 took off without a flaw. After reaching an altitude of about 30 meters, however, it began to rotate slightly. Then it turned over to the west, became erratic, and, while flames shot out sidewise, flew crazily toward the airfield of Peenemünde West—a kind of sister organization under the command of the Luftwaffe where guided air-launched bombs, and also the buzz bomb (later to be called V-1), were under development. The explosion at impact destroyed several aircraft that were parked there.

Dornberger and von Braun, understandably, were stunned. Later, von Braun related the episode. *"Himmler,"* he said, *"remarked with a sarcastic smile: 'This now removes any doubt on my part. I will go ahead and order the production of ground combat weapons.' Fortunately,"* von Braun continued, *"the sting of this acid remark was blunted somewhat by one of Dornberger's staff officers who drily suggested that the A-4 could now really be called a 'revenge weapon' because a few days earlier, the Peenemünde West people had erroneously dropped one of their guided air-launched bombs over Dornberger's Peenemünde East where it dug a deep hole not far from one of the A-4 assembly hangars."*

Von Braun was too much of a realist not to have prepared himself for the possibility of a launch failure during Himmler's visit. Less than one hour after the unsuccessful launch attempt, another A-4 stood on the launch table, filled with alcohol and liquid oxygen, checked out, and ready for launch. This time, it was a picture-book launching. The rocket impacted less than one quarter of one percent from the predicted impact point in the Baltic Sea.

As von Braun told his associates later, he could not tell whether Himmler was impressed by the sight; his mind remained impenetrable. At least, he did not make another nasty remark. Von Braun, trying to make the best of the situation, pointed out to Himmler that the potentialities of the A-4 were demonstrated by the second launch, while the first launch clearly indicated how much development and testing remained before production of the rocket as an operational missile could be started. Himmler remarked that he would talk to the Führer about it.

Himmler did indeed talk to the Führer about it, but it was not in the way von Braun had wished and hoped, but in the way he had feared.

Himmler's dark scheming must have already begun before his visit to Peenemünde, but that visit obviously made him even more determined to pursue and achieve his goal. In his efforts to gain control over the A-4 program, he received unexpected help through a long-feared event that befell Peenemünde on 17 August 1943: A bombing raid by the British Royal Air Force, described earlier in this chapter (3-3).

The bombing raid on Peenemünde was a clear indication that the Allies were well aware of its importance. So Hitler ordered that production facilities for the A-4 be constructed under ground; Himmler would be responsible for assuring the order was carried out.

Von Braun's earlier suspicion proved correct. With this move, Himmler acquired control and command over mass production of the A-4, and over its deployment as a military weapon.

Casual observers might have seen Peenemünde as a safe haven whose people were in no danger of getting entangled in the web of Nazi Party activities and intrigues, in contrast to those who lived and worked at less restricted places in Germany. The SS, likewise, left the common man in Peenemünde alone—but only because Himmler was out for bigger game. Considering his almost unlimited power, coupled with a total lack of technical understanding, this was a dangerous situation for von Braun. With his strong sense for sound engineering, and for ethical demeanor as well, he was often tempted to make statements that would not at all be appreciated by his counterparts.

Years after the war, more of this struggle became known, mostly through Speer's books *Inside the Third Reich* [3-4] and *Infiltration* [3-5], and by Dornberger's book *V-2* [1]. It is a confusing story, full of morbid ambition, intrigue, recklessness, ignorance, megalomania, and stupidity on one side, and enormous human efforts and sacrifices on the other. Himmler did succeed in acquiring far-reaching influence over mass production and military deployment of the A-4, but not over technical development and testing. The fact that a complete take-over of Peenemünde never occurred, although the SS had some well-placed informants and collaborators within the complex [3-5 and 3-11], attests to the superior leadership and steadfastness of Dornberger, von Braun, and others among the Peenemünde hierarchy.

Initially, the A-4 Project even faced danger from two fronts: Speer's ministry, and Himmler's SS. As the war dragged on, the two fronts merged into one.

Speer became acquainted with the Peenemünde establishment during the late 1930s. As a thoroughly technically oriented and talented person, he became fascinated with the fast-moving project [3-4], and he did not hesitate to give the establishment substantial and continuing support, even without Hitler's concurrence (Chapter 3-3).

In December 1942, after the first A-4 had been successfully launched, Hitler gave in to Speer's urging and signed an order for the production of A-4s, without, however, approving any particular priority for the project. Dornberger and von Braun were not at all happy about this turn of events. Although driving forcefully toward completion and perfection of the A-4, they were in no hurry to have the rocket handed over to a mass production facility, and to the SS for military deployment. Again and again, they demanded more time for testing, for technical improvements, and for the achievement of higher reliability. Better target accuracy would be obtained only by systematically increasing accuracies of components. Speer's ministry, however, wanted mass production immediately after the first successful test launching in October 1942. When Dornberger and von Braun laid out a program for further improvements and intensified testing of the A-4, Hitler appointed a missile production czar, Gerhard Degenkolb, a member of Speer's staff who had made a name for himself by organizing and enforcing the monthly production of 2,000 war locomotives. With that achievement to his credit, Hitler thought that Degenkolb would qualify as manager-in-chief of an A-4 production program that would produce 3,000 missiles per month, as Hitler had originally ordered.

Thus, production of the A-4 was forced out of the hands of its developers while the rocket was still in a premature state. From the beginning, there was much friction and tension between Degenkolb and the Peenemünde people. Dornberger described the missile czar as *"violent, menacing, vain, distrustful, and without any regard for rule and order"* [1].

While Degenkolb was busy preparing the mass production of A-4 rockets, another high-priority action got underway in Germany. Speer, responsible for maintaining and even increasing the productivity of German industry, was painfully aware of the vulnerability of existing factories to Allied bombing. An effort was started to look for underground facilities, such as tunnels, mines, quarries, and other subterranean structures where industrial activities could proceed without the danger of being destroyed in air raids.

One such structure was found in the Harz Mountains near the town of Niedersachswerfen. Back in 1917, a chemical corporation, Badische Anilin und Sodafabrik, had driven tunnels into Kohnstein Mountain to exploit its deposits of gypsum. Mining continued until 1934; from that time on, the tunnels were utilized, and also expanded, as storage areas for chemicals, including large amounts of petroleum and gasoline. During the spring of 1943, it was decided that A-4 production should be carried out at that place, together with a number of other weapon systems; it was to be called Mittelwerk (Chapter 3-3). Conversion of the storage tunnels into facilities for industrial production started immediately, and with it began one of the darkest chapters in German history.

In an attempt to obtain more support for the work at Peenemünde, Speer wanted Dornberger and von Braun to meet with Hitler. He succeeded on 8 July 1943. After von Braun had made his presentation, in which he showed a model of the A-4 and a movie of a launching, he emphasized the urgent need for more development and testing before production could begin, Hitler stepped up the budget allotments, and he made Speer *"responsible for the A-4 Program"* [3-4]. One month later, Hitler informed Speer that *"Himmler suggested the use of concentration camp inmates for A-4 production to assure secrecy."* Speer and Dr. Karl Otto Saur, one of Speer's department heads, were against Himmler's suggestion. Hitler told Speer to discuss that point with Himmler. However, by that time Himmler had been promoted to Minister of the Interior; that put him organizationally above Speer, and the Minister of Armament and Munitions lost his argument. Himmler always came out the winner.

After the SS had established its grip on the A-4 project, at least on production and military deployment, high-ranking SS officers often came from Berlin to Peenemünde and wanted a guided tour through the rocket development facilities. Von Braun usually obliged with politeness and patience—what else could he have done?—but sometimes the arrogance of his visitors drove him to a bit of sarcasm. One officer in a group of visitors, to whom von Braun had just shown an A-4 on the test stand, asked him how long it would take to make the A-4 ready for troop training. *"Three months,"* was the answer.— *"How long would it take you if I sent you a contingent of 200 SS men to help you?"* the officer wanted to know. *"Herr Standartenführer"*, von Braun said, *"in that case it would take us six to eight months, because we would have to repair all the damage those untrained men would do to the rocket."*

At another time, an SS officer came to von Braun's office and saw his desk which was always full of notes, reports, drawings, and other documents that are the unavoid-able ingredients of a busy man's daily chores. As usual, all the papers were neatly stacked and carefully arranged on the desk. *"Dr. von Braun"*, the visitor said, *"what a mess of papers you have on your desk! This is intolerable! My General in Berlin never has more than one paper on his desk at any time!"*— *"Yes, sir,"* von Braun replied, *"I know. It is the paper in which his wife wrapped his sandwich for him."*

It may be understandable that such replies did not create an amiable atmosphere between von Braun and the SS, even though Himmler, as one of the gimmicks with which he tried to lure von Braun away from the army and over to his SS, had personally bestowed an honorary SS rank upon him (Untersturmführer, equivalent to second lieutenant in the U.S. Army) on 1 May 1940. At that time, von Braun was greatly upset by Himmler's fake show of generosity. He discussed the situation with some of his closest associates, and they all agreed that declining this *"honor"* would only result in a fit of rage on the part of Himmler, with unpredictable consequences. So von Braun accepted the rank, but he quietly stowed his SS uniform away in a closet. Himmler, continuing his attempts to win von Braun over to his side, promoted him further, and made him Sturmbannführer (equivalent to major) on 28 June 1943. Since all these shows of benevolence were to no avail, Himmler had von Braun put into a Gestapo jail in Stettin in March 1944 (Chapter 3-3). That's where von Braun spent his thirty-second birthday.

6   UNDERGROUND FACTORY MITTELWERK

Himmler had begun the systematic establishment of concentration camps during the spring of 1943, obviously in order to create a store of cheap labor for an enormous program of industrial expansion and production that he planned first as part of the war effort, and later for a gigantic postwar build-up [3-5]. The average citizen in Germany heard about the *"KZ,"* as concentration camps were called. It was known that certain criminals, dissidents who had expressed their anti-Nazi feelings too loudly, and persons the government wanted out of the way, were hauled off to the KZ without any orderly legal procedures. Almost everyone knew of some hapless person whom the Gestapo had picked up and sent to the KZ. Also, Party functionaries and other hard-boiled Nazis used it almost as a standard threat: *"If you don't conform, we'll send you to the KZ!"*

Himmler also imprisoned in his concentration camps many of the resistance fighters captured in countries occupied by the German Army. It was not known at that time, though, that the road to the concentration camp would be a way with no return for many of the inmates.

When Himmler suggested the use of concentration camp inmates for A-4 production at Mittelwerk, he based his proposal on the availability of thousands and thousands of inmates from a number of concentration camps, all of which were under his command as supreme concentration camp commander in the Third Reich.

While the debate about A-4 production at Mittelwerk, and about the use of concentration camp inmates, was still underway, Peenemünde suffered the British air raid. Hitler subsequently ordered *"the entire German industry"* underground, and he concurred with the suggestion that concentration camp inmates should be used in A-4 production. However, he decreed that *"only Germans"* should be employed in A-4 work [3-4]—an order that later was ignored.

Under the Degenkolb program, production of A-4 components began at Mittelwerk in September 1943. When Himmler, who had assumed full responsibility for A-4 production in August, put his SS General Hans Kammler in charge, he totally disregarded Speer's existing assignment! Speer retained the responsibility for development, while Kammler, in response to Himmler's promise given in August, set out to force the production of *"5,000 A-4s in the shortest possible time . . . ;"* Hitler had asked for 3,000 A-4s per month.

Dornberger, who at that time was still in the position to give the formal orders for A-4 production to Himmler's underground factory Mittelwerk, was slow in carrying out that order, incurring Himmler's and Kammler's displeasure [3-4]. Finally, in October 1943, Dornberger asked for *"the production of 900 A-4s per month, up to a total number of 12,000 rockets"* [1].

The actual production numbers were lower. During all of 1944, only 4,120 A-4s were produced. Production finally stopped on 18 March 1945 after a total of 5,784 A-4 rockets had left Mittelwerk.

Hitler's orders to put the entire German industry underground led to frantic activities at Mittelwerk. More and more tunnels were driven into the solid rock, more machine rooms and assembly hangars were blasted out. Thousands of inmates from nearby concentration camps, particularly from Camps Dora and Ellrich, were transported to Mittelwerk every morning, and back in the evening. Some of the inmates had to stay in the tunnels all the time. Large numbers of civilian engineers, craftsmen, and technicians also worked in the underground factory; those civilians who were assigned there to A-4-related work had been transferred from the three A-4 production plants south of Peenemünde, near Vienna, and at Friedrichshafen that had been bombed out in September 1943.

Manufacturing of components and assembly of entire weapon systems were underway in workshop rooms near the tunnel entry, while blasting went on more deeply into the mountain. Until summer of 1944, a large portion of the inmates had to work in the tunnel-blasting areas under unbelievably harsh and insane conditions. Those assigned to technical work were the luckier ones. Besides the Germans, there were Russian, French, Polish, Belgian, and Italian nationals among the inmates.

Working and living conditions at Mittelwerk must have been horrible, bad enough for the civilians, far worse for the inmates who worked in the shop areas, and worst for the tunnel blasters. Speer visited the Mittelwerk for the first time on 10 December 1943. In his book *Inside the Third Reich* [3-4], he described the conditions in the tunnels as *"barbarous,"* and in his book *Infiltration* [3-5] as *"scandalous."* He immediately ordered more food, better living conditions, cleaner sanitary facilities, and more humane treatment for the inmates. In particular, he ordered the construction of barracks near the Mittelwerk for 10,000 inmates. Jean Michel, a former inmate of Camp Dora, wrote [3-12]: *"Late March or early April [1944] the barracks were completed, and the inmates could sleep outside the tunnels."* Speer wrote that during December 1943, when he first visited the Mittelwerk, 630 (or 5.7 percent) of the 11,000 inmates died of diseases; during August 1944, only 100 (or 0.8 percent) out of 12,000 inmates died, a clear indication that his measures had brought at least some improvements. Michel mentioned that Speer's actions indeed brought some relief.

Beginning in September 1943, Arthur Rudolph and several other members of the Peenemünde rocket center were transferred to the Mittelwerk for shorter or longer periods to help set up the production and test facilities, and to train the workers. Rudolph was the technical director for A-4-related work.

While A-4 component production, organized under the Degenkolb program, had begun already during the summer of 1943, assembly of complete A-4 missiles started in December 1943.

Rudolph stayed with the A-4 production program at Mittelwerk until the end of the war in May 1945. The total number of employees under his technical direction, civilians and inmates, varied between about 6,900 and 8,400. At first, the number of inmates exceeded that of the civilians; later, there were more than twice as many civilians as inmates. The civilian employees were professionals, or at least had some training for their work assignments; most of the inmates were untrained for their work. None of those inmates who worked under Rudolph stayed in the Mittelwerk overnight.

Rudolph's functions, and those of other civilians in management positions, were strictly limited to technical work. Administration of the Mittelwerk, including the procurement of camp inmates, their transportation, housing, clothing, feeding, health care, and general treatment, was entirely up to Kammler's SS, under the broad responsibility of Himmler. The latter's responsibility also included meeting the preset production quotas, and providing the work space and the work force needed to produce the desired production numbers. All of that had to be achieved not only for the A-4 project, but for half a dozen other weapon systems eventually crammed into the Mittelwerk underground factory.

After the war, Rudolph told his friends from Peenemünde about the nightmarish conditions at Mittelwerk. *"When I first saw what was going on, I was totally shocked,"* he said. *"I immediately tried to talk to one of the SS supervisors, but he cut me right off, saying: 'That is none of your business. Shut up, or you will wear the same uniform!'—A little later, I tried another approach with a higher SS guard. 'Look here', I said, pointing to some manufactured pieces, 'this work is not good enough. It does not have the high accuracy we demand of these pieces. This is certainly not a result of ill will or sabotage, it simply reflects a state of extreme fatigue and emaciation on the part of the workers. Unless we keep them in a decent state of physical fitness, we will not achieve acceptable products, and we cannot meet our production quotas!'—The result was some modest improvement, at least for the inmates in my A-4 directorate."*

Rudolph, during the many postwar interrogations to which he was subjected, always made emphatic statements to the effect that while he was technical director of A-4 production at Mittelwerk, not one person died in that area at Mittelwerk under his technical supervision.

Likewise, von Braun testified repeatedly that during his short visits to Mittelwerk, he never saw a dead person (Chapter 3-7).

However, large numbers of inmates died in the camps, such as Dora and Ellrich, where conditions were repeatedly described as ghastly. Diseases were rampant and sanitary facilities were practically nonexistent.

How many people, civilian and forced labor, worked at Mittelwerk? The figure 32,000 has been cited for the time of maximum activity late in 1944. For those who

Labor Involved in A-4 (V-2) Production at Mittelwerk

Date	Technical Supervision	Administration	Skilled Labor	Common Labor	Total Civilians	Forced Labor	Total
July 44	500	1,000	1,500	400	3,400	5,000	8,400
Oct. 44	600	800	2,000	600	4,000	3,500	7,500
March 45	800	600	2,500	1,000	4,900	2,000	6,900

From: Bilet, V. H., and J. D. McPhilimy, "Production and Disposition of German A-4 (V-2) Rockets", Staff Study No. A-55-2167-N1, DDC No. ATI-18315, March 1948, Headquarter Air Materiel Command, Wright Field, Dayton, Ohio.

worked in the A-4 (V-2) program, detailed numbers were reported in a staff study by the Air Materiel Command in Wright Field in 1947 [3-13]. These figures are shown in the table above. After the initial build-up, the number of forced laborers was continuously reduced and the number of professional civilians increased, because, as the report states, unskilled inmates were not able to perform work of the necessary professional quality.

Von Braun was called to the Mittelwerk repeatedly, the first time on 25 January 1944, but always briefly—for a few hours up to two days—and only for the discussion and solution of very specific problems of manufacturing or testing. Each time, he was taken very quickly to the meeting room and back out again.

Although each visitor was ordered not to talk about what he had seen, von Braun could not desist from sharing his experiences with some of his closest associates who still remember his words: *"It is hellish. My spontaneous reaction was to talk to one of the SS guards, only to be told with unmistakable harshness that I should mind my own business, or find myself in the same striped fatigues! I would never have believed that human beings can sink that low, but I realized that any attempt of reasoning on humane grounds would be utterly futile. Such arguments as decency, fairness, morality, or ethics simply did not count here. These individuals had drifted so far away from even the most basic principles of human morale that this scene of gigantic suffering left them entirely untouched."*

Von Braun took a manufactured part, went to one of the higher-ranking SS officials, and told him that such poor workmanship simply cannot be accepted. *"How can you expect better work quality,"* he said, *"when you keep your workers so far below a normal state of health? Our capability to produce acceptable V-2 rockets depends fully on the good work these people are doing. If they don't have better living and working conditions that enable them to concentrate on their work with a clearer mind and more skillful hands, we will never reach a higher level of work quality than we have now. We badly need an improvement of the quality of your output. That is now in your hands! The engineers and scientists who train the inmates cannot do more than what they are doing now. It is up to you to improve the physical and mental capabilities of the workers! I represent the customer here, and I have to reject such miserable stuff. If you cannot provide better products, your entire operation here is a total failure! Put your workers under better conditions, and they will do better work!"*

Von Braun's reaction, and even his words, were very similar to Rudolph's. It must have been obvious to both of them that this approach would be the only one that might have some positive results. Those totally degenerate and inhuman SS functionaries had only their orders in mind; showing them that they were failing their orders might be a way to bring about an improvement of the lot of the prisoners.

Although Rudolph's and von Braun's efforts had some positive effects, both of them remained deeply disturbed. Years later, von Braun said that the vision of those luckless prisoners has haunted him ever since. *"The most depressing thought,"* he said, *"is the fact that I was absolutely without power to do anything substantial. Even if I had left the place and my work and gotten to jail, Himmler would have given orders to continue, but only under harsher and more stupid conditions. The inmates would undoubtedly have suffered even more."*

On several occasions, Dornberger and von Braun spent hours trying to think of steps they could take to relieve the dreary lot of the inmates. *"We did not arrive at any good idea,"* von Braun recalled later. *"Even if both of us had resigned—a step that would have converted us into inmates immediately—we would not have helped the prisoners. Hitler and his SS commanders, in their frenzied determination not to give up their mad race toward doom, would certainly have continued all the Mittelwerk operations—V-2 rockets, airplane engines, anti-aircraft missiles, submarine components, fighter planes. Inmates and civilian workers would have been driven only more relentlessly."*

Even if all technical work at Mittelwerk had been suspended completely, that would not have set the inmates free. On the contrary, they would have been kept in the concentration camps day and night, exposed to growing famine and disease. As the world learned after the end of the war, this actually became the fate of many concentration camp inmates shortly before the terminal breakdown of Germany. Many of them lost their lives during the final months, weeks, and days before the war's end by hunger, disease, and wanton killings. The SS commanders obviously tried to prevent inmates from falling into the hands of the Allies.

Von Braun and his team members became aware of these final tragedies, particularly of the mass killings by the SS during the waning days of the Third Reich, after they had come to the United States.

The only person who might have had a chance to persuade Hitler, over the influence of Himmler, to give the inmates a more humane treatment would have been Speer. Reminiscing about the past, he expressed this thought himself. *"I could have made decisions in a minute that would have improved the situation of the unfortunate inmates,"* he wrote in his book *Infiltration* in 1981 [3-4]. *"By simple means, I could probably have increased the survival chances for countless numbers of people . . . [This] would not have spelled any danger for me. But I hid my conscience behind the innumerable problems that I had to settle at such times. Furthermore, I was always in a hurry. I barely had 5 or 10 minutes to hold a conversation in peace and quiet. One decision after another had to be made . . . Why did I waste my chances to help? . . . Why did it not occur to me that I acted carelessly when I did not think of my greater responsibility, but only of my immediate administrative duties? . . . I overlooked the human part of our duty . . . We did not do what we could and should have done to save the lives of all these people . . ."*

Speer did take a number of actions to improve the lot of the prisoners, but he could have done much more. He realized and admitted this when it was too late. Those countless others who were very painfully aware of the need to do something, but were totally paralyzed by the power structure of the most ruthless dictatorship, had no chance of doing anything substantial, even if they had been ready to sacrifice their own lives.

The world would learn the full extent of Nazi concentration camp atrocities when the inmates were liberated toward the end of the war, and subsequently as the Nuremberg and other war crime trials unfolded after the war. Relevant books include those by Davidson [3-4], Speer [3-4; 3-5]; Bornemann [3-5]; Bornemann and Broszat [3-16]; Michel [3-12]; Ordway and Sharpe [11]; Tusa and Tusa [3-17]; and others. While it will always remain incomprehensible how it could happen that such inhuman sufferings were inflicted upon so many by a small self-styled *"elite"* whose normal human feelings had totally degenerated, these books at least give an account of the development, structure, and apalling conditions in the concentration camps; and, in the particular case of Dora and its satellite camps, of their relationship to Mittelwerk.

Toward the end of 1944, about one quarter of Mittelwerk's entire workforce worked at the V-2 production lines. During the summer of that year, about 60 percent of the V-2 workers were inmates from various camps. However, because of the nature of the highly technical V-2 work, more and more of the unskilled inmates had to be replaced by trained civilian technicians and engineers. By March 1945, only 30 percent of the V-2 work force consisted of inmates; most of the inmates from Dora and Ellrich worked on the mass production of other weapons. Earlier, many of them had to blast new tunnels into the mountain, a truly murderous assignment that continued until late in 1944. The *"tunnel blasters"* came mostly from the nearby camps Ellrich and Harzungen which, together with Dora and other satellites, formed the Mittelbau complex of concentration camps.

7   THE MITTELWERK TRAGEDY

Using prisoners as workers, including those held in concentration camps and in prisoner of war camps, was widespread in Hitler's Third Reich. When added to the ever-present pool of volunteer foreign laborers, these men represented a substantial source of manpower to assist farmers, to help with civil construction and military support activities, and, particularly during the final years of the war, to provide manpower for the huge production empire established by Speer and Himmler.

Although Speer argued frequently against what became a standard 12-hour day, and in favor of a more humane treatment of such workers, even proposing that they be rewarded for exceptional service, he revealed no philosophical aversion to their employment. Toward the end of the war, he did try to reduce the number of concentration camp workers in his far-reaching enterprise, but without success. This fact was recognized when Speer faced judgment before the Nürnberg Tribunal; but, it seems, the reason for concern stemmed more from an aversion to Himmler (who finally controlled virtually the entire forced labor pool) than from humanitarian considerations.

To organize the forced labor program, Hitler in March 1942 named the Gauleiter [Governor] of Thuringia, Ernst Friedrich Christoph (*"Fritz"*) Sauckel, as Plenipotentiary of Labor Mobilization. A Nazi party member since 1923, Sauckel pursued his new job with enthusiasm, and soon increased greatly the number of foreigners, including volunteers, working on behalf of the Third Reich. As pointed out by Eugene Davidson [3-14], *"Sauckel's recruiting drive started in a relatively humane fashion—or at least with certain humane intentions and instructions. From the beginning, however, working and living conditions for thousands of those laborers were subhuman. For one thing, there simply was not enough habitable space available for all these thousands of people; for another, many camp managers either had no interest in how foreign laborers lived, or they just enjoyed mistreating them . . ."*

Statistics for 1942 show that 5,124,000 individuals from German-occupied territories, including volunteers, forced laborers, concentration camp inmates, and prisoners of war were working inside Germany, a number that remained more or less constant throughout the war. It is estimated that workers in the munitions and armaments area made up a full 40 percent of that figure.

The decision in August 1943 to move production facilities for weapons systems underground was followed later that month by a proposal from Professor Karl-Maria Hettlage, director of the Bureau of Economy and Finance in Speer's Armaments Ministry in Berlin, to establish a *"limited liability corporation"* (GmbH) with Dr. Kurt Kettler, director general of the Borsig Lokomotiv-Werke GmbH in Berlin and Federal Railway Councillor, as its managing director. The firm's name would be Mittelwerk GmbH, and financing would flow through Speer's ministry. Overseeing the entire operation would be Dr. Karl Otto Saur, director of the Technical Bureau under Speer. With that move, Speer secured at least some influence on the A-4 program for himself, and prevented a total sellout to Himmler's SS.

Months before the Royal Air Force raid, plans for a small preproduction manufacturing program of the A-4 at Peenemünde were underway, independent of mass production elsewhere at a later time. Then, missile czar Degenkolb in Speer's ministry began to prepare and later coordinate mass production of the missile on his own terms. At that time, A-4 parts were being manufactured at more than 100 locations in Germany and other countries occupied by the German Army. Preliminary plans were drawn up by Degenkolb to produce 300 rockets monthly from October to December 1943, and 900 units monthly thereafter. Assembly was to take place in the pilot production works at Karlshagen near Peenemünde; at the Luftschiffbau Zeppelin in Friedrichshafen in southern Germany; and at the Henschel-Rax-Werke in Wiener-Neustadt in Austria.

Extreme vulnerability of these surface facilities to air attack had been recognized even before the raid on Peenemünde. Degenkolb therefore looked for alternatives, one of which was the very Harz mountain site that would later be selected by Kammler for underground weapon production.

On 28 August 1943, the SS transferred the first inmates from Buchenwald to an emerging 'Häftlingsarbeitslager' [inmate labor camp] at the south end of Kohnstein Mountain that would soon become the infamous Camp Dora. Although Kammler theoretically reported directly to Speer, the SS general was also subordinate to Himmler and therefore could take particularly aggressive action to secure the required labor force for Dora from camps anywhere in Europe. Speer remembered: *"In the course of my enforced collaboration with this man, I discovered him to be a cold, ruthless schemer, a fanatic in the pursuit of a goal, and as carefully calculating as he was unscrupulous"* [3-4].

Conversion of the old Kohnstein storage tunnels into a huge production facility began in the summer of 1943. A shipment of one thousand workers, including several hundred concentration camp inmates from Buchenwald, arrived in September 1943. Equipment was shipped from Peenemünde that same month. Mittelwerk management expected to deliver the first missiles before the end of the year, and to accelerate production to a monthly rate of 400 missiles in May, and 600 in August 1944.

By making a supreme effort, the first three Mittelwerk A-4s were ready on 31 December 1943. They were shipped in five railway cars to the Demag Vehicle Works (Demag-Fahrzeugwerke, GmbH) in Berlin-Falkensee on 1 January 1944 for the installation of electrical components, and then to Peenemünde where, upon inspection, numerous manufacturing and assembly flaws were discovered. Flight testing began with an unlucky start; the first A-4 produced at Mittelwerk, like numerous others following it, failed shortly after launch.

Problems with the Mittelwerk-produced A-4s brought complaints from many sources. So desperate was the war situation for Hitler that only few individuals in Speer's ministry or in the SS involved with A-4 production were willing to face the fact that the weapon was still in the research and development stage, and by no means ready for field deployment. Von Braun's warnings to this effect were brushed aside as irrelevant, while pressure built up to mass-produce the missile. He was ordered to visit Mittelwerk repeatedly, and also to detail there a few of his engineers to coordinate design changes with resident manufacturing personnel. Von Braun's long-time colleague Arthur Rudolph was assigned to the Mittelwerk for more than a year.

The efforts of civilians assigned to Mittelwerk, such as Rudolph, were hampered by strict SS-imposed prohibition of direct contact between plant employees and prisoners. In fact, on 30 December 1943, Dora camp commandant Sturmbannführer (Major; later Lieutenant Colonel) Otto Förschner issued explicit instructions that there would be no personal interaction between German civilian personnel and inmates. Förschner and his staff were ever concerned that inmates might try to escape, or to sabotage production. Opportunities for sabotage were ample, for the A-4 was an extremely complex system with some 20,000 parts, all of which had to function to assure a successful mission. It appears that the French and the Russians were the most actively engaged in this courageous, but extremely risky business.

The role of Förschner was two-fold: running the Dora concentration camp, and simultaneously being directly involved in the administration of the Mittelwerk GmbH, plant security, and mobilization of labor. Förschner had come to Dora from Buchenwald. He remained at Mittelwerk until late January 1945. Soon thereafter, he was captured by American officers, and on 13 February, he was sentenced to death by a military court. He was executed at Landsberg am Lech on 28 May 1945.

As plans for assembling A-4s at Mittelwerk further crystallized, the preposterous production figure of 1,800 units per month emerged in October 1943. Over the strong protests of Dornberger, von Braun, and others, this proposal was approved by Degenkolb. But soon afterward, General Emil Leeb, head of the Army Weapons Department, followed Dornberger's advice and prepared a production order for half that number, or 900 missiles a month. Accordingly, Mittelwerk was assigned responsibility for:

1. Production of 900 A-4 rockets monthly, with a total quantity of 12,000 units supplied without interior electrical fittings, warheads, and packing.

2. Final assembly of these 12,000 rockets, including interior fittings, warheads, and packing at a unit price of RM 40,000 for a total contract price of RM 480,000,000. [This would have been US $115,000,000 at the wartime Reichsmark quotation (through Switzerland) of $0.238].

As development and production of the A-4 and several other weapon systems, including the Jumo 004 jet engines and the fighter plane He 162, expanded at Mittelwerk, so did requirements for labor supplied by Dora, and by a growing number of subcamps in the Harz mountain region. Soon, Dora became known as Mittelbau I, and its two main subcamps as Mittelbau II (Ellrich) and Mittelbau III (Harzungen). In October 1944, Dora, Ellrich, Harzungen, and all other satellite camps in the area were elevated in status from a subunit of Buchenwald to a completely independent system, with Dora serving as administrative headquarters.

Dora itself contained more than 50 inmate barracks with multilevel bunks and little else. The camp also included four administrative barracks, an infirmary, a crematorium, and such other adjuncts as a power station and laundry plus a cinema for the favored few. Just beyond the gate houses was a large parade ground, a characteristic of all concentration camps. Close by were the twenty-five or so buildings that accommodated the SS garrison.

As the Mittelbau complex grew, so did the number of prisoners assigned to Dora and its subcamps. By October 1943, here were some 4,000 inmates, 5,000 in November, 10,000 in December, and 12,500 in February 1944. During that five-month period, most of the tunnel excavation, concrete lining, and similar exhausting work was undertaken with severe suffering on the part of the inmates. According to Bornemann and Broszat [3-16], of the approximately 17,000 individuals transferred into the Mittelbau camps between October 1943 and March 1944, about 15,000 were assigned to the tunnels. During the same period, there were 2,882 verified deaths, suffered, in descending order, by Russians, French, Poles, Germans, and Italians. Some 3,000 who were too weak to function as laborers were simply shipped out of Mittelbau. Many, if not most, of them must be presumed to have perished.

With the completion of most construction and related heavy work, and the concentration on weapon production assignments, the lot of inmates began to improve in the spring of 1944. This led Bornemann and Broszat to observe that inmates began to receive *"relatively considerate treatment,"* experiencing *"greater freedom than was possible in other concentration camps."* The two authors also noted that the German civilian workers in Mittelwerk *"seem, in general, to have made the prisoners' working conditions easier. At any rate, it meant a step forward for the prisoners in that after rocket production had begun, they worked to a greater degree under the supervision of plant foremen, and were no longer exposed to the bullying of SS personnel."*

In spite of this, security was extremely tight in the camps. To assure that it was enforced, a special unit of the Gestapo was brought in under SS Obersturmbannführer [Lt. Colonel] Helmut Bischoff, reporting directly to Kammler. The unit was specially trained to prevent sabotage and escape. Attempts at both were dealt with harshly. It was Bischoff who developed the deterrent practice of hanging saboteurs on a gallows before assembled prisoners.

As new production assignments were thrust upon Mittelwerk, even more sub-camps sprouted up in the area, and the already existing ones grew in population. By the end of 1944, Dora alone counted at least 15,000 inmates, and the population of the various subcamps had reached approximately 19,000. Among them, Ellrich had be-tween 7,000 and 8,000 inmates, and Harzungen over 4,000. It is noted that workers in these two camps became involved in heavy mining and construction work, and thus suffered more than their corresponding numbers in Dora who by then were largely involved in manufacturing. The most numerous prisoners were, in descending order, Russian, Polish, French, German, and Belgian. The first Hungarian Jews arrived in Dora in late May, 1944, followed by a second shipment in mid-June.

The end of Dora and its satellite camps was particularly tragic. As Russian forces closed in on Germany from the east, prisoners housed in concentration camps in Poland and other occupied countries were progressively herded into homeland installations such as Dora. Drawn from Auschwitz and elsewhere, they arrived in lamentable physical condition, and in numbers that overwhelmed the camps to which they were assigned. The death of thousands shortly after arrival so overtaxed Dora's crematorium that a new one had to be installed at nearby Ellrich. The plight of Mittel-bau complex prisoners is revealed by the monthly statistics: in October, 1944, 200 died, while in March, 1945, the number had soared to 2,400.

Camps of the Mittelbau complex began to be evacuated in April. At the same time, the increasingly desperate SS was executing more and more prisoners by hanging, 162 in March alone. Around the same time, an Allied air raid on Nordhausen killed another 1,500 prisoners. During the night of 4 to 5 April 1945, the final exodus from Dora began; it was completed a day later, just ahead of advance units of the U.S. Third Armored Division. Before they arrived, an estimated 25,000 to 30,000 prisoners had been stuffed into freight cars and sent to Bergen-Belsen where those who had survived the ordeal were liberated by the British on 15 April. Two other trains carried Ellrich prisoners to Oranienburg and Dora prisoners to Ravensbruck, while a third moved prisoners to Mauthausen in Austria.

Verified total deaths in the entire Mittelbau complex of camps reached 12,500; but, investigators feel that 20,000 would be a more accurate number. More than half of them perished during the last three months of operations (January, February, and March 1945) as Mittelbau was forced to accommodate prisoners transferred from the east.

What did this frantic effort to mass-produce an immature weapon, ordered by Hitler and supported by Himmler and Speer against the pleas of its developers, really achieve? Approximately 5,800 A-4s were produced at Mittelwerk; of these, about 3,200 were launched operationally. Their total warhead capability, accumulated over a period of seven months, amounted to about 3,000 metric tons of explosives. During a single major air raid by Allied bombers, up to 10,000 tons of bombs were dropped on a given target within a few hours.

Prior to and after his arrival in the United States, von Braun had to explain the relationship between Peenemünde and the V-2 production program at Mittelwerk in great detail. His candid descriptions satisfied the Allied investigatory authorities to the extent that, after checking numerous other records, statements, and testimonies, von Braun and over a hundred of his colleagues were permitted to come to the United States. Eventually, they were granted U.S. citizenship and high security clearances, and after some time of joint work, the Germans enjoyed the virtually unrestricted confidence and trust of most of their American colleagues.

Twenty years after the war, circumstances arose that caused von Braun to clarify again his and Peenemünde's relationship to the Mittelwerk. These events started with the French. Citizens of that nation had played an important role in the Mittelwerk work force as inmates of concentration camps. No one who was caught in that abysmal tragedy would ever forget the horrifying experience.

By the mid-1960s, not only the top Nazis—Hitler, Bormann, Himmler, Goebbels, Göring—but also those specifically connected with concentration camps and with Mittelwerk—Kammler, Sauckel, Förschner, Sawatzky, Saur—had long been dead. Tormentors of lower status either had never been known to inmates and the public by name, or they had just disappeared. During the early 1950s, a man began to find public recognition whose name had not been known publicly before: Wernher von Braun. It was learned, in the United States as well as in Europe, that he was campaigning for satellites and manned flight to the Moon and Mars, and that he had been the guiding force behind Peenemünde. It became also known that V-2 rockets, developed at Peenemünde, had been mass-produced at Mittelwerk, and that concentration camp inmates had made up a part of its work force. It is not surprising that camp survivors began to associate von Braun with their wartime ordeals, and that they particularly resented the growing and usually positive publicity given him.

Around 1964, the work of Ordway, co-author of this book, brought him into frequent contact with editors of the French weekly *Paris Match*. They had become intrigued with American and Soviet achievements in space, resulting in enthusiastic coverage of the subject in their magazine.

Ordway briefed them and also organized tours of NASA installations, including interviews with von Braun. The editors, impressed with von Braun and his team, between 1964 and 1966 published a number of glowing reports on their work. In the autumn of 1965, an Air France charter flight was organized that took a number of distinguished and influential Frenchmen, Belgians, and Swiss, accompanied by Ordway, from Paris to NASA installations in the United States. At the Marshall Center in Huntsville, von Braun treated his visitors to a test firing of a powerful F-1 rocket engine that powered the mammoth Saturn V Moon rocket. Obviously, the Huntsville program left the visiting Europeans with a feeling of deep admiration for von Braun and his NASA team, reflected in the *Paris Match* 23 October issue. When, a year later, von Braun and Ordway published a book, *History of Rocketry and Space Travel*, in New York and London [1-2], *Paris Match* arranged with publisher Larousse the publication of an expanded French edition, *L'Histoire mondiale de l'astronautique* (1968), for which the authors subsequently were awarded the prestigious Diplôme d'Honneur of the French Commission de Bibliographie, d'Histoire et d'Art.

The laudatory tone of the magazine's reports about von Braun caused grave irritations to former inmates of concentration camps who had formed an organization known as the Amicale des Camps de Dora-Ellrich [Friends of Deportees of the Dora-Ellrich Camps]. Their displeasure took the form of a number of letters directed to the editors of *Paris Match*, written between October 1965 and March 1966. The composers of these letters felt that if von Braun hadn't developed the V-2 in the first place, and he hadn't pressed for rapid production after its development, Dora and Ellrich would never have existed, and hence no camp inmates would ever have had to suffer. They overlooked the simple fact that concentration camps existed in Hitler's Third Reich before production of V-2s began. Inmates for Mittelwerk were transferred from other camps to Dora, Ellrich, and other Mittelbau installations. Had there been no V-2, the luckless inmates would have been forced to work on other weapons, and perhaps would have suffered even more.

The letters contained bitter accusations against von Braun who was seen as the central cause, and also as the main perpetrator of the misery of the inmates, of their inhuman working and living conditions, and of their high mortality rate.

It was unthinkable that the editors of *Paris Match* could ignore these letters. On 4 April 1966, they wrote their bureau chief in New York: *"Knowing of your relations with von Braun, we wonder whether you can ask him to give some explanations with regard to these accusations which, in fact, do not appear to be based on any precise proof."*

On 26 April 1966, von Braun wrote a rather lengthy reply:

"Thank you for letting me see the letters that Paris Match *has received from the 'Friends of Deportees of the Dora-Ellrich Camps'. I can readily understand the irritation that a former French inmate of a wartime forced labor camp in Germany must feel when he sees a leading French magazine giving a big publicity buildup to a man whose wartime engineering creations have caused him so much unforgettable suffering and anguish. However, my personal role in these past events was quite different from the one in which some of your correspondents seem to depict me . . ."*

First, von Braun stated that from their position as inmates, it would not have been possible for them to know what roles the various organizations and personalities played in the V-2 program. *"As much as I understand their bitterness,"* von Braun wrote, *"I am appalled by their false accusations aimed at me. I know and appreciate how they have been wronged; but doing me a wrong in this way will certainly not erase the ignominious treatment that they have suffered."* Then, von Braun described how all facets of his personal background were carefully studied by U.S. Government investigators before immigration to the United States, and later citizenship, were granted to him. The records of the War Crime Tribunal (including testimonies of former inmates, guards, and administrative personnel from Dora), and of the Allied investigations of the German rocket program were thoroughly screened. Had he been involved in any way with any atrocities, it would surely have been revealed at that time. He also mentioned that mountains of documents of this period had been examined by many scholars interested in the general history of rocketry. Their findings, which by then had become a matter of public record, were also based on the simple fact that there are still thousands of people around (and not all of them von Braun's friends!) who were intimately familiar with von Braun's duties, the limits of his authority, the anguish to which he himself was subjected, and, last but not least, the kind of man he really was.

A brief summary of von Braun's background followed in *Paris Match*, beginning at the time when he joined the German Army Ordnance Department as a civilian employee in 1932, the year before Hitler's ascendance to power. A total lack of funds for private rocket research in Germany would have made it impossible to continue his early rocket experiments with the German Society for Space Travel in Berlin. Under the auspices of the German Army, continuation of this work became possible, first at Kummersdorf, and from 1937 on at Peenemünde where he developed an evolving family of rockets from the A-1 to the final family member A-4, later called the V-2.

"After our research and development got far enough along, and a few reasonably successful flights had been performed with the new V-2 rocket, the decision was made by Speer's Ministry of Armaments and Munitions in Berlin to mass-produce the V-2," von Braun wrote. Originally, he explained, it was the ministry's plan to activate assembly lines at three or four different locations in Germany and Austria, all in existing factories above ground. The thousands of parts and components from which the rockets were to be assembled were contracted to numerous manufacturing plants throughout the country. During the tooling-up period, but before assembly operations began, he recalled, all four facilities had been destroyed in air raids.

"At this point, Hitler himself gave orders to move the assembly operations for the V-2 mass production program underground," von Braun stated. He went on to tell how existing jigs, fixtures, and tooling were shipped to an abandoned mine south of the Harz mountains in Central Germany. A special organization to operate this new subterranean production facility was established; this is how 'Mittelwerk' came into being. The civilian management of Mittelwerk, noted von Braun, reported to Speer's Ministry of Armaments and War Production. SS General Kammler was instructed by Hitler and Himmler to provide skilled and unskilled forced labor. The prisoners were selected from various concentration camps and moved to Camps Dora and Ellrich. SS Major Otto Förschner was appointed Camp Commandant by Kammler.

As the technical director of the research and development operations at Peenemünde, von Braun at no time had any authority in the Mittelwerk management, in the affairs of Camps Dora and Ellrich, or in the setting of production goals. His task at Peenemünde consisted of (and was limited to) the development of prototypes of the V-2 rocket, and delivery of drawings and construction specifications to Speer's Ministry. As developer of the rocket, Peenemünde was also held responsible for the quality of components fabricated by hundreds of companies all over the country. This made it necessary that quality control representatives from Peenemünde had to be stationed in all major plants involved in the V-2 program, and this included Mittelwerk.

Not surprisingly, the attempt to press a still immature design of a radically new system like the V-2 rocket into mass production led to a host of technical difficulties. While Speer's Ministry pressed the Mittelwerk management for rapid buildup of the production rate, the rockets' experimental prototypes launched at Peenemünde and also by the military units in training were still exploding at their launch sites, failing in mid-flight, or flying astray due to a faulty guidance and control system. This situation compelled von Braun to make numerous trips to manufacturing plants that were supplying faulty parts to Mittelwerk, and a few trips to Mittelwerk itself. *"Each visit,"* von

Braun observed, *"lasted only hours, sometimes one or two days, and was solely concerned with quality control problems. I would like to state emphatically that during my visits to Mittelwerk I never saw a dead prisoner, I never saw a man beaten, I never saw a man hanged or otherwise killed, and I never participated in any acts of violence or physical mistreatment of prisoners. Nor have I ever called upon anyone else to perform such acts. Any testimony to the contrary can only be the result of mistaken identity."* However, von Braun stated that during the latter part of 1944, he learned during visits that many prisoners had died as a result of malnutrition, disease, mistreatment, inadequate medical care, and other causes, and that there had been incidents where prisoners were hanged as a result of sabotage acts. *"I readily agree,"* he continued, *"that the entire environment at Mittelwerk was repulsive, and that the treatment of the prisoners was humiliating. I felt ashamed that things like this were possible in Germany, even under a war situation where national survival was at stake."*

Von Braun's responsibility for quality control forced him to continuously interfere with the flow of production, a role that made him quite unpopular with Mittelwerk managers who were hard put to meet production goals. Kammler, who pressed for accelerated deployment, and Förschner, who had become responsible for meeting production goals, drove the workers, civilians and inmates, harder and harder.

Von Braun mentioned that in the spring of 1944, he was arrested and held in a Gestapo jail for two weeks under the accusation that he was sabotaging the V-2 production program by thinking too much of the future of rockets for space travel, and too little of the immediate needs of the V-2 war production program. *"I think,"* he said, *"this accusation stands in noted contrast to the belief apparently still held by some of the unfortunate Dora prisoners that I was personally to blame for their and their dead comrades' suffering."*

Von Braun enclosed a letter dated 12 April 1963 from another inmate of Camp Dora. *"His attitude differs greatly from the one expressed in the letters from the Friends of the Deportees of Dora-Ellrich,"* von Braun said. During his time in the United States, he received several such letters. However, he refrained from publishing any of them.

Von Braun's letter to the editors of *Paris Match* obviously did clear the air—for the time being. Then, nearly a decade later, the subject of wartime production of the V-2 missile at Mittelwerk resurfaced. In 1975, another wave of accusations against him arose when former Dora inmate Jean Michel published a book about his wartime experiences, *Dora* [3-12]. Author Michel once again tried to lay the blame for the suffering at Dora directly at the feet of von Braun and some other top members of the Peenemünde center.

Although von Braun, like certainly all his associates, was convinced that if there had never been an A-4 (V-2), the SS would have established and operated just as many concentration camps—the inmates would only have been forced to work on other weapons—he chose not to engage in any further debate with former inmates. *"These unlucky people have been mistreated so terribly,"* he once said to some of his close associates. *"I would feel even more miserable if I stood up now and quarreled with them, telling them that they blame the wrong persons. This would help neither them, nor those of us who had a glimpse at the inside of Mittelwerk, to ease our memories . . ."*

8   LIFE GOES ON, AND SO DO THE DREAMS

Most of the rank and file members of the Peenemünde work force had no contact with the production facilities in the Mittelwerk, besides providing blueprints and design data, and occasional consultations about tolerances or modifications for easier manu-facturing. In fact, they knew very little about any activities beyond their immediate areas of responsibility and concern. Dornberger managed to receive a substantial number of the A-4s from the early production runs for test launchings and troop training first in Heidelager, a test firing range near Blizna in southeast Poland, and later in Heidekraut, a test site farther to the southwest. These tests continued to show the need for increased reliability and accuracy, a need that was to govern work at Peenemünde to the last days of the war. This need also prompted continuing urgent requests from von Braun and Dornberger to Himmler's organizations that deployment should be withheld until better rockets became available.

Even before the heavy British air raid on Peenemünde in August 1943, many of the laboratories and shops had been moved to a variety of places all over Germany. Industrial contractors and universities expanded their participation in the work pro-grams. New test laboratories and workshops were established in schoolrooms, ware-houses, and temporary buildings. Much traveling by rail between Peenemünde and other places in Germany was necessary, often under most difficult circumstances because of the frequent air raids. Delays of hours and even days, caused by the bombardment of railroad stations, bridges, and control centers, were the rule. Even communication by telephone became a matter of only sporadic success as the devasta-tions of war grew from day to day. In spite of all these encumbrances, work on the A-4 proceeded.

The abundance of technical and scientific problems that had to be tackled during those years was overwhelming. It was only natural that they filled and occupied the minds of the Peenemünders completely, at least while they did not have to cope with the most basic necessities of life and survival.

There were endless discussions and debates about the problems that came up during their work. Von Braun participated in the larger meetings whenever he could, particularly when some difficulties had to be resolved. His presence in a meeting always had two immediate effects: First, the style and tone of the discussions differed markedly from those in other meetings. Each speaker tried to express himself as clearly as possible, without hiding facts or shunning responsibility. There were no nasty accusations against others. If something had gone wrong, there was a joint effort to correct the errors and assure proper functioning in the next test. Second, von Braun never allowed the discussion of a technical problem to terminate before all the details had been analyzed and clarified to the best capability of all those present. This drive for clarity often required most vigorous efforts on the part of his co-workers. His inquisi-tive and often relentless questions, his insistence on discussing every potential source of failure, his ingenuity in suggesting chains of events and failure modes, and his stunning ability to anticipate future failures, always amazed everybody at such meetings.

Enlisted men in particular enjoyed and appreciated meetings with *"the boss."* Not only were they extremely helpful for the clarification of complex questions and for reaching decisions; there was still another reason: When the Army called many engineers and scientists back from the battle fronts in 1942 and 1943 and sent them to Peenemünde, these men—mostly Pfc.s and corporals—retained their military status and their uniforms. Had they been *"civilianized,"* they would have fallen prey imme-diately to the relentless draft board and would have been sent back to the active troops. As soldiers, they could stay in Peenemünde; however, colleagues in civilian clothes, and particularly young officers, often found it difficult to accept a man in Pfc. uniform as an equal partner in a technical or scientific discussion. Meetings in which von Braun presided were different. They gave the *"scientists in disguise"* an opportunity of being colleagues among engineers and scientists, not just lowly Pfcs. Von Braun, for one, was not bothered at all when a man wore a soldier's uniform. It did bother him, though, when a man failed to recognize and to tackle a problem which fell under his responsibility; he made everybody aware of his concern, regardless of whether the man was a Pfc., a civilian, or a high-ranking officer.

Von Braun's characteristic spirit stimulated the entire Peenemünde workforce. Besides their individual expertises, the men and women who worked on the little island possessed one common feature: dedication to their joint project. They felt that they stood at the threshold of a totally new technology, and that they had the means, both mental and material, to transform a dream into a real accomplishment. If the project turned out to be successful, the new technologies would be a firm possession of mankind from then on.

Although the SS had been given authority over the production of A-4 missiles in the Mittelwerk by fall 1943, Himmler was *". . . embittered about the lack of influence on rocket development . . ."* [3-4]. The schism between SS and Army grew; Hitler, too, became distrustful and contemptuous of the Army after the unsuccessful attempt on his life. This allowed Himmler to assume more and more authority over the total A-4 program. Paris was bombarded with A-4 rockets (from then on called the V-2) for the first time on 8 September 1944, and London was hit on the same day.

When the news reached von Braun over the public radio that A-4s had been launched against Paris, his secretary, Dorette Kersten (now Mrs. Rudolf H. Schlidt of Huntsville, Alabama) was present. She still recalls details of this fateful event [3-18]: *"Von Braun was completely devastated. In fact, never before or afterwards have I seen him so sad, so thoroughly disturbed. 'This should never have happened,' he said. 'I always hoped the war would be over before they launched an A-4 against a live target. We built our rocket to pave the way to other worlds, not to raise havoc on this earth. Should this really be the fruit of our work?' We almost felt as if the A-4 hitting Paris had hit each of us personally."*

One could argue, of course, that von Braun and his co-workers should have expected that a rocket which was built to military specifications, and under the auspices of the armed forces, might eventually be used as a weapon against an enemy. Von Braun was, of course, fully aware of this possibility. However, he was convinced, like most of his co-workers, that the A-4 with its very limited explosive power, its modest range, and its small production numbers would be irrelevant as a weapon when compared to the potential of the huge wartime bomber fleets. Primarily, though, von Braun always hoped and expected that the war would be over before an A-4 could be launched as a military weapon.

The last phases of the war remain deeply impressed in the memories of all who lived through those fateful and depressing times, wherever they may have been. For the Peenemünders, there were two modes of existence between which their lives alternated. Each of these two modes was absolutely real, and each was relentlessly demanding.

One mode was the daily work: The development of a rocket system of high precision and high reliability that would be capable in its first version to cover large distances on Earth, and in subsequent versions to reach some distinct target in outer space, such as the Moon or the planet Mars. Within a period of less than five years, a powerful, but finely controllable rocket motor had come into existence; precision guidance and flight control systems had been invented and built; supersonic aerodynamics had become *"terra cognita"*; radio guide beams and communication links had been developed and built; and electronic simulators to handle lengthy mathematical procedures and to help solve complicated equation systems—forerunners of modern computers—had begun to take shape.

Then, there was the other mode of existence, one in which the men and women simply tried to cope with the cruel realities of life. The war was going on, every day and every night. Newspapers and radio announced *"strategic shortening of certain sections of the front line."* Vapor trails of high-flying bombers crisscrossed the sky. Industrial installations succumbed to the bombs; entire cities were flattened under the impact of bombing attacks. Life for the Peenemünders was an irregular sequence of working and waiting; it oscillated between laboratories, design rooms, test stands, assembly hangars, meetings, and hours of data evaluation, interrupted by standing in the chow line at Fischer's cafeteria, by soldierly chores in the barracks, and by a short sleep at night, frequently broken by long hours in an air raid shelter or in a trench between the trees.

Traveling was always an adventure in its own right. Only rarely could a traveler find a hotel to spend the night. Sleeping on a bench in a railroad station, or on an overcrowded train, or in a schoolroom, or even in the hall of a post office, was part of the life of the average Peenemünder during the last two years of the war.

Hardly any one among them had not felt the cruel impact of war. Family members, friends, neighbors, relatives had been killed at the front or in air raids. Dwellings and houses had been destroyed by bombs. And yet, the men scarcely talked about this. They did talk, however, about another question that lay heavily on their minds: How will it all end? But even such talks were restricted to small groups of chaps who knew that they could trust each other. Peenemünde, as a military installation, was nonpolitical; jurisdiction was in the hands of the Army. The network of organizations of the Party did not cover the Peenemünde establishment, at least not directly. However, there were still a few *"convinced and ardent Nazis"* among the Peenemünde workforce, ready to jump on everyone who showed signs of disbelief or sagging spirits. It would not only have been imprudent, but totally futile to try any debate with those characters. There was simply no comparing of opinions, no pitting of wits. Their number was shrinking continuously, but the few remaining ones meant danger. In their frantic and crazy belief that doom could be averted, they reported the imprudent ones who expressed doubt in the righteous cause of the Nazi regime. There was always the threatening spectre of the concentration camp—although at that time, it was not known that many of the luckless ones would not return. Neither was it known that the regime had started a systematic program to annihilate the Jews. Only very few people knew about these happenings at that time.

Although Peenemünde was relatively isolated from the rest of the country, the Peenemünders were not spared the miseries of war. Many of the married men lived with their families in the *"Siedlung,"* a housing project in Peenemünde; the families of others lived in other parts of Germany. One of the men had his family—wife, three children, and his parents—in the city of Dresden where all were killed in the devastating British and American air raids in February 1945. Within two or three days, an estimated 130,000 to 160,000 people in Dresden lost their lives, just a few months before the war ended. Many of them, mostly women and children, were refugees from the east. Stalin once said: *"When a person dies, it is a human tragedy. When a million people die, it is statistics."*

No! When a million people die, it is a million tragedies! What had happened to the man's family in Dresden had happened to millions of others, not only in Dresden, Hamburg, and Cologne, but in Paris, Antwerp, Warsaw, London, Coventry, Kiev, Moscow, Stalingrad, Tokyo, Hiroshima . . . With all their sympathy for their friend from Dresden, the Peenemünders—and countless others—felt involved in a far greater tragedy . . .

why couldn't it be stopped? How was it possible that it all started? How could it be brought to an end? Everything looked so hopeless, so miserable, so gloomy.

Again and again, people asked themselves: How could all this happen? With so many Germans being against the Nazis, how could they wield such absolute power? What went wrong? How could a government, after having been elected in purely democratic fashion, turn so violently against its own people, against most of the other nations, and against every rule of logic, reason, decency, and ethics? What could be done now?

Long after the war, there was still the simple question: *"Why didn't you just say no?"* Those who asked had never lived under a dictatorship. Actually, there were numerous no-sayers. Either, their *"no"* remained without any consequence because it did not impress, or even bother, the functionaries of the regime, or, they were picked up by the Gestapo and just disappeared.

Those who, in retrospect, give that advice, are not aware of the fact that large numbers of the concentration camp inmates were upright Germans who had *"just said no."*

There were other thoughts that always found their ways into the secret discussions of trusted friends. It was well known how strong the tendencies of resistance had grown among the people in Germany, particularly within the Army. Rumors spread quickly and profusely in those days. Everybody had heard of attempts on Hitler's life during the later war years. Many of these rumors were confirmed after the war [3-9]. Why shouldn't one of these attempts succeed, it was argued? Couldn't this nightmare come to a quick ending tomorrow, or even tonight?

Also, there were rumors that small, but carefully organized resistance groups had established contacts with the western Allies through the governments of neutral countries. Some people claimed to know that Field Marshal Erwin Rommel, probably the most brilliant tactician among all the military leaders in Germany at that time, was playing a prominent role in these efforts. These rumors were verified by the aftermath of the abortive assassination attempt on Hitler on 20 July 1944. As was learned later, Rommel was forced by two army generals, Burgdorf and Maisel, on Hitler's orders, to take his own life, or face the ill-famed People's Court. He chose the former.

As was also learned later [3-19], Winston Churchill had instructed the Foreign Office on 20 January 1941 to ignore any peace feelers from inside Germany: *"Our attitude towards all such inquiries or suggestions should be absolute silence . . ."*

If the Führer and the Nazi regime were removed, a livable situation might eventually have been restored. Some people hoped—too naively—that the western members of the Allies would see things in a similar light, and that they might even help bring about a solution of this kind. This hope persisted day after day, to the very end. Many Germans would never have believed that the western Allies would allow the Soviets to penetrate so deeply into the heartland of Europe and to establish their firm foothold only 1,000 kilometers (600 miles) from Paris and London.

Of course, these were unrealistic thoughts at a time when the Allies were certain that their sweeping victory was imminent. However, it was typical of countless *"what-if"* questions with which many people in Germany tried to maintain a last, faint glimmer of hope.

Well, it surely would come to an end one day. Then, life would go on for millions of Germans, regardless how deeply Germany was lying in shambles. A terrific task of rebuilding would wait for the survivors. Not only houses, streets, hospitals, factories, farms, schools, churches, railroads, bridges would have to be rebuilt, but also a society with community lives, local and state governments, administrations, food production and distribution, a postal system, social services, newspapers, industries. Perhaps most important of all, something like a new German nation would have to be raised from the ashes, with an appreciation for human values, with mutual trust, with a will for rebirth, with confidence in the future, a nation that would work and find its way back into the world community.

Many people in Germany felt the enormity of this task, and they knew that the men and women who had to tackle it were already living among them. Even for this task alone it would be worth while to hold out at the places where everybody happened to be, rather than wasting away in some obscure Nazi dungeon.

There was still another little spark in the saddened minds of the Peenemünders, another dream, quite familiar to many of them. *"If there should be a life hereafter,"* they sometimes said, *"we wish we could work, without the pressures of war, on the development and perfection of rockets that would be used exclusively for peaceful exploration of the high atmosphere, the Moon, the planets."*

The first of these dreams did not come true. The war continued. Both sides had to fight to the bitter end. But the second dream found its splendid fulfillment. Twenty-five years after the last Peenemünders had left their little island for good, the giant Saturn V rocket launched the Apollo astronauts to the Moon. Von Braun and his team, which included a number of the Peenemünde oldtimers among thousands of American colleagues and friends, had a decisive hand in this project. When von Braun was asked which aspect of Project Apollo seemed the most important to him, he said: *"The fact that this marvelous project had a totally nonmilitary purpose. It was undertaken solely for peaceful exploration, and the American people gladly paid for it!"*

9   DRAMATIC ENDING

The British night raid on Peenemünde in August 1943 was followed a year later by three American daytime raids: on 18 July, 4 August, and 25 August 1944. The damage to technical installations was not too great, but these attacks were an unmistakable indication of the Allies' intent to destroy the Peenemünde works.

Beginning in 1943, some of the activities at Peenemünde were transferred to other locations less accessible to bombing raids. Test launchings of A-4 rockets were made from a launch site far to the east, Heidelager near Blizna in Poland. Soviet armies overran Heidelager in September 1944. Anticipating their arrival, Dornberger had transferred during the summer months all test launching activities to a place farther to the west, Heidekraut.

At the same time, many of the laboratories and shops were moved from Peenemünde to places in central Germany where development and testing of rocket components could be resumed after some hectic days and weeks of relocation. In some instances, room and even some basic facilities could be found at factories or universities; in other cases, new laboratory and shop facilities had to be built up literally from scratch before a laboratory could resume its development and testing activities at a place removed from Peenemünde.

As the days and weeks slowly moved through the winter of 1944/45, as the Allied troops closed in on Germany from all sides, and as the collapse of practically everything that constitutes the normal structure of a country proceeded relentlessly, the members of the large Peenemünde team tenaciously held on to their work, although they were spread out over all reaches of remaining Germany. This was certainly not the result of an imperturbable faith in final victory; it was rather a frantic attempt to retain one last mental haven that provided some sense of stability, of reason, and of hope. Most of the Peenemünders had always seen their work for the rocket as part of a large program that would provide the means to explore space. They were realistic enough to know that their rocket, in spite of its remarkable technical abilities, would not influence the outcome of this war.

Spirits were low, and they became lower every day. Everybody suffered from hunger and cold. Family members, relatives, colleagues, friends fell victim to the war. The utter hopelessness of Germany's situation was so obvious. In the middle of chaotic circumstances everywhere, von Braun kept his balance. He decided and directed the move of one department of Peenemünde after the other toward the south, and he always had words of consolation, encouragement, and optimism. He certainly knew that Germany would be overrun by the Allies, but he held on to his belief that somehow his team's work would survive. Although the conclusion that all this would end in a final cataclysm was inescapable, he never appeared desperate. He never made frantic decisions or unwise moves. Did he have a sixth sense that made him anticipate that the sun would shine again on his rocket team sometime in the future?

By the end of January 1945 the Soviet armies stood less than 150 kilometers (90 miles) east of Peenemünde. The Western Allies had penetrated deep into German territory. The distant rumbling of artillery fire was a constant companion in those days. Early in February, SS General Kammler, whom Himmler had made commander of the V-2 program half a year earlier, ordered the evacuation of Peenemünde, and the move of all personnel, machines, and equipment to Bleicherode in central Germany.

Around the same time, von Braun received another order from the Gauleiter of Pomerania, also a high-ranking member of the SS. Peenemünde belonged to his state. That order commanded *"the defense of Peenemünde against the Soviet army at all cost."* The utter senselessness of that order was obvious. It was equally obvious, though, that the Gauleiter aimed at the complete extinction of Peenemünde and the entire rocket project and its team so that no part of it would ever fall into Allied hands.

Choosing between these two contradicting orders, both from powerful SS functionaries, was no problem for von Braun. It was a choice between no future at all, and a chance for some future, perhaps.

Von Braun called some of his closest associates together to assess the situation, and the options that were still open. There was immediate agreement: Accept Kammler's marching order to Bleicherode and, if possible, move further toward the southwest, hoping that the advancing armies of the western Allies would capture the Peenemünde group before the Russians had a chance to do so. Although it was not until after Stalin's death that the appalling conditions in his nation were fully revealed to the world [3-20], von Braun and his teammates knew enough in 1945 to cause them to avoid at all cost being captured by advancing Soviet troops.

Hitler used numerous devious means to make the world believe that every German was a Nazi and stood firmly behind him: consummate induction of government employees into the Party; forced participation in gigantic mass demonstrations exalting the Führer; falsification of the results of public elections; absolute control over the news media; total suppression, under the threat of imprisonment, of opinions deviating from the Nazi dictum. Stalin, in contrast, was not bothered by world opinion. He did not even try to prove that the Russian people stood behind him; he just held them in his iron grip. This spared the citizens of the Soviet Union the onus of *"collective guilt."*

This sinister picture of Stalin's regime was underpinned by reports of the unspeakable sufferings of the refugees from the east that poured into Germany as Soviet forces advanced toward the Reich in 1944 and 1945; about 12 million of them sought protection and survival in the fast-shrinking territory that was left over from Germany after six years of war.

By that time, more than 4,000 people still worked at Peenemünde. On 17 February, the last test launch of an A-4 rocket from Test Stand P-7 took place. On the same day, the first train, and the first of about 1,000 trucks, all loaded with rocket parts, equipment, documents, and personnel, left Peenemünde for the long trek south. Even barges on the river Oder were used in the mass exodus. Meanwhile, von Braun had flown south in advance to determine where, in the Bleicherode area of the Harz Mountains, an interim camp for his people could be established. At the same time, test stands and other facilities at Peenemünde were ordered destroyed along with those remaining archives that could not be carried south.

Those days are vividly described in D. K. Huzel's book *Peenemünde to Canaveral* [3]. As a personal assistant to von Braun, Huzel had intimate knowledge not only of the day-by-day events, but also of von Braun's thoughts and plans. *"When we evacuated Peenemünde,"* he wrote, *". . . many of us had given up all hope of ever again being able to work in the field of rocketry. Then and now, to most of us this meant 'space travel'— the greatest challenge of the 20th Century—the embarkation to new worlds, exploration more bold in spirit and on a grander scale than anything since the days of Columbus."*

By March, Soviet forces were only 30 kilometers (19 miles) away from Peenemünde. Most of the rocket people had been evacuated, and only a few maintenance crews, plus a contingent of SS personnel to watch them carry out their orders to blow up the buildings and test stands, remained to await the Russians. The wait, it turned out, would be longer than expected. Peenemünde was not a prime target. Early in April, Marshal Georgi Zhukov began massing more than 750,000 troops in his sector along the Oder, while to the south along the Neisse, Marshal Ivan Konev readied another 500,000 men. At five o'clock in the morning of 16 April, these powerful forces launched a coordinated offensive under a massive artillery barrage and harassment by several thousand fighter and other planes. One inconspicuous side event during this mighty thrust was the capture of Peenemünde on 5 May by units of the Second White Russian Army under Major Anatoli Vavilov.

Meanwhile, von Braun was trying as best he could to organize a rudimentary new base, including primitive accommodations for his people. One of his prime concerns was the safekeeping of the priceless technical documents. The exciting story of how they were secretly buried in an abandoned mine in the Harz mountains by two trusted men, Dieter K. Huzel and Bernhard Tessmann, was told dramatically in Huzel's book [3]. He wrote: *"These documents were of inestimable value. Whoever inherited them would be able to start in rocketry at the point where we had left off, with the benefit not only of our accomplishments, but of our mistakes as well . . ."*

While these two men carried out their classified mission, von Braun received another order from Kammler: *"Leave Bleicherode immediately and move further south to Oberammergau in the Bavarian Alps."* On 5 April, a detachment of 500 Peenemünders left by train. Von Braun, who had broken his arm in a car accident—his driver had fallen asleep at the wheel and run into a tree—was permitted to travel by automobile.

Oberammergau, where the rocket people had to crowd together in army barracks, was full of SS troops. It soon became obvious that the SS men were under orders to keep a very close watch over von Braun and his team members. *"Kammler,"* von Braun remarked to his associates, *"undoubtedly wishes to keep us as his personal hostages, as a kind of ransom with which he hopes to buy his own freedom when the Allies close in on him. Or, even worse, these SS people may destroy us and everything we have done in one last deadly blow."* The correctness of von Braun's suspicion was confirmed later by Speer, who wrote in 1981 [3-5]: *"SS General Hans Kammler intimated to me in March or April 1945 that plans were underway within the SS to remove the Führer, and that he, Kammler, intended to make contact with the Americans and offer to them, in return for a guarantee of his freedom, the complete technology of our jet planes, of the A-4, and of plans for an intercontinental rocket. For this purpose, Kammler continued, he will now concentrate all the experts of these developments in Upper Bavaria to have them ready for delivery to the Americans. He suggested that I may like to participate in this action . . ."*

Another hint to that scheme is found in Jean Michel's book *Dora* [3-12]: *"SS Obergruppenführer Hans Kammler was not the only one with sufficient authority to control the Gestapo . . . and who, in November 1944, could suggest to the Allies: 'I can negotiate with you about the future of the secret weapons . . .'."*

The picture that von Braun painted of the immediate future that might expect the rocket people in Oberammergau did not look rosy. *"Let's move out of here,"* Dornberger decided. He, von Braun, and Steinhoff succeeded in persuading the SS officer in charge that this tight concentration of precious Peenemünde specialists in one place is really inviting disaster—a single low-flying fighter-bomber could wipe out all of them in one instant. So the officer agreed to have the people disperse in the neighborhood, but each group had to have SS watchdogs around.

Dornberger, von Braun, and a number of their associates moved to Oberjoch, a small village high up in the mountains, and took residence in Haus Ingeburg, still closely, although indirectly, guarded by SS men. It was there where the news of Hitler's suicide reached them on 30 April. The most visible immediate effect of this event was the quiet disappearance of the SS men, one by one. There was no SS General Kammler. Rumor has it that he was shot and killed by his adjutant in Prague during the final days of the war. Himmler, likewise, faded into nonexistence.

On the morning of 2 May, von Braun announced to his associates: *"My brother Magnus, who speaks English well, has just left by bicycle to establish contact with the American forces at Reutte. We cannot wait here forever . . ."*

Magnus met American troops near the town of Schattwald; they belonged to the Antitank Company of the 324th Infantry Regiment, 44th U.S. Infantry Division. The dramatic, at times even comical story of this historic event has been told repeatedly [3; 11]. Private First Class Frederick P. Schneikert from Wisconsin made the first contact. *"Komm vorwärts mit die Haende hoch!"*—*"come forward with your hands up,"* he ordered. Soon afterward, the little group of rocketeers was firmly in Allied hands. Von Braun, Dornberger, and all their companions were taken to the nearby town of Reutte in Austria for preliminary interrogation by personnel of the Counter Intelligence Corps (CIC). Shortly thereafter, they were transferred to Peiting in Germany, and finally to Garmisch-Partenkirchen for questioning by a number of technically trained Allied specialists.

Among the interrogators was Dr. Richard W. Porter of the General Electric Company, who had been hired by U.S. Army Ordnance to secure as much information as possible on German progress in rockets and guided missiles. The ultimate aim of the armed forces, organized under the umbrella-designation Project Hermes, was the development of long-range American rocket systems for research and military applications. Porter was attached to the Combined Intelligence Operations Subcommittee, CIOS, Team 183.

At Garmisch-Partenkirchen, von Braun was asked by the CIOS team to prepare a summary of the developments undertaken by his team of rocket specialists during the preceding ten to twelve years. He promptly went to work and soon delivered a report entitled *"Survey of Past Liquid Propellant Rocket Development in Germany and of Future Prospects"* [Übersicht ueber die bisherige Entwicklung der Flüssigkeitsrakete in Deutschland, und deren Zukunftsaussichten] [3-21].

Emphasizing that the modern precision rocket is still in its infancy, he compared it with the first airplanes that also needed substantial technical improvements, as well as the investment of considerable funds, before the performance and the reliability of the modern airplane was achieved.

This fact had been his and Dornberger's continuous, but totally futile argument with Himmler, Kammler, and Degenkolb. In order to corroborate his point now, von Braun wrote: *"Some 60,000 to 65,000 drawing modifications were required before the first experimental A-4 rocket had become ready for production. This should indicate the number of absolutely new problems that arose during the testing phase of the A-4 . . ."*

"As a next step in rocket development," von Braun's report went on, *"we should expect rockets with longer ranges, and also anti-aircraft rockets that can be guided to their targets with radio guide beams, or with automatic homing devices. Future developments will certainly include rocket-launched satellites for Earth observations and astronomical studies; manned rocket flight; and also orbiting space stations with permanent human occupancy. In the long run, developments will provide opportunities to travel to the Moon and to planets."*

Von Braun concluded his essay with the assertion that systematic development of the art of rocketry will have revolutionary consequences for science and also for the military, as well as for our society in general, similar to the development of aviation which has brought revolutionary changes during the past fifty years.

The existence of the Peenemünde rocket program had been known to the Allies for some time. Early in 1945, while the war was still raging, U.S. Army Colonel Gervais W. Trichel requested Colonel Holger N. Toftoy, head of the Ordnance Corps Rocket Branch in Washington, to start planning how to obtain captured rockets and to interrogate the personnel responsible for their development. Subsequently, Toftoy became chief of Army Ordnance Technical Intelligence in Europe. From that position, he and his assistant, Major James P. Hamill, orchestrated their mandate.

As Allied troops entered German territory and moved eastward during the spring of 1945, Toftoy was asked by Trichel to locate V-2 rockets, and to arrange shipment of about a hundred to the United States. Much of the work in the field was carried out by Major Robert B. Staver and Major William Bromley. Staver's official position was Chief, Jet Propulsion Section, Research and Intelligence Branch, Army Ordnance Technical Division, located in London; Bromley had been designated by Toftoy as head of *"Special Mission V-2."*

Staver wrote several reports to the Chief of Ordnance about his various impressions and findings during his scouting activities in Germany during the summer and fall of 1945. In one subreport, *"The Liquid Fuel Jet-Propulsion Program of the German Ordnance Department"* [3-22], he wrote (17 December 1945): *"The writer knows most of the German group and can say without fear of contradiction that there is only one basic incentive which has led this group to come to the United States—the future possibility of carrying on research and development as citizens of the United States . . ."*

Later in the report, he emphasized that: *"The times call for some visionary planning, and not through prewar spectacles. The world has only been scratching the ground in the field of jet propulsion during the past fifteen years. Basic research must be stimulated. If a sound program to utilize the German scientists be evolved, and if a major research and development program be instigated, within twenty-five years this country will find itself about twenty-five years ahead of the rest of the world. During the next hundred years, the program which will soon be initiated will result in one of the most exciting scientific ventures in history."*

Speculating on the future, Staver discussed satellites, space stations, and possibilities of lunar flight using a space station as an assembly and departure facility.

At the underground factory Mittelwerk, Army Lieutenant Milton S. Hochmuth proved invaluable in helping locate parts and components from which operational V-2 missiles could later be assembled on the other side of the Atlantic.

The dramatic story of how this masterpiece of *"military procurement"* was accomplished by Staver, Bromley, Porter, and Hamill, supported by some of the Peenemünde engineers, gives a lively insight into conditions in Germany after the shooting had ended [11; 3-22]. Not only did these men have to find the rockets, rocket parts, instruments, and materials; they also had to load all this material on several hundred freight cars, and then railroad this convoy through war-torn Germany and Belgium to the port city of Antwerp. Moreover, this huge caravan had to be spirited through the checkposts of overzealous officials of the Allied forces who stuck to the Yalta agreement, according to which it was not allowed to remove any technical equipment from its location in occupied territory. The U.S. Army Transportation Corps, for example, refused to accept the assignment of transport because it feared a possible *"international incident"* among the Allies. As Hamill later remembered, *"the Ordnance Department was required to run its own railroad during that period."* The entire operation had to be achieved within nine days after the unassembled rockets and the documents had been found near Nordhausen because after that time, Soviet occupation forces would move into the area, which had been assigned to them in the Yalta agreement.

Working feverishly against the clock, Staver and Hochmuth arranged for the first trainload of V-2s to leave for Antwerp and then for the United States on 22 May 1945. In total, 341 freight cars were necessary to transport the vital cargo through Germany and Belgium to the port city.

Surprisingly, and very fortunately, the freight cars with parts for about one hundred V-2 rockets finally arrived in Antwerp. After the material had been crated, it was loaded on sixteen Liberty ships for a strictly subsonic transatlantic voyage to New Orleans at the mouth of the Mississippi.

Retrieving those priceless Peenemünde documents which had been buried earlier that spring in an abandoned mine near the town of Dörnten required some special action. Staver, with the help of Karl-Otto Fleischer and Eberhard Rees, was able to locate the hiding place, and to enlist local helpers to dig an access tunnel to the mine whose entrance had been blasted shut after the documents had been safely hidden inside. The documents were crated and loaded into Army vehicles that transported them westward to the American occupation zone, a few days before the Soviets and the British took over those parts of Germany. *"One of the greatest scientific and technical treasures in history is now securely in American hands,"* one of the American officials remarked.

By mid-June, Toftoy's team members, particularly Porter and Staver, had rounded up about 1,000 Peenemünders who lived in the areas of Nordhausen, Bleicherode, Ilmenau, and farther east. The men were urged to move across a demarcation line to the west by 19 June with their families and their modest belongings. Everybody fearfully anticipated what the demarcation line and the deadline meant, although this was not explained by the American officers. Almost everybody complied with the urgent suggestion. Beginning on 20 June, Soviet forces moved into Saxony, Thuringia, Mecklenburg, and some other areas that they had not occupied before, but which had been given to them in the Yalta Conference.

This action of locating and collecting former members of the V-2 project in those regions that were soon to be occupied by the Soviets, and to move them quickly to places west of the demarcation line, came under the personal responsibility of Porter. It was an action no less frantic than Hamill's because of the same time pressure, but it was even more difficult because the *"charge"* included hundreds of women and children, all homeless, weary, and hungry.

During an interview in 1989 [3-23], Porter remembered many details of his dramatic, often quite heroic efforts to carry out his assignment. Before war's end, he had headed the Aircraft Equipment Department at the General Electric Company in Schenectady. In November 1944, Army Ordnance asked General Electric to undertake a broad program for the development of rockets and guided missiles; Porter was put in charge of this task.

"The contract called for some intelligence work," Porter said. He received a lot of intelligence documentation, put a team of experts together, and left for Europe towards the end of March in 1945.

They first traveled to London and joined a team that included Colonels Holger N. Toftoy, Gervais Trichel, John A. O'Mara, and Horace B. Quinn, and Majors William Bromley, James P. Hamill, and Robert B. Staver. Porter and two associates then moved on to Germany and stopped first in Darmstadt whose Technical University had been doing work for Peenemünde.

"I discovered a young fellow there, an X-ray specialist, whom I gave a ride home in my Jeep . . . He had been at the wind tunnel at Kochel . . . None of us knew where that was . . . it turned out to be on the Kochelsee [in southern Bavaria]," Porter began the tale of his odyssey. He found a man from the Naval Technical Mission to Europe who had been a professor at Princeton, and who recognized immediately the need of doing something before the 10th Army went across that area; Kochel hadn't been captured yet. *"When the troops go across,"* Porter said, *"it's important to have somebody with them to tell them what not to break up . . ."*

Porter found Dr. Rudolf Hermann and his wind tunnel staff in a miserable state; there was simply no food. *"The Prussians who were moved in on the Bavarian farmers were not popular . . . So we helped obtaining food and medical supplies to take care of Hermann and his people . . ."*

Fortunately, Porter's men were able to protect all the wind tunnel facilities when the troops arrived.

Eventually, Hermann, most of his people, and the wind tunnel arrived in the United States. The tunnel went to the Navy. General Simon was not interested, saying that the tunnel wasn't all that important. Porter countered: *"Sure, but the instrumentation is in advance of anything you've got,"* but he did not prevail. Part of the reason was because of an eminent scientist, astrophysicist Fritz Zwicky. He was on Porter's team, but he worked for the Navy. He told Simon *"You don't want the tunnel, it's not important,"* and Simon believed him. After all, Zwicky was a famous professor from CalTech, so Porter lost. In May, he and his team went back to London to celebrate VE Day; from there, they flew to Garmisch-Partenkirchen where they met with von Braun and his people who were guarded by the 10th Army at a Gasthaus [hotel]. *"He spoke a pretty good English,"* Porter remembered.

Interrogations went on for weeks. *"Each day we would write things down,"* Porter said, *"but one day Zwicky vanished with most of our notes. Just disappeared . . ."* Two days later a major showed up, telling Porter that the former Peenemünders in the Nordhausen area had to be moved out of there in a hurry because the Soviets would arrive in something like twenty-four hours.

Porter, taking von Braun and some other Germans along, drove to Munich where he got a DC-3 Dakota airplane and flew to Nordhausen. He telephoned all the Army bases in the neighborhood and asked for everything that could roll from half-tracks to trucks and Jeeps. *"We even had some donkey carts. No kidding!"* he remembered. The Americans told the Germans that they had to go west, and that there was a pretty good chance that they would get to the United States, some day. But for now, they added, the Russians were due in shortly. *"I told them that they had about three hours notice, and that they should take with them only what they could carry, and that included food . . ."*

Then, Porter located some freight cars, although he still didn't know where to take the men and their families. Finally, two places were named where to move: Witzenhausen and Eschwege. Then Porter learned that one could not go by train from Witzenhausen to Eschwege because the bridges had been bombed out. They were still in what was to be Russian territory, and they never knew whether around the next bend they would run into Russian ground troops.

Slowly, things began to move; then, at Mühlhausen, the engineer decoupled his locomotive and took off for Nordhausen *"to get some water for the locomotive, and some drinking water,"* and that's the last Porter ever saw of him! There he was with eight or nine boxcar loads of men, women, and children at Mülhausen, and no locomotive.

"It was getting dark," Porter continued, *"and we had been going all day . . . The station was full of displaced people who had been released from the camps in the neighborhood . . . We went to see the station master, but he said that he didn't have a locomotive, but he would give us the first one that came in . . . After some time, one came in, but it had a busted injector and was just limping along . . . there was a hill outside Mühlhausen . . . Finally, a working locomotive came in, but it was the smallest I have ever seen, and it could only pull about half of our cars up that hill."*

They had to cut the train in half, but there was no way to switch the engine. Then Porter observed that there were no handbrakes on any of the cars. He didn't dare to stay until morning for he was pretty sure that the Russians would arrive, and if they did, some of the Americans might be doing time in Siberia. Finally, a place was found to switch the engine on top of the hill, but the switch house was locked, and there was no switch operator. At three o'clock in the morning, an American Jeep came along, and Porter could persuade the driver to take him to the home of the switchman. *"They even gave us some food—we had not eaten since morning. Actually, we gave most of the food to the railroad crew for they had nothing to eat, either."*

Well, it took several days and nights, but finally all three hundred odd people arrived safely in Eschwege and Witzenhausen. Porter and his helpers found some emergency housing for them, and some food.

"Then," he said, *"we had to decide what to do next with the Germans."* It was there in Witzenhausen where he sat down with von Braun, Axster, and some group leaders, and where von Braun proposed to develop a two-dimensional winged ramjet missile. *"Von Braun wanted to bring over a complete operating group, as I would have, too, in his place. That included draftsmen, tool makers . . . Being a project manager myself, I knew exactly what he was talking about. He was right, and we ended up with a group of about 500, or maybe even 600 . . . I went off to Paris to talk to Toftoy, by Jeep . . . He told me: Oh, no, that's way too many people."* He knew that his higher-ups would never accept such a number. There were weeks of debates and arguments with the people back in Washington, and also with the British who wanted V-2s and a launch crew for test

launchings in Cuxhaven. Certainly, plans to ship a number of the Peenemünde people to the United States did not materialize overnight.

Porter, Staver, and Toftoy as well, were convinced that the transfer of rocket engineers and scientists to the United States would be of great benefit to the armed forces and also to American industry. As early as May 1945, they had drafted a telegram to the Chief of Ordnance, as Porter remembered. The cable was signed by General Eisenhower; it read in part: "Have in custody over 400 top research and development personnel from Peenemünde. Developed V-2 . . . The thinking of the scientific directors of this group is 25 years ahead of US . . . Recommend that 100 of very best men of this research organization be evacuated to US immediately . . ."

On 20 June, U.S. Secretary of State Cordell Hull approved the transfer of a limited number of German rocket specialists to the United States, under the auspices and responsibility of Army Intelligence. Von Braun suggested 500 as a nucleus for a new rocket research, development, and testing program. Porter thought that there was no hope for more than 300 to be permitted; the Army finally agreed to 100. Toftoy and Porter, with the help of von Braun and some of his associates, were to select the 100 men. When they arrived in the Untied States, their total number was 127. *"I am really sorry,"* Toftoy later told them with a chuckle, "but mathematics has always been my weak spot. I often had difficulties adding and subtracting plain numbers." For the Germans, going to the United States was entirely voluntary. They were invited, not forced or lured. For each of them, extremely thorough background investigations were made. Every corner of their lives, professional and private, was checked for possible links to war crimes, or to Nazi activities. Their relatives, their neighbors, their colleagues and friends, and even their high school teachers were interrogated at length. Each of those men who were finally offered contracts had received a clean bill of health.

The offers to go to the United States were not accepted without some reservations. Characteristically, the first question of every married man was: *"What will happen to my family?"* closely followed by the second question everybody asked: *"Will I be able to work in my professional line?"* Eventually, those who had been invited accepted the offer, with a very few exceptions. Some wanted to take over their fathers' businesses, some others wished to continue a university career they had begun before the war.

Even before these negotiations had proceeded very far, another event intervened. The British Government planned to test-launch some V-2 rockets in order to obtain *"a thorough evaluation and documentation of the missile"* [3]. More than one hundred of von Braun's associates joined British engineers at Altenwalde near Cuxhaven in this *"Operation Backfire."* Several V-2s were assembled from many parts and components that had been picked up at random by British troops at several places in central Germany. A first launch over the North Sea took place on 2 October; it was a complete success. Another successful launch occurred on 4 October. The third launch, on 15 October, also was a full success. With these three launchings, Operation Backfire was terminated, and the German engineers returned to southern Germany. In the meantime, the U.S. Joint Chiefs of Staff had officially established *"Operation Overcast,"* a *"project of exploiting German civilian scientists . . . on an island in Boston Harbor . . .".* One of the first actions Toftoy undertook after the project had obtained official status was to set up a camp in Germany for the dependents of the rocket specialists who were to transfer to the United States. He succeeded in establishing a dependent camp in Landshut on the Isar, 70 km (45 miles) northeast of Munich. This camp was to become a temporary home for the families of the Peenemünde people until they finally, late in 1946 and through 1947, could join their husbands and fathers in the United States. While the men worked in the States, their salaries would be paid to the families at home. The men would subsist on a per diem of $6; part of this amount had to be paid back to the Army for housing and food. Toward the end of September 1945 the families began to move into the Landshut quarters. At that time, nobody could estimate how long they might remain there.

Transferring German rocket specialists to the United States in the fall of 1945 posed some unprecedented questions. Will they be immigrants? Do they need visas? Are they still enemies of the United States? Should one expect acts of sabotage? Will they be held under continuous surveillance by the FBI? Finally, the U.S. Army agreed to assume custody and responsibility for the German *"resident aliens."* They would *"immigrate without visas, but with the knowledge of the President."* Operation Overcast was renamed *"Operation Paperclip,"* a designation derived from the fact that in the huge pile of dossiers at Army Ordnance, those individuals who had been selected to come to the United States from Germany were distinguished by paperclips.

It was a strange situation in which the Germans found themselves as they faced the beginning of a new life in America. For lack of a more descriptive designation, and with some sense of wry humor, they called themselves *"PoPs,"* prisoners of peace. But all in all, they were optimistic, and grateful for their fate. They felt that there might be a path for them into the future that would permit them to continue what they had begun in Peenemünde, a path that would eventually lead to our neighboring worlds in space.

Army Ordnance offered the German specialists a six-month contract, but von Braun, and at least some of his teammates, suspected that they might remain in the United States longer than that. Accompanied by six co-workers, he was taken in mid-September by truck to Le Grand Chesnay west of Paris. On 18 September, they were flown from Orly Field by a U.S. Army Air Corps C-54 first to the Azores and then to Newfoundland for refueling, and finally on to the New Castle Army Air Base just southwest of Wilmington, Delaware. From there, they proceeded on 20 September to Boston by air, and then by boat to an Army Intelligence Service post at Fort Strong on Long Island in Boston Harbor.

After a couple of weeks, the men, except for von Braun, were transferred to Aberdeen Proving Ground in Maryland where they began organizing the vast store of Peenemünde documents that had arrived earlier from Europe. Von Braun was taken to Washington for conversations with Major General Gladeon M. Barnes, Chief of the Technical Division of Army Ordnance, and Colonel Leslie E. Simon, Chief of Research and Development in the same division. Their principal subject was the question how best to integrate von Braun's men and participating American engineers and technicians into a group that would first reassemble the V-2s brought over from Germany, and then launch them. After that discussion, von Braun, in the custody of Hamill, traveled by train to Fort Bliss in Texas where he was to live and work for the next five years.

Between November 1945 and February 1946 three shipments with 118 Peenemünde Germans arrived by boat in New York. Two of the three were processed at Fort Strong in Boston before traveling by train to Texas, along with the group temporarily stationed at Aberdeen to sort out the documents. The third shipment went from New York to Fort Hunt near Washington, D.C. It arrived at Fort Bliss on 23 February. Two further shipments later in 1946 completed one of the most unusual single transfers of technical brainpower on record, 127 men in all. A new chapter in rocket history was about to be written.

Fifteen years later, von Braun reminisced about Peenemünde: *"From those humble beginnings,"* he said, *"rocket engineering has advanced to the threshold of space exploration . . . Peenemünde has become a legend . . . it gave life to an idea that far transcended its immediate application as a weapon of war . . ."*

CHAPTER 4

A NEW START IN TEXAS AND NEW MEXICO

1 DESERT STATION FORT BLISS

Colonel Toftoy's initiative met with success. Beginning in the fall of 1945, 127 Peene-münders prepared for their transfer to the United States. Some left Germany five months after the war had ended; the last members of the group waited for about a year before they were shipped. Each of them had his own thoughts about leaving his country—particularly at a time when it was in utter distress—and seeking a new existence across the Atlantic. At that time, it was not known how long the time abroad would last: a few months, several years, or even longer? *"Will I be needed at home?"* they asked themselves. Germany lay in ruins at that time. A tremendous effort would be needed to rebuild a basis for normal existence, not only in the physical sense, but also with regard to the acceptance of Germany as a nation by other nations. *"Will we be in a position in the United States to do useful work? Will our families be able to join us? Will the Americans accept us in their midst? Will we be permitted to build up a team with American colleagues? Will we have a chance to become integrated in the community? Will we be allowed to send food parcels to our folks in Germany?"* There were questions with no end.

Before the war, when relations between the two countries were normal, almost every youth in Germany dreamed of going to America, a country offering unlimited opportunities for everyone who came in peace, and with the will to work. Now, that great country opened its doors and invited each of the 127 to come, but under conditions unforeseen a few years earlier. Each of them would certainly come in peace, and with the will to work. But they would come as citizens of a defeated nation, and their own government had carried the torch that started the war. Hitler, with his Propaganda Minister Goebbels, had tried to convince the world that every German was a Nazi. Would that image of *"the Germans"* persist? Would the Paperclippers have the opportunity of proving themselves as the people they really were?

These thoughts roamed through the minds of the young men, most of them in their early thirties, as the Victory ships on which they were traveling slowly ploughed their ways through the stormy Atlantic during the winter of 1945/46. But as the New World came closer and closer, other thoughts began to take over.

Almost every teenage boy in Germany goes through a phase in his life when he devours the books by Karl May, those true epics of high adventure. Written in the 1880s, many of them tell of the Indians of North America, their encounters with the white settlers, their deadly fights, and their touching, faithful friendships. Some of the novels have the Rio Grande as a backdrop with its narrow green banks and the wide desert lands to the east and west, with the jagged mountain ridges and deep-cut gulches, and with the colorful trading post, El Paso del Norte, at the place where the river has broken a passage through the rocky Sangre de Christo range.

When the Germans arrived in El Paso during the fall of 1945 and early in 1946, they saw a landscape totally different from anything they had ever seen in their home country, but still not really foreign. The seemingly endless desert-like prairie stretching toward the east, the stark mountain ranges rising in the west and south which were so colorful during the day, but became so totally black when night fell, and that unbelievably clear, blue, and deep sky—it was exactly as the Wild West had always lived in their imagination. Now, suddenly, all this had become real, the desert lands, the sharply contoured mountains, the bustling and booming city of El Paso, the magnificent Texas sky. This was now the stage on which a new phase of their lives was to begin, full of unknowns, but also full of promise and hope.

Fort Bliss, a large Army post at the northeast edge of the city of El Paso, had been chosen by the Army as the new home for the Paperclip people. A group of barracks was selected apart from the other buildings, partially protected by a chain link fence. They contained simple living quarters as well as larger rooms suitable for drafting rooms and storage hangars.

The group was put under the command of Major (later Colonel) James P. Hamill. Providing housing, maintenance, and support service for the German engineers and scientists was the responsibility of the 9330 Technical Service Unit under Captain (later Colonel) William E. Winterstein who had been transferred for that purpose from the Aberdeen Proving Ground in Maryland to the *"Fire-Ball Project"* at Fort Bliss. This was the official code name for the Fort Bliss operations. In a rare spell of humor, Major Hamill changed that code name into TAGSOE for *"The Absolutely Greatest Show On Earth,"* but when that acronym one day was punched inadvertently into a telegram to Washington, confusion resulted, and the name TAGSOE had to be dropped [4-1].

Working and living conditions at that time were really primitive, as Winterstein recalls; however, after six years of war, the Germans were used to primitive conditions. In another respect, though, it would be difficult to imagine a more radical change of life-styles than was experienced by the Peenemünders. There was no pressure of work, no scenes of total destruction, no emaciated and hopeless faces, no anxiety, no fight for survival, no need to carve out a new base of existence. Everything was serene, peaceful, and quiet. And, there was plenty to eat! The food, after wartime years of hunger and deprivation, was excellent. Kitchen service was performed by German prisoners of war. The *"Paperclip specialists,"* a designation used at that time, stayed in the camp. Once a week, each of them was permitted to make a short trip to town, accompanied by three other Germans, and escorted by an Army sergeant with a car. These weekly excursions followed a standard routine: shopping, dinner in a restaurant, a movie, and back to the barracks.

The nature of the work program for the German group in Fort Bliss was broadly defined by Major General Gladeon M. Barnes, Chief of the Technical Division, Office of the Chief of Ordnance, Washington. Basically, the Germans were to train military, industrial, and university personnel in the intricacies of rockets and guided missiles; to help refurbish, assemble, and launch a number of V-2s that had been shipped from Germany to the White Sands Proving Ground in New Mexico, about 130 kilometers (80 miles) north of Fort Bliss; and to study the future potential of rockets for military and research applications. The Army contracted with the General Electric Company to provide technical support to the group and, at the same time, absorb as much as possible of the group's knowhow as to the design, fabrication, and testing of guided rockets. A number of military personnel had joined the German and General Electric Company experts in their daily work.

While this program of activities provided a certain framework and substance for the eight-hour workdays, it was a far cry from the intense, fast-moving pace of project work to which the Peenemünders were accustomed. Very soon, the men began to miss the assignment of a definite project that would have allowed them to use their experience and knowledge, and to continue their work of developing rockets that had come to an end with the fall of Peenemünde. Not only did they wish to carry on a technical program in which they firmly believed; in some way, they felt that such work would justify the effort the Army had expended in bringing them to the United States, as well as their own decision to leave their home country and to start a new rocket development program in America. Their desire to continue rocket development work became even more urgent when it became known that those of their former colleagues who had been captured by the Russians were busily working on the improvement of V-2 missiles, and on more advanced rocket systems.

Winterstein remembered those days [4-1]: *". . . any requests for funds for basic research were almost doomed from the start. Some members of Congress were apparently not apprised of the fact that we had a group of German rocket scientists under Dr. von Braun, due to the relatively tight security envelope under which the Germans were held. It included a total news and public information blackout, with rather tight restrictions of movement outside the barracks area. Even when the presence of the Germans became known in December 1946, the general attitude of Congress appeared to be apathetic, with comments similar to: 'The War is over, what further need do we have for the future rocket research and development?' . . . To my knowledge, there were no funds available in the early days for any basic research that Wernher would have been most happy to get involved in . . . The Office of the Chief of Ordnance, with Colonel Toftoy at that end, gave as much support as possible; however, that Office, in trying to get money out of Congress for any basic research, just ran into a stone wall."*

Von Braun suggested several rocket projects. Finally, he succeeded in initiating one project, a long-range cruise missile, that would permit his group not only to apply its knowledge and experience, but also to utilize a number of the V-2 rockets available at the nearby White Sands Proving Ground. For von Braun, this was not a new idea; in fact, he outlined and discussed plans for a *"two-dimensional winged ramjet missile"* with Dr. Porter in Witzenhausen, Germany, in June 1945 [4-2].

Eventually, four different activities took shape for the Paperclip specialists in Fort Bliss. The first, requiring and receiving immediate attention, was the sorting, refurbishment, repair, and assembly of the V-2 parts that had been shipped over from Germany with the goal of building a number of complete, launchable rockets. This work was carried out almost completely at White Sands. Day-to-day operations for this program were supervised by Lieutenant Colonel Harold R. Turner, commander of White Sands Proving Ground.

The second activity, designated the Hermes Program, was primarily the responsibility of the General Electric Company (G.E.). Using designs and also some real components of the German wartime Wasserfall missile, a liquid-fuel surface-to-air guided rocket, the company planned to build several Hermes A-1 missiles, and then to proceed toward the design and manufacture of more advanced Hermes I guided antiaircraft missiles.

A third project, Hermes II, followed von Braun's suggestion to combine a V-2 booster with a high-flying, air breathing, supersonic ramjet missile. Six ramjet engines with rectangular intake cross sections would be fitted integrally into stub wings. The range of this missile would be several thousand miles. Although this project evolved promisingly through the phases of design, and even underwent some ramjet testing in a special high-altitude wind tunnel facility that had been rigged up in the mountains of the High Sierra in California, it did not survive. The reason was the fact that in 1947 the newly created U.S. Air Force decided to transfer Hermes II technology to its own Navajo long-range missile program. No sooner did the Air Force appear on the American scene than it sought supremacy over the Army in missile projects. Missiles, to the Air Force, were simply aircraft without wings, and not extensions of artillery as the Army preferred to believe. The Navajo project, using rocket power to launch an air breathing cruise missile, was under development at that time under Air Force auspices at the Rocketdyne Division of North American Aviation, Inc.

The fourth activity in this program covered work in several different fields to improve the major components of a guided rocket, including propulsion, control, guidance, aerodynamic features, instrumentation, and thermal systems. Most of that work had to remain restricted to paper studies because of an almost total lack of appropriate laboratories, tools, machine shops, wind tunnels, test facilities, and funds.

2   ROCKET SPECIALISTS UNDER MILITARY COMMAND

Most of the Germans were stationed at Fort Bliss under the command of Major Hamill. For many of the former Peenemünders, it came as a surprise that Major Staver, who had been most active and successful in rounding up the members of the von Braun team right after the war, and who was decisively instrumental in having a number of them transferred to the United States as a nucleus of a future American rocket development group, was not put in charge of the Fort Bliss Germans. Colonel Toftoy decided in favor of Hamill, perhaps because he happened to know him much better than Staver.

A large number of the rocket men had served in the German Army, either before or during their assignment to the Peenemünde works. It was natural for them to pay the traditional respect to a commanding officer. As Hamill remarked much later, he was surprised to receive this respect—with some unmistakable Prussian flavor—from people who were not American soldiers, but German engineers and scientists. For a professional Army officer, the situation must have been quite unusual, to say the least. For the rocket people, a military commander presiding over their technical work was not new. Their primary loyalty belonged to the project, and they felt that the commander over their project should be included in this loyalty.

All the normal aspects and functions of the lives of military men, in war as well as in peace, are prescribed and regulated by written and unwritten laws, and by long-standing tradition. Not so for *"Major Hamill's Paperclip Estate."* Still, things worked out quite well—disregarding temporary ups and downs—because both sides did their best to have the unusual enterprise succeed. Hamill gradually realized that the Paperclippers wanted to be genuinely cooperative, and the rocketeers appreciated and respected Hamill's endeavor to carry out his military assignment as a distinguished officer.

"Wernher and Jim Hamill got along quite well, most of the time," Winterstein reminisced in 1988 [4-1]. *"Von Braun, on one hand, was quite firm in what he spoke about, but he had a more even-tempered nature. Jim, on the other hand, had a 'short fuse' sometimes."* In general, the operation ran quite smoothly. Von Braun got along very well with most of the Americans. Some of them still harbored an edge of animosity toward the Germans, and it showed, but there was never a real disruption of the peace.

In retrospect, it turned out that the Fort Bliss Germans came to know their commander far better after their formal association in the Fort Bliss camp had ended.

After the von Braun team had moved from Fort Bliss, Texas, to Huntsville, Alabama, in 1950, Major Hamill accepted a new position in the Pentagon. He kept contact with many of *"his Germans,"* and the stiff *"Yes, Major"* changed into a very jovial *"Hi, Jim." "That was certainly the most difficult assignment I ever had,"* he once said, remembering the old Fort Bliss days. *"Any soldier, wherever he might serve, is taught to fight, outsmart, trick and otherwise coerce the enemy into full defeat. The Germans were our enemies during the time when I received my military education. And then, after the armistice, but before peace had been officially declared, I found myself surrounded by 127 Germans . . . My military books did not give any hints for such a situation. I don't believe that there has ever been a precedent to our case in the whole course of history!"* Hamill said. *"Both of us made our mistakes,"* he conceded, *"but we had the best intent to make a success out of it. I am really glad that we succeeded."* At another time, he said: *"When I look at the wonderful programs that came . . . out of those early beginnings in Fort Bliss and White Sands, I am mighty proud of each of you, and I am deeply grateful that I was privileged to be your commander."*

Hamill also remembered a little anecdote. During the first months in Fort Bliss, when the Germans were still the PoPs and Hamill had to keep them constantly under close guard, some of the men found a hole in the fence that shielded the camp toward the desert. Sometimes, at night, some of them would quietly slip through that hole and take a long walk over the sand dunes. When they returned, they carefully camouflaged the hole again. *"You had no idea that I knew about it, and that I even had you watched,"* Hamill said. *"Neither did you know that I was glad that you undertook this little adventure; it was a much-needed safety valve against all this pressure that confinement in the camp must have built up in your minds! In fact, this hole in the fence did much to convince me of your absolute trustworthiness!"* But he had one question: *"What did you do when you walked through the desert at night?"*—*"Contemplate the universe."*—*"Do what?"*—*"Contemplate the universe."*—*"Oh, I see. Yes. Well, I always believed that I had come to know you fellows quite well after these five years in Fort Bliss, but I must say that a few mysteries will always remain . . ."*

Hamill had several staff members who maintained contact between himself and the von Braun team members. Most prominent among them was Pfc. (later Sergeant) James J. Fagan, a chemical engineer who had been drafted into the Army shortly before he was assigned to Hamill's command. Fagan was not only an excellent engineer and scientist; he also had a genuine understanding for both the military and the civilian aspects of this unprecedented situation in Fort Bliss. He often played the role of a two-way ambassador between Hamill and the Germans, and he succeeded in smoothing out many rough spots that were unavoidable in the daily life of this strange symbiosis between military and civilians, soldiers and scientists, victors and vanquished.

"My first impression of von Braun," Fagan recalled in 1988 [4-3], *"was exactly the same that I still have more than forty years later. He was a man filled with an absolutely unbounded enthusiasm! He was enthusiastic about everything, not only rockets and space. To be near him was always most exciting. His enthusiasm was so infectious. He would always talk and involve you in a discussion. He always had something interesting to talk about, to explain, to relate. His desire to express himself was without limits, but he never was really overbearing. He made you part of the talk; you felt that he was deeply interested in you, and for the moment everything else had lost importance for him."*

Fagan had some very interesting and revealing comments about the relationship between Hamill and his charge. *"Major Hamill had been assigned to the von Braun group as its commander,"* Fagan said. *"It was an unusual situation for a military officer, and Hamill was not always at ease in his position. On the one hand, there could be no question that he was in complete and sole charge of the group. It was Major Hamill's Command, not von Braun's team."* On the other hand, as Fagan observed, Hamill did not really know what to do with those Germans. He was proud to be their commander, but he often ridiculed the men, and also von Braun, in their attempts to find their ways in this totally new and unprecedented environment.

Integrating into the American way of life, Fagan remarked, certainly was not easy for the Germans. *"They had some contact, but not much, with the few officers and enlisted men in Hamill's command, but they were almost completely isolated from other American citizens, and from civilian life in El Paso. Aggravating was the fact that they had no library; no technical books or journals; no reports, papers, data sheets; nor information material at their disposal that would have brought them into contact with those rocket projects that were underway in the United States at that time . . ."*

Did Fagan sometimes have to play the role of a mediator between Hamill and the Germans? *"Well, yes. I think I really did have to build a bridge between Hamill and the Germans, and sometimes also between the enlisted men and the Germans . . ."* Hamill was torn between the natural attitude of an Army officer who only recently had to fight a war, and the responsibilities of a leader of a group of engineers and scientists who were supposed to transfer experience and knowledge of a remarkable new technology from another country to the United States. Captain Joseph Sestito, in charge of security under Hamill, a well-balanced, warmhearted square shooter with a good technical background, had a better understanding for the situation. His attitude was far more relaxed, natural, and reasonable. The same was true for Winterstein. *"The two of them and I often debated and argued with Hamill. He never really accommodated to von Braun,"* Fagan remembered.

Assembly and launching of the V-2s at White Sands Proving Ground was under the command of Colonel Turner. Several of the Germans were permanently assigned to White Sands, others shared their time between White Sands and Fort Bliss. Members of the General Electric Company, and a number of Army officers, NCOs, and enlisted men formed the bulk of the work force at White Sands.

One of the most active members on Colonel Turner's staff who will always remain alive in the memories of the Peenemünders was Major Herbert Karsch. An officer of flawless military attributes, he had a broad and genuine understanding for technical things. He wanted to know as much as possible about rocket engineering, and he was always anxious to help with the procurement of parts, equipment, and facilities needed for the production line of White Sands V-2s. *"If you are really certain that you need it,"* he used to say, *"I will get it for you,"* and he did get it! There were not only rocket parts that he got for the PoPs. When he realized that during their long evening hours many of the Germans began to build crude pieces of furniture from scrap wood they found at a huge dumping place near the barracks, he lost no time giving them permission to use the well-equipped Army woodworking shop in the evenings, with the result that the frugal barracks quarters soon began to be furnished with expertly built tables, easy chairs, bookshelves, and cabinets. Some of them were still in use more than forty years later, long after the Germans had become full-fledged American citizens with respectable homes and modern, high-quality furniture.

On Sundays, some of the White Sands Germans were eager to go hiking in the nearby Organ Mountains, a rugged range of cliffs and rocks that rose majestically behind the White Sands barracks camp. Major Karsch not only granted them permission to do so, he also gave orders to the kitchen that each Sunday hiker should be provided with a generously stuffed lunch box. *"Just tell the officer on duty in which direction you*

are going, and report to him when you are back. We don't want to lose any one of you.
And watch out for rattlesnakes and mountain lions!" Those who did take to the
mountains on weekends had a wonderful time there. They met rattlesnakes and the big
desert tortoises, and they saw bobcats and even an occasional mountain lion. One of
the intrepid hikers, Helmut Horn, did not take Karsch's advice seriously; he was bitten
by a rattlesnake when he reached up on a ledge. The doctors at Beaumont Hospital in
El Paso took good and successful care of him, but when he returned after a week in sick
bay, he insisted that it was not the rattlesnake that did all the harm, but only those
countless injections he had to endure in the hospital!

3   DAILY LIFE IN THE BARRACKS

During the long evenings and weekends of their first year in Fort Bliss, the Germans
were left to their own resources within the confinement of the camp. Many of them
were eager to do what they had no time to do during the previous years: read books,
play chess, listen to a record player; improve their knowledge of English, mathematics,
physics, thermodynamics, and other basic sciences; or work out details of rocket and
satellite projects. Von Braun involved himself in a bold study; he wrote an essay, later
to be published as a book [4-4], on a manned expedition to the planet Mars. His study
was strictly based on technology that was within reach at that time. With the cooperation
of some of his team members, he described many details and aspects of the journey, and
he also provided the exact mathematical framework that proved that a manned round
trip to Mars would indeed be feasible on the basis of technology available in 1945. This
essay, *"The Mars Project,"* will be described in Chapter 5-3.

All of the Germans from the very beginning endeavored to improve their English,
with varying success. They practiced constantly, and they soon managed to understand
what they heard and read. Progress in their ability to express themselves was slower,
and none of them succeeded in speaking the new language without the unmistakable
Germanic accent, even many years after they had become American citizens. The only
possible exception was Magnus von Braun, Wernher's brother. *"Small wonder,"* he
would say. *"At the time when I learned to talk, twenty-five years ago, I had a British
nanny. Even my first words in German sounded English."*

The second best achiever in this language-learning endeavor was Wernher. He
quickly acquired a marvelous command not only of the English vocabulary, but also of
a great variety of idioms with which he spiced his language, and of many of the special
words and expressions used in the science and engineering of rockets. One evening in
the summer of 1946, several of the rocketeers, including von Braun, returned from a
busy field day at White Sands. Crouched together on the flatbed of a half-ton truck, most
of the men dozed sleepily while the truck rumbled over the bumpy desert road. Not so
von Braun. Holding a flashlight in one hand and a few pages torn from a vocational
dictionary in the other, he learned the pipefitter's words for the essential parts of
plumbing systems: faucet, valve, plunger, elbow, grommet, washer, sealant, O-ring . . .

Almost every evening after the end of the workday, many of the Germans played
ball games on a crude field between the barracks—volley ball, soccer, softball. They
were quite systematic in their efforts to stay physically fit. One afternoon every week,
they were permitted to enjoy the swimming pool on the Army post. Von Braun was
always an active participant in these outdoor sports, in contrast to his brother Magnus
who preferred the quiet and leisurely environment of his barracks room, reading or
playing his accordion.

Sometimes during one of those hot Texas summer nights, the unused energy of the rocketeers would put them into a state of high spirits, with the result that a mock fight would break out between the folks in two neighboring barracks. Empty cans and bed cushions would fly, paper bags filled with sand or water would be tossed through the air. *"We outnumber you, why don't you surrender!"* one party would yell below the balcony of the *"enemy"* barracks. Von Braun, leading the other party, would shout back: *"But we have the higher potential energy!"* He would grab a fire hose from the barracks fire fighting system, open the throttle full blast and, spraying the siege forces with rusty fire hose water, chase the enemy into wild retreat.

There were other activities with which the Peenemünders filled their after-duty hours. They modified an aging cabin of unknown former use into a club house. Jim Fagan, reminiscing about those early times, said in 1988 [4-3]: *"I particularly remember the weekends in Fort Bliss. There was the beautiful club house, an old, run-down ramshackle structure of crooked boards and tar paper which the Germans had converted into a cosy recreation building with sofas, easy chairs, rugs on the floor, and a bar that was tended by Sergeant Eric Wormser, and stuffed with delightful native drinks: whisky, rum, gin, tequila, beer, and, of course, lots of soda."* Winterstein even remembered another detail [4-1]: *"They had a drink formula posted on the wall behind the bar which ran something like this: 1st drink, 2 oz. of scotch, 4 oz. of soda; 2nd drink, 1½ oz. scotch, 5 oz. soda; 3rd drink, 1 oz. scotch, 6 oz. soda; 4th drink, pure soda."*

The club house was decorated with paintings by Gerd deBeek, a technical illustrator from Peenemünde. Every Saturday evening, the Germans had a good time there. Magnus von Braun played his accordion, and there was singing, laughing, story telling, and drinking through most of the night. On Sunday afternoons, classical concerts were played on an old phonograph. The loudspeakers were outside where the Germans had transformed part of the dry desert land into a garden with trellises and flowers; there were plenty of the fast-growing castor oil plants and huge sunflowers that provided *"instant shadow"* under the relentless Texas sun.

That flower garden was a major after-hours project for the PoPs. It featured a trellised walkway around the large square and also a pergola, all built from scrap lumber on a stretch of brown desert near their barracks. By tapping a water main that ran close by, they even created a little creek with forget-me-nots and marsh marigolds. Morning glories, bee plants, sunflowers, scarlet runner beans, cosmos, and climbing pumpkins formed a colorful and unusual oasis in the barren land. As Fagan told them, Major Hamill sometimes took his visitors to the garden, saying: *"Come and see what my Germans have made out of this dreary old piece of desert!"*

Some of the men began to feed the stray cats that roamed the Army post, with the result that they soon shared their rooms not only with the homeless cats, but also with the rapidly growing numbers of their offspring. One of the specialists once caught a porcupine while it ate the squash that another specialist had planted behind the barracks. He lifted it carefully into a cardboard box and carried it into his room, but the animal did not appreciate the hospitality. When it was offered a carrot, it turned around and slapped the feeding hand with its powerful tail, leaving thirty-two barbed quills in the flesh! *"Don't try to pull them back out with all these barbs,"* a well-meaning room neighbor told his colleague. *"Better push them right through and pull them out on the other side of your hand."*

Soon after their arrival in the United States, the Paperclip specialists requested, and later in 1946 were given permission to send gift parcels of food to relatives and friends in the old country. Buying the foodstuff from a local grocery—mostly lard, sugar, flour, oil, bacon, spaghetti, corned beef, shortening, honey, noodles, rice, coffee, tea, condensed milk, soap, knitting wool. Filling and wrapping the parcels and taking them to the post office was well organized as an after-duty activity every four weeks. Major Hamill provided half-ton trucks for the transportation, and military escorts for the *"buyers"* and the *"mailers."* The quantity of these gift parcels increased when, in November 1946, the Germans were given new contracts that included civil service type salaries, replacing the former $6 per diem. From then on, team members received a yearly pay on the order of $4,300 to $6,800; von Braun's salary topped the pay scale at $7,500 per year.

"The daily life was quite regulated due to security requirements," Winterstein remembered. No social gatherings were permitted. The rule in the early days was that no large group of Germans with their military escorts would appear at any one place in public. The exception to this rule were the scenic military bus trips on Sundays out into the country. *"The dread that any of the German team may become involved in a public disturbance or accident hung over our heads at all times during those days before it was announced officially that they were in the United States,"* Winterstein said [4-1].

While the Germans accepted these restrictions as a matter of loyalty toward their host country, they were not happy to be *"put on ice,"* as Major Hamill said, without an opportunity to continue their work in the rocket field. Winterstein recalled his conversations with von Braun about this subject. *"His reaction to the apathetic attitude of Congress in granting funds for rocket research,"* he remembered in 1988 [4-1], *"was one of disappointment and anger."* Von Braun began to realize that he was going to face a long, hard fight in trying to get sufficient funds for meaningful rocket research. The majority of congressional members at that time evidently thought that the war being over, there was no reason for further rocket research; the possible use of space benefits for mankind was not even a glimmer in the far reaches of their imagination. *"Wernher's dreams of exploring space would just have to wait,"* Winterstein remarked.

A first spark of hope lighted up in October 1946. At that time, the entire von Braun group moved into new quarters. There was an *"annex"* of the Fort Bliss Beaumont Hospital not far from the old barracks area that had been built during the war. It was no longer needed, so Toftoy and Hamill obtained permission to move the Paperclip specialists into the former hospital wards and medical personnel quarters. There was still a guarded gate, but this move from the old dilapidated barracks to the Beaumont Annex really lifted the spirits of the Peenemünders. Here was very visible proof that the American Government was considering the work, and the very existence of the von Braun team in a positive sense, perhaps even with plans to integrate the team eventually into a new, comprehensive American rocket development program.

4   FIRST CONTACTS WITH AMERICAN COLLEAGUES

Congressional decisions to put the Peenemünders *"on ice"* also had the result that von Braun had almost no opportunities to meet American colleagues who worked in the rocket field. He knew that several projects were underway early in 1946, among them the Wac Corporal Project at the Jet Propulsion Laboratory (JPL), the Viking Project at the Naval Research Laboratory (NRL), and several cruise missile projects under Army Air Corps auspices. He would have loved to talk shop with the project engineers and offer some of the experiences, successes as well as mistakes and failures, that the V-2 program had provided so abundantly.

Gradually, some contacts did develop. In March 1946, Dr. Ernst H. Krause and Milton W. Rosen, the leading members of the fledgling Viking Project at the NRL in

Washington, decided to stop at Fort Bliss and talk to von Braun on their way back from California, where they had visited Clark B. Millikan, Frank J. Malina, and Louis G. Dunn [4-5]. Von Braun looked forward to that visit; it would be his first opportunity to discuss the problems and prospects of rockets with peers. Late in 1945, Krause had been the driving force behind the establishment of the Rocket Sonde Research Section at NRL, and the use of German V-2 missiles for high altitude research. Rosen was one of the most knowledgeable rocket engineers among his American colleagues at that time.

Von Braun spoke about the visit to his associates the next day. He was pleased that the old V-2s were put to good use by the scientists at White Sands, and that a new rocket, the Viking (Rosen's first large-scale endeavor), was developed strictly as a high altitude research rocket for scientific purposes. And yet, that meeting obviously did not produce the comfortable atmosphere von Braun would have enjoyed so much. Rosen, in an interview in 1988 [4-5], said: *"Krause . . . was one of the men who had gone over to interview the German scientists and engineers while the U.S. Army was still advancing into Germany. So he was pretty much like a prosecutor as he started to grill von Braun . . ."*

Rosen's own position was a little different. Anticipating that he would occupy an important position in the country's future rocket development programs, he tried to establish himself by questioning, and even criticizing, almost everything that von Braun suggested. Von Braun, on the other hand, had hoped for a straightforward, open-minded discussion with facts and sound technical arguments. Considering the vast difference in practical rocket experience between von Braun and his guests, it may be understandable that von Braun felt a little less than comfortable when all his comments immediately met with objections. There was, for example, the question whether rockets should be built of aluminum or steel. The V-2 had a steel skin and aluminum tanks. Rosen wanted to build the Viking with integral tanks of aluminum. Von Braun stated that there are three major conditions that must be met by the material: strength, heat resistivity, and weldability. At the time when the V-2 was developed, these conditions could not be fulfilled with available alloys and methods. Rosen, however, interpreted von Braun's caution as a *"closed mind."* Actually, von Braun built all his rockets except the V-2 with integral aluminum tanks, but not before he had laboratories and workshops at his disposal at the Redstone Arsenal in 1950, where he initiated a development program for advanced welding techniques that made the manufacturing of high-quality aluminum tanks possible.

That first visit in 1946 marked the beginning of a long period of working relations between Rosen and von Braun's group that covered almost thirty years. Rosen left the NRL and joined the National Aeronautics and Space Administration (NASA) in 1958. At the time of his retirement from NASA in 1974, he was deputy associate administrator (Engineering) in the Office of Space Sciences. Throughout the many interactions with the von Braun team, he was always held in high regard as an excellent engineer and a very dedicated spaceman, although his views and those of his colleagues often diverged [Chapter 9-4]. *"We enjoy our mutual discussions,"* one of his counterparts in Huntsville said, *"but it takes a lot of patience. Milton is always against it, no matter what subject we are discussing. It takes time to open his mind at least to the half-way point."* A co-worker in Washington had more picturesque words: *"Milton always sees the hole in the doughnut, whereas von Braun always sees the doughnut!"*

Relations with Ernst Krause were different. He organized a brilliant high-altitude research program, and he made very productive use of the V-2 rockets in White Sands. His reputation in the von Braun group as a fine scientist as well as an energetic program manager could not have been better, but he always kept his distance from *"the Germans."*

One of the young scientists who followed the Army's invitation to utilize the access to high altitudes which the V-2s at White Sands offered *"for free"* was Dr. Herbert Friedman at NRL. He put little argon-filled Geiger counters into the nose section of V-2s, and he succeeded in detecting X rays from the Sun—the first discovery of X rays arriving from outer space [Chapter 4-6].

Friedman recalled the days of rocket launchings in the White Sands desert during an interview in 1990 [4-6]: *"Having those V-2 rockets was a real boon to us because we had nothing as capable to handle heavy payloads. All we had were military solid propellant rockets that were toys by comparison. The V-2 gave us 2,000 pounds of payload for instruments, and this immediately paid off very handsomely."*

How did Friedman feel about the fact that the United States brought former enemies and their rocket technology over to this country? *"We treated it in the scientific community as a war prize. We held the German scientists off at arm's length, and, in effect, tried to avoid any substantive contacts with them. We felt that American engineers would pick up the technology pretty soon, and we would then be working with our own people."*

The scientists who came to White Sands to fly their instruments on the V-2s, or at least to see how high-altitude research could be conducted with rockets, included Homer E. Newell, James A. Van Allen, Richard Tousey, Fred L. Whipple, John E. Naugle, Ernst H. Krause, John W. Townsend, Milton Rosen, M. J. E. Golay, George K. Megarian, William G. Stroud, and others—an impressive selection of present and future space scientists.

As Friedman said, they did keep their distance from the Germans. Some of the former Peenemünders were scientists themselves, at least before Hitler's Army gobbled them up. Stuhlinger, for example, had been a cosmic ray physicist under Professor Hans Geiger, working with Geiger counters. He is credited with the successful operation of the first proportional counters for electrons and cosmic ray particles in 1935, the subject of his thesis. Experiments to use such proportional counters for X-ray spectroscopy began at that time at Geiger's institute, first in Tübingen, and later in Berlin. Stuhlinger would have been most happy to share his experience with his American colleagues and to exchange views about cosmic ray measurements at high altitudes, but no such conversation would develop.

Was Friedman surprised when, at a later time, von Braun and his associates were asked to remain in this country and eventually become citizens? *"I wouldn't have predicted that at the beginning. But, as time went on, there was a gradual accommodation; and, as we got to know them, we found that many were admirable people dedicated to rocketry as a means for exploration, rather than for weapons. In the long-range perspective, you wonder what the Americans might have done if the situation were reversed. We often develop military weapons even though we hope that they will never be used."*

When the Peenemünde group began to settle in Fort Bliss late in 1945, and engineers from the General Electric Company were contracted by the Army under the Hermes Program to work with the Germans, G.E.'s assignment included designing the Hermes A1 missile, a guided ground-to-air rocket very similar to the German anti-aircraft missile Wasserfall that had been under development at Peenemünde.

How well did the PoPs and the G.E. personnel work together? Certainly, both parties made an honest effort, and person-to-person relations were very friendly, but still the going was a little rough at times. Jim Fagan recalls the situation [4-3]: *"As far as I could notice, American industry was not entirely happy with von Braun and his team. My observations are limited to the cooperation between the von Braun group and the*

G.E. Company . . . Von Braun had his own ways of doing things. He always knew exactly what he wanted and how it should be done, and he did not give in easily to suggestions from colleagues at industry who wanted to try different approaches. Von Braun's co-workers were of the same frame of mind . . ."

To understand this difference in attitudes, one should note some of the special circumstances. For the Germans, many of the American design practices were new: inches instead of centimeters; different ways to define and to add tolerances; different symbols; different ways to show cross sections, fits, and other details; and a different language! On the other hand, the Germans were totally familiar with the V-2, and they had already designed, built, and successfully flight-tested complete Wasserfall missiles similar to the one they were now designing. Their American colleagues, in turn, faced a group of people with unusual design practices who had difficulty in expressing their thoughts in plain English. Is it reasonable to expect a person speaking flawed English to offer flawless engineering?

Components of Hermes A1 were flight-tested on V-2s, and five complete A1 missiles were flown in 1950 and 1951, but the project was cancelled thereafter.

By 1946, the predecessor of the U.S. Air Force, the Army Air Corps, had already started to develop several projects of the cruise missile type. The best known was the Navaho, an air-breathing missile built by North American Aviation (NAA). It was boosted by three liquid fuel rocket engines and then continued its horizontal flight with ramjet engines. The rocket motors were developed by NAA's Rocketdyne Division, headed by Samuel K. Hoffman.

Shortly after the launching of captured V-2 rockets at White Sands began in 1946, Hoffman and members of his rocket engine group showed great interest in the V-2 engine. Eventually, active working relations developed between the two groups.

The president of NAA, J. Leland Atwood, said in an interview in 1988 [4-9]: *"Undoubtedly, the example of the V-2 had a definite influence on the Navaho engine work . . . I think Rocketdyne made great contributions in heat transfer, valves, turbo machinery, etc. . . . Von Braun and his team . . . undoubtedly contributed much in ideas and technical critique . . ."*

Even closer ties grew between Hoffman and von Braun, leading to a most fruitful alliance between Rocketdyne and the von Braun group which was still in full action forty years later, after the Redstone, the Jupiter, the three mighty Saturns I, IB, and V, and the space shuttle orbiter had been successfully powered by Rocketdyne engines. Hoffman, in an interview in 1988 [4-8], remembered the beginning of this unique symbiosis: *"The V-2 engine certainly was of decisive influence on our rocket engine work . . . The development of the F-1 engine for the big Saturn rocket, which began in 1958 or so, stepped up our company's interaction with von Braun. He and I had become very close friends. Our relations were just perfect, between the two of us as well as between our teams. I could never have imagined a better cooperation between our company and any other group . . ."*

What did Hoffman think of von Braun as a person? *"He had a terrific charisma! In fact, it became immediately evident that he was a very unusual individual. I was deeply impressed from the first moment on, and this very positive impression even increased as I came to know more of him. I always had unlimited respect for him."*

The Rocketdyne Division of NAA, later to become Rockwell International, was not the only company with which the von Braun group developed pleasant working relations. By the time the Saturn-Apollo Project was at its peak, about 20,000 American industrial firms worked under Saturn-Apollo contracts. All the larger ones, and many of the smaller ones had contracts with von Braun's George C. Marshall Space Flight Center in Huntsville, Alabama. At that time, the Germans were only a minute fraction of von Braun's total work force of almost 8,000 men and women. Having lived now for more than twenty years in the United States, they were completely integrated in the great American society in every respect—except for their German accents—and they were as familiar with American design practices, feet and inches, project management, and almost all other aspects of life in their new home country as any of their innumerable native-born colleagues and friends.

5   A TASTE OF FREEDOM

December 4, 1946 was a memorable day for the Germans: The front page of the *El Paso Times* showed a picture of Major Hamill and von Braun, accompanied by an article *"German V-2 Experts Stationed in El Paso."* This was the first public acknowledgment of the fact that the Paperclip people lived and worked in the United States under the auspices of the American government, more specifically under the U.S. Army. The PoPs happily took it as a sign that they might eventually become members of the great American family.

Winterstein explained the situation many years later [4-1]: *". . . it was about a year and a half that Germany had surrendered, and that public attitudes had mellowed . . . I believe that the time had arrived to come out with a forthright disclosure of the facts and who was really firing the V-2s in White Sands . . . I had briefed my son, [aged four] that he would not discuss the nature of my job at Fort Bliss . . . with anyone, especially not to mention rockets or Germans. My son came home from kindergarten one day with a congratulatory note from the teacher on what a very fine drawing of a rocket he had made! For this infraction my son received a dressing down. It was a hard thing for me!"*

How did the public in El Paso take this exciting disclosure? Fagan remembers those days [4-3]: *"The city's reaction was overwhelmingly positive! The Germans were most welcome to the Texans. The natives were not only full of curiosity and interest for the 'German rocket scientists,' they were proud of having them in their city! Surely, there were occasional negative voices, but those rare criticisms were really irrelevant. The Chairman of the El Paso Chamber of Commerce, Chris Fox, was enthusiastic about the project, and he made sure that most of El Paso's citizens shared that feeling."*

Virginia Strom, a reporter from the *El Paso Times* (later to become its editor), interviewed several members of the von Braun team. A little uproar arose when Walther Riedel, chief design engineer of the von Braun group, bluntly stated that much of the food was tasteless, and that the chicken served for lunch gave him the impression of being rubberized. Some El Paso citizens were indignant; many of Riedel's colleagues were shocked. After all, the Germans had been invited to the United States and appreciated the generous supply of food that was offered every day—particularly after long and difficult war years. Some of the Germans expressed their embarrassment to their American colleagues, but they learned what freedom really means: *"Why? Don't forget that you are living in a free country where everybody is entitled to his own opinion, and to express it as he pleases!"*

Army Ordnance, having custody over the Peenemünde people, had pondered the eventual integration of the von Braun team into a greater rocket development program since the summer of 1946. Gradually, the desire to keep and utilize the German scientists and engineers for an indefinite period became a decision to do so. This decision led to a number of pressing personal matters that needed attention. For example, the families who had been left behind in Camp Overcast in Landshut, Bavaria, would have to be brought to the United States. So, arrangements for their travel from Germany to Texas were made, and on 8 December 1946, the first of a large group of family members arrived in Fort Bliss to join their husbands and fathers. By mid-1947, all of the families were reunited in the Beaumont Annex of the Fort Bliss Camp. *"The arrival of the initial group of families in 1946,"* Winterstein recalled [4-1], *"was a big morale booster for the Germans."*

However, contacts between the Germans and American citizens, other than those dictated by their work assignments, was still limited to the weekly shopping trips under military escort, with few exceptions. In the summer of 1946, some of the Peenemünders had asked an English teacher at Texas A&M University in El Paso, Professor Dennis Moses, to help them improve their ability by teaching them English conversation. One evening every week Professor Moses would come out to the camp, and his students would enjoy two or three most stimulating and pleasant hours with a man who had lived all his life in the United States, but quickly developed a genuine interest, and even a warm-hearted attachment to his resident alien students. When Christmas time approached in 1946, the Paperclippers were still strictly confined to their well-guarded barracks camp. Professor Moses went personally to Major Hamill and asked him for permission to invite four of his students, who were bachelors, to his home in town for a family dinner on Christmas Eve. *"I will pick them up with my car in the camp, and I will return them to the camp before midnight. I will personally vouch for each of them,"* he said. Hamill agreed, and the four had a most delightful Christmas Eve with the Moses family. That was the first private home they entered in the United States, almost one year after they had come into the country.

A few of the Germans enjoyed an occasional respite from their daily monotony. *"My wife and I invited small groups of the Germans to our quarters . . . in Fort Bliss,"* Winterstein remembered [4-1]. *"We introduced them to the Western style of barbecue dinners along with conventional American cuisine . . . As of this date I still have the home-made bar we used at Fort Bliss, and over which a number of 'successful' launches into outer space were planned. One estimate at that time, in early 1946, was that with all-out effort, we could reach the Moon for about 3 billion dollars."*

On 16 January 1947, von Braun gave his first speech to a public audience in the United States, the El Paso Rotary Club [4-9]. He chose to talk about *"The Future Development of the Rocket"*; this would be the first time that he was entirely free to express his own thoughts about the evolution of the rocket from an Earth-bound weapon to a vehicle that would one day carry human astronauts to the Moon and to planetary space.

Beginning with a brief description of the principles of rocket propulsion, he continued, anticipating a question on the minds of his listeners: *"You might ask me why the rocket was used first . . . as a weapon of war . . . It seems to be a law of nature that all novel technical inventions that have a future for civilian use start out as weapons . . ."* Citing the airplane and atomic energy as examples, he said: *"Each of these developments offers a unique chance to improve our standard of living. The only hope we can have right now is that in the future an everlasting peace will allow the rocket to be used only for peaceful purposes."*

He described a 90-foot [27-meter] high three-stage rocket powerful enough to boost its upper stage into an orbit around the Earth. *"When the 'cut-off' of the rocket engine takes place,"* he explained, *"there is a queer sensation in the cockpit—everything just floats weightlessly . . ."* El Paso Rotarians had never heard such a talk before!

"When the rocket reaches a horizontal velocity of about 22,000 feet [6,600 meters] per second," von Braun continued, *". . . it will not fall down toward the Earth, even when its propulsion system stops. It will just continue to circle the Earth . . . A manned platform can be established and used for various purposes, including the exploration of the universe. Such a platform may look like a wheel . . ."* Within a few years, the idea of the space station would become familiar to millions all over the world through a host of illustrated lectures and popular magazine articles.

A space platform, von Braun explained further, could serve as a refueling station for a rocket traveling to the Moon. This, then, would be the beginning of space travel. *"The first man who puts his foot on the Moon or another planet,"* von Braun concluded his talk, *"will be much in the position of Columbus when he discovered the New World. With mankind visiting and exploring other planets, the future history of our world is both unlimited and unpredictable."*

The Rotarians gave their speaker a standing ovation.

This was the first of about 500 public speeches von Braun was to give during the next thirty years. Most of them dealt with rockets and spaceflight, but some digressed into other fields that were close to his ever-active mind: the profound importance of education; or the interplay between technology, science, and politics; or his ideas about religion and Christian faith. More about his presentations will be said in later chapters. While each of his speeches dealt with a specific subject, all of them had one comprehensive purpose: to show that the exploration of space is a basic element of human destiny, and that its time to become manifest is now.

"I see the purpose of my life in the promotion of spaceflight," von Braun once said while he and a group of his co-workers were sitting on a sand dune in the White Sands desert, waiting for the take-off of a V-2 rocket. *"My gut feeling is that these years in Fort Bliss and White Sands will mark a decisive step in this endeavor . . ."*

It would be wrong to assume that von Braun's invincible optimism spread like permanent sunshine over the Paperclipper's days, weeks, and years in the camp. Von Braun had his gloomy days, too. *"The lack of resources,"* Winterstein said [4-1], *"was one of the uppermost problems confronting the group at Fort Bliss, and particularly von Braun."* In fact, this was cause for low morale and a discouraging situation of a team wanting to engage in research and development, without the materials to do so. *"At that time,"* Winterstein recalled, *"any large-scale operational research facility for conducting basic research on improved rockets for national defense or space ventures was still a far distant dream during the early times at Fort Bliss."*

There was no lack of attempts on von Braun's part to obtain at least some very basic support. He talked to his boss, Major Hamill, and he wrote urgent memoranda to him in which he asked for laboratory facilities, tools, access to a library, and contacts with other groups engaged in rocket work. He pointed out the utter waste that this situation meant for the government that brought over, at great expense, a group that offered a remarkable amount of experience, knowledge, cooperative spirit, and will to work for the development of a promising and very important new technology, and now lets this opportunity for outstanding accomplishments waste away in a little desert camp.

Hamill never responded to von Braun's pleas. Long after the Fort Bliss camp had closed its doors and the von Braun group was working on the Saturn-Apollo project, Major Hamill told his former wards at an oldtimer reunion in Huntsville: *"Von Braun was so impatient. He wrote me notes, threatening that he would leave the organization if I did not do this or that. I always ignored what he said, and what he wrote I threw into the waste paper basket."*

Actually, von Braun meant what he said and wrote. A breakup of the team was not averted by Hamill's wisdom, but by other circumstances. Winterstein shared this bit of inside knowledge with his old friends forty years later [4-1]: *"The lack of resources for any extensive rocket research . . . concerned von Braun quite a bit. One evening [during the 1946/47 winter], my wife and I took Wernher and several other Germans out for dinner at the Hacienda Restaurant . . . on the road to Las Cruces, New Mexico. After dinner, Wernher and I . . . went out on the patio, where we were quite alone. It appeared that he was on the verge of deciding to leave the organization and go to private industry."* Obviously, von Braun did not see any future in the realm of rockets or anything related to space while he was an employee of the government.

What was holding him back was the simple fact that no private corporation at that time had the necessary resources to sponsor work concerning space travel. *"I advised him to 'hang in there',"* Winterstein recalled, *"and [I predicted] that someday Congress would ease up and grant funds for space research. I also told him at that time that someday he would be known as the greatest rocket scientist in the United States, and probably in the world."* Though the immediate outlook was bleak, von Braun decided to ride the rough times out, and to hope for better days.

"Lack of a real project to work on," von Braun remarked to his associates repeatedly in those days, *"has a severe impact on the mood and morale of our men. If they have no scientific or technical problem to sink their teeth in, they create human problems."* In fact, von Braun spent many hours at that time trying to soothe spirits that got upset over bagatelles. People even called on him as an arbitrator in marital disputes. *"I really wish,"* he said, *"we could work on a tough technical problem again!"*

But there were sunny days, too, and by and large von Braun's deep-rooted joy of living gained the upper hand again. One day in February 1947, von Braun did not show up for breakfast or lunch, and he even missed the usual after-dinner volley ball game. Rumor spread quickly that the Army had whisked him away very quietly and had flown him to Germany—to get married! Sure enough, after a week or two he returned with his young bride, Maria, beaming with happiness and pride. The two of them had been married in the Lutheran Church of Landshut, Bavaria, on March 1. Wernher recommended strongly to all the bachelors in his team to follow his example. From the beginning, Maria was greatly admired by everybody for her youthful beauty and grace, and was deeply respected because she played her role as *"First Lady"* with so much dignity.

Wernher and Maria were relatives; they shared the same grandfather, Dr. Wernher von Quistorp. Von Braun often told the touching story how, as a youth of seventeen, he was privileged to hold his baby cousin Maria in his arms during her baptism in the Lutheran Church. *"That was the moment,"* he never failed to add with a chuckle, *"when I looked into her eyes and decided to marry her."* Maria would never quite confirm that story, though.

Another step toward freedom for the Germans occurred in the spring of 1947, their second Texas spring in the Fort Bliss camp. By that time, the tight restrictions of the rocket people's freedom of movement were gradually lifted. They were permitted to take brief walks outside the camp, albeit with the strict order not to enter, or even approach, any public or private building whatsoever. One day, it so happened that one of the men hiked through the desert in the direction of the El Paso Airport; at that time, that entire area was still totally undeveloped. All of a sudden, one of those quick desert thunderstorms broke loose, and the man was threatened by a drenching downpour. Oblivious to his orders, he sought shelter in the hallway of the airport, but he was spotted by an officer and reported to Major Hamill.

In wise anticipation of such disciplinary problems, Hamill had asked von Braun earlier to establish a kind of *"people's court"* within his team that would exercise jurisdictional powers when needed. Von Braun appointed Dieter K. Huzel as chief judge, and a few others as jurors. When the hapless fellow was accused of violating the order not to enter any building, the court convened, took testimony, debated and judged, and finally pronounced the verdict: for one week, the man had to sweep the clubhouse every evening.

A more serious incident occurred when a rocket expert, who had been an amateur radio operator for many years in Germany before the war and had been in radio contact with another ham radio operator in El Paso, one day went to town, in defiance of his orders, and paid a visit to his ham friend. For some reason, he was stopped by the police; but alas, he had no identification papers whatsoever, and he spoke only broken English—but not with the usual Mexican accent! This time, the city judge had to handle the case. After lengthy court procedures, the man was reprimanded and released. Later, he told his friends in the camp: *"The first thing the judge did after the thing was over was to request that he be admitted to our ham radio club!"*

Fortunately, these restrictions did not last long. By mid-1947, children of the *"resident aliens"* were permitted to enroll in public schools. The Germans were free to buy automobiles and acquire driver's licences, to drive through the town and its environs without limitations, to spend weekends in the beautiful mountain country of Cloud Croft and Ruidoso, and even to take vacation trips to Colorado, Yellowstone, Arizona, and California, provided that they submitted a detailed itinerary ahead of time. Many of the Germans embraced this newly won freedom of travel avidly, as far as their vacation time permitted. Most of them had developed, by the summer of 1947, a life-long love affair with the country.

For the American government, there was still the sticky problem of the status of all the Germans, the men and their families alike. The Federal Bureau of Investigation was reluctant to authorize security clearances for the engineers and scientists, and the State Department was uncertain as to how to consider the *"prisoners of peace"* whose stay in the United States was to have been only temporary.

As relations between the United States and the Soviet Union chilled during the postwar years, Army Ordnance became increasingly convinced that the Germans must stay. Early in 1948, Army Intelligence and the Department of State jointly began to make definite plans for an orderly entry of the German specialists into the United States that would give them the status of lawful immigrants, and enable them to submit requests for First Papers as the initial step in a lengthy and complicated process of obtaining American citizenship. In May of that year, Army Intelligence Director Lieutenant General Stephen J. Chamberlain persuaded FBI Director J. Edgar Hoover to do all he could to make it possible for the Germans to obtain official resident status in the United States. In collaboration with the Department of State, a plan was devised for the Germans to go over the Rio Grande Bridge in El Paso to Ciudad Juarez in Mexico, and then to officially enter the United States upon their return to El Paso. This procedure was, to say the least, unusual. The first group of the Germans *"double-crossed"*—as one of the escorts wrily remarked—the Rio Grande late in 1949; by the spring of 1950, most of the Peenemünders had legally immigrated. The backgrounds of all of them had been searched and screened very thoroughly several times during the previous four years, and even J. Edgar Hoover saw no further reason why their clean records, their loyalties, and their values for the United States should be doubted.

Well protected by a contingent of Army guards, the German immigrants first walked across the international Rio Grande Bridge from El Paso in the United States to Ciudad Juarez in Mexico. On both sides of the bridge, customs officers discreetly refrained from asking questions. The group proceeded directly to the U.S. Consulate where everyone received an immigration visa. This accomplished, they walked back across the bridge under the watchful eyes of American customs officers. Upon the question *"Where do you come from?"* the Germans dutifully answered *"From Mexico,"* showing their visas. The officers then certified to the Army guards that these people had lawfully entered the United States *"via street car"* from Mexico, and could proceed at will.

That brief walk across the bridge was a happy event for von Braun and his team. It meant for them an outstretched hand, a voice that said: *"Stay with us, and share with us the beauty, the wealth, and the freedom that this country is offering to all who come to its shores . . ."*

6   V-2 ROCKETS IN WHITE SANDS

"A few hundred feet away from me the rocket towered on its launching stand. Gleaming white, it stood in the mid-morning sunlight pointing toward the cloudless blue sky. Fully loaded, the V-2 now awaited its release to roar away into the azure heights above it. . .". These were the words of Dr. Homer E. Newell—a young scientist at the Naval Research Laboratory in Washington, later to become NASA associate administrator and chief scientist—after he had witnessed his first A-4 launching at White Sands Proving Ground in New Mexico in the summer of 1946 [4-10].

"As I watched and waited, the impression bore down upon me that this behemoth was actually alive, now still and motionless, but ready at a moment's notice to spring into action . . . Propellants were pumped into the missile, and as the tanks took on their full load. . . , the rocket acquired a latent power that seemed to bring it to life . . ." The same feelings that Newell expressed so poetically are known to thousands who have witnessed the launching of a great rocket during these past fifty years. *"Twenty, nineteen, eighteen . . . At the count of zero, flames burst forth from the tail of the rocket . . . The control cable connecting the missile to the blockhouse dropped away. The jet roared with an awful din. Under full thrust, the rocket climbed powerfully toward the sky. All about us the air thundered with the noise of the motor. The ground trembled. In only a matter of seconds, the rocket had climbed so high that we had to crane our necks to watch it . . ."*

Regardless of how many times even an oldtimer in rocketry has seen the launching of a big rocket, each launch event overwhelms him again with the same powerful, captivating impression. Seeing that slender, gleaming body emerge from a wild cauldron of fire and smoke and head straight up, unperturbed by all the roaring thunder at its rear, is an unforgettable sight indeed.

"That V-2 firing was the first rocket launching that I had ever witnessed", Newell continued. *"Nothing could match the excitement, the thrill, the exhilaration that went with that beautiful, inspiring, awesome sight . . . I was impressed with the power and portent of the magnificent achievement that was embodied in the V-2. It was the world's first giant rocket. As a weapon, it had already begun to revolutionize the deadly art of war. As a research vehicle, it could carry a ton of equipment and instruments to over a hundred miles above the Earth to explore the upper atmosphere. Here was the first real promise of space travel. Here, in fact, was something new!"*

This launching of a V-2 that Homer Newell watched in White Sands in the spring of

1946 occurred only a little over a year after the last V-2 had been test-launched in Germany. What had happened in the meantime?

The story of the long overland and overseas travel of the V-2 parts from the middle of Germany to the mouth of the Mississippi was briefly told in Chapter 3-9. The sixteen Liberty ships were unloaded at the pier of New Orleans. From there, railway freight cars transported the rocket parts to Las Cruces in New Mexico, and after a short trip on flatbed trucks over the Augustine Pass, they finally found temporary resting places in hangars, and even on the open desert floor, at White Sands Proving Ground in August 1945.

About a year earlier, Army Ordnance had established this proving ground for rocket test launchings near Las Cruces, 130 km (80 miles) north of El Paso, Texas. Lieutenant Colonel Harold R. Turner was put in charge. He had to start really from point zero—his first action was to drill for water in the desert, causing him to remark that he felt like Moses in the Old Testament—but by mid-summer in 1945, there were barracks to house troops and civilians, and hangars for some limited equipment storage and assembly work.

It turned out that some of the essential parts had not been shipped in sufficient numbers, or not at all. Other parts had been damaged beyond repair during disassembly, loading, shipping, unloading, and storage, all by unskilled labor. Replacements for those parts had to be manufactured by General Electric. At first, assembly of the rockets proceeded slowly, not only because there were practically no tools, no machines, no shop facilities, and no cleanrooms for the highly specialized work, but also because the ubiquitous desert sand, blowing into all the buildings with relentless force, was a constant problem that often made the lives of the rocketeers quite miserable.

By springtime in 1946, the first V-2s were ready for launching in the White Sands desert. After a static firing on 15 March, veterans from the Peenemünde launch crew, reinforced by enlisted men and General Electric engineers, prepared and launched the first missile on 16 April. It reached an altitude of only 6 km (3.8 miles), but the five following launches were completely successful.

Between April 1946 and September 1952, no less than 70 V-2s were launched, 67 of them from the rocket testing grounds in White Sands, 2 from Florida, and 1 from the aircraft carrier *Midway*. In spite of the harsh treatment and the hostile environment to which these rockets had been exposed for more than a year after their completion in Germany, and in spite of the primitive facilities available for their assembly and checkout, the success rate of the launchings was reasonably good. Of the 70 V-2s brought to the launch pad, 3 fizzled upon ignition; 20 reached altitudes between 4 and 100 km (2.5 and 65 miles), and 47 soared to peak altitudes between 100 and 213 km (65 and 140 miles). Most of them carried scientific payloads; some were used for guidance and control studies. About 75 percent of the rockets carried payloads that were heavier than the payloads for which the V-2 had been designed originally.

Eight of the V-2 rockets had WAC Corporal rockets from JPL as upper stages. These true two-stage vehicles reached considerable altitudes. The record was set on 24 February 1949 with an apex of 387 km (240 miles).

In Germany, the total flight history of V-2 rockets, from the first test launch to the last firing, covered only two and a half years. In White Sands, V-2s were launched for scientific research purposes over a period of six and a half years.

Army Ordnance, motivated by Colonel Toftoy, initiated these test launchings in White Sands primarily because of the technology transfer that would result from such launchings: field training for the troops, and rocket know-how for industry. It soon became obvious, though, that the considerable payload capability of the V-2 rocket would offer a tremendous opportunity for scientists to explore the high atmosphere, the ionosphere, and the space beyond as it had never been possible before.

Probably the first scientist in the Untied States to see this possibility was Gerard Kuiper, an astronomer in Tucson, Arizona. The idea must have occurred to him in 1944 when he was sent to France as a member of the ALSOS Mission to interrogate German prisoners of war. Arthur C. Clarke, in February 1945, wrote to the editor of *Wireless World* and proposed V-2s for ionospheric research, with the observational data telemetered to a ground station. The National Advisory Committee for Aeronautics [NACA], one month later, suggested that atmospheric data up to altitudes of 100 miles could be acquired by V-2 rockets. Physicists and astronomers at other places began to recognize the unprecedented research opportunities. Leo Goldberg wrote to Donald Menzel at Harvard Observatory later in 1945 that he *"would like nothing more than to be involved in a project to study the solar spectrum outside the Earth's atmosphere"* [4-11].

In the meantime, Ernst H. Krause, a physicist at the Naval Research Laboratory, had returned from Germany where he had interrogated German scientists involved in high altitude physics. He was determined to bring the United States up to speed in guided missile research [4-12]. In December, he and Milton Rosen established the Rocket Sonde Research Section at the NRL. Toftoy strongly supported the use of the captured V-2 rockets for scientific research, and the Army generously offered free instrument flights to interested scientists, an offer that met with enthusiastic response from the Naval Research Laboratory in Washington, from the Applied Physics Laboratory at Johns Hopkins University, and from a number of other scientific institutions in the country.

Numerous high-ranking scientists became actively interested in high-altitude research with the V-2, among them R. Ladenburg and Lyman Spitzer, Jr. at Princeton; Merle Tuve, M. H. Nichols, J. J. Hopfield, and James Van Allen at the Applied Physics Laboratory; W. B. Klemperer at the Douglas Research Laboratory; Richard W. Porter at General Electric; T. H. Johnson at Aberdeen Ballistic Research Laboratory; J. Allen Hynek at Ohio State University; Jesse Greenstein at Yerkes Observatory; Fritz Zwicky at CalTech; Richard Tousey, Homer E. Newell, and Herbert Friedman at NRL; and others.

In order to provide planning and management support for these manifold interests, Krause organized the V-2 Upper Atmosphere Research Panel whose members represented all the institutions and agencies which at that time were interested in high-altitude research. Among the panel members were G. K. Megarian from G.E., James A. Van Allen from Johns Hopkins University, and Fred L. Whipple from Harvard University. Krause acted as chairman until 1947 when he was succeeded by Van Allen. This panel *"became the aegis for the country's first sounding rocket program,"* as Newell remarked later [1-4]. One of the first actions was the advice to Army Ordnance to organize the allocation of space in the V-2 nose cones for scientific research projects on an orderly, well-planned basis. The Army gladly accepted this advice.

"During the period of the V-2 upper atmosphere program, the German missile served as an admirable vehicle for high-altitude research. It often carried more than a ton of payload to altitudes better than 160 km (100 miles)," Newell wrote later [1-4].

Von Braun was very happy about these peaceful uses of his rocket. In April 1946 he wrote a paper on *"Investigation of the Upper Atmosphere with the A-4 (V-2) Rocket Missile"* [4-13], in which he described the great importance of knowledge about the high atmosphere not only for scientific research, but for a better understanding of our immediate environment, particularly the weather. *"Measurements of the uppermost layers of the atmosphere, in addition to their purely scientific value, will have considerable influence on progress in meteorology, radio wave propagation, navigation, and aeronautics. They will help pave the way for future flying at such altitudes,"* he wrote.

The Naval Research Laboratory contributed more than a group of enthusiastic scientists to this research program. It provided a redesigned nose cone instead of the heavy-weight military warhead, suitable for the accommodation of a variety of scientific instruments. NRL also initiated the development of a new telemetry system, based on modern electronic technology, which was more capable, lighter, and more reliable than the old telemeter that had been developed and used in Peenemünde. A talented young electronics engineer, John R. Kauke, patiently and successfully nurtured this Raytheon-built NRL telemeter through thirty-three V-2 launchings during the late 1940s.

Instruments and experiments carried aloft by V-2 rockets in White Sands make a most impressive list. In total, 223 different experiments were launched; 38 of them measured cosmic rays, 32 made solar observations, 26 studied the ionosphere, 25 determined the temperature profile of the atmosphere, 25 its pressure profile, and 19 its composition. Photographic pictures of the Earth's surface were taken on 18 flights. Other experiments performed biological studies, observed meteoroids, measured the Earth's magnetic field, or studied features of the atmosphere.

"By the time the last V-2 was launched in the fall of 1952, a rich harvest of information on atmospheric temperatures, pressures, densities, composition, ionization, and winds, on atmospheric and solar radiations, on the Earth's magnetic field at high altitudes, and on cosmic rays had been reaped," Newell wrote in 1980 in his book *Beyond the Atmosphere* [1-4].

While the V-2 proved its utility as a tool for high-altitude research, the time was in sight when the stockpile of V-2 parts would be exhausted. Van Allen, wishing to continue this line of research for a long time to come, initiated the development of a smaller, lighter, and cheaper research rocket, the Aerobee, with a payload capability of 65 kg (143 lb) and a peak altitude of about 120 km (75 miles). He was also guided by the strong desire to have a rocket at his disposal whose payload compartment he would not have to share with a number of colleagues, each of them working by his own schedule, and by his own specifications concerning time of launch, trajectory, attitude control, and telemetry.

The first Aerobee was launched in November 1947; by the end of 1952, almost one hundred Aerobees had flown. Financed by the Navy, the Aerobee was developed and produced by the Douglas Aircraft Company and the Aerojet Engineering Corporation.

A larger research rocket, Viking, was developed by the Glenn L. Martin Company under the project direction of Milton W. Rosen at NRL. It reached an altitude of 219 km (137 miles) with about 180 kg (400 lb) of payload. A total of eight Viking rockets, powered by Reaction Motors, Inc. engines, were successfully launched between 1949 and 1952.

The primary beneficiaries of the science program on V-2s and other high-altitude rockets in White Sands were the experimenters on cosmic rays, on solar radiation, and on atmospheric and ionospheric data. Van Allen had his and his co-workers' Geiger counters on 13 V-2s from 1946 to 1952, and on 10 Aerobees. Cosmic ray scientists at NRL used 17 V-2s, 4 Aerobees, and 3 Vikings during the same period. Among all the enthusiastic users of high-altitude research rockets in White Sands at that time, the most consistent and untiring experimenter was Richard Tousey, a solar physicist at the NRL. He applied several different methods to measure the solar spectrum as far into the ultraviolet region as possible. Tousey's first—and historic—success came with a V-2 flight on 10 October 1946, on which he recorded the solar spectrum with a grating spectrograph down to a wavelength of 220 nanometers. Previously, balloon flights had provided spectra only down to 300 nanometers.

Solar X rays with a wavelength below 0.8 nanometers were detected for the first time by T. R. Burnight who exposed photographic plates, covered with thin beryllium foils, to solar radiation on a V-2 flight that reached an altitude of 168 km (105 miles) on 5 August 1948. Using selected phosphors and appropriate filters, Tousey could cover the entire spectrum down to the soft X-ray region around 0.8 nanometers wavelength, although with very limited resolution, on a V-2 flight on 17 February 1949, and again a year later, on 17 February 1950.*

Using Geiger counters with special gas fillings and a variety of windows, Friedman and his co-workers obtained more definite X-ray results on a V-2 flight on 29 September 1949. Their measurement covered the solar spectrum from about 200 nanometers down to the soft X-ray region around 0.6 nanometers. *"In one simple set of measurements,"* he said, *"we identified the Lyman alpha radiation as the source of D-region ionization, and identified soft X-rays with E-region production."*

Leo Goldberg, Director of Kitt Peak National Observatory, said of Herbert Friedman on the occasion of his sixtieth birthday in 1976, that he was like a prospector of the past, but his claims were not gold mines, *"they were staked out on the virgin territory of the electromagnetic spectrum"* [4-18].

Actually, these experiments in White Sands were not the first scientific payloads that had been planned for high-altitude flights of V-2 rockets. As early as 1942 at Peenemünde, von Braun had suggested to Professor Erich Regener, physicist at the Technical University in Stuttgart, that a set of instruments, mounted in the nose cone of a V-2 and carried to a high altitude during a test flight, would be in an excellent position to measure pressure, temperature, and composition of the high atmosphere, and the ultraviolet spectrum of the Sun's radiation. Instruments could even take and retrieve samples of the ambient air. Regener subsequently built the *"Regener Tonne,"* a capsule containing instruments for all these measurements, including a spectrograph with quartz optics for the ultraviolet spectrum. The capsule was to be released at the apex of the trajectory and to be recovered by parachute. Unfortunately, by the time the Regener Tonne was ready for flight, von Braun had lost the necessary authority over the use of even the test vehicles to go forward with the launching of the scientific instruments. In a report on war research in Germany, F. Zwicky described details of this joint, but unfinished von Braun-Regener project [4-14].

Von Braun followed with keenest interest the program of scientific research that unfolded in the White Sands desert. Not only was he excited and intrigued by the new knowledge that came from these high-altitude launchings; he was greatly relieved because, as he said, *"our V-2 is finally approaching its bona fide destination, the vast reaches of space beyond the narrow confines of the low atmosphere . . ."*. Homer Newell, one of the architects and users of the V-2 research program, who retained close contact with von Braun throughout his professional life, wrote in 1961 [1-4]: *"One of the impelling motives drawing many of the German workers into the field of rocketry was the anticipation of travel through space. Even when developing the V-2 missile, Wernher von Braun and his colleagues were ever conscious of the call of outer space. They retained this interest after coming to the United States. Because of it they were ready, when the call came, to launch the first U.S. artificial satellite, Explorer 1. They accomplished the launching with a Jupiter C (Juno 1) rocket, based on the Redstone, which was in many ways an enlarged and improved version of the V-2."*

---

*As Dr. Herbert Friedman pointed out in a letter to Ernst Stuhlinger, these early observations could not be fully confirmed by later, more accurate measurements.

7   ROCKETS FOR DEFENSE AND EXPLORATION

What impact did the V-2 rockets in White Sands have on the American rocket program? Homer Newell wrote in 1980 [1-4]: *"Neither Goddard's work nor the JPL rockets provided the initial impetus to the space science program in America. Circumstances made rocket sounding in the United States the beneficiary of the two decades of vigorous rocket development work by German experimenters that ensued following the publication of Oberth's* Rocket Into Planetary Space. *Nourished by German military support, the German experimenters rediscovered and reinvented for themselves much of what Goddard was learning in the United States. Going well beyond what Goddard could accomplish in his self-imposed isolation, Walter Dornberger, Wernher von Braun, and their colleagues produced the V-2 . . . The Army took the captured V-2s to the United States . . . [and] made it possible for interested groups to instrument them for high altitude scientific research . . ."*

Scientists were not the only ones who took a lively interest in the V-2 flights at White Sands. Among the most ardent observers was Colonel Toftoy, under whose initiative the *"rocket people"* had been rounded up in Germany and brought over to the United States. Shortly after they had settled at Fort Bliss, Toftoy tried to influence members of the government to provide support for the build-up of some basic laboratory and shop facilities at Fort Bliss to enable the Germans to begin some useful development work. Impressed and encouraged by the V-2 launchings, he thought that a missile of 500 to 1,000 miles (800 to 1,600 km) range would be a very useful project for the Army, and that it would be a logical and also a feasible development project for *"his"* guided missile people at Fort Bliss.

However, Army authorities in Washington were not interested in such a project. No need for further weapon systems development was perceived at that time. Only a far less ambitious project, the cruise missile Hermes II, to be boosted to cruise altitude by a V-2 rocket and then to continue its horizontal flight with a supersonic ramjet propulsion system, was finally permitted as a research project at Fort Bliss, to be done jointly by the von Braun team and the General Electric Company.

Erik Bergaust [2-3] recalled a conversation with von Braun on that subject. *"It was in some respect a good and interesting project,"* Bergaust wrote. *"Many tests were made with supersonic ramjet diffusers, injection methods, flameholders and the like, and a considerable body of knowledge in a new field was acquired. Von Braun and his men, until recently accustomed to the lavish Peenemünde test facilities, demonstrated surprising capability to get good work done with a shoestring budget, and with makeshift facilities."* Two old Army trailers were converted into diffuser and combustion test stands. Air was supplied by a series of mobile Army surplus compressors, and in order to run tests at more representative flight altitude conditions, the whole rig was simply towed up a mountain road in the Sierra Nevada. Runs were made at the reduced atmospheric pressure at 10,000 feet (3,000 meter) elevation.

Around that time during the late 1940s, several project studies for ballistic rockets and long-range cruise missiles were under way at Glenn L. Martin, North American Aviation, Republic Aviation, Northrop Aircraft, General Electric, and other companies.

In an attempt to contribute to these various development projects, von Braun presented a proposal to Army Ordnance in 1949, suggesting the development of *"A Large Multipurpose Booster Rocket"* [4-15]. This booster could be applied as an initial thrust stage to all these missiles, greatly enhancing their performance and usefulness. The report began with a strategic assessment of long-range guided missiles. Unlike long-range bombers, von Braun wrote, long-range guided missiles can effectively be applied against targets over which air superiority cannot be established. On such targets, long-range guided missiles may even be cheaper than the application of bombers because of the high risk factor of the latter.

After enumerating and describing some technical features that must be met by a long-range guided missile, he included the following brief, but very characteristic comment: *"A number of additional applications of this multipurpose booster exist. It could be used . . . as a first stage of three-stage arrangements such as: Booster/V-2/Wac Corporal; Booster/Viking/Wac Corporal; Booster/V-2/Nativ; Booster/Viking/Nativ. Preliminary investigations indicate that . . . some of these combinations would be capable of reaching satellite velocity."*

After this plug for spaceflight, von Braun continued with the technical details of his proposal. He stated that the propulsion system would be the most important component of the booster, while the final booster configuration could be adapted to the various second stages.

The proposed propulsion system contained several features which, as von Braun remarked, *"may appear unusual in comparison with conventional rocket propulsion system design."* In particular, the conventional de Laval nozzle was replaced by a *"spoke wheel"* design. In this arrangement, a number of nozzles are packed closely together so that a cross section through the nozzles would look like a spoke wheel. The total length of a spoke wheel engine would be much shorter than the length of a conventional one-barrel engine with equal performance.

In retrospect, von Braun's Multipurpose Booster Report was a remarkable milestone in the history of American rocket development. Composed during 1948, it described an advanced rocket developing 200 tons of thrust, with a variety of innovative features, based on more than ten years of densely-packed experience with rockets that had culminated in the V-2 missile. That booster would have provided a powerful and efficient first stage for a number of rocket vehicles under development at that time, and it could have led to an American satellite of substantial size in 1955 or 1956.

Shortly after von Braun had completed his Multipurpose Booster Report, he wrote a paper entitled *"Space Superiority as a Means for Achieving World Peace"* [4-16]. That was the time when the Soviets had just exploded their first atomic bomb, and when they were building up their military power at a terrifying pace. It was a time of growing anxiety; the dream of eternal peace that had blissfully spread over many minds began to vanish quickly. *"The West finds itself obliged to arm to the teeth in the interest of maintaining an uneasy peace in this tortured world,"* von Braun wrote. He saw two simultaneous problems: First, a deterrent power must be created which is sufficiently effective to inhibit the East from continuing its aggressive expansion; and second, a fighting power is needed. *"First priority . . . must be given to . . . the deterrent power,"* he wrote.

Airplanes and atomic bombs, von Braun continued, will no longer represent an effective deterrent. *"There is but little use in wildcatting in the exhausted oil fields of conventional armament . . . We must find our deterrent to a Third World War at new horizons, in a field where test drillings have already revealed a plentiful supply of the treasures we seek . . . The field to which I refer is that of rocketry."*

Paraphrasing a statement by General George C. Marshall, von Braun continued his essay: *"The most distinguished military thinking of our time concedes that the only way to win a Third World War is to prevent its outbreak."* He argued that one of the most decisive steps toward that goal would be the establishment of observing posts in satellite orbits that would deny any would-be aggressor the possibility of a clandestine build-up of military preparations. *"Rocketry is, I believe,"* he wrote, *"capable of solving the world's peace problems more effectively than any other branch of science and engineering."* Besides its deterrent effect upon would-be aggressors, he pointed out, it will be capable of serving a multitude of humanitarian ends.

Although von Braun's detailed description of an observing platform in orbit, and of its peace-keeping activities, may sound a little over-optimistic today, it must be acknowledged that there has not been a World War III, and that rockets with nuclear warheads, and also *"spy-in-the-sky"* observing satellites, on both sides have probably been the most decisive contributors to this prolonged period of peace.

As the 1940s came to an end, neither the Multipurpose Booster nor the observing platform in space had become an active development project. Instead, under the shadow of the Korean War, the Army remembered Toftoy's old proposal of building a 500-mile (800 km) surface-to-surface rocket as a strategic weapon. Von Braun was given the order to build the missile, later to be named the Redstone. It was the first real development project the Army assigned to him, and he and his team charged ahead with full power. It gave him the opportunity to apply the knowledge and experience he had acquired through almost twenty years of active rocket work, and it sparked the hope— still hidden deep in his mind—that one day this rocket would put the first man-made satellite in orbit.

8   CAMPAIGNING FOR SPACE

The Army's decision to build a 500-mile ballistic missile, and to assign the project to the von Braun team, coincided with the move of the rocket group from Fort Bliss in Texas to Huntsville in Alabama during the summer of 1950. During their four and one half years in the Texas camp, the rocketeers had stayed busy with the V-2 launchings at White Sands, and with their self-chosen study project, carried out jointly with members of the General Electric Company, of a V-2-boosted, ramjet-driven cruise missile. That project study also provided the framework for individual studies of guidance and control instruments, magnetic amplifiers, celestial mechanics problems, supersonic aero- dynamics, electric propulsion systems, and other advanced work related to rocket flight. Von Braun, together with some of his associates, focused in on a subject that had occupied his mind for more than twenty years: a manned expedition to Mars.

It was not only his leisure time during the low-key years in Fort Bliss that made von Braun decide to write down, in a concise technical report, his concept of a journey to Mars by human spacefarers [4-4]. His rocket and spaceflight presentation to the Rotarians in El Paso early in 1947—his first exposure to a public audience in the United States—had prompted a heartwarming response. Encouraged by this demonstration of interest, von Braun accepted more invitations for public speaking, and he realized that the world of outer space, and its exploration by men and women from planet Earth, had the potential of casting its magic spell over an audience, provided that it were presented in the right way.

The Mars Project essay would give von Braun the opportunity of describing in a sound and sober way the technical problems that confront the planners of a Mars expedition, and also the methods by which those problems could be solved.

"Soon after the publication of the first serious papers on space travel," von Braun wrote in the introduction to his booklet, *"a spate of fanciful tales appeared. The central figure in these stories was usually the heroic inventor. Surrounded by a little band of faithful followers, he secretly built a mysteriously streamlined space vessel in a remote*

backyard. Then, at the hour of midnight, he and his crew soared into the solar system to brave untold perils—successfully, of course."

Von Braun used every opportunity to emphasize that true space travel cannot be attained by any backyard inventor, no matter how ingenious he might be. It can only be achieved by the coordinated might of scientists, engineers, technicians, and organizers from nearly every branch of modern science and industry. *"Interplanetary exploration must be done on a grand scale,"* he said.

Von Braun did not deny the possibility that nuclear energy might someday propel space vehicles. He was always hesitant to use the word *"impossible"* when speaking of technical developments. However, he said, atomic energy all by itself does not constitute a reactive propulsion system. *"I am still to be convinced,"* he wrote, *"that within the next twenty-five years an atomic rocket drive will be able to compete in cost and performance with chemical propulsion . . . The study that follows,"* he said in the introduction to his Mars study, *"intends to prove that we can thrust an expedition to Mars with conventional chemical propellants."*

Von Braun's study dealt with all the major phases of the Mars expedition; Chapter 5-4 describes the broad concept of his proposal. Written in 1948 and 1949, his essay was published as a ninety-page booklet in Germany in 1952, and in the United States in 1953 [4-4]. However, long before its publication, von Braun talked about the results of his work whenever he had an opportunity to do so.

While the pundits of rocketry and spaceflight hailed the study as a true milestone in the evolution of their art, von Braun himself realized that papers of this kind might appeal to the few professionals, but all the effort put into them would not do much to bring space travel closer to reality. A change in strategy would be necessary. Von Braun decided to make that change, and it came in a dramatic outburst.

Actually, it was not a change, but rather an addition to the basic strategy he had been following for years: hard work of a dedicated team to develop the science and technology of rockets for spaceflight. Besides this work, von Braun argued, an effort must be made to awaken public interest in spaceflight directly and forcefully.

Dr. Adolf K. Thiel, a theoretician of rocket physics and celestial mechanics, and a long-time associate and friend of von Braun, told Stuhlinger of the crucial event many years later [4-17]:

"One day, I showed the boss some recent calculations I had made about rockets to the Moon. Von Braun at first discussed the matter with great interest, but suddenly he said: You know what? Even if we continued our calculations until hell freezes over, we will not touch or move anybody. You may continue your theoretical studies, but I will talk to the people! I will go public now, because this is where we have to sow our seeds for space exploration!"

From then on, and for the following twenty-five years, von Braun grasped every opportunity, every forum to talk and write about rockets and space flight. Characteristically for him, the *"people"* were not only citizens who just read the journals and listen to the daily news; he particularly had the active ones in mind, the writers and publishers, the educators and politicians, the industrialists, generals, and statesmen— the more prominent, the better!

Going *"public"* with an idea as novel and as far-reaching as spaceflight required an unusual degree of delicate diplomacy. Fortunately, von Braun was a master in this art. Partly inherited through a long line of ancestors in prominent public positions, partly acquired through a very careful upbringing by his parents, von Braun's skill in persuasion reached legendary dimensions. *"Diplomacy is the art of letting someone else have your will,"* he said, and he practiced this rule. Whether he talked to engineers or lawyers or car dealers or members of Congress, his audience would follow him and believe what he said.

"*We are living in a democracy,*" he sometimes remarked to his co-workers, "*where the will and the mood of the people count. If you want to accomplish something as big as travel into space, you must win the people for your idea. Being diplomatic is necessary, but it is not enough. You have to be filled with a burning desire to bring your idea to life. You must have absolute faith into the righteousness of your cause, and into your final success. In short, you must be a kind of a crusader!*"

CHAPTER 5

HUNTSVILLE, ALABAMA:
ROCKET CITY AND SPACE CAPITAL, U.S.A.

1 INVASION FROM TEXAS

Fort Bliss had provided the rocket people a modest, but relatively comfortable place to live; facilities for technical work, however, were very limited.

Around 1949, the political skies over the nation began to darken. Storm clouds accumulated over Korea, and the Beaumont Army Hospital needed its former annex. That was the signal for General Toftoy to look for another place for his Guided Missile Development Division that in the meantime had grown to about four hundred people and was still expanding. He traveled all over the country to look at places where he might find a new home for his rocketeers.

During this search, Toftoy came upon the Huntsville Arsenal, a large, deserted Army post at the outskirts of the City of Huntsville in northern Alabama. This facility, together with the adjacent smaller Redstone Arsenal, had served as a chemical weapons production plant during the war. The two arsenals covered an area of about 65 square miles (160 square km). There were good road and rail connections, a small harbor on the big Tennessee waterway, and even an airplane landing strip. A number of barracks and hangars also existed on the arsenal grounds.

Toftoy thought that this would be a good place for the group, mainly because it would offer excellent growth capabilities for the future. In the summer of 1949, he contacted the Industrial Expansion Committee in Huntsville, chaired by Senator John Sparkman. However, Toftoy could not generate much resonance. The reason was simple. At that time, the Air Force was looking for a southeastern location at which to establish a large aeronautical research, engineering, and testing laboratory. Two places figured on top of the list: Tullahoma in Tennessee, and Huntsville in Alabama. Senator Sparkman had staged a very determined effort to obtain the Air Force laboratory for Huntsville, and that is why he gave Toftoy the cold shoulder. Then, the Air Force decided in favor of Tullahoma. Disappointment in Huntsville was great, but Sparkman was quick to offer to the city an alternative that, as he said, might well prove to be more lucrative in the long run than the Air Force facility. This was to be a research and development center for Army rockets and ballistic missiles. Toftoy lost no time in grasping the opportunity. After convincing his superiors in Washington, he, von Braun, and some of von Braun's team members traveled to Huntsville in the fall of 1949 on an inspection tour. In March 1950, an avant-garde of a dozen resident alien *"Texans"* arrived there to take up residence, and the rest of the Guided Missile Development Division moved from Fort Bliss to Huntsville during the following months.

To the former Peenemünders, this move meant a significant step in their personal histories. In Texas, they had to live in the Army compound behind the gate; all their travels were carefully monitored. Now, they were free to move around, and to rent or buy houses wherever they wished. They went to parent-teacher meetings, joined churches and civic clubs, took out library cards, attended concerts, helped establish a symphony orchestra association, and participated in various other community activities.

Huntsville opened a new chapter in the lives of von Braun and his team members. The first real project had been assigned to them, the Redstone ballistic missile. By the time the Redstone had its first flight test in 1953, the team was also ordered to develop the longer-range Jupiter rocket followed by the Pershing; then a family of satellites; then the Saturn-Apollo rocket for the voyage to the Moon; then Skylab, America's first station in space; then the major components of the space shuttle, its main rocket engine, its external tank, and its solid rocket motor; then the Hubble telescope; then substantial parts of the Space Station Freedom.

This new chapter in Huntsville was also resplendent with that wonderful, warm, glowing southern way of life with which the Germans were quite familiar from *Gone with the Wind*, but which they would never have dreamed of meeting in reality. There were no fences between the houses; neighbors called them by their first names, offered them unlimited help in any situation, and shared their daily problems with them. The German children made friends quickly among the neighbors' children. They soon spoke English like the natives, with and without southern drawl, and most of them did well in school.

Von Braun, in spite of his prodigious workload resulting from the fast-moving Redstone missile project, took every opportunity to establish contacts with the community. He spoke at the Rotary Club and at other civic organizations, and he took part in parent-teacher meetings. He joined the Episcopal Church. He met with the social leaders of the community. And, perhaps most important of all, he made known to the Chamber of Commerce, and to the business leaders in town, his optimistic outlook on Huntsville's future as a booming center of modern technology and industrial growth. The closeness of the Tennessee River with its dams and beautiful lakes rekindled his love for water sports; he became one of the local pioneers for the fledgling sport of water skiing. Also, he resumed flying at the local airport, received his American pilot's license, and on weekends rented a Piper Cub or a Stinson for $6 an hour.

At the same time, von Braun visited many of the leading companies all over the country in a determined effort to help build an industrial base for the rocket projects that he was certain would evolve in the near future. One of the first companies to respond to the challenge was North American Aviation in Los Angeles.

The citizens of Huntsville, most of whom were used to the more leisurely versions of southern living, at first eyed the *"invasion from Texas"* with caution. The last invasion of their home grounds, still alive in their minds as an historical event of secular significance, was made by the armies of Union Generals Sherman and Grant almost a hundred years ago. What would this new invasion of rocket people from the west, and even some from Germany, do to their peaceful city that had long enjoyed a serene life based on the four C's, cotton, corn, cattle, and cress of water? Fortunately for the invaders, the anxious wait-and-see phase did not last long. Reserve turned into curiosity, then into interest, and before long the newcomers had been accepted as *"most welcome citizens,"* as the mayor of Huntsville, R. B. (Spec) Searcy, would put it.

Wilson D. Smith, a very active and successful building contractor in Huntsville who was about ten years old when the Germans arrived during the summer of 1950, remembers the day when a moving van appeared in his street and began to unload furniture and household goods at a neighboring house that had stood empty for some time. He and his pals watched for a while, then he ran back to his home and told his father: *"There are new people moving into that empty house, they speak such a strange language, I believe they are Germans, it sounds funny,"* whereupon his father exclaimed: *"Oh, oh! Here goes our neighborhood to the dogs!"*

The new people moved into their house; they were Wernher and Maria von Braun and their one and a half year old daughter Iris Careen. In no time, the Smiths and the von Brauns had become close friends, and the neighborhood did not go to the dogs.

A number of years later, Wilson married the daughter of another German who worked on the von Braun team, Heide Segewitz. *"That was about the best thing I ever did in my life,"* Wilson said with a happy smile when he told the story in 1988 [5-1].

A highlight for the people from Peenemünde occurred on 15 April 1955. In an impressive ceremony, attended by 1,200 Huntsvillean citizens, von Braun and forty of his associates became naturalized citizens of the United States. This event documented for all time that the City of Huntsville, and the United States of America, had become a beloved home for the former prisoners of peace and invaders from Texas, now proud and happy Americans by choice.

Leaving Germany, and pledging allegiance to a new country, was not a step the young Germans took lightly. The main reason for taking it—a reason with which most members of the vast Peenemünde establishment would have agreed—was, as von Braun put it in 1952 [5-2], *"because this would give us the hope, and perhaps the opportunity, to continue our work toward the realization of space flight."* He gave yet another reason: *". . . because Americans have a reputation for having an especially intense devotion to individual freedom and human rights."* How fervent his and his colleagues' quest for freedom and human rights must have been can be understood from von Braun's description of life and work during the twelve years of Hitler's ruthless dictatorship.

"I had assumed I would encounter plenty of hostility as an 'ex-enemy big shot,' but I never did," von Braun wrote in his essay. *"In America you don't seem to bear grudges, as do many Europeans who had been enemies . . ."* He and his companions were pleasantly surprised when they met with warm friendliness from most of the Americans with whom they came in contact; at the same time, it was a new experience for them to realize how free Americans are to criticize even the highest government officials.

Most of the newcomers became enthusiastic and active members of Huntsville churches. Many of them also became red-hot hometown boosters. *"I've been a guest speaker at luncheons of the local Rotarians, Elks, Kiwanis, and Lions. Some of us are even members of the Huntsville Junior Chamber of Commerce. In fact, one of us (Walt Wiesman) is presently Jaycee vice president,"* von Braun wrote.

One of his serious misconceptions he had about this country, he admitted, concerned the role of churches. He thought that churches in America were something like clubs, a notion he had picked up years ago from Sinclair Lewis's *Babbitt*. How surprised he was to see a very active church life everywhere! *"All of this indicated to me a terrific pioneer spirit . . . wherever I went, I found myself admiring the work churches are doing in making Christianity alive in the community, and I became grateful for all they did in helping our German families feel at home, including my own . . ."*

Von Braun was twenty-five years of age when, in 1937, he became technical director of the Peenemünde establishment. Most of his thousands of co-workers belonged to the same age group. They had their formative years during the late 1920s and early 1930s. At that time, Germany was going through a period of economic depression, coupled with inflation, staggering unemployment, and growing stagnation of many of the normal activities of a healthy national community. Against this backdrop, America offered a glorious image to the eyes of the teenagers. Colorful success stories of American self-made men abounded in their reading fare. America was the country of wealth and plenty, of fabulous freedom, of healthy growth, of unlimited opportunities for everyone who was willing to accept the challenge and to throw his hat in the ring.

For many young Germans during those years, emigration to America became a dream that they hoped to fulfill one day. They would join the huge flow of emigrants who had gone from Europe to the New World during the past 400 years. Among all the European countries, Germany had furnished the largest number of emigrants, 7 million in total, who sought and found a new home in America (this is true if England and Ireland are counted as two separate countries; otherwise, Great Britain is the largest, and Germany the second largest supplier of emigrants to the United States). The list of Americans who descended from German ancestors is almost endless. President Eisenhower's paternal grandfather immigrated from Germany. Lt. General Bernard A. Schriever, architect of the Air Force's guided missile program, was born in Bremen in Northern Germany in 1910; he came to the United States with his parents in 1917 and was naturalized in 1923.

"Going to America" for young Germans, and for other Europeans as well, did not just mean the exchange of one home country for another. It was more like a step in the natural course of a demographic evolution that had gone on for hundreds of years, the expansion of densely populated European countries into the wide lands of the New World. Neither the war, nor even the tremendous propaganda activities on both sides during the war, could change this very positive picture that most young Germans had of America.

For von Braun, the situation had still another aspect. He had anticipated—correctly, as it turned out—that each of the two superpowers would be eager to lay hands on the team of rocket specialists, and that a hunt for Peenemünders would begin as soon as Allied forces from the west and the east had penetrated far enough into Germany. There was even a third power that reached out for the von Braun team, with macabre objectives indeed: Himmler's SS. Strangely enough, while Germany's power to decide and to act was dwindling rapidly in every respect, destiny would have it that von Braun faced the opportunity to make a profound decision: Should he and the core of his team fall into the hands of the SS, or the Russians, or the Americans? There could be no doubt how he would decide.

Actually, it was not a choice. It was a question of *"to be or not to be,"* at least *"to be"* as a team of young people who wanted to develop rockets for space. Surely, their rocket in Peenemünde, ordered by the German Army, had been conceived originally as a weapon of defense, and as a deterrent for a would-be aggressor. For its young developers, it was more: it was a means to explore the world around them, even eventually to leave Earth and travel through space.

As the war came to its end, considerable know-how and experience in the building of long-range precision rockets had been accumulated by von Braun's group. Both potential uses of such rockets, as guardians of peace and as vehicles for spaceflight, appeared feasible and promising. If there should be any possibility, von Braun argued, to continue his and his team's work in that sense, this possibility would exist only in America.

However, there would still be a weighty question: Will the Americans accept a group of German rocketeers? There had been a murderous war between Germany and its neighbors, and America had fought this war on the side of the neighbors. There had been a violent Nazi dictatorship in Germany, and Hitler, supported by his propaganda minister Goebbels, had tried to make the world believe that every German was a ruthless Nazi. Would the Americans see technicians, engineers, and scientists, and eventually even co-workers and colleagues, behind the rocket people from Peenemünde?

Von Braun's decision to accept the invitation in 1945 to come to America may appear natural and logical today. And yet, to go to America, and to continue his rocket work on the other side of the Atlantic, was not so much a rational decision in the spring of 1945. It was rather the fulfillment of a hope, a dream-come-true to which von Braun and at least some of his co-workers had clung during many hours of utter despair.

2   ROCKET PROJECTS FOR THE UNITED STATES ARMY

General Toftoy's urgent plea for the development of an Army guided missile, based on the available experience of the German V-2 rocket team, led to the assignment of a rocket development project to the von Braun group in the spring of 1950. Planning work for a large ballistic rocket for the Army had already started in Fort Bliss in 1949; after von Braun and his people had settled in Huntsville, project work could go into high gear.

A sense of urgency for this project resulted from two recent events: Soviet Russia had successfully tested its first atomic bomb in 1949, and the Korean War had broken out the following year. In July 1950, the Office of the Chief of Ordnance formally ordered the Guided Missile Development Division at Redstone Arsenal in Huntsville to make plans for a guided missile with a range of several hundred miles. The rocket was named Redstone in April 1952 when it neared completion.

Like the V-2, the Redstone could be launched from mobile launch platforms, but it featured several innovations, all of which had been under consideration and even some development in Peenemünde. The body of the missile was a monocoque structure, consisting only of welded aluminum propellant tanks without an external steel hull. The nose cone with the warhead and the guidance system separated from the rest of the rocket after burning cutoff. The Redstone was designed for a range of 200 miles (320 km). Originally, the warhead design weight was 6,500 lb (2,950 kg); however, that figure was reduced considerably later when smaller nuclear bombs became available.

As the Army's missile project at Redstone Arsenal proceeded, it faced only one severe problem: low funding. Buying laboratory equipment and machine tools proved cheaper than giving contracts to industry. The Guided Missile Development Division therefore decided to build complete Redstone missiles in its own fabrication laboratories at the Arsenal, except for the rocket motors that were bought from Rocketdyne. The rocket scientists and engineers even had to pitch in with some of the construction work for the buildings. They converted a former Army hospital into a guidance and control laboratory, and when the new Redstone rocket neared the time of its first static test, test director Karl Heimburg and his men gathered some steel parts at a scrap yard and built a test tower. They organized three old railroad tank cars, cut out doors and viewing ports, covered them with sand and soil, installed control facilities, and had a complete static firing test stand for less than $1,000! Today, that test stand is a Historic Land Mark on Huntsville's Redstone Arsenal grounds, protected by federal law.

Sixteen Redstones were built on the premises of Redstone Arsenal, but as the time of flight testing came closer, the Guided Missile Development Division was permitted to negotiate a contract with the Chrysler Corporation for the remaining twenty missiles scheduled for the program.

At first, there were questions whether an automotive company, used to leaving quality testing of its products to customers, could change its habits and make quality testing to the high standards of a rocket system an integral part of its work philosophy. That fear proved to be unjustified. Very close working relations soon developed between Chrysler and the Arsenal group. Chrysler lived up to the demands of the Redstone project management, and a healthy spirit of cooperation prevailed between the two partners throughout the remaining Redstone project that continued through the Jupiter project, which originated while work on the Redstone was in full swing. Chrysler also contributed substantially to the Saturn project during the 1960s.

Questions were also asked in the opposite direction: Is it correct to leave a major technical development in the hands of a government agency, rather than assigning a consummate contract to industry? For the first large rocket development projects, the *"arsenal concept"* was certainly the logical choice, as proven by the success of this concept in all of von Braun's rocket projects. Development work was assigned to the people and to the place where years of hands-on experience existed, and where proven expertise was available. Transfer of that expertise to industrial contractors would go on while project work proceeded. Substantial savings in time and in money were the result. Typically, criticism of the arsenal concept that characterized von Braun's projects was not raised by those companies that worked directly with the von Braun group, but by outsiders who were not familiar with the true situation.

The first launch of a Redstone rocket took place on 20 August 1953, about one week after the Soviet Union had exploded its first hydrogen bomb. That Redstone failed after a short flight, and so did the second Redstone, but the third flight test a few weeks later was a full success, followed by many more successful Redstone test launchings.

Guidance and control of the Redstone was achieved with an all-inertial guidance system using a gyro-stabilized platform.* Design and component testing of such a system had been started at Peenemünde during the war, and some further theoretical work had been carried out by the von Braun group at Fort Bliss. Full-scale development of an inertial system began at Redstone Arsenal; the in-house group was joined later by colleagues from industry, particularly the Ford Instrument Company on Long Island that manufactured the guidance and control systems for Redstone and Jupiter rockets. Substantial support for the Jupiter guidance system was provided by the Sperry-Farragut Company.

In an effort to incorporate the most up-to-date technology in the Redstone guidance and control system, a magnetic amplifier program was initiated, and also a program to use a newly invented, but still largely unknown gadget, the transistor. Transistor and magnetic amplifier stages were combined, resulting in guidance and control computers far superior to the amplifiers and mixing stages used in the old V-2 systems. The new components were tried out on V-2 flights at White Sands Proving Ground. At that time, the transistor made its maiden flight as a component of modern rocketry, with full success. When the Redstone missile was technically complete in 1953, it did not contain a single glass body electron tube; this was a dream-come-true for many of the rocket engineers at Redstone Arsenal.

Transistors also quickly found their ways into the simulator technology that had been started at Peenemünde. The first simulator systems, huge, clumsy, hot monsters with electric and mechanical components, were analog computers that simulated the flight path of rockets, and also their stability behavior under various conditions. Transistors with their very short response times and low power dissipation permitted the transition to digital systems that could tackle more sophisticated problems, such as vehicle instabilities caused by propellant sloshing, aerodynamic flutter, or cross-wind-

*The platform was developed by Dr. Fritz Mueller at the Kreiselgeraete Company in Berlin. Mueller had pioneered rocket gyro guidance systems beginning with the A-3 rocket in Kummersdorf in 1934, and he subsequently developed gyro-stabilized guidance platforms for the A-4, Redstone, Jupiter, Pershing, Saturn I, Saturn IB, Saturn V, and even for the SINS-system of the Navy. Rockets guided and controlled by gyro-stabilized platforms do not need radio or radar links between the missile and the ground.

introduced shear forces. Another field that owed rapid progress to the new transistor was telemetry. The V-2 telemeter in Peenemünde had six channels, and was the size of a bookcase. Traditionally, launch time of a V-2 was *"X minus telemeter."* Telemeters developed for Redstone and Jupiter had hundreds of channels; they were housed in small boxes, and they always worked well.

Gyroscopes and accelerometers for the guidance and control platform were equipped with air bearings which proved very successful on all of the team's future rockets. In the Saturn-Apollo Moon project, the Redstone-developed platform guided the Saturn-Apollo vehicle up to the point where the lunar spacecraft separated from the Saturn V; at that point, guidance was taken over by a system developed at the Massachusetts Institute of Technology (MIT) under the direction of Charles Stark Draper. That system used liquid bearings instead of air bearings for gyroscopes and accelerometers. Similar systems, also developed by Draper at MIT, were used on the Air Force-developed missiles Thor, Atlas, Titan, and Minuteman.

In June 1958, Redstone rockets were deployed at strategic points in Europe. Neither the Redstone, nor any of the other later—and more powerful—guided ballistic missiles built by the United States or any other country, has been launched against an enemy target so far.

At the time when the first Redstone was test launched, military planners began to think of rockets with longer range. Trevor Gardner, special assistant to Air Force Secretary Harold E. Talbott, urged the development of a missile that could bridge intercontinental distances (ICBM). Atlas became the first ICBM to be developed. Later, Titan, Minuteman, and the intermediate-range (IRBM) Thor were added to the program.

Army planners thought of longer ranges, too. The next step in distance should be about 1,500 miles (2,400 km), with a warhead of 2,500 lb (1,125 kg). The missile should be launched from fixed or mobile bases. Von Braun proposed a rocket, later to be called Jupiter, based on a Rocketdyne engine of advanced design; it was the same engine that powered the Atlas, and later, with further modifications, the Thor, Saturn I, and Saturn IB rockets. In contrast to the Redstone engine, it burned kerosene and liquid oxygen, and instead of the double-walled combustion chamber and nozzle, a system of parallel shaped tubes formed the combustion chamber and the nozzle (*"spaghetti-type"* engine). Vehicle control was not achieved with jet vanes, but by swiveling the entire rocket engine.

Increasing the range of a guided missile from a few hundred up to 1,500 miles required the solution of a specific problem: the heating of the warhead skin upon reentering the Earth's atmosphere.

As soon as prospects for an Army long-range missile became realistic around 1952, von Braun began to tackle the problem of reentry heating of rocket nose cones. Among several possibilities of protection, two systems found closer consideration: the heat sink method, and the ablation method.

The first method utilizes the heat capacity of a very massive layer of a good heat conductor, such as copper, as the outer wall of the warhead. It will heat up during reentry, but due to its large heat capacity its temperature will not reach unacceptable levels.

In the second method, the warhead wall is much thinner and lighter, but it consists of a material with very low heat conductivity, and with a melting temperature slightly below the stagnation temperature to be expected during reentry. The flow of hot air melts the surface material and blows it away before the heat can penetrate deeper into the wall material.

The Air Force, facing the reentry heat problem with the Atlas warhead, chose the first method and began to develop heat sink warheads, spearheaded by H. Julian Allen at Ames Aeronautical Laboratory. Von Braun's group, together with members of the General Electric Company, developed ablation-type reentry shields. Sample materials of various combinations, shaped like warhead tips, were exposed to the hot blast of a rocket engine mounted on a static test stand. In addition to a substantial program of such laboratory tests, flight experiments were prepared in which scaled-down nose cones were to be launched under conditions similar to those encountered by IRBM and ICBM warheads.

Long-range flights of this kind would require rocket vehicles that did not yet exist. However, the Redstone rocket, beginning its flight test program at that time, offered excellent opportunities for reentry heating tests. If equipped with two upper stages of relatively simple solid-propellant rockets, a Redstone would be able to carry a scaled-down ablation nose cone over a range comparable to that of IRBMs, and even ICBMs.

For the upper stages of the test vehicle, von Braun proposed clusters of the solid-propellant rocket Loki, a simple antiaircraft rocket that was in production by the Aerophysics Corporation. The possibility of building a reentry test vehicle for warheads on the basis of the Redstone must have appeared in von Braun's mind during the early 1950s. At that time, he also realized that by putting three stages of small solid-propellant rockets on top of a Redstone, a launch vehicle capable of putting a small satellite into orbit would result (Chapter 6-1).

It is not known which of the two concepts emerged first in von Braun's thinking, Redstone as a reentry test vehicle, or Redstone as a satellite launcher. Both applications of a launch vehicle had been obvious to him for years. When the opportunity arose, he was prepared. Either application would immediately have enabled the other one.

Had it not been for some high-level decisions to the contrary, an American satellite, the first in history, could have been launched in 1956, or even in 1955.

The first Redstone reentry test rocket, called Jupiter C for *"composite,"* took off on 20 September 1956, with two upper stages of solid-propellant rockets developed by Jet Propulsion Laboratory; it reached an altitude of 682 miles (1,090 km) and a distance of 3,400 miles (5,440 km), a world record at that time. That rocket did not yet carry a reentry nose cone. The second test rocket also took off well, but its guidance system malfunctioned, so the nose cone could not be found and recovered from the ocean. The third test on 8 August 1957 was a full success. The nose cone was recovered after a trip of 1,200 miles (1,920 km). Careful analysis of its surface and of the thermal sensors on its inside proved that the ablation method worked well, and that the reentry problem could be considered solved. President Eisenhower showed the Army's recovered warhead during his news conference to the nation—but, he said that the Air Force had now solved the reentry problem!

During most of the year 1956, prospects for a continuing active role of the rocket people at Redstone Arsenal in the American rocket and space program looked good. Test launchings of the Redstone proceeded well. The Jupiter project quickly approached its first test firings. Ablation-type nose cones for Jupiter were available. First reactions to von Braun's proposal for a minimum satellite, to be launched with a Jupiter C, found positive responses, at least at some places in the government, and from many space engineers and scientists.

Working relations between von Braun's group and their industrial contractors were excellent. A special joint Army-Navy project to develop an inertial guidance system for ship-launched missiles proceeded to the fullest satisfaction of both parties.

For many observers at that time, the rocket group in Huntsville seemed to be on its way to an effective, successful, and stable element in a comprehensive American rocket and space program. However, these expectations were not to be fulfilled.

Three years earlier, after the Army's Jupiter project had been assigned to Redstone Arsenal, Secretary of Defense Charles E. Wilson permitted the Air Force's Air Research and Development Command to develop a missile, Thor, that was practically identical in design, size, and performance to Jupiter. Thor could be launched only from fixed bases, while Jupiter was able to take off from fixed as well as mobile launch platforms.

Penetrating questions from both Congress and the public concerning duplication of effort ensued, but Wilson remained firm in his decision that Thor should be developed in parallel with the Jupiter project.

That situation led to very unfortunate interservice rivalries that cast their shadows over much of the guided missile development work during the mid-1950s. General Medaris, who courageously carried the Army's flag in that fight, described the details of the Army-Air Force struggle in his book *Countdown for Decision* [5-3]. Von Braun tried to stay out of the firing line. Again and again, he would urge his co-workers: *"Let's not get involved in this inter-service bickering. Let's concentrate on that work which is assigned to us. We must never relax in our efforts to do the best work we possibly can."*

Two months after the first successful flight of the long-range Jupiter C composite rocket, on 26 November 1956, a lightning bolt struck out of that thundercloud that had been hanging dark and heavy over Redstone Arsenal. Secretary of Defense Wilson issued his *"Roles and Missions Directive,"* which decreed that the Army's rocket building activities will be limited to missiles with ranges below 200 miles. Redstone Arsenal would be permitted to complete the Jupiter project—the first launch was only a few months away, and it was ahead of Thor—but operational control of Jupiter, as well as funding of the project, would be the Air Force's authority.

"This meant," Medaris wrote, *". . . that we were now producing a weapon that was not really wanted by the people who would hold responsibility for its use . . ."* [5-3].

Besides a storm of disappointment and criticism, this DOD directive created a number of difficult problems concerning transfer of technical know-how, project responsibilities, funding channels, budget requests, troop training, deployment planning, and so forth. Finally, General Schriever and General Medaris, in a man-to-man effort, worked out a compromise that was in agreement with Wilson's directive, but avoided at least severe losses among the many accomplishments of the Army's projects of past years.

Von Braun took the blow in stride. The ill effects of interservice rivalry had always been a source of grave concern to him; on many occasions, he pleaded for a unified rocket and space program in which military and civilian organizations would have their well-defined and well-considered responsibilities. After the Roles and Missions decision, he continued his efforts to make the Redstone and Jupiter rockets as perfect as possible. The first successful Jupiter launch occurred on 31 May 1957, four months before the first Thor launch. In August 1958, the first operational Jupiter, with ablation nosecone, was delivered to the Air Force. More than sixty Jupiters were eventually produced and deployed in Italy and Turkey during the following years. Thor missiles were deployed in Great Britain, beginning in April 1960.

Work on the Redstone and Jupiter rockets had a double aspect for von Braun. *"In common with so many technical achievements of recent years,"* he wrote in a paper [5-4] presented in 1952 at the Third International Astronautical Congress in Stuttgart, Germany (translated here from the German original), *"the development of rocketry has two faces, like the Roman God Janus. One of these faces is turned toward the solution of a truly super-national endeavor, the exploration of space. The other looks upon the relentless fervor with which nations devote billions of tax dollars, rubles, pounds, and francs to the creation of frightful new methods of destruction . . ."*

The prospect of another global war in which rockets would deliver their deadly payloads was a horrifying thought for him, but he reminded his listeners that rockets have become integral parts of national armaments from which they cannot be segregated—as little as this could be done with airplanes or computers.

Developing rockets that would be used also for military purposes, and not only for spaceflight, was a subject that occupied von Braun's mind probably more consistently throughout his adult life than any other subject. In 1951, he wrote an essay entitled *"Why Guided Missiles?"* [5-5].

Atomic energy, he observed, with its great potential of freeing mankind from the yoke of heavy physical labor, is being abused in the dreadful atomic bomb. The modern rocket, conceived to carry astronauts to the Moon and to planets, is coming to life through funds allocated for the development of guided missiles.

At a very early age, von Braun began daydreaming of trips to the Moon and to Mars, and he decided to devote his life to this challenging goal. He lived up to this decision, but then he found himself tagged with the label of designer of weapons of war. *"Why,"* he asked in his paper, *"are guided missiles necessary?"* He tried to formulate an answer: *"As long as wars are not outlawed by worldwide legislation and agreement, every nation is compelled to employ the most modern technology in order to be able to enter into a potential war with better chances of survival than its opponent . . ."*

"Do not forget," he often said when a conversation turned to this subject, *"that the development of aviation, particularly during its decisive phases, was financed by military funds."*

The existence of horror weapons does not necessarily promote the outbreak of wars. If both antagonists possess such weapons, their potential consummate destructive power may persuade both parties not to apply them. In fact, the tremendous power of nuclear-tipped long-range guided missiles as deterrents of war has been pointed out numerous times in recent years.

When von Braun's life neared its end in a hospital in Alexandria during the summer of 1977, two of his long-time associates and friends, Rees and Stuhlinger, visited him—it was to be the last time. Almost too weak to talk, he said with a feeble voice: *"Do you think it was right that we developed these rockets? . . . We did it for spaceflight, but we needed the support of the military . . . we hoped they would never be used in a war against people . . . looking back, I am very happy to realize that guided missiles turned out to be guardians of peace rather than weapons of war . . ."*

3   VISIONS OF SATELLITES, SPACE STATIONS, MOON, AND MARS

To build the Redstone rocket, the first large, precision-guided missile in the American arsenal to reach maturity, was not only a technical challenge for von Braun. This assignment gave him the opportunity to prove that Colonel (later General) Toftoy was right in 1945 when he suggested to the Army and the government that the Peenemünde rocket team would be capable of serving the United States well with its experience in rocket technology.

There was, however, also another thought: The Redstone would be a natural successor to the V-2 rocket, only bigger and better in every respect. It would be a decisive step toward spaceflight.

In the United States, as was not the case in Germany, von Braun was free to talk about his ideas of future activities in space. He relished and fully utilized this new freedom. During his early years in Huntsville, he stepped up his activities of public speaking and writing. Over the next twenty-five years, he would publish about five hundred essays on spaceflight with its exciting opportunities for exploration, its tremendous potential for scientific research, its enormous stimulation of technological progress, and its unequalled challenges to the restless human mind.

Going public with his thoughts on space travel was, as von Braun realized, absolutely vital. If he wanted the nation to devote substantial resources to space-related work, he would have to promote his ideas outside the confines of an Army installation.

Typically for his approach, his first publications dealt with satellite stations that would orbit the Earth with human astronauts onboard. The spacefarers could observe and photograph the complete surface of the Earth; they would look at the Moon, the planets, and the stars with fantastic magnifications; they would carry out scientific research programs; and they would, totally free from the Earth's gravitational force, just enjoy life. These were prospects for exciting experiences in which the readers and listeners could participate at least with their minds, experiences that would make them aware that spaceflight and space exploration could play important roles in mankind's future on Earth.

Von Braun's publications on Earth-orbiting platforms were not the first published essays on that subject. About eighty years before his time, Edward Everett Hale had presented his still-famous story *"The Brick Moon"* [5-6], a sphere of 200 feet (61 m) diameter that orbited the Earth at an altitude of 4,000 miles (6,500 km). Its prime purpose was to serve as an aid in ocean navigation. *"It will forever revolve in its obedient orbit, a blessing to all seamen . . . ,"* Hale wrote in 1869.

Shortly thereafter, in 1883, the great Russian space pioneer Konstantin Tsiolkovskii presented his first thoughts on rocket-propelled space vehicles. Twelve years later, in *"Dreams about the Earth and the Sky, the Effects of Universal Gravitation"*, he described a small Earth-orbiting satellite. Expanding his thoughts, he wrote about manned space vehicles, and by 1920 had proposed permanent orbital stations [5-7].

Hermann Oberth [5-8] suggested that orbiting spacecraft would be useful as communication links, as refueling stations for spaceships, for the monitoring of weather patterns, as astronomical observatories, and for watching details on the Earth's surface.

Years before Oberth published his studies, ideas about orbiting space platforms were expressed by Robert Esnault-Pelterie [5-9] who began talking and writing about astronautical subjects as early as 1912. Further proposals and suggestions for Earth-orbiting space stations appeared during 1928. Among the proposers were Guido von Pirquet [5-10] in Austria, and Willy Ley [5-11] in Germany and Hermann Noordung [5-12], originally from Slovenia, in Austria. Noordung's proposed station was to operate in a 24-hour orbit *"to facilitate observation of the Earth."* In 1929, J. D. Bernal in England [5-13] speculated that the day would come when man would build permanent homes in space. *"At first space navigators,"* he wrote, *"and then scientists whose observations would be best conducted outside the Earth, and then finally those who for any reason were dissatisfied with earthly conditions would come to inhabit extraterrestrial bases."* His proposed space station was spherical, with a diameter of 10 miles (16 kilometers)!

Von Braun, still a teenager during these years, avidly devoured whatever space-related literature he could find. Orbiting space stations were quite familiar to him, but even closer to his mind was the fact that no object could ever be put in orbit without a very powerful rocket propulsion system. His work during the late 1920s and early 1930s, therefore, was devoted to the development of rockets, rather than space stations.

During the war years in Germany, any discussion of spaceflight matters was strictly *"verboten,"* because *"spaceflight does not contribute to the war effort."* And yet, thoughts of rocket flight into space, of satellites, and of probes to the Moon and planets were alive in the minds of von Braun and at least some of his associates throughout the Peenemünde years.

Some of von Braun's early thoughts found their expression in his lecture to the El Paso Rotary Club in January 1947. Two years later, H. E. Ross in Great Britain published a paper that described a large station to be used for meteorological and astronomical research, for studies of the zero-gravity condition and of high vacuum physics, for investigations of cosmic and solar radiations, and as a communications relay [5-14].

Meanwhile, in the United States in the autumn of 1948, the Air Force School of Aviation Medicine organized its first symposium on space medicine. This was followed, two years later, by a similar symposium at the Professional Colleges of the University of Illinois in Chicago. In his introduction, Major General Harry G. Armstrong, head of the U.S. Air Force Medical Corps, said: *"I believe that some day we will travel beyond the stratosphere . . . With this in mind, a new department of the School of Aviation Medicine was created which we refer to as the Department of Space Medicine . . ."* [5-15].

General Armstrong's introduction was followed by von Braun's presentation entitled *"Multi-stage Rockets and Artificial Satellites"* [5-16]. Explaining first that a two- or three-stage rocket will be the proper vehicle to place a satellite into an orbit around the Earth, he summarized his convictions in three concise statements:

1. *"With a multi-stage rocket ship, the hauling of considerable payloads into a satellite orbit around the Earth appears possible.*

2. *If the final stage of such a rocket ship is fitted with wings, the ship can safely return to Earth.*

3. *The size and cost of such a multistage rocket ship will be tremendous, but the size, at least, does not represent an unsurmountable technical difficulty."*

Then, he described his concept of a wheel-shaped large manned space station, 200 feet (60 meter) in diameter. *"What are the potential applications of such an artificial satellite?"* he asked, and then explained its use for Earth and weather observations, and for astronomical work. He also mentioned the potential uses of a space station as a military observation post, and possibly even as a weapon carrier. *"But,"* he was quick to add, *"there is a brighter aspect, too. The orbiting station will help us reach out into deep space, well beyond the confines of our trouble-ridden home planet . . ."*

Whenever prospects of spaceflight are discussed, the question of economical benefits of interplanetary travel is raised. Von Braun often answered with the question: Was it really economical necessity that set our great explorers in motion? We may doubt whether Columbus was driven by a burning desire to cut the freight rates on Indian tea when he decided to sail toward the west. Magellan, Henry Hudson, Vasco da Gama, *"theirs was the fire of genius, the response to the challenge of the unknown. . . ,"* von Braun said [5-16].

In contrast to his proverbial boldness and exuberance, von Braun could be extremely cautious when he felt that circumstances required this. *"We don't want dead heroes,"* he used to say, *"we want live workers!"*

During the early 1950s, he once made a round trip with some of his associates and with the agency's airplane to a number of contractors. On the last evening of their trip, they had to make a refueling stop. The weather ahead was bad. *"Should we continue our flight, or rather spend another night in a motel?"* von Braun asked. The pilot thought that it would be alright to go ahead. *"You give the word, and I'll fly,"* he said. Each of the associates opted for continuation. *"We have had rough sailing before; we wouldn't mind,"* they remarked. But von Braun, who had been a pilot since age seventeen, and who had done a lot of night and foul weather flying himself, said no. *"As we stand here,"* he argued, *"we represent a significant portion of the American rocket and space program. We really should not take any unnecessary risks. Let's go to the motel."*

After dinner, von Braun suggested that they go to his room and do a little talking. They did, and, as usual, von Braun did the talking, until long after midnight. *"I am really encouraged by what we have seen and learned on this trip. Redstone and Jupiter are coming along well; I'm certain that we can put the first satellite into its orbit soon. We should now begin to make realistic design drawings, and also think of how to solve the guidance and control problems."*

His words were received by eager minds. He continued: *"Once the first satellite is in orbit, others will follow. Also, there will be probes to the Moon. Then, we should think of putting man into space, first on a ballistic flight, and then in an orbiting satellite. There will be larger satellites, and also a permanent station in space. We will then begin to make plans for a manned expedition to the Moon. Really, I couldn't think of a serious technical problem that would prevent us from traveling to the Moon. Mars will be the most challenging mission in our lifetime. We should not leave it out of sight . . ."*

These were not the words of a dreamer; they came from a mover and achiever who stood solidly on firm ground not only with his plans for action, but also with his visions of the future. These short hours in the motel, spontaneously born out of an unexpected weather delay, passed quickly, but they stayed alive in the memories of those who were there, and who saw von Braun's visions come to life during the next twenty years.

4 PLANNING FOR A SPACE PROGRAM

A flurry of satellite and space station papers appeared soon after the Illinois symposium. Many of them proposed huge facilities with crews of dozens or even hundreds of astronauts. While von Braun pursued his own concept of a large, manned *"space wheel"* as a distant goal, he used every opportunity to point out that before such stations in space can become a reality, a number of smaller projects must be planned, designed, and built in order to create a technical base from which the design of a large space station with all its complex operations can evolve.

Most of the space enthusiasts who spoke and wrote about satellites and planetary expeditions before the mid-1950s did not give much thought to the Earth-to-orbit transportation problem. Von Braun saw an urgent need to draw the attention of potential space project planners to this sober fact. In 1951, he wrote a paper for the Second International Astronautical Congress in London with the title *"The Importance of Satellite Vehicles in Interplanetary Flight"* [5-17]. In his absence, it was read by Frederick C. Durant III, at that time one of the directors of the American Rocket Society (ARS).

"I learned that von Braun had a paper . . . but he was not allowed out of the country for security reasons. . . ," Durant remembered in 1988 [5-18]. *"So I sent him a letter . . . , suggesting that we meet . . . we met in New York, and within 3 to 5 minutes we felt closely associated."* This *"close association"* was to develop quickly into a lively friendship that lasted to the end of von Braun's life.

"Rocket designers generally agree," von Braun wrote, *"that at least three stages are required for a satellite rocket with chemical propellants."* If such a rocket is to transport

components of a large orbiting space station, or of a planetary space vehicle, *"it must be capable of carrying aloft a liberal amount of payload."* He often said that what we need is *"a stable with some mighty good workhorses."*

Von Braun's paper was written at a time when large guided rockets were still in their infancy. Thirty years later, he would certainly have argued that two-stage rockets make good systems for Earth-to-orbit transportation, as proven by the two-stage members of the Saturn rocket family, or the space shuttle system. Even single-stage rockets can be built that are able to reach orbit.

"There is a widely held belief, even among space travel enthusiasts," he wrote in his London paper, *"that interplanetary voyages with chemically propelled rocket ships require such tremendous quantities of propellants that the technical feasibility of such trips could be questioned, even for very limited payloads. It has therefore become a habit to hint at mysterious 'atomic propellants' and 'nuclear rocket drives' that could do the trick better . . . We should not forget that all speculations about nuclear power sources for rockets are still founded on rather shaky grounds . . ."* Even if and when nuclear space propulsion systems have been developed, he wrote, such rockets will in all probability start from orbit rather than from the Earth's surface.

Twenty years later, the NERVA project to develop a useful and reliable nuclear-thermal rocket engine was underway, directed by Harold Finger. Von Braun was greatly interested in this project, and he included nuclear propulsion systems in his mission studies, but he pointed out that even if the nuclear rocket program should not produce the desired results, a manned Mars expedition could still be undertaken with chemical rocket engines. He also mentioned that some Mars mission planners begin to focus on nuclear-electric systems; they offer the advantage of a highly concentrated energy source, but neither with the extremely high temperatures and radiation levels, nor with the need for large quantities of liquid hydrogen over long periods of time, which are characteristic of nuclear-thermal systems on planetary missions.

Elaborating on the need for the man-carrying upper stage to return to Earth, von Braun described the *"winged stage,"* and he discussed the interrelations between wingloading, stagnation temperatures, orbital altitude, angle of atmospheric reentry, landing speed, and vehicle weight. Today, his words sound almost like a preliminary design study for the space shuttle, built twenty years after he wrote his IAF paper.

Thoughts about travel to Mars followed. Von Braun described an expedition of seventy men, traveling in ten spaceships from a satellite orbit around the Earth into a satellite orbit around Mars. Landing on the Martian surface would be performed with three winged *"landing boats,"* two of them capable of returning to the spaceships left circling in the circum-Martian orbit.

Von Braun's study contains the words: *"The bottom density of the Martian atmosphere is only about one-twelfth of the sea-level density of the terrestrial atmosphere,"* followed by a description of the aerodynamic properties of the landing craft.

At this point, von Braun's concept of landing procedures on Mars needs a correction. Winged landing craft, as he proposed them, would not be feasible on Mars. When he wrote his essay, planetary scientists believed that the atmospheric density near the Martian surface is on the order of 8 percent of the density of the Earth's atmosphere. Twenty-five years later, unmanned probes to Mars discovered that the density of the Martian atmosphere at the surface is not greater than 0.6 to 0.8 percent of that of the Earth's atmosphere. Winged landing vehicles, therefore, would not be practical on Mars. Landing, as we know today, must be achieved with a combination of aerobraking and retro-rockets.

Von Braun himself was always acutely aware of the possibility of erroneous assumptions because of insufficient or incorrect input data. Whenever he had an opportunity, he suggested and urged research programs to fill the gaps in our store of knowledge. *"Let us not forget,"* he often said, *"that the major portion of our space efforts must take place right here on Earth!"*

If rewritten in the 1990s, von Braun's original concept of a Mars project would undergo several further modifications. Rocket motor efficiencies have increased considerably during the past four decades. Hydrogen-oxygen rockets have come of age. Nuclear-thermal propulsion studies have been revived. Besides chemical and nuclear-thermal rocket motors, electric propulsion systems have shown high reliabilities, high efficiencies, and long operational lifetimes. If combined with nuclear-electric power sources, they offer space propulsion systems of impressive performance on planetary voyages.

Although a manned expedition to Mars, if planned in 1999 or 2009 instead of 1949, would differ considerably from von Braun's early concept, that proposal marked not only a milestone, but a turning point in the evolution of manned spaceflight. It was the first proposal for a round trip to Mars that described all the technical steps and phases from beginning to end, with figures and numbers, making it clear that a visit to our neighbor planet is really within our technical capabilities. It showed the voyage to Mars not through the eyes of the heroic space adventurer, but through the drawing boards, data sheets, and computers of the design engineer. *"Sheer size of a project,"* von Braun used to say, *"has never been a deterrent to creative engineering. Just think of the pyramids, the Great Wall of China, the Panama Canal, or a modern oil tanker!"*

Grandiose as von Braun's huge space wheel, or his seventy-man expedition to Mars may sound, it should be noted that he never lost contact with the real world, with sound engineering, and with up-to-date scientific knowledge. How deeply von Braun concerned himself with innumerable details of the projects he tried to promote is illustrated by a paper he wrote for the Third International Astronautical Congress in Stuttgart, West Germany, in September 1952: *"Space Travel—Its Dependence Upon International Scientific Cooperation"* [5-4]. Again, he was not permitted to leave the United States, so Durant presented the paper for him.

Addressing a space-minded audience composed of members from many countries, von Braun emphasized the great need for scientific and technological research in various fields, and he urged all his research-oriented listeners to contribute somehow to the great common goal of space exploration. Members of space societies, he argued, are in excellent positions to help further the cause of spaceflight, even without belonging to a large industrial research and development team. There are still uncounted numbers of technical and scientific problems that must be solved in preparation of spaceflight missions, he said; many of them can be tackled by small groups, or even by individual researchers.

He quoted numerous examples of projects in technology, physics, chemistry, biology, medicine, even in simple activities of housekeeping and daily routine chores that should be worked out in anticipation of future space ventures. A storehouse of knowledge, scientific and technical, will be needed for the large spaceflight projects of the future. Everyone with some special knowledge in one of the numerous fields of modern technology can make his contribution.

Durant read a third IAF paper for von Braun, *"We Need a Coordinated Space Program,"* at the Fourth International Astronautical Federation Congress in Zurich, Switzerland, in August 1953 [5-19]. Excerpts of that paper are presented in Chapter 5-7.

5   *COLLIER'S* PRESENTS SPACE TO THE PUBLIC

A fantastic opportunity to preach and spread the spaceflight gospel to a large audience arose in late 1951 with a sequence of events, almost dramatic in retrospect. Stimulated by von Braun's and some other space enthusiasts' talks and writings about the exploration of space, the Hayden Planetarium in New York hosted its First Annual Symposium on Space Travel on Columbus Day, 12 October 1951. It was organized by Frank H. Forrester; speakers included Dr. Albert E. Parr, director of the American Museum of Natural History; Robert E. Cole, chairman of the Hayden Planetarium; Willy Ley, rocket authority and spaceflight pioneer; Robert P. Haviland, research engineer for General Electric's Hermes Project; Dr. Fred L. Whipple, chairman of the Department of Astronomy at Harvard University; Dr. Heinz Haber, U.S. Air Force Department of Space Medicine; and Oscar Schachter, acting assistant secretary general of the United Nations Legal Department. Also present were Dr. Joseph Kaplan, Arthur C. Clarke, Dr. Fritz Haber, Dr. Hubertus Strughold, and Chesley Bonestell. Von Braun was not among the attendees.

Schachter, who presented a paper on space law, remarked later [5-20]: *"I didn't expect the large audience that it turned out to be. I thought it was going to be a kind of school kid affair. And what was memorable about it, what impressed me most was the number of people from the armed services. . . ."* Whipple, an outspoken space enthusiast for many years, said: *"I had been pushing for satellites for a long time, and they obviously knew of my interest in the subject . . . you may recall that I invented the meteor bumper back in 1946"* [5-21].

The papers given at the symposium, and particularly the very animated discussions that followed the talks, must have offered an unusually exciting menu to the listeners. Strughold, a specialist in aviation medicine and a strong promoter of manned space-flight, immediately began to organize a follow-up symposium on manned flight into space, with a broad panel of invited speakers, to be held in San Antonio, Texas, from 6 to 9 November 1951. Von Braun was invited to the meeting, but he did not present a prepared paper. Whipple, in an interview in 1986 [5-21], gave an explanation: *"At that time, von Braun was sort of in the doghouse, for some people did not want a German engineer sending up our first satellite. So he did not participate as an active contributor for that reason . . . That attitude held on actually until the Vanguard failure."*

Whipple met von Braun for the first time at the symposium in San Antonio. What was his initial impression of him? *"I knew him by reputation, and I was not surprised in any way when I met him. He was a very vigorous person, and extremely devoted to his subject. Yes, I was delighted to meet him because I felt that he would be the man who was going to put us into space. We became good friends."*

Among the audience at the earlier Hayden symposium were members of the editorial staff of *Collier's* magazine. Inspired by the content of papers and the enthusiasm of lecturers and audience alike, they tried to persuade Gordon Manning, managing editor of *Collier's*, to have an article about the symposium published in the magazine. Among the staff people who attended the Hayden symposium was Cornelius Ryan, associate editor of *Collier's*. At that time, he was not a space man at all. *"I remember that he was extremely skeptical about the whole thing. He had only a peripheral interest in space,"* Whipple said later. But, as Mrs. Kathryn Morgan Ryan, Cornelius Ryan's widow, recalled in 1986 [5-22], Ryan did report about the symposium to his boss, Gordon Manning. Editor Louis Ruppel, *"an ex-Marine who hated Germans"* [5-23], suggested to Ryan: *"Connie, go to San Antonio and find out what these nutty Germans are doing."* So, Ryan also attended the San Antonio symposium.

Von Braun saw and grasped the extraordinary opportunity, as described by Whipple: *"I remember . . . the late afternoon when Wernher, Joe Kaplan and I cornered Cornelius Ryan at a table in the dining room there in San Antonio. He was still extremely skeptical when he found himself amongst two super salesmen, von Braun and Kaplan, and I'm not a complete slouch at salesmanship either."* The three scientists talked to Ryan through drinks, through dinner, and through after-dinner drinks on into the night, and they sold him on the idea that it was really possible to put a satellite up into orbit. But he would not believe that it was possible to go beyond that and place a man on the Moon, or to put numbers of people into orbit. *"Of course,"* Whipple said, *"he may have been playing a bit coy, but I would say that he didn't believe it, nor did others at* Collier's, *until the three of us really got a hold of Ryan. That was the beginning of it . . ."*

Mrs. Ryan had a vivid recollection of her husband's experiences at the San Antonio symposium [5-22]. *"He was sent to cover the space symposium in San Antonio to determine if it might merit a magazine article. At that time, Cornelius knew absolutely nothing about the subject. When he returned, he said he was sitting in a room where this rather striking blue-eyed blond German was at the blackboard, chalking all sorts of mathematical equations. Suddenly, there was a sort of collective gasp around the room; there seemed to be a tremendous amount of excitement in the air. Connie happened to be seated next to Chesley Bonestell, whom he knew, and Chesley was as excited as everyone else. Connie asked Chesley: 'What's going on here?' Chesley replied: 'Dr. von Braun has just shown us a way to go into space!'"*

Was Connie convinced by von Braun's arguments? *"He was absolutely convinced,"* Mrs. Ryan said. *"He came back trying to figure out how to get* Collier's *interested in space stations, spaceships, and flights to the Moon. He told me: 'This man could convince anybody. His dreams, his ideas are mesmerizing. He is so effective that he could sell anybody anything. Even used cars!' Wernher exuded this kind of confidence that could win over others,"* Mrs. Ryan continued. *"He could suffer the slings and arrows from people who still harbored feelings against him, particularly because of the V-2 rockets. He could surmount that."*

Back at *Collier's*, Ryan did succeed in persuading managing editor Gordon Manning to publish articles about space in the magazine. To start things off, Manning decided to organize a *Collier's* in-house round table conference on these spaceflight ideas, and then publish the results [5-23]. Lavish, yet realistic illustrations would accompany each article.

Associate editor Cornelius Ryan was a war correspondent during World War II, first in Europe, and later at General Douglas McArthur's headquarters in Japan. He joined *Collier's* in February 1951. Later, he would gain world renown for his book *The Longest Day* that described the Allied landing on the Normandy coast. After the San Antonio symposium, he was given responsibility for *Collier's* spaceflight project.

Ryan organized the round table meeting and invited Whipple, Ley, Heinz Haber, Schachter, von Braun, Kaplan, and artists Bonestell, Rolf Klep, and Fred Freeman. Von Braun presented his big space station. Ley followed with a description of life and work on the station. Whipple spoke about astronomical observations that could be made from a platform, entirely unencumbered by the Earth's atmosphere that hangs in front of earthbound telescopes *"like a dirty basement window,"* while Kaplan described studies of the outermost layers of our atmosphere that will be possible from a station in orbit. Haber's presentation was entitled *"Can we survive in space?"* *"The crews of space ships,"* he concluded, *"while they can never be completely protected against hazards such as meteors, will probably be safer than pedestrians crossing a busy street during rush hour."* Schachter, the legal expert, discussed the question *"Who owns the universe?" "Why not extend the same principle that is now applied to the open seas also to outer space and other celestial bodies? These areas would then be considered as belonging to all mankind . . ."*

Collier's published the proceedings of this round table discussion in the magazine's 22 March 1952 issue under the title *"Man Will Conquer Space Soon."* The editors predicted that *"this may prove to be one of the most important scientific symposia ever published in a national magazine. It is the story of the inevitability of man's conquest of space . . . What you will read here is not science fiction. It is serious fact . . ."*

Mrs. Ryan remembered the story many years later [5-22]: *"It was utterly fascinating. It drew . . . a large readership, especially high school students . . . And my husband and Wernher, they became very, very close friends."* So successful was the *Collier's* story that an expanded version followed, also edited by Ryan, with the title *"Across The Space Frontier."* Planning for a second Hayden symposium got under way almost immediately. It took place on Columbus Day, 1952, and this time von Braun—who didn't attend the first symposium the previous year—was present along with the former participants. Milton W. Rosen from the Naval Research Laboratory was also on hand.

In his introduction, Hayden's chairman Cole remarked that *"it is obvious . . . that any project of such magnitude as the conquest of space can be successful only if it enjoys the full support of the public . . . It is very doubtful that those responsible persons whose support is needed for such an undertaking would show much enthusiasm without such a backing."*

Von Braun predicted that within ten to fifteen years, the Earth will have a second satellite, a man-made moon circling the Earth. He then described his orbiting station concept and the many functions this outpost in space will serve. For the spacefaring astronauts; it will be a *"home away from home,"* whatever their missions in space will be.

When he talked about the uses of an orbiting space station, he never failed to mention its tremendous potential as a deterrent to war. *"With its fantastic reconnaissance capabilities, a space station can pull up an Iron Curtain, no matter where it is being lowered,"* von Braun said at the *Collier's* round table discussion in 1952.

The Earth received its first man-made moon just five years later. It was unmanned, and it was made in the Soviet Union. Von Braun's and the Free World's first satellite, Explorer 1, followed after four months. The first American manned space station, Skylab, began its orbital life in 1973, twenty-one years after the second Hayden symposium; it trailed the first Russian station, Salyut, by two years. A series of station-like short-duration orbital flights began in 1981 with the U.S. space shuttle. Ten years after Skylab, a new Soviet space station, Mir, appeared in orbit to be occupied permanently by cosmonauts.

Public reactions to the two Hayden symposia, the *Collier's* issues of 22 March, 18 October, and 25 October 1952, and the Viking book *Across The Space Frontier* were enthusiastic beyond expectation. Sales of *Collier's* magazine soared. Ryan, who had masterminded and edited all these publications, became the editor of yet another book: *Conquest of The Moon*, written jointly by von Braun, Whipple, and Ley, and illustrated by Bonestell, Freeman, and Klep. Published by Viking Press in 1953, it was based on articles that had earlier appeared in *Collier's*. That book, written years before the first man-made object began to orbit the Earth, is a surprisingly true-to-life account of a lunar expedition, and at the same time a delightful story of the life and work, the excitement and the anxieties, the hardships and the final triumph of the first human travelers to the Moon. In 1954, *Collier's* ended its eight-part series by publishing von Braun's plans for an expedition to Mars.

Writing for the *Collier's* publications on space was a most enjoyable pastime for von Braun. *"After a day of excruciating meetings for the Redstone Project with all these contractors, laboratory and shop workers, Army officers, designers, budget people, and test engineers, hammering out performance data, safety rules, flight test programs, production quotas, contractor bonuses, acceptance criteria, and what-have-you, it is such an enjoyable relaxation to transpose yourself to the lunar surface and simply charge ahead with a colorful description of all the exciting adventures that expect you there . . . I mix me some martinis, put a Brandenburg concerto on the record player, and just write and write . . . until Maria gets out of bed and reminds me that I must be in the office two hours from now . . ."*

6   WALT DISNEY TAKES TO OUTER SPACE

Unexpected support for the spaceflight idea came from a man for whom von Braun always had highest admiration: Walt Disney.

When Disney conceived the idea of the famous Disneyland park at Anaheim, California, he envisioned four areas: Adventureland, Fantasyland, Frontierland, and Tomorrowland. To help finance it, he developed a TV series dealing with aspects of each. He had material for the first three segments; but what about Tomorrowland? Disney looked to Ward Kimball who had been on his staff since the mid-1930s; Kimball was one of the animation supervisors on *Snow White* and other Disney classics. He remembered [5-24] that in the early 1950s, *"Walt came to me and said: 'You guys are the modern thinkers around here . . . , can you think of anything we can do on Tomorrowland?' And that's when I said I had been following some very interesting articles about space in* Collier's *magazine. It was fascinating for me to realize that there were these reputable scientists who actually believed that we were going out into space."*

Kimball studied the *Collier's* articles and, assisted by layout man Ken O'Connor and sketch artist Bill Bosché, prepared tentative screen treatments. They were shown to Disney on 17 April 1954. *"We want to do something new this time . . . ,"* Kimball said. *"We are trying to show man's dreams of the future, and what he has learned from the past . . . He has wanted to fly all through history . . . Now he wants to get out on Mars . . . We should be careful and keep our serious stuff separate . . . We are known for fantasy, but the same tools we use there we should apply here to the facts, and give a scientifically factual presentation . . . men dealing with fantasy and men dealing with facts coming together . . . we open up this world to the people . . ."*

Disney was impressed by what his associates had prepared. *"When we had finished,"* Bosché recalled, *"Walt was enthusiastic about it. He walked out of the story room, stopped at the desk, and ripped off a blank sheet of notepaper. Handing it to Kimball, he said something nobody had ever heard him say before: 'Write your own ticket!'"*

With this backing, Kimball went to work. A three-part show was envisioned: *"Man in Space"*; *"Man and the Moon"*; and *"Mars and Beyond"*. First, he needed some rocket and space experts. Remembering the *Collier's* series, he contacted Willy Ley, who responded eagerly. *"Willy turned out to be a real encyclopedia,"* Bosché recalled. *"He had information on just about everything you wanted . . . He was a very amusing fellow, we all got a big kick out of him!"*

Then, von Braun and Haber were contacted. Both immediately agreed to join the project. With his frequent visits to contractors in the southern California area in connection with the Redstone and the Jupiter projects, von Braun could spend evenings at the Disney studios. He often would arrive at six o'clock in the evening and work until well after midnight, sometimes until three or four o'clock in the morning.

Of greatest interest to the Disney crew were accurate models of the launch rocket, the spacecraft, the space station, the Moon ships, and the Mars vehicles. Here, von Braun really was on home ground; he quickly embraced the opportunity to reach an audience far greater than he could by attending the Hayden Planetarium symposia, or through the pages of *Collier's*. Besides models for the rockets and space vehicles, he provided a wealth of information on technical details, from in-orbit fueling operations down to problems of cooking and eating under weightlessness.

The first show, *"Man in Space,"* was aired on 9 March, and again on 15 June 1955. Ley started out with a brief history of rocketry; Haber discussed the medical aspects and potential problems of spaceflight; and von Braun described the launching of the huge Earth-to-orbit rocket with its winged upper stage.

Shortly after this first Disney space show had been aired on TV, President Dwight D. Eisenhower, according to David R. Smith, director of Walt Disney Productions archives, *"borrowed the show to run it for the brass in the Pentagon."* Six weeks later, he announced American plans for orbiting a small artificial unmanned satellite as part of the nation's contribution to the International Geophysical Year.

For the second show, *"Man and the Moon,"* full-scale portions of the space station and of the Moon ship were constructed at Disney Studios, including many of the details that convey the impression of a true-to-life adventure. Assembly work in orbit made it necessary that space engineers left the pressurized interior of the space station in *"bottle suits,"* miniature space vehicles with their own atmosphere and rocket propulsion system, and with manipulator arms to accomplish the assembly work.

The script called only for a circumlunar reconnaissance flight, without a landing. The omission of a landing on the Moon may have disappointed many viewers; however, this was one of Disney's ground rules for this series: *"A factual science presentation . . ."* At that time, almost nothing was known about the Moon's surface. Is it reasonably firm? Is it a sea of loose dust? Is it strewn with boulders? Can a space vehicle find a smooth and level spot to land? Will it sink into dust and fine debris? Divergent theories were abundant, but nobody really knew. Disney did not want to speculate in any direction, and von Braun was fully supportive of this cautious attitude.

The third show in this series, *"Mars and Beyond,"* was the most ambitious of the three, as far as reaching out into new territories was concerned. Long-time exposure to the emptiness of space, recycling of waste products to produce drinking water and breathable air, artificial gravity for the spacefarers, even the growth of vegetables onboard the spaceship, are among the problems that confront the planners and designers of a Mars expedition. Again, the knowledge and the conceptual ideas of von Braun and his colleagues were in high demand at the Disney Studios.

What should the Mars ships look like? What kind of propulsion systems should they use? In his Mars project studies carried out in 1948 and 1949, von Braun had suggested a flotilla of chemically propelled vehicles, designed on the basis of 1948 technology, which was, after all, not very different from the 1942 technology of Peenemünde's V-2 rocket. *"Can't you think of something more modern, but still technically feasible?"* Disney asked. Von Braun brought his associate Stuhlinger aboard, who for several years had been studying electric space propulsion systems. He proposed a spaceship for a manned round trip to Mars that would produce electric power with a nuclear-electric generator; thrust would be generated by a flow of ions, accelerated to a high exhaust velocity by an electric field. A space propulsion system of that kind had never been built, but in the judgment of the experts its principle was technically sound. Von Braun had no qualms seeing it incorporated in Disney's Mars expedition, even more so because the electric system, as compared to chemical rocket motors, would allow a considerably greater payload fraction, and also a shorter travel time.

Disney Studios built models of six electric Mars ships, some of them equipped with landing craft, that were shown traveling to Mars, and entering into a circular orbit around Mars.

Again, Disney was anxious to keep his show within the boundaries of *"a factual science presentation,"* leaving speculations about the nature of the Martian surface, and about any kind of live organisms that may be found there, to the fantasy of the viewers.

Von Braun thoroughly enjoyed working with the Disney people. He often told his co-workers in Huntsville about the good times he had there in the evening after a day's hard work with contractors; at that time, both the Redstone and the Jupiter projects were going full blast.

Kimball had a full-size steam locomotive—bought from a scrap yard—and several hundred feet of standard railroad track, on his property. Sometimes after a spaceflight design session, the locomotive was fired up, and each of the men was allowed to drive the locomotive back and forth on the rails—bell ringing, whistle blowing, and steam puffing out everywhere!

"During one of his visits to Disney," Kimball recalled [5-24], *"I invited him and Willy Ley to a barbecue dinner on our patio. At that time, Wernher was planning to visit his friend Arthur C. Clarke and to go scuba diving with him off the Great Barrier Reef near Australia. He had bought diving equipment, and it just so happened that he had face mask, breathing tube, and swim fins in his traveling bag. While we were waiting for the steaks to cook, Wernher made endless underwater practice runs back and forth in the Kimball swimming pool! I remember the final night he spent with us, working with Stuhlinger on nailing down the nuclear-electric rocket hardware . . . It was a tough night, we were sitting there in our shirtsleeves, sweating it out . . . When he was through, he threw down his pencil and turned around to a piano, and for ten minutes played Bach, without notes. I didn't even know he played the piano. He just played—flawlessly. He was such a genius. He just could do anything. Then he stopped, clapped his hands, and said: 'Well, Wahd (that's the way he pronounced my name), how about taking us back to the hotel?'"*

When Explorer 1 was put in orbit, the Disney people sent a congratulatory note *"To Wernher and Ernst from your friends at Disney,"* together with a typical Disney cartoon. It showed the launching of a big rocket, with a water hydrant on top! At the time of the Explorer launch, the dog Laika was in orbit onboard the second Russian Sputnik; the Americans are sending a complimentary water hydrant to the lonely dog in orbit.

7   BACK TO THE GRASS ROOTS

Von Braun spent twenty years in Huntsville, from 1950 to 1970. While the second of these two decades belonged almost entirely to the Saturn-Apollo program, the first ten years were filled with a variety of projects and activities. Some of them ran in parallel, others overlapped for a shorter or longer time. A situation like this cannot be portrayed chronologically, because events that actually occurred simultaneously can be described only in sequence, requiring a frequent stepping back and forth in time.

During Von Braun's first decade in Huntsville, the Redstone and Jupiter missiles for the Army were developed and completed, and work on the solid-propellant ballistic missile Pershing began. Ablative heat protection for nose cones was developed; the first American satellite was launched, and also the first probe to fly by the Moon. Von Braun was the main contributor to the *Collier's* articles about the orbiting space station, a trip to the Moon, and a voyage to Mars; and he worked with Walt Disney for the triple TV series *"Man in Space."* Von Braun became thoroughly engrained with life in America during that decade. He built his own house; two of his children were born during those years; he became active as a water skier, a scuba diver, a motor boater, and a sailor; and he acquired private and commercial pilot's licenses. He established close relations with the city government, particularly the Chamber of Commerce. He joined the Episcopal Church, and he participated in numerous community activities. He wrote essays and gave presentations about space matters. He established contacts with leaders in industry and in the state and federal governments that led to numerous public appearances, including congressional speeches and testimonies. He began a number of close friendships that lasted to the end of his life.

Casual observers at that time might have concluded that von Braun's very broad spectrum of activities was just an outgrowth of his hyperactive mind. This may have been partially true; however, those who were in close contact with him saw a very systematic trend at least in his major activities. Von Braun was deeply convinced that in order to reach the goal of man's travel into space, he would have to achieve a number of other goals first, and he approached them with determination.

"The idea of spaceflight must be popularized to arouse public enthusiasm," he would tell his associates, and he offered his suggestions whenever there was an opportunity: Friends of space exploration have to be won among influential people. Industrial leaders should be stimulated to recognize the great promise of space projects for technological progress. Scientists are to be alerted to the opportunities for space research. Prominent politicians in government must be made aware of the tremendous prestige value of accomplishments in space.

While extolling all the glorious aspects of spaceflight, von Braun was most anxious not to raise false expectations. Building space vehicles will require long and strenuous efforts; most of these efforts will just be hard work. A program of step-by-step evolution must be started, beginning with available rockets, and proceeding through unmanned satellite projects, ballistic flights with animals, ballistic flights with human astronauts, satellites with humans, space rescue systems, simple orbiting stations, shuttle-type Earth-to-orbit transportation, unmanned and manned flights to the Moon, elaborate space stations in orbit, and expeditions to Mars.

Emphasizing the necessity for a careful, logical, step-by-step approach to the goal of spaceflight became even more urgent in the light of glowing proposals for luxurious castles in orbit, huge industrial activities on the Moon, and extended human colonies in space that were published by well-meaning space enthusiasts who happily jumped over the vast gap that separated existing technical capabilities from the gigantic requirements of such space ventures of the future.

The need to go back to the grass roots and to build a solid base for future accomplishments was a constant concern for von Braun. Spaceflight requires a well-coordinated program that extends over a number of years; each step in this progression must dovetail with the previous and the next step. He made these points whenever he had a chance.

"How far in the future is the flight of man through space?" he asked in a paper

entitled *"We Need a Coordinated Space Program"* [5-19] which he prepared for the Fourth International Astronautical Congress in Zurich, Switzerland, in 1953.

There are some *"who advocate extreme caution and a slow . . . almost organic development process . . ., while others wish to rush in where even angels might fear to tread, and to construct out of hand one or more multi-stage, manned space vehicles . . ."* von Braun cautioned. Certainly, no one with any experience could recommend that we should build a manned rocket ship without a series of intermediate steps.

In his paper, von Braun urged a standardization of essential components of large rockets. We need a coordinated space program, and we need it now, he said. *"Any fond belief that we can have a successful space program without a well-coordinated effort is not speculation, it is just an illusion."*

One by one, von Braun discussed those problems which still exist and must be solved before manned space will come of age. Navigational systems for spacecraft, hypervelocity aerodynamics, protection against meteoroids and radiations, methods to return to Earth through the atmosphere, studies of the effects of weightlessness on animals and humans, life support systems for the crew members, emergency ejection capsules, quick-response vehicles for rescue from orbit—there are many open questions that need answers, but they can be answered in due time in a well-coordinated, logically evolving program.

How far in the future is manned spaceflight?—Very far, without a well-planned and well-coordinated program, von Braun insisted. However, he contended, if we chart a carefully coordinated course and stick to it, we will require but a few years to take our first steps into space. *"I only hope,"* he added, *"that we will not wait to adopt this program until after our astronomers have reported a new star that moves across their field of vision with menacing speed . . ."*

Laying the technical groundwork for a well-coordinated space program was one part of von Braun's suggestions. The other part of his *"back to the grass roots"* proposal concerned a campaign for public and governmental support for the idea of spaceflight.

In an essay written in 1954 [5-25], von Braun offered some suggestions on how to sell the idea of spaceflight. Protagonists for space projects face a dual task, he said. They must gain support for the great program from the broad public that controls the politicians as well as from the high and mighty who control dollars and priorities. In order to succeed in this dual task, they must stimulate people's imagination while carefully avoiding any speculations that would not stand scrutiny by a critical audience. In particular, *"if [the campaigner] is not careful in holding that narrow line between . . . sound concepts and unrealistic dreams, he will easily fall prey to the very critics he sets out to win over to his side."*

How should the idea of spaceflight be sold? *"First,"* von Braun advised, *"you don't sell large rocket and space projects by small-scale, door-to-door peddling. You must succeed in capturing the imagination of those people on whose support you project depends."* *"Those people,"* he felt, would include the broad public, government, scientists, and industry.

Second, von Braun emphasized that *"in technological developments, you will always be in trouble if you cannot arrange your plans in such a way that each intermediate step pays for itself."*

Von Braun's third lesson concerned the crucial importance of teamwork. *"Rocket and spacecraft development,"* he said, *"embraces many aspects of engineering and science, and it is utterly dependent upon good teamwork . . . You must have a good team at your disposal before you begin a project . . . It takes a long time to build up a team; even an excellent group of professional football players requires extensive coaching before the players can be amalgamated into a team fit for the superbowl."*

Then, von Braun urged that the proposer of a large project must lay out and show a carefully planned and coordinated program for his space project. *"Be cautious with time tables!"* he warned.

Finally, he reminded his audience of the impressive progress in aviation, atomic energy, radar, and rocketry during World War II. *"If we move forward with the same perseverance and determination that made these advances possible, in a mere 10 to 15 years man's presence in space will have been established."*

Von Braun's own history shows that he practiced what he preached. As his military rockets Redstone and Jupiter neared completion, he turned his efforts toward projects that evolved naturally from these achievements. Explorer 1, the first American satellite, was launched with the modified Redstone-based Jupiter C (or Juno I, to distinguish it from the former's role as a reentry test vehicle). Explorer 2 did not make orbit; after a successful take-off of the Redstone and ignition of the first and second upper stages, the third stage failed to ignite, and the satellite came down several thousand miles east of Florida. Explorer 3 in March 1958 was again successful, and so was Explorer 4 in July 1958. While that satellite with its cosmic ray counters was in orbit, another Redstone rocket launched a hydrogen bomb from Johnson Island in the Pacific for a high-altitude explosion test. Satellite counters recorded the radiation intensities and their decay, providing valuable data on the effects of nuclear blasts in the atmosphere, and also of the capturing and decay mechanisms of charged particle radiations in the Earth's magnetosphere. A Redstone rocket launched the first American astronaut, Alan B. Shepard, on 5 May 1961 on a ballistic trajectory.

Jupiter rockets also served as space launchers under the designation Juno II. On 3 March 1959, Pioneer 4 was launched by a Juno II; it became the first successful flyby of the Moon. The first successful animal passengers, small monkeys Able and Baker, traveled over a 1,600 mile (2,560 km) trajectory in a Jupiter-launched space capsule on 28 May 1959. Miss Baker subsequently lived at the U.S. Space & Rocket Center in Huntsville for twenty-seven more years! The first Juno II satellite, Explorer 7, was launched on 13 October 1959. It carried a variety of instruments to further explore the Van Allen radiation belts and other radiations beyond the atmosphere.

Thor, likewise, found application as a launch rocket for spacecraft; its numerous versions included Thor Able, Thor Delta, Thor Epsilon, and Thor Agena. Thor-based Delta-configuration launchers were the mainstay of American satellite launch systems for several decades, enjoying a remarkable success rate. And they are still flying.

Around 1958, a new and powerful rocket made its appearance, the Air Force's Atlas missile. Like Redstone, Jupiter, and Thor, it also served as a space launcher, mostly in combination with Able, Agena, or Centaur as upper stages.

Von Braun's suggestions and predictions of 1954 came surprisingly close to reality. A space program evolved step-by-step; each step dovetailed into previous and succeeding projects, and each step had some utility of its own. The continuing quest for larger and larger projects was kept alive. Ten years after the *"Selling of an Idea"* paper, in 1964, nine Soviet cosmonauts and four American astronauts had been in orbit around the Earth. Fifteen years after this paper, in 1969, four American astronauts had walked on the surface of the Moon, and eight more followed during the ensuing three years.

Another prediction, expressed timidly in 1954 as a possibility, also came true: During the night of 4 October 1957, astronomers discovered a new "star" that moved across their field of vision with menacing speed.

CHAPTER 6

TROUBLED BIRTH OF EXPLORER 1

Satellites had been orbiting in von Braun's mind ever since he read, at the age of fourteen, Hermann Oberth's book on rockets and spaceflight. When he was fifteen, he had learned how to calculate the speed that a rocket must acquire in order to put a satellite into a permanent orbit around the Earth. Later, as technical director at Peenemünde, he would talk about satellites, but he soon learned that it was wiser not to, so he followed the French admonition: *toujours y penser, mais jamais en parler* (always think of it, but never talk about it).

Many years later, von Braun confided to a friend: *"When I landed on the American continent in 1945, I had one burning hope: that this step may enable me to contribute to the launching of the first satellite!"*

Probably the earliest written account of man-made satellites of our Earth is found in Isaac Newton's monumental *Principia*. If you fired a cannon from the top of a mountain in a horizontal direction, he explained, and if you could impart to it sufficient muzzle velocity, and if there were no air resistance, the cannon ball would not fall to the ground, but rather continue to fly around the Earth. Eventually, it could even hit you from the rear!

Over the years, novelists, science fiction writers, and serious spaceflight planners wrote about artificial Earth-circling satellites. Von Braun first mentioned *"stations in space"* in a story he wrote in 1927. Nearly two decades later, at Fort Bliss, he found the leisure and the freedom to expound on this new dimension human experience would acquire as soon as man reached out into space. He described how satellites could be put in orbit, and how they would benefit mankind. In his Christmas address to his team members at Fort Bliss in 1945, he gave a glowing, but technically sound report on the launching of satellites, Moon landers, and Mars expeditions with rockets that could evolve from the Peenemünde V-2 rocket.

Von Braun was not the only one who studied the feasibility and the potential uses of Earth satellites at that time. In the fall of 1945, the U.S. Navy established a Committee for Evaluating the Feasibility of Space Rocketry (CEFSR). This committee recommended a satellite project, and it contracted with the Guggenheim Aeronautical Laboratory at the California Institute of Technology (GALCIT) for a theoretical study.

The director of GALCIT was Theodore von Kármán, one of the all-time giants of theoretical aerodynamics. He had established a rocket research project in 1936 together with Frank Malina, Martin Summerfield, and some other early rocket enthusiasts. Their first experiments with liquid propellant rocket motors during the late 1930s were almost identical with those of the Verein für Raumschiffahrt in Berlin in 1930 and 1931. A young engineering student from China, Hsue-shen Tsien, joined the experimenters in 1937. He soon impressed his colleagues by his brilliance in mathematics as well as in practical engineering. He rose quickly through the ranks, and in 1943, von Kármán,

Malina, and Tsien jointly wrote a proposal for an energetic rocket research program which, as von Kármán pointed out, would have *"immediate military usefulness."* This proposal led to the establishment of the Jet Propulsion Laboratory (JPL) within the California Institute of Technology (CalTech). Its primary assignment was the development of guided missiles for the military, but von Kármán wished to include *"those branches which are more important for peace applications."*

Tsien, a Chinese citizen working in the United States while his country was under communist rule, was caught in Senator Joseph R. McCarthy's inquisition during the early 1950s. Being declared an undesirable alien, he was to be deported; but, because of his knowledge of classified information, the federal government instead put him under *"preventive detention"* and denied him access to classified material. He remained at CalTech until 1955 when he was allowed to leave the United States. His old country gave him a hero's welcome. During the ensuing years, Tsien became the chief architect of China's nuclear bomb development, as well as its intercontinental ballistic missile program.

Interest in space rockets and satellites began to grow in the United States during the mid-1940s. Von Braun beat the drum at local chapters of engineering societies, and in articles for the journals of the American Rocket Society, the American Astronautical Society, the British Interplanetary Society, and other organizations. His comprehensive study of a manned expedition to the planet Mars was written in 1948 and 1949 and published several years later [4-4].

Among the reports that appeared during this period was the Navy's *"Investigation of the Possibility of Establishing a Space Ship in an Orbit above the Surface of the Earth"* by O. E. Lancaster and J. R. Moore, published in November 1945. *"It is estimated,"* they wrote, *"that above five hundred miles the resistance of the air would do little to slow the ship, and in such an orbit the ship would remain indefinitely. This orbit may prove more desirable . . . for communications or for scientific observations. Of special interest is a circular orbit at 22,300 miles (35,680 km) above the surface of the Earth, where the ship would make one revolution per day. In this orbit the ship may be kept over a designated point on the surface of the Earth."*[*]

The Douglas Aircraft Company proposed a satellite in a report dated May 1946 [6-1], and the Glenn L. Martin Company wrote a report on *"Orbit Project"* in September of that year [6-2].

Navy scientists tried to obtain the cooperation of the Army Air Force; however, at that time the AAF had its own satellite study underway at the RAND Corporation in California. In 1947, a technical evaluation committee established by the Department of Defense (DOD), chaired by Clark B. Millikan, failed to identify any military uses for satellites [6-3]. Secretary of Defense James V. Forrestal therefore stated in 1948 that current satellite activities in the United States will include only studies and component designs, but no development projects [6-4].

In spite of this official DOD stance, von Braun continued to make recommendations to Army Ordnance to permit analytical studies of an Earth satellite based on modified V-2 technology. Toftoy supported these efforts. For several years, satellite studies continued in the von Braun group on an informal and limited basis.

Systematic work on the Redstone missile began in 1950. Even before the name Redstone had become official, von Braun remarked to Stuhlinger: *"With the Redstone, we could do it!"* *"Do what?"* was the puzzled reply. *"Launch a satellite, of course!"*

---

[*]This is only correct, of course, when the satellite is orbiting exactly in the equatorial plane. If it is orbiting in any other plane at that specific altitude, it will describe a figure-eight trajectory in a plane perpendicular to the equatorial plane, centered around a point directly above the equator, and tangent to the circular orbit through that point.

Von Braun then described how the Redstone rocket could carry three stages of clustered solid-propellant rockets to the apex of a steep trajectory, high above the atmosphere. The three-stage cluster would be housed inside a cylindrical container that would spin around its longitudinal axis, driven by an electric motor, to assure that slight differences in the burning rates of the individual rockets would not cause lateral deviations of the cluster. Oriented in a horizontal direction by the time the Redstone reached apex, the three upper stages would be fired in quick succession to build up the required orbital velocity of about 7.7 km per second. Calculations showed that a payload of several pounds could be injected into orbit. *"This will certainly not be the most efficient way to put five pounds into orbit,"* von Braun admitted, *"but it is the only one available this side of the Iron Curtain for the next couple of years."*

While proposals for an American satellite project languished in the maze of government channels, a spark lighted up at another place: the American Rocket Society (ARS). For some years its journal, and that of the British Interplanetary Society as well, had featured articles on space rockets, satellites, and planetary flight. Among the authors were Leslie R. Shepherd, Arthur V. (Val) Cleaver, Kenneth W. Gatland, Krafft A. Ehricke, S. Fred Singer, and—not surprisingly—Wernher von Braun.

In 1952, the ARS established a Space Flight Committee under the chairmanship of Milton W. Rosen. On 24 November 1954, this committee submitted a report to the National Science Foundation entitled *"On the Utility of an Unmanned Earth Satellite"* [6-5]. It recommended that the Foundation *"sponsor a study of an unmanned Earth satellite vehicle,"* explaining that the ARS was making this proposal *"in the normal exercise of its function."* The proposal stressed the utility of such a satellite to astronomy, astrophysics, biology, communications, geodesy, geophysics, and to experiments *"arising from the unusual environment of space."* A number of appendixes were included, written by experts in the fields.

The National Science Foundation did not choose to respond to this proposal. Disappointed, the ARS used its own resources to promote the idea further.

Meanwhile, toward the end of 1953, two men in Washington felt that the time had come for some concrete action: Commander George W. Hoover at the Office of Naval Research (ONR), and Frederick C. Durant III, president of the International Astronautical Federation (IAF). Durant reminisced about the beginnings of the satellite project during an interview in 1988 [6-6]. *"It was in February or March 1954 when we got that program underway. I brought Wernher and George Hoover together; they had known of each other independently . . . We set up a meeting attended by Fred Singer and others . . . The name Orbiter was not used then; we called it Project Slug—we needed a code name because of military politics; not security, just politics. George Hoover had just been made a commander, and he was sticking his head way, way out. George had a history of doing many avant-garde things. He had come out of Admiral Louis De Florez' Special Devices Center on Long Island; had introduced Otto Winzen to high-altitude plastic balloons; and, with Al Mayo, had worked on an advanced cockpit design. I recall he invented a flat-plate television screen for the cockpit of aircraft, and a 'road in the sky' . . ."*

Durant and Hoover arranged a meeting at the Office of Naval Research with von Braun that included Dr. Fred L. Whipple, chairman of the Department of Astronomy at Harvard University; Dr. S. Fred Singer, physicist at the University of Maryland; Dr. David Young of the Aerojet General Corporation; Alexander Satin, chief engineer at the Air Branch of the Office of Naval Research; and some of von Braun's associates from Huntsville.

Hoover opened that historic meeting with words that will be long remembered by all who were present: *"Gentlemen, the time has come to stop talking and start doing. We will now go ahead and build a satellite."*

At that meeting, von Braun proposed using his Redstone with a three-stage solid-propellant rocket cluster on top. Those rockets could be Lokis derived from the German World War II antiaircraft rocket Taifun. The Loki rocket had been developed at the Jet Propulsion Laboratory; Lokis were manufactured in large numbers by president Bill Bollay's Aerophysics Development Corporation. Bollay had been one of von Kármán's assistants during the late 1930s.

All participants at the meeting immediately and unanimously agreed that von Braun's proposal should be accepted and pursued further. Singer, who had worked out plans for a 100-pound (45 kg) satellite called MOUSE (minimum orbiting unmanned satellite of the Earth) in 1953, happily settled for the smaller satellite since a launch rocket for MOUSE was neither available nor in sight in the foreseeable future.

"After the meeting," Durant recalled [6-6], *"we went to the Statler Hotel at 16th and K Streets—Wernher, Ernst Stuhlinger, Gerhard Heller, [Rudolf Schlidt] and others. We were sitting around in one of the hotel rooms, on the bed and so on . . . we were counting on four of Wernher's Juno missiles . . . if we had these Junos available, when could we launch? . . . We established a date of October or November 1957 . . . maybe earlier, in the fall of 1956 . . ."* Actually, the bar diagram on Durant's yellow pad spanned the period from January 1955 to January 1958.

The chief of Naval Research approved the continuation of conversations between Navy and Army experts. In August 1954, a meeting was held at von Braun's home base in Huntsville. At the insistence of Toftoy (by then Brigadier General), commander of Redstone Arsenal, approval of the meeting was sought and obtained from Major General Leslie E. Simon, chief of Ordnance Corps Research and Development. *"Project Orbiter"* was born at that time. Hoover became project officer. It was agreed that the Navy would design the satellite and provide NRL's Minitrack system, ground tracking facilities, logistics support, and data acquisition. The Army would design, procure, and operate the Redstone with its cluster of small upper stage rockets. Launch was to take place in 1956 from a site on an island near the equator. The chief of Naval Operations, Admiral Robert E. Carney, reacted positively to the proposed project. *"Tell us what you want moved,"* von Braun reported him saying, *"and where it should go, and we will ship it!"*

Around that time, von Braun came up with a new idea. *"It looks like our Orbiter project is taking shape now. We have a pretty good grasp of the vehicle system and other technical aspects of the project. What we need is a real, honest-to-goodness scientist on our bandwagon, a true representative of the scientific elite of the country. Without having a man of that stature on board, scientists will justifiably criticize our project."* Turning to Stuhlinger, he continued: *"You know many scientists here in the country. Why don't you approach one of them and try to persuade him to prepare a small instrument for our satellite?"*

Stuhlinger agreed that this was a splendid idea. About fifteen years earlier, while working on cosmic ray research under Professor Hans Geiger, inventor of the Geiger counter, he had studied a paper on a similar subject written by one James A. Van Allen in the United States. In 1946, he had the pleasure of meeting Van Allen in person at the rocket test facility in White Sands. There, Van Allen mounted some of his own Geiger counters in the nose cones of V-2 rockets that Stuhlinger helped prepare for launching.

Following these early rocket experiments in White Sands, Van Allen had perfected the art of making high-altitude cosmic ray measurements with balloons, rockets, and a combination of the two, so-called rockoons. He had launched them from all over the globe: the Arctic, Florida, along the equator, even from Antarctica. He was also the mastermind behind the development of the Aerobee and its successor, the Aerobee-Hi, two most successful rocket systems employed for high-altitude research from the late 1940s on.

Van Allen had become head of the physics department at the State University of Iowa in 1951. Three years later, he spent a sabbatical year as research associate at the Princeton Institute of Advanced Studies. It was there that Stuhlinger visited him in the autumn of 1954 with the desire to discuss a possible collaboration in the satellite project. After a delightful family dinner, the two men withdrew to the study. Van Allen settled in the corner of the sofa and, characteristically, surrounded himself with a huge cloud of pipe smoke. His visitor unfolded the story of the Redstone with its clustered upper stage assembly, the rocket's potential as a satellite launcher, and the possibility of mounting such instruments as Geiger counters with their supporting equipment in the satellite. Pulses of the counters could be transmitted easily to the ground.

Van Allen sat in his sofa corner without motion. The only sign of life was the vivid smoke production of his pipe. *"When I had finished,"* Stuhlinger recalls, *"he showed no signs of interest, let alone excitement. All he said was: 'Thanks for telling me all this. Keep me posted on your progress, will you?'"* Stuhlinger thought that he had blown the whole thing, and that his mission was a complete failure. Depressed, he traveled back to Huntsville.

Von Braun's associates did keep Van Allen posted on their progress with Project Orbiter. But it would take three years, until December 1957, before they had really good news for him. By that time, Van Allen had signed up, with his cosmic ray counters, for the Vanguard satellite project.

In September 1954 von Braun and some of his co-workers completed a paper entitled *"A Minimum Satellite Vehicle Based on Components Available from Missile Development of the Army Ordnance Corps,"* and presented it to Army authorities [6-7]. Classified Secret until declassification in 1962, the paper provided details of design, performance, and operation of the suggested satellite system.

"A satellite vehicle circling the Earth would be of enormous value to science, especially to upper atmosphere, meteorological, and radiological research . . . This memorandum proposes to show that, by limiting the payload of a first minimum satellite vehicle to approximately 5 pounds, such a project is feasible with presently available missile hardware," von Braun wrote. He then described the joint work that had been done by his group at the Redstone Arsenal and the Office of Naval Research.

"The establishment of a man-made satellite, no matter how humble, would be a scientific achievement of tremendous impact," von Braun continued. *"Since it is a project that we could realize . . . it is only logical to assume that other countries could do the same. It would be a blow to U.S. prestige if we did not do it first."*

Von Braun then described the technical details of the four-stage rocket. Summing up his report, he emphasized that the proposed satellite with a payload of 5 pounds (2.3 kg) could be built with components available from weapon developments of the Army Ordnance Corps. In view of the launching and tracking problems of such a vehicle, he suggested that a joint Army-Navy-Air Force Minimum Satellite Vehicle Project be established.

Unfortunately, the response to this proposal was different from what its authors had hoped for. Before describing the ensuing events, some other developments of that time should be mentioned.

The desire to have an Earth satellite in orbit was not the only reason why von Braun, as well as others who were anxious to stimulate some action on the part of the government, were so eager to obtain an official go-ahead for an American satellite project. Activities in the Soviet Union, visible to all who were willing to look and listen, clearly suggested the beginning of a *"race into space."*

In October 1951, a distinguished Soviet scientist, M. K. Tikhonravov, stated that the USSR had plans to orbit artificial satellites. Two years later, in November 1953, A. N.

Nesmeyanov of the USSR Academy of Sciences announced at the World Peace Council in Vienna that the launching of Earth satellites by the Soviet Union had become a realistic possibility.

Since the early 1950s, American and Russian space scientists would meet at the annual congresses of the International Astronautical Federation, and they often discussed satellites. Delegates from the Soviet Union quite freely talked about their intentions to launch scientific satellites. In 1955, at the Fifth International Astronautical Congress in Copenhagen, American attendees asked Professor Leonid Sedov, member of the Soviet Academy of Sciences, and highly respected as a dean and patron saint of Soviet space scientists, whether the first astronaut in space will be Russian or American. *"Neither one,"* he answered with a smile. *"The first astronaut in orbit will be a dog. A Russian dog, of course."*

For space-minded Americans, the tremendous prestige value of being the first to orbit a satellite was obvious. Their convictions, however, were not shared by high officials in the Department of Defense, and in the three armed services. Moreover, rivalries between Army, Navy, and Air Force personalities overshadowed the perception of joint responsibility for the good of the nation. A cartoon appeared in a journal at that time, showing an Army and an Air Force general and a Navy admiral standing together; a satellite orbited overhead with a hammer and sickle painted on it. The Army general says to the admiral: *"Gosh, am I glad that it is not the Air Force!"*; the admiral says to the Air Force general: *"I am so happy it is not the Army!"*; and the Air Force general, in turn, says to his Army colleague: *"Golly, am I glad it is not the Navy!"*

In 1950, Dr. Lloyd V. Berkner, a world-renowned geophysicist, suggested that a joint effort on an international basis be made to study the Earth and its environment. His suggestions led to the creation of the International Geophysical Year (IGY). A special committee for the IGY was set up in 1952 under Dr. Sidney Chapman, president, and Berkner, vice president.

On 4 October 1954 the special committee recommended to the IGY participants *"that thought be given to the launching of small satellite vehicles . . ."* as an integral part of the international effort. In March of the following year, this recommendation was approved.

As early as 1952, von Braun had begun to make plans for using Redstone rockets with simple upper stages for the testing of heat-resistant nose cone surfaces during high-speed reentry into the atmosphere (Chapter 5-2). The modified Redstones would carry two upper stages of solid-propellant rockets, integrated into a spinning cluster. That system would be very similar to the rocket von Braun proposed for the satellite launch, except that the satellite rocket would have one more stage on top of the spinning cluster. Gerhard Heller and Rudolf Schlidt headed the planning effort for the reentry test rocket.

By the end of 1954, preparations for the nose cone testing had proceeded to the point where the reentry test version of the Redstone (named Jupiter C because it tested a Jupiter-type nose cone) had been equipped with elongated tanks; it was to use hydyne instead of alcohol as fuel [unsymmetrical dimethyl hydrazine, $(CH_3)_2 N_2H_2$]. These changes would result in a satellite launch capability of 15 pounds (6.8 kilograms). Launching of a satellite in the summer of 1956 would be possible. Von Braun sent a copy of this newest proposal to the Jet Propulsion Laboratory in Pasadena in December 1954.

Meanwhile, another satellite launch system was under study by Milton W. Rosen and his colleagues at the Naval Research Laboratory. That launch system would consist of a modified version of the Viking high altitude rocket as the first stage, a modified Aerobee Hi as second stage, and a new solid propellant rocket as third stage. It was a very interesting design, but much modification work, and substantial new developments, would be necessary before one could count on a reliable launch rocket. Rosen promised a payload of 40 pounds (18 kilograms), and a flight readiness also by summer 1956.

The Air Force advised that it, too, was working on a satellite project; it was to be launched by the future Atlas rocket.

At about the same time, there were signs of renewed interest in satellites within the Department of Defense. Taking advantage of this improved situation, members of Project Orbiter early in 1955 requested permission from Army authorities to brief assistant secretary of defense for Research and Development, Donald Quarles, and to present to him the essence of von Braun's *"Minimum Satellite Vehicle"* proposal of September 1954, but updated with the new performance figures obtained in the meantime.

Quarles received this request, but instead of responding to it with some action, he set up a new committee. It was chaired by Dr. Homer Joe Stewart, professor of physics at CalTech. The committee was to recommend which of several competing proposals for a satellite should be accepted and activated.

Against this background, the White House announced on 29 July 1955 that the United States would launch an Earth satellite sometime during the International Geophysical Year.

This announcement was followed quickly by an announcement in Moscow to the effect that the USSR was also planning to launch a satellite during the same period.

Instead of giving a briefing to Assistant Secretary of Defense Quarles on Project Orbiter, as he had requested and hoped, von Braun gave a presentation to the Army Policy Council on 3 August 1955. After describing the technical features and the way of operation of his proposed satellite launcher, he said: *"All of the subcontractors have worked closely with Redstone Arsenal in developing the rocket, whose fabrication is now being rapidly turned over to the Chrysler Corporation. This being the case, the Guided Missile Development Division at Redstone Arsenal has the capacity and organization to undertake the satellite project without interference with the Redstone missile development . . ."*

Later in his presentation, von Braun said: *"When comparing our Army satellite proposal with the Air Force and Navy proposals, it is necessary to realize that we have carefully refrained from utilizing any hardware that would require extensive development . . . We have a booster that has been successfully flight tested . . . We also have the Redstone guidance system, all of whose components have been successfully flight tested. In addition, the Loki motors used for the upper stages are existing items of hardware. About 10,000 of those Loki motors have been produced under Ordnance production contracts . . ."* Von Braun also mentioned the possibility of exchanging the Loki rockets with scaled-down Sergeant rockets, as JPL had recently suggested. These rockets could be mounted on the same spinning container that had been developed and tested at Redstone Arsenal for the Loki rockets.

In the same month, August 1955, the nine members of the Stewart committee voted on the question which of three satellite proposals should be accepted for the American IGY program: Rosen's Vanguard, von Braun's Redstone Orbiter, or the Air Force satellite which, however, dropped out because it did not have a launcher. Six members cast their votes for Vanguard, while three members, including Stewart, voted for the Redstone Orbiter.

Upon learning of the Stewart Committee's recommendation, the Secretary of Defense instructed the Army to stop all work on satellites, and buckle down to its main business: the development of military missiles. When the news reached Huntsville, an air of depression began to creep in. The general feeling went something like this: *"We could hardly believe it. After all, we wanted to launch an American satellite, not an Army or a Huntsville satellite. We knew how close the race with the Soviets was, and how difficult it would prove for the Vanguard people to make good on their promise, with all their brand new, untried components that had to be developed, including a new rocket motor."* Spirits were low when von Braun called a meeting to discuss the situation. To everyone's surprise, he arrived with his usual beaming smile. *"They stopped us in the tracks with our satellite,"* he said, *"but we are still in business with our reentry tests. Let's go to work right away! We will build the upper-stage system for the testing of Jupiter nosecones which we have been preparing since 1953, and we will launch the first Jupiter C next year, as planned. This will be perfectly legal,"* von Braun added; *"in fact, we have to do this anyway for our Jupiter missile project. At the time when we will be called upon to launch a satellite—and I'm sure that time will come—we will quickly add that third solid rocket stage, modify the guidance system, put the satellite on top, and we are in business, and even without transgressing the limitations they have clamped on us!"*

Shortly after this new beginning, in September 1955, Stewart visited Huntsville, accompanied by Dr. William H. Pickering, director of JPL, and Dr. Jack E. Froelich, a close associate of Pickering. Stewart, who was as downcast as von Braun's co-workers had been a few days earlier, wanted to discuss how Project Orbiter, and America's prospects for an early satellite launch, could possibly be saved.

When Stewart learned about the active development state of von Braun's multistage Jupiter C reentry test vehicle, he quickly shared the optimism of the Huntsville people. Pickering now definitely offered JPL's scaled-down Sergeant rockets for the Jupiter C upper stages; they would be more powerful and efficient than the Loki rockets, but still fit into Redstone's spinning tub. In addition, Pickering offered his laboratory's help with a super-sensitive tracking system, Microlock, designed by Eberhardt Rechtin, and to be prepared for the satellite as soon as the satellite development would be authorized. He also offered JPL's support with instrumentation, tracking operations, and data transmission.

A number of events that happened at Redstone Arsenal while the Orbiter satellite project went through its birth pangs during the years 1955 and 1956 were described in Chapter 5-2.

Several identical launch vehicles of the Jupiter C type were built and ground-tested. Nose cone testing began in the fall of 1956. In this test program, von Braun's Development Operations Division enjoyed the active support of JPL and the Aerophysics Development Corporation. General Medaris, who had become commander of the Army Ballistic Missile Agency (ABMA) on 1 February 1956, saw the need for a very tight organizational structure of all those Army Ordnance agencies that contributed to the rocket and missile projects under his responsibility.

With tongue in cheek, von Braun decided that one of the Jupiter C vehicles should be set aside and carefully subjected to a *"long-time storage test"*; it was quietly understood that this vehicle represented a potential satellite launch rocket. As soon as permission could be obtained, that vehicle would be taken out of storage, and a third Sergeant stage, an attitude orientation system, and an ignition command receiver would be added. In a parallel action, Jack Froelich at JPL put a number of Sergeant rockets into a controlled environment *"to study long-time effects on the propellant,"* just in case.

On 20 September 1956 the first launching of a Jupiter C with two Sergeant-powered upper stages took place, but not before Medaris, under orders from the Pentagon, had verified personally that the nose cone did not contain a third Sergeant stage that might *"inadvertently"* ignite and place a test payload into a satellite orbit!

As described in Chapter 5-2, the nose cone test program met with full success. But in spite of this technical accomplishment, von Braun and his team at ABMA encountered rough sailing. Secretary of Defense Charles E. Wilson, in his *"Roles and Missions Directive"* of 26 November 1956, significantly reduced the Army's role in the national guided missile program. This decision threatened to spell the end of the Jupiter program, and to render useless all the time, effort, money, experience, and success related to its development and operational deployment. In fact, it was feared that the Wilson decision would just eliminate the proven capability built up by Toftoy, Medaris, von Braun, and their widespread team of government employees, military personnel, and industrial companies.

During that twilight period of anxiety and fear in late 1956 and through 1957, a bizarre sequence of events unfolded. Army Colonel John C. Nickerson, one of Medaris's staff officers and a West Pointer, virtually sacrificed his career by uncovering and exposing some obvious high-level misjudgments related to ballistic missile and other defense matters. The upshot was a highly publicized court-martial with Nickerson accused of transgressing security and hierarchical channels and going public with the facts as he saw them. Nickerson got a slap on his wrist, but the decision to cancel Jupiter was withdrawn. The project was permitted to continue, on the condition that Medaris and his Air Force counterpart, General Bernard A. Schriever, could work out a Jupiter-Thor compromise. Fortunately, the two generals succeeded in reaching an agreement. Wilson's successor, Secretary of Defense Neil H. McElroy, authorized Jupiter for production along with the Air Force's Thor missile, but the Air Force would be responsible for Jupiter's operational and funding control (Chapter 5-2). This decision allowed the Jupiter C nose cone test program to continue. Thus, the multistage Redstone-based rocket was available as a satellite launcher when it was needed later in 1957.

While Project Orbiter was still an approved study project back in 1954 and 1955, von Braun initiated the development of three subsystems that would be needed for a rocket system that was to launch a satellite. The first of these was an attitude control system that would turn the upper portion of the rocket, after burning cutoff of the main propulsion system and separation of the forward section from the burnt-out main stage, in such a way that it would be exactly horizontal at the moment of apex. The first of the upper stages would have to fire at this moment. The second subsystem, an *"apex predicter,"* would accept signals from mutually independent radio, Doppler, and radar measurements made during ascent, and, after forming a weighted average of these signals, would compute the exact moment when the first of the three upper stages would have to be ignited. At that moment, it would transmit an ignition signal to the vehicle. The third subsystem was the satellite capsule that had to accommodate tracking equipment, Geiger counters, data transmitter, batteries, and antennas. Design engineers Josef Boehm and Helmut Pfaff were responsible for the satellite design, and for the mechanical components of the attitude control system; Walter Haeussermann, Fred Digesu, and Hans H. Hosenthien worked out the theory for that system. The apex predicter was designed by Stuhlinger at the Research Projects Laboratory, and built in Wilhelm Angele's shop. Ernst D. Geissler, Rudolf Hoelker, and some of their colleagues did the celestial mechanics work. Charles A. Lundquist developed a method to determine the satellite's orbit based on a limited number of observations from the ground.

This work could not be continued after the Army had been directed, in the autumn of 1955, to terminate all satellite-related study, research, development, and design work. However, there was no reason why the men behind these studies could not carry on their work on their own time, at least as long as their activities were limited to paper studies. They did, even at home, and when the door opened at long last for Army participation in space, the designs were ready. It must be said, though, that General Toftoy, and after him General Medaris, always turned very generously the other way when they visited a laboratory and spotted on one of the drawing boards a sketch that looked suspiciously like a little satellite.

Fortunately, relatively little hardware was necessary for all three subsystems. This fact helped keep the implementation time short once the official go-ahead signal for the satellite project had been given. Vanguard testing began in 1956, and with it also a string of bad luck for the Vanguard project crew. Although of an impressive design, the three-stage vehicle was so complex that the brief available time was just not sufficient to iron out all the technical problems that inevitably crop up in a project of that nature. Vanguard director Dr. John P. Hagen, chief engineer Milton W. Rosen, and their team mates fought valiantly against heavy odds to bring the project to fruition.

On 29 October 1957 von Braun said in a presentation to the Association of the United States Army [6-8]: *"We have a number of excellent missile development teams in this country, and their achievements, despite all the unavoidable set-backs of early test programs, are beyond reproach. I should like to specifically include in this statement the technical team in charge of the Vanguard Project."*

Von Braun, and his representatives, repeatedly offered to the Navy their readiness to join forces with the Vanguard team, even to the extent that a Vanguard satellite would be launched with a Redstone rocket under the name of Project Vanguard, and under the auspices of the Vanguard team, but the Navy officers in charge always responded with a firm *"no."*

During 1956, and even more during 1957, indications that the Soviets might launch a satellite became more frequent. Journal and newspaper articles, presentations by scientists, even newscasts contained hints that the USSR was serious about meeting its IGY satellite commitment [1-2]. Thus, at a meeting of IGY planners in Barcelona, Spain, in September 1956, Professor I. Bardin advised all present that the Soviet Union *". . . would use satellites for pressure, temperature, cosmic ray, micrometeoroid, and solar radiation measurements"* [6-9]. Similar statements were made during 1957. The fact that the Soviet Academy of Sciences had started a satellite program in April 1955 had been known for about two years. In June 1957, Professor Nesmeyanov stated publicly in the press that a satellite launcher and its payload were ready, and that a launch should be expected within a few months. Around the same time, Lloyd Berkner, the U.S. member of the IGY Committee, received information of an impending satellite launch by the USSR from the president of the Soviet Academy of Sciences [6-10]. On 18 September 1957, Radio Moscow stated that a satellite would be launched soon.

Soviet program planners were known to their western colleagues for their tendency not to talk about a new project unless its realization was imminent; therefore, these hints of an impending USSR satellite launch caused growing tension for at least some of the satellite planners in the United States. But only few people in the United States took these developments seriously. For these few, the crisp statements of the Russians, the depressing plight of the Vanguard project, the tied hands of the Army-JPL team, and the almost complacent disregard of many Americans of the possibility that their country might be outranked by the USSR with a brilliant technical accomplishment, added up to the expectation of a major shock.

Von Braun, bound by the secretary of defense's order not to build and launch a satellite, forced himself into stoic tranquility. His associate Stuhlinger was less restrained. By the end of September, he suggested that another attempt be made to obtain permission from DOD to proceed with the Redstone-boosted satellite, either Orbiter or Vanguard. But von Braun, chafed by pressures from two opposing sides, quipped: *"If you wish to become nervous, do so—but leave me out! I cannot move anyway, as you well know!"*

Then, Stuhlinger pleaded with Medaris: *"I am firmly convinced that a Soviet satellite will soon be in orbit. General, couldn't you approach the secretary again and ask for permission to go ahead? The shock for our country would be tremendous if they were first into space!"*

"Now, look," Medaris replied, *"don't get tense. You know how complicated it is to build and launch a satellite. Those people will never be able to do it! Through all my various intelligence channels, I have not received the slightest indication of an impending satellite launch. As soon as I hear something, I will act. When we learn something about their activities, we will still have plenty of time to move. Go back to your laboratory, and relax!"*

On 1 October, an official announcement by Radio Moscow gave transmission frequencies of the forthcoming satellite, so that everybody could tune in to its signals.

Less than one week after Stuhlinger's discussion with Medaris, on 4 October 1957, the shock came when Soviet Russia proudly announced that Sputnik 1 was in orbit. Everybody with a little radio receiver could hear its gentle but insistent beep-beep every 96 minutes, and on clear nights one could see the little star traveling quickly across the sky. Von Braun asked Stuhlinger: *"Did the General talk to you since it happened? I think he owes you an apology!"* *"Yes,"* was the answer. *"All he said was: 'Those damn bastards!'"*

2 THE SPUTNIK SHOCK

Only few events in the history of spaceflight have met with such powerful emotional reactions by the public and the professionals as the launching of Sputnik. At the Army Ballistic Missile Agency in Huntsville, the future birthplace of the first American satellite, the news of the great Soviet success led to some dramatic outbursts of tensions that had been pent up for many months.

On 4 October 1957, Secretary of Defense-designate Neil H. McElroy was visiting the Army Ballistic Missile Agency, accompanied by Secretary of the Army Wilbur M. Brucker, Army Research and Development chief General James M. Gavin, Army Vice Chief of Staff General Lyman L. Lemnitzer, and other high ranking officials. During the cocktail hour that followed the orientation program, Gordon Harris, director of the Public Affairs Office, burst into the room, shouting: *"Soviet Russia has launched a satellite!"*

His words struck like a thunderbolt. *"We could have done it with our Redstone two years ago!"* von Braun exclaimed, looking at his visitors. Then, he pleaded with Secretary McElroy: *"Give me the word, and we will have an American satellite in orbit in sixty days!"* Medaris quickly intervened: *"Wernher, let's make it ninety!"* McElroy, who had yet to be confirmed by Congress, had no power to act. And there was nobody above him who would have felt a desire or an urge to act.

Among the first responses in the country, besides the immediate reactions of the news media and countless comments by citizens, was a renewed offer from the

Secretary of the Army Brucker to the Navy to build and launch six Army-JPL satellites for 12.7 million dollars. It would take three weeks before that offer was answered.

During these three weeks, the *"Sputnik Shock"* expanded. Passionate, even angry pleas were made to the government to put more effort, more funding, more emphasis, more determination into the nation's space program. The loss of national prestige was hard to swallow. Being pushed from the number one place in the esteem of the world, and even by a country that was believed to lag in almost every aspect of modern civilization, had been totally inconceivable to most Americans, and to many citizens of other countries, too. Calls for changes were loud and clear; loudest were cries for a better educational system in this country.

The rocket people, particularly those who *"could have done it two years ago,"* waited anxiously for a signal to go ahead and help restore the country's image as a first class achiever.

About two weeks after Sputnik's appearance in the sky, and three weeks before the definite order to develop the Army's Orbiter satellite was received at Huntsville, von Braun was invited by the Association of the United States Army to present his thoughts on the situation. He was happy to be afforded this opportunity, and he wrote one of his classic essays, *"The Lessons of Sputnik."* Von Braun gave the presentation in Washington on 29 October 1957. His audience included Secretary of the Army Brucker and Army Chief of Staff Maxwell D. Taylor.

Von Braun's paper was a stirring assessment of an unfortunate situation that first was brought to light by Sputnik's sudden appearance, and then was hammered in by the satellite's insistent beep-beep every 96 minutes while the calamity was lamented by reproachful voices from almost all walks of life.

"October 4, 1957, the day when Sputnik appeared in the skies," von Braun said, *"will be remembered on this planet as the day on which the Age of Space Flight was ushered in."*

The international fraternity of scientists, he noted, will see it as a truly great scientific and technological achievement. To the Western world, looking to America for leadership in science and technology, it came as a surprise and a shock. *"For the United States,"* he said, *"the failure to be the first in orbit is a national tragedy that has damaged American prestige around the globe."*

He conceded that mistakes are made wherever people live and strive.

"The right to make a mistake," he often said in conversations, *"in particular a mistake in judgment, is one of man's most important birthrights, at least in a free country."*

His presentation continued: *"None of the things we can learn from the Soviet success involve questions of a scientific or technological nature, or of project management. But we made some grave errors in judgment. We failed to recognize the tremendous psychological impact of an omnipresent artificial moon, visible to anyone with a pair of good eyes, and audible to anyone with a simple radio receiver."* He added that the United States also failed to correctly appraise the research and development capabilities of a country run by a totalitarian government.

Von Braun offered several suggestions for improvement of existing practices in research and development programs, such as a shortening of the time between conception of a project and its completion, or the handling of large-scale defense contracts. As an example of questionable management decisions, he mentioned that during the past twelve years, the government activated no less than 119 different guided missile contracts, *"and every one of them involved the expenditure not only of a substantial number of professional manhours for engineering analysis and design work, but to a considerable degree also shop time and testing."*

What other suggestions did von Braun offer?

"First and foremost, let's give more appreciation to the value of the team in modern research and development efforts! Successful R&D teams are the most valuable assets this country has in its continuous struggle for scientific and technological leadership; therefore, let's protect the integrity of those teams . . . , and I wish to include all our missile competitors in this plea . . ." One of the reasons, he said, why the significance of teams is often overlooked is because people tend to identify achievements only with individuals; actually, those individuals who get the publicity rarely deserve more than a fraction of the credit they receive. *"I myself am a case in point,"* von Braun added. *"There may be differences in the degree of ignorance among rocket engineers, but there simply is no such animal as a 'rocket genius.' Neither at the Army Ballistic Missile Agency, nor in the Navy, nor—mark my words!—in the Air Force."*

The most important lesson one should learn from Sputnik, in von Braun's mind, was that the Soviet Union had grasped the full significance of man's reach into space, while America had not. One should be prepared, von Braun warned, for a few more dramatic Soviet *"firsts"* in the new field of astronautics. For several years they have pursued a consistent, well-coordinated spaceflight program, supported with their extensive military rocket know-how and hardware. One certainly cannot say that the American public is not ready for spaceflight. The industry seems to be ready to accept it, too, and even some military leaders have expressed their belief in the great future and significance of manned spaceflight.

Why, then, is it that the Soviets have beaten us to the punch? von Braun asked. He offered an answer by reading from a report one of the American delegates to the International Astronautical Congress in Barcelona, Spain, had written after a long conversation with Professor Leonid Sedov, Soviet delegate to the congress, who had a strong personal hand in the Russian satellite project. That congress opened on the day of the Sputnik launch. Here are excerpts from this report:

"One thing we [in the Soviet Union] could never understand," Sedov said, *"is why you chose such a complicated, difficult, and really marginal design for your satellite vehicle. It was an entirely new development! And, furthermore, it had no growth potential. A little device of 20 pounds was all you could hope to launch . . . Why, for heaven's sake, didn't you take one of your powerful engines that you have been flight-testing for a considerable time now? They would be the right thing for your satellite project . . . We just could not understand why you did not choose this natural, straight-forward approach . . ."*

Later, the report said:

"We in Russia considered the satellite as a project of highest importance for our country, not only from the scientific angle, but from the political viewpoint. For us, it was a national concern of first order . . . we avoided any experimenting with novel designs as much as possible. We just could not understand why you did not do the same. You would have been in an excellent position, as far as that goes."

At no time in this revealing discussion did Professor Sedov make any reference that Sputnik was the product of the Soviet Army, Navy, or Air Force. When pressed for an answer, he proudly replied that it was just a plain Soviet satellite.

"The real tragedy of Sputnik's victory," von Braun wrote, *"is that this present situation was clearly foreseeable two years ago, when the separate U.S. satellite program was established."* But he ended his presentation with words of optimism: *"We*

have lost a battle, and we may lose a few more, but we have not yet lost the war. If we only remember that it is more important to get United States satellites up there, rather than Army, Navy, or Air Force satellites, we will soon be in good shape again."

Von Braun's *"Lessons of Sputnik"* paper reflects one of his typical traits, well known to his co-workers, but rarely recognized by those who knew him only from a distance. This was his relentless analytical dissection of a failure, and his constructive suggestions for a repair of the damage. There was no useless fault-finding and blaming, no breast-beating, no futile lamentation, no ashes on the head, only a sober assessment of the situation, a charting of new courses, a dropping of unnecessary ballast, an upbeat proposal for action, and then a plea for full speed ahead.

To his co-workers, von Braun said: *"The Russians have given us Americans a free lecture. We better put it to good use!"*

3   EXPLORER 1 COMES TO LIFE

Did anybody heed the lessons of Sputnik? Did von Braun's words, concise, and determined, contribute to the government's decision to let the Army-JPL satellite project go ahead? The answer may never be known. It is safe to assume, though, that Secretary of the Army Brucker and Army Chief of Staff General Taylor, to whom the presentation was given, subscribed fully to von Braun's words, and that they were as anxious as the people at Redstone Arsenal and at JPL to see the U.S. Army's satellite launched.

October came to its end, but no word arrived from Washington. As time went by, there were more painful delays of Vanguard, and more critical comments and accusations through the news media. On 3 November 1957, the Soviets launched their second Sputnik, a capsule of 1,120 pounds (504 kg) with the dog Laika onboard. Again a public outcry, and again a glimmer of hope at Redstone and JPL that the red stoplight hanging over their Orbiter Project might now turn green. Finally, several days later, Secretary of Defense McElroy received authorization from President Eisenhower to go ahead with the Army's satellite project. The papers picked up the good news first and reported that the Department of the Army had been directed *"to proceed with the launching of an Earth satellite, using a modified Jupiter C . . ."* However, ABMA and JPL members rejoiced too soon. The official order to General Medaris, arriving after the newspaper publication, read differently. Medaris showed it to his people at ABMA: Prepare a satellite, it said, but don't plan to launch it until you receive the actual go-ahead signal . . .

This was an uncertain trumpet sound that Medaris was not willing to accept as a directive. *"Either give me a clear-cut order to launch a satellite, or I'll quit,"* he wired to General Gavin, the Army's chief of Research and Development. Von Braun as well as Pickering at JPL also offered their resignations in preference to such a wishy-washy assignment.

That did it. The clear order came on 8 November, permitting ABMA and JPL to shift into high gear. Arrangements were made immediately with Van Allen to incorporate his instrumentation into the satellite's payload capsule. He had begun to prepare a cosmic ray experiment for the Vanguard satellite as early as 1956. Two years before that, as described in Chapter 6-1, he had asked the von Braun group to keep him posted on the project's progress. He received the progress reports, and when the modified Jupiter C project finally got the green light, he was ready with an instrument that *"just happened"* to fit also into the satellite's payload shell. In his typically modest way, Van Allen would later remark: *"When I built my little instrument for Vanguard, I thought it wise to prepare it in such a way that it would fit Vanguard as well as Jupiter C, so that I would be prepared in either case . . ."*

Members of the Army Ballistic Missile Agency and the Jet Propulsion Laboratory had worked closely together during 1955 and 1956 while the Jupiter C vehicle was being readied for nose cone reentry testing. It had been JPL's responsibility to build and test the scaled-down Sergeant rockets that the ABMA people would then integrate into their *"spinning tub"* on top of the Redstone rocket. Now, JPL's part of the joint Orbiter project would be more involved; the Laboratory would be responsible for the Microlock communication system, for part of the onboard instrumentation, for much of the tracking and ground station systems, for the ignition of the second and third Sergeant stages, for the integration of Van Allen's Geiger counters into the data system, and for other components of the project. Von Braun named Robert E. Lindstrom as ABMA's project engineer for the Orbiter project, an experienced and very energetic technical manager of previous projects. As compared to the ninety-day Orbiter crash program that started on 8 November 1957, the earlier joint reentry project had progressed at a leisurely pace. At that time, the inherent differences in the structure and work style of the JPL and the ABMA organizations had little impact on the conduct of the project. Each of them had proceeded in its own way according to its own traditions. The working relationship was such that ABMA's liaison engineer for the project, Rudolf H. Schlidt, did not encounter any significant problems beyond the normal interface activities.

Now, as pressure built up under the extremely tight time schedule, opinions and desires expressed by the two organizations sometimes went in different directions. In the ABMA organization, responsibilities and assignments were defined very clearly; complete visibility was one of ABMA's natural trademarks. JPL, a government-owned, contractor-operated facility, enjoyed the stability of a federal entity, and at the same time the freedom and intellectual independence of an academic institution. After all, it was run by the prestigious California Institute of Technology. Salaries at JPL were approximately twice as high as at ABMA for comparable positions. Dr. Homer E. Newell, former NASA Associate Administrator for Science, vividly described in his book *Beyond the Atmosphere* [1-4] the specific traits of JPL that set it aside from all other NASA field centers. Most conspicuous among these, Newell said, was *"an unbound quest for independence, coupled with a remarkable superiority complex."*

In spite of such different characteristics, cooperation between JPL and ABMA in the joint satellite project was completely successful. Lindstrom effectively coordinated JPL's and ABMA's activities. Work on the project proceeded on schedule, in spite of occasional rough spots, and even times of tension and disagreement. Hearing of such cases, von Braun would talk turkey to his people: *"Are you grown men, or young schoolboys? Is your precious little ego more important to you than a satellite in orbit? Now, you go back and work out your differences. If you can't, I will replace you on this project!"*

At one occasion, von Braun and several of his associates flew out to California in ABMA's Gulfstream to discuss a certain problem that had come up in the joint work. The associates did not want to accept a particular proposal made by their JPL colleagues, being convinced that its only purpose was to satisfy tender egos. On the way out to California, they suggested that von Braun should politely, but firmly decline to accept the JPL proposal. Typically, von Braun tensed. *"Absolutely not,"* he decided. *"We have a job to do, and we will do it together. We will discuss your point with the JPL people, but we will accept their proposal. If you fellows feel that you cannot go along with this, I'll tell the pilot to turn around in midair and fly back to Huntsville."* The trip continued, of course, and JPL got its way.

Members of ABMA were not the only ones who were willing to yield to JPL's wishes.

Dr. T. Keith Glennan, NASA administrator from 1958 till 1960, wrote many years later [6-11]: *"I think that JPL was the beneficiary of tolerance by NASA peers . . ."*

Despite JPL's assertive and independent nature, the relationship between ABMA and JPL was productive. In general, the joint work proceeded very well, and there were always occasions for joint joking and merrymaking. Without doubt, a number of highly talented engineers and scientists were at work at JPL who spontaneously gave their very best when the joint ABMA-JPL satellite project came to life. John (Johnny) Small and Manfred (Fred) Eimer built and tested the cluster of Sergeant rockets. Eberhardt Rechtin substituted a very sensitive and reliable Microlock radio tracking system for the previously planned Minitrack system that had been developed by the Navy. Albert R. (Al) Hibbs worked on trajectory and celestial mechanics problems. Jack E. Froelich acted as JPL's project manager for the joint satellite project. Homer Joe Stewart, the physicist, gave his support wherever needed. William H. Pickering, who remained a scientist at heart throughout his twenty-two years in the top position of the laboratory, insisted that no American satellite should be launched without scientific instruments onboard, a principle that was deeply appreciated by a number of von Braun's associates. Pickering was elated to learn that Van Allen was ready with a Geiger counter package which would fit into the capsule of the Redstone satellite. As a former cosmic ray physicist, Pickering had been in contact with Van Allen for years.

A somewhat bitter pill was waiting for von Braun and his co-workers when the brief implementation period for the Army's satellite began. Josef Boehm, laboring for years in his design office, and also during his spare time, to design the satellite capsule, expected that it would now be built quickly. But his JPL colleagues had different plans. During a visit to ABMA, Pickering had a private discussion with Medaris. Afterwards, von Braun was told to forget about the Boehm design; JPL would build the capsule. Von Braun swallowed hard, but did not comment. Boehm and his co-workers swallowed even harder.

Pickering recalled this particular event in 1986 [6-12]: *"Medaris had a big meeting on 9 November [1957] with about twenty people, including Stewart, Froelich, and myself. At that meeting, he announced that JPL would be involved [with the satellite design]. I think that came as quite a shock to the Germans . . . we could sense the reaction. But we worked very well together, right up to the launching."*

Medaris always had a soft spot in his heart for JPL. The von Braun team belonged to him simply because it was part of the army, and he was commanding general. JPL, in contrast, was a civilian academic organization. He realized that only the human relations bond, strengthened by considerable generosity on his part, would assure JPL's loyalty to a military organization.

For both ABMA and JPL, the go-ahead signal for their satellite marked the beginning of an extremely busy work program. The same was true for Van Allen and his co-workers in Iowa City, among them Leslie H. Meredith, Carl E. McIlwain, George H. Ludwig, and G. H. Ray. They had built and tested their Geiger counter package for the measurement of cosmic rays on the basis of Van Allen's long-time experience in flight projects; the JPL colleagues insisted that it underwent some rebuilding procedures at their laboratory.

At ABMA, the Jupiter C rocket that was waiting in long-time storage under the code name *"Missile #29"* had to be fitted with an attitude control system that would slowly turn the separated forward section into an exactly horizontal position while it coasted upward on its steep trajectory. The apex predictor, determining the exact moment near the apex of the ballistic path when the first of the three Sergeant stages would have to fire, was to be completed, tested, and integrated into the launch operations system at the launch site in Florida. Finally, all the tracking and telemetry stations along the expected path of the satellite had to be coordinated and alerted for the launching.

Besides ABMA, JPL, and Van Allen, several contractors of ABMA were deeply and decisively involved in the satellite project, among them the Chrysler Corporation in Detroit and Huntsville, and the Ford Instrument Company in New York. To the amazement of some outsiders, there was never anything like a *"roles and missions"* document that would have spelled out what each member of this big and complex family was supposed to do. There was a job to be accomplished, and everyone pitched in with his best ability.

On 6 December 1957, Vanguard was ready for launch, the first time with all three stages active. The booster stage ignited, but after a few seconds it was one big cataclysm of fire and smoke.

Work on the Army-JPL satellite continued at a fast pace. The Jupiter C rocket, in its four-stage configuration often called Juno I, was assembled in ABMA's Fabrication Laboratory, and then transported to Cape Canaveral in Florida by a C-124 airplane. On 17 January 1958 it was hoisted into vertical position on Launch Pad 26A. Takeoff was planned for 29 January. There were only few days available for launch, because the firing range was needed for other launches, mostly from the Air Force. The Vanguard group was also preparing for another launch early in February, and that launch would take priority over an Army launch. Tension among the ABMA and JPL people was considerable, and it even mounted when the weather outlook turned out to be bad, threatening a delay in the otherwise normal countdown proceedings.

Medaris joined the people at the Cape; von Braun, Pickering, and Van Allen were directed to stay in a room at the Pentagon, equipped with communication channels to the Cape and to Goldstone Station, JPL's big tracking and radio communication center in California. With them were a number of high-ranking Army officials. The evening before launch, Kurt H. Debus, director of the rocket launch center at Cape Canaveral, made the round once again to see that all hands were prepared to carry out their functions before, during, and after the launch. Looking at the little apex predicter that had been set up in an extra room in one of the big hangars with direct telephone lines to radar, Doppler, telemetry, and launch stations, he remarked: *"Do you really want to rely upon this mechanical system alone to give the ignition signal for the upper stage? I would definitely use a hand-operated push button in parallel to this system, and push the button at the moment when you see that the automatic contact is to occur!"*— *"Sir,"* was the answer, *"this is exactly what I'm prepared to do. Here is the push button, and I will push it at the right moment!"*—*"That's good,"* Debus said. *"Good luck!"*

As the hour of launch approached, the weather turned worse. Strong winds were reported at high altitudes, resulting in possible shear forces across the rocket that might be too powerful for the rocket's control system to handle. Medaris wisely cancelled the flight for the day. The next day brought a repeat performance. The following day, 31 January, things looked a little better. The weatherman predicted lower wind forces, and Medaris decided to go ahead.

The Jupiter C (Juno I) rocket looked beautiful as it stood erect and alone on its launch pad, glistening against the black sky in the bright searchlight beams. Beginning a few minutes before scheduled launch, the cluster tub on top of the rocket was spinning fast, with the little satellite—6 inches (15 cm) in diameter and about 4 feet (1.20 m) long—pointing straight up toward outer space. From there on, everything worked like a charm. The big booster engine ignited at 22:55, the rocket rose majestically out of a sea of fire, climbing first slowly, and then faster and faster into the night sky where it soon disappeared behind the clouds. Tracking and telemetry data on the big viewing screens showed that the rocket followed exactly its predetermined path. The signals from radar, Doppler, and telemetry arrived, the apex predicter, including the hand-operated backup button, worked, the three upper stages ignited in sequence as planned—and then, everything was silent. It did not take long, though, before signals were received at the first downrange station in the Bahamas, indicating that obviously the satellite was on its correct course.

Among those who had support functions during the launching were Al Hibbs from JPL and Fridtjof A. (Fred) Speer from Huntsville. In a joint effort, they had prepared charts allowing them to make a first estimate of the orbital parameters of the satellite as soon as the travel time between cluster ignition and Antigua overflight was known. While they were frantically working their charts, Medaris wanted to know: *"How long will it stay in orbit?"*—*"Well"*, Hibbs answered, *"when you allow a certain inaccuracy in the first reading, and then consider a slight deviation in direction, you probably could tentatively estimate . . ."* Here, Medaris' patience had run out. *"Keep all that stuff for yourself and tell me how many years, but quick!"* Hibbs promptly replied: *"Ten years, Sir!"* He was surprisingly close; Explorer 1 spent a little over twelve years in orbit.

Medaris and many of the people who had been involved in the launching then moved a few miles south to Patrick Air Force Base. A number of reporters and other guests had been invited to gather at a communication center on the base that was in contact with the Goldstone station and with the Pentagon where von Braun, Pickering, and Van Allen were waiting.

It would take about 90 minutes, counting from the moment of lift-off, before a signal could be expected at Goldstone. For many who were waiting, those 90 minutes may have been the longest ever in their lives. Would the satellite have obtained the right velocity to achieve an orbit trajectory? Would it have been accelerated in the right direction? Would it really follow Newton's law and arrive over the coastline of California? Would the Microlock system work? Would the telemeter work? As the critical time came closer, Medaris—contrary to his normal composure—became tense, then restless, then nervous. He called Pickering in Washington: *"Do you hear anything?"*— *"No, not yet, Sir,"* was the answer. Two minutes later, Medaris called again: *"Bill, do you hear anything?"*— *"No, Bruce, not yet."*—Two minutes later: *"Bill, why in the hell don't you hear anything?"*— *"Well, Sir, there just ain't anything to hear!"* Medaris then paced the room, looking alternately at his watch and at a clock in the room. There was dead silence, but the air was thick with tension and suspense. At about that time, a young scientist from ABMA, Chuck Lundquist, stormed into the room. With his arms waving wildly, he shouted: *"Goldstone has the signal! It's in orbit!"*

After that, a torrent of noise broke loose in the briefing room, everybody congratulating everybody. Von Braun, in Washington, looked at his watch: *"It is several minutes late,"* he said. *"It must be in a relatively high orbit. It will have a long lifetime."* A little later, when he talked to reporters, he spoke more prophetically: *"We have firmly established our foothold in space. We will never give it up again."*

That night, there was dancing in the streets of Huntsville, and jubilation all over the country.

Shortly after the little satellite had settled in its orbit, President Eisenhower gave it the official name Explorer 1. Its orbital altitude was 223 miles (357 km) at perigee and 1580 miles (2566 km) at apogee, with an orbital period of 113.2 minutes. It remained in orbit for 12.3 years.

Explorer 1 carried Van Allen's Geiger counters, and also micrometeoroid and temperature sensors. The Geiger counters discovered the first indications of high-intensity radiation belts around the Earth that subsequently became known as Van Allen radiation belts.

Van Allen met Stuhlinger shortly after the Explorer success. *"Do you remember that evening in Princeton, three and a half years ago?"* he asked. *"I was sitting in my corner, listening to you through my screen of smoke, and I said to myself: Either, these guys are crooks. Or, if they are not, they have something absolutely fantastic on their minds, and even on their hands. At that time, I did not know the correct answer. Now, I do!"*

The papers published a photograph taken during a press conference the day after the Explorer triumph; it showed three happy men with an Explorer replica over their heads. When Van Allen saw the picture, he remarked: *"Wernher, as usual, carries the brunt of the load!"*

A delightful story that happened in the aftermath of the Explorer launching was told by Pickering [6-12]:

"There was this Eisenhower dinner at the White House [on February 4, 1958], commemorating the Explorer success . . . [The President] decided there should be some joint sessions with the military and the scientists, and [Wernher and I] were brought in almost at the last minute. We were both staying at the Dupont-Plaza . . . Wernher called up my room while he was dressing for dinner and asked: 'Have you got a spare white tie? . . . You see, I have rented this suit, and there is no white tie!' . . . Well, I also had rented a suit, and of course I didn't have a spare white tie . . . Later, he called back, saying that surely the White House ought to be able to handle this problem, so let's go. We went to the White House . . . and explained to the guard our dilemma. The guard said 'No problem', and by the time we reached the portico, someone grabbed Wernher, took him off to the side for about ten seconds, and there he came back with a white tie on!"

"The dinner was arranged so that we were seated military-science, military-science . . . Maria von Braun ended up next to General LeMay! LeMay, his usual grumpy self, said hardly a word to Maria, except to state once that he wished he would be home in bed. Poor Maria. And Wernher was next to Mrs. LeMay, and both of them were talking a blue streak . . . Eisenhower did not have much to say. He arrived late, and he apologized for two things, first, for being late, and second, for wearing a black tie. 'We looked all over the White House,' he said, 'but we could not find my white tie '"

Personal relations between von Braun and Pickering, and all other members of the JPL with whom von Braun had contact, were always very easy-going and pleasant. They remained so for more than twenty years after the von Braun team and JPL had started their first joint project. However, this first project, Jupiter C/Juno I and the Explorer satellite, remained the only project that the two teams carried out together.

There were several opportunities for further cooperative projects in which the specific skills and experiences of the two groups could have complemented each other ideally. Potential joint activities included planetary missions with the Saturn I and Saturn IB launch vehicles, and also an early space station carried into orbit by the giant Saturn V. Missions to planets, to planetary moons, to asteroids, and to comets with electric propulsion systems might also have been pursued jointly. But neither von Braun nor Pickering made any attempts to bring one of these potential projects to life as a joint enterprise. Von Braun's reason was probably that in 1958, he had already taken his first steps toward the manned Moon mission, a project that, as he correctly anticipated, would completely absorb him and his team during the forthcoming ten-year period.

Immediately after the success of Explorers 1, a flood of congratulatory messages from all over the world reached Medaris, von Braun, Pickering, Van Allen, and also the crews and the companies that had contributed to the project. Perhaps the most noteworthy among all the congratulations was a telegram from the man who had masterminded the big bombing raid on Peenemünde in August 1943, and who had specifically designated as prime target the housing area where the civilian scientists and engineers lived: Duncan Sandys, Junior Minister in Britain's War Office, and son-in-law of Winston Churchill. Von Braun showed the telegram to his associates:

"To Dr. Wernher von Braun through Department of State, Washington D.C. Please accept my warmest congratulations on your great achievement which has thrilled and delighted us here in Britain. You and I had some differences in the war. I am so glad that we are now working together for the same cause. I hope we may meet personally one day. Best wishes, Duncan Sandys."

CHAPTER 7

DAWN OF THE SPACE AGE

1   VEHICLES FOR SPACE

When did the space age begin? The best answer may be 4 October 1957, the day when Sputnik I reached its orbit. During its first four years, from late 1957 to the end of 1961, 78 satellites were put in orbit, 63 by the United States and 15 by the Soviet Union. Two U.S. astronauts were launched through ballistic trajectories, two Soviet cosmonauts orbited the Earth, four unmanned probes flew towards the Moon, two of them settled in orbits around the Sun.

In the United States, Explorer 1 was followed a few weeks later by Explorer 2, again built and launched by the joint Huntsville-JPL-Van Allen teams. Takeoff was normal. The cluster of solid-propellant rockets received its ignition signal from the apex predicter at the correct moment; Sergeant stages 1 and 2 fired properly, but the third stage, to be ignited by an automatic signal after burnout of stage 2, did not fire. Orbital velocity was not reached by the payload, and Explorer 2 found an early grave in the Atlantic. Explorers 3 and 4, launched on 26 March and 26 June 1958, were completely successful. The Vanguard project, too, finally met with at least some success. After another heartbreaking failure on 6 December 1957, a small Vanguard satellite, weighing 3.25 pounds (1.5 kg), reached orbit on 17 March 1958. Precision tracking of this satellite from ground stations provided data for a refined determination of the Earth's shape; it was found that the Northern Hemisphere is a little more *"slender"* than the southern hemisphere. A second Vanguard satellite of 22 pounds (9.8 kg) was successfully put in orbit on 17 February 1959, and a third one a few months later.

A detailed report on the Explorer satellites launched during 1958, entitled *"The Explorers"* [7-1], was written by von Braun in 1959 and presented at the Ninth International Astronautical Congress in Amsterdam.

Von Braun first expressed the deep appreciation of scientists all over the world for the International Geophysical Year organization under whose auspices the satellite projects had come to life, and which *"has rendered mankind such convincing and heartening proof that even in times of tension and crises the world's scientific community can work together for the mutual good."* Congratulating the Soviet colleagues for their recent achievements in space, he said: *"We all appreciate the derivative values of competition that can be extremely beneficial in wholly peaceful scientific endeavors . . ."*

Von Braun then described the Redstone rocket and its Jupiter C and Juno I modifications for reentry nose cone and satellite firings; the successful cooperation between ABMA, JPL, and Van Allen's Iowa group on the one hand and the Air Force Cambridge Research Center and other agencies on the other—including the Navy's Project Vanguard (which helped out with tracking and data acquisition and reduction).

The discovery of the giant radiation belts around the Earth by Explorer 1 came as a big surprise. *"You may recall,"* von Braun said, *"that the diameter of the Explorer satellite cylinder is only six inches (15 cm). The total weight of the instrumentation performing all three experiments on Explorer 1 was a mere 10.83 pounds (4.9 kg). It was from this inauspicious springboard that a major scientific discovery in physics developed . . ."*

The satellite's radiation counts, as expected, showed 30 to 40 particles per second at altitudes of 200 to 300 miles (320 to 480 km). At higher altitudes, which the satellite reached because of its elliptical orbit, the radiation count increased, first slowly, then rapidly, and finally climbed to more than 35,000 counts per second. This was about the limit of what the counters and the recording instruments could accept; the actual number of counts must have been even higher.

Explorer 1 permitted the collection of data only while it was in direct line of sight with at least one of the few receiving stations on the ground.

"In order to achieve a more complete data gathering," von Braun wrote, *"Explorer 3 was equipped with a tape recorder that stored information acquired throughout the entire orbit. It reported this information on command when the satellite passed over a . . . receiving station . . ."*

Only a small portion of the recorded rays could have high energies that would classify them as cosmic rays; most of them appeared to be low-energy electrons or protons.

"The instrumentation on Explorers 4 and 5," von Braun continued, *"was designed to investigate this exciting radiation phenomenon more closely. To permit the maximum exploitation of our relatively small carrier, the micrometeoroid and temperature gages carried on Explorers 1 and 3 were eliminated. Even the tape recorder [used] on Explorer 3 was sacrificed."*

Weight savings in the upper two stages of the launch vehicle, and the use of more powerful propellants, resulted in a total satellite instrumentation weight of 18.26 pounds (8.3 kg) on Explorers 4 and 5. All instruments served one purpose: To determine the energy spectrum of the radiation. It was found that two separate, huge regions of very dense radiation surround the Earth like belts. The particles are held captive by the Earth's magnetic field, while they oscillate constantly between southern and northern latitudes.

"The satellite instrumentation for Explorers 4 and 5," von Braun wrote, *"was designed, built, assembled, and tested under the supervision of Joseph Boehm at the Army Ballistic Missile Agency in Huntsville. Van Allen's institute again furnished the counters. For telemetry, we used JPL's proven Microlock system."*

Von Braun's essay also described all essential technical components of the Jupiter C (Juno I) vehicle that launched the first Explorer satellites. The spinning tub, carrying the upper stages, was one of the subsystems that was developed for the earlier nosecone reentry test flights with two upper stages; it was then used for the satellite launchings with three upper stages. Referring to a picture of the Juno I rocket, von Braun wrote: *"Rockets for the first and second upper stage are hidden within the tub, while the third stage with the satellite as payload appears at the top. The tub is an empty aluminum cylinder . . . The third stage, however, is mounted atop the second stage in a conical holder attached to the forward end of the second stage. The satellite payload is mounted at the top of the third stage . . ."*

Two heavy ball bearings, mounted in the nonrotating support structure of the nose section, support the spinning tub. Two electric motors provide the spin-up power; they drive the tub over two sprocket rubber belts.

Shortly before launching, the motors are energized, driving the tub at 550 revolutions per minute. The rocket takes off while that speed is maintained. About 70 seconds after takeoff, a governor controlled by a tape programmer on board the rocket changes the governor setting so that the spin rate slowly increases up to 650 rpm. At 115 seconds after takeoff, it rises to 750 rpm.

This procedure of slowly increasing the spin rate was necessary to avoid resonance between the spin frequency of the tub and the bending frequency of the booster. The latter increases as propellants are consumed.

"In summary," von Braun concluded his presentation at the Amsterdam space congress, *"we think that with our Explorer satellites we have made a valuable contribution to man's knowledge and scientific comprehension of the airless spaces surrounding the Earth . . . This past year has brought mankind closer to the stars, and it has made all of us alarmingly aware of the fact that we must learn to peacefully live and strive together on our own Earth. For this little planet, which people once called 'the world,' and which our satellites now circle in 90 minutes, has become too small for war and strife."*

Building and launching the first U.S. satellite, and working closely with JPL and the Van Allen group on a project that combined scientific objectives, advanced technologies, and the challenges of pioneering exploration in an ideal way, was a matter of utmost delight for von Braun. His presentation to the Amsterdam congress reflects this feeling. However, he permitted himself such extravagances only rarely. Before the year 1958 came to a close, he devoted his time again to other subjects that he considered of decisive importance for a continuing evolution of the fledgling space age. Typical for him, he worked simultaneously on different fronts: Talk to the people, talk to colleagues, talk to the high and mighty, work out and present well-organized plans for an evolving program, and, perhaps most important, initiate technical developments of those basic components which stand out as long-leadtime items in the new projects.

President Eisenhower established the National Aeronautics and Space Administration (NASA) in the summer of 1958; it was created from the National Advisory Committee for Aeronautics (NACA) that had been in existence since 1915. The President appointed Dr. T. Keith Glennan as administrator of the new organization. Dr. Hugh L. Dryden, for many years the director of NACA, became deputy administrator of NASA. The Jet Propulsion Laboratory joined NASA soon after its establishment; von Braun's Development Operations Division at ABMA would become a member of NASA two years later, in 1960.

On 15 December 1958, von Braun gave a presentation to NASA officials, entitled *"Present and Future Space Vehicles and their Capabilities"* [7-2]. In his presentation, he divided space projects into two categories: military and civilian. Civilian projects, he said, will be either scientific or commercial in nature. He predicted intense scientific programs throughout the solar system, paralleled by commercial activities in near-Earth space, but also on the Moon. He had no doubt that there will be human presence in space before long.

Von Braun foresaw six classes of space launch vehicles, representing six different levels of payloads for low Earth orbits if combined with proper upper stages. These were:

Class	Launch Vehicles	Payload range, lb
1	Scout, Vanguard, Redstone	3 to 100
2	Jupiter, Thor	100 to 1,000
3	Atlas, Titan	1,000 to 10,000
4	Juno IV (future Saturn I and IB)	20,000 to 50,000
5	Juno V (future Saturn V)	150,000 to 250,000
6	Nuclear-thermal (uncertain configuration)	not determined

Von Braun proposed a cluster of 1.5 million lb (675,000 kg) thrust single-barrel engines for class 5 launch vehicles with the argument that it would be the logical next step, simply because such an engine could not be flight-certified before it had gone through a test period of three to five years. *"At that time,"* he said, *"we would not be satisfied with a mere doubling of the thrust level we already have in use today."*

Ideas of using a nuclear reactor to heat up hydrogen and produce rocket thrust were not new. About half a year after Hahn and Strassmann had discovered the fission of uranium nuclei in December 1938, Krafft Ehricke, at that time a member of von Braun's rocket group in Peenemünde, made a study of nuclear rocket engines. Around 1942, von Braun conferred with Heisenberg in Berlin on possibilities of using nuclear power for rocket propulsion (Chapter 1-3).

Two British authors, Leslie R. Shepherd and A. Val Cleaver, published results of a study *"The Atomic Rocket"* [7-3] in 1948 and 1949. More papers followed, and around 1954 the Rover program for the development of nuclear propulsion for airplanes and rockets was initiated in the United States. A few years later, the Kiwi project got under way with static tests in 1959 at the Jackass Flats, Nevada test area, followed in 1961 by testing of the NERVA (Nuclear Engine for Rocket Vehicle Application). NERVA engines developed 760 seconds specific impulse and 50,000 lb (23,000 kg) thrust beginning in 1964. In June 1968, a nuclear rocket engine was tested at 4,000 megawatts and about 200,000 lb (90,000 kg) thrust. The highest specific impulse registered during the program was 850 seconds.

The technical accomplishments in these projects were impressive; however, problems arising with the application of nuclear reactors working at power levels of 2 to 5 million kilowatts onboard rockets—particularly manned rockets—were no less impressive. Also, there was the rising public resistance against nuclear engines operating on or near the Earth's surface. On top of these problems, there was the sober fact that the specific impulse obtained at that time was not high enough to make the nuclear rocket competitive with modern chemical rockets.

While he expressed the doubts of the conscientious engineer who always keeps the total picture of his proposed project in mind, he still included nuclear rockets in his proposed future rocket program, simply because a rocket with the alleged high specific impulse would result in very impressive payload capabilities. However, he always added his caveats when he mentioned nuclear rockets, and he showed that the projects he proposed could also be achieved with all-chemical propulsion, although with less payload, or with longer flight times.

The United States discontinued its nuclear heat-exchange type (*"nuclear thermal"*) rocket program on 5 January 1973, but studies and some development work on nuclear rocket motors were resumed fifteen years later.

Von Braun wrote his space vehicle essay at a time when only the first Sputniks, Explorers, and Vanguards had been launched. And yet, even at that time, he had the evolutionary line of projects clearly staked out in his mind. Real developments during the ensuing years followed his predictions with surprising fidelity: satellites from 1958 on; lunar flybys from 1959 on; Atlas-launched satellites and lunar probes from 1960 on; manned space flights from 1961 on; Juno IV class rockets (Saturn I and IB) from 1961 on; television satellites from 1962 on; Titan-based orbital and planetary spacecraft from 1965 on; manned lunar expeditions with the giant Juno V rocket, Saturn V, from 1969 on; America's first space station, Skylab, in 1973; and, at a slower pace, the first Earth-to-orbit roundtrip vehicle, the shuttle, from 1981 on—all of them within twenty-three years after von Braun had written his report.

One of von Braun's predictions did not come true: his expectation that the family of powerful Saturn launch vehicles, Saturn I, IB, and V, would become the mainstay in the U.S. program of heavy space launchers *"for this generation of spacefarers."* A total of 32 members of the Saturn launch vehicle series were erected for firing at Cape Canaveral. Though all took off without incident, some developed technical problems during flight—sloshing of propellant in their tanks, lengthwise oscillations ("Pogo") in the propellant feed system, and a broken hydrogen pipe. Fortunately, the causes of these malfunctions were detected and eliminated. By the time the Saturn-Apollo missions had been completed, Saturns had achieved a 100 percent success rate. In spite of this impressive performance record, NASA cancelled the Saturn production program in the early 1970s (7-4).

2   EDUCATION IN THE POST-SPUTNIK ERA

Thirty-seven years after Sputnik, it may be difficult to understand the shockwave that the sudden appearance of the little satellite sent through the Western world. Emotions, even fears ran high. How could it happen that the great United States was pushed into second place? What imminent dangers to the free world would accrue from this demonstration of superiority by the Soviets? After all, it was the time of the cold war.

For months, Americans asked: What should we, what can we do to regain our leading position among nations, in the perception of the public as well as in international relations?

Proposing a course of action for the American space program was one of the contributions von Braun offered. He felt, though, that talking to technically-oriented space planners would not be enough. During the summer of 1958, he wrote a paper, *"The Acid Test"* [7-5], in which he suggested how we should react to this defeat, and what we might do to climb back to first place among the modern high-technology nations.

"The acid test of men and nations is the measure of their courage and resourcefulness in the face of adversity and peril . . . ," he wrote. *"Our country has faced agonizing tests more than once during its relatively short history. It emerged each time from the crucible not without scars, but with greater confidence and richer maturity . . ."*

The Sputnik shock created an air of doubt in the American people. *"Overnight,"* von Braun said, *"it became popular to question the bulwarks of our society: our public educational system, our industrial strength, our foreign affairs approaches, our economic policies, our defense strategy and forces, the capabilities of our science and modern technology. Even the moral fiber of our people came under searching scrutiny . . ."*

Understandably, the most immediate reaction was the fear among Americans of a military attack on their country.

"Actions have been taken by the Defense Department, fully supported by the Congress, aimed at achieving operational capabilities with intermediate and intercontinental ballistic missiles at the earliest practicable date," von Braun wrote, but he emphasized that *"the Soviet challenge is by no means restricted to military technology . . . It will not be enough to perfect weapon systems that have at least equal capabilities with those of a potential aggressor . . . The real peril lies in the enormous momentum the Soviets have built up that certainly will yield other dramatic by-products along the way. They have . . . embarked upon a dynamic program to achieve supremacy in science and technology . . . , turning out competent scientists and engineers in greater*

numbers than ours. It is upon this broad foundation that the Russians are waging their effort, and not upon the gleanings of the brain-picking of some captive foreign scientists, as many people in this country still seem to believe. Clearly, we must accelerate our effort at a rate calculated to overtake and surpass the Russian advantage . . ."

"Our educational offerings," von Braun urged, *"must come under scrutiny since it is tomorrow's generation that will have to cope with the problems developing today. If our young people's preparation is to be compatible with the kind of world they will inhabit, they must be taught basic and essential knowledge at the earliest practicable age—in the elementary schools . . . They must understand mathematics and the physical sciences, which means that we need more and better teachers, and expanded offerings in scope as well as in number. Higher salaries, improved professional status, and more adequate classroom and laboratory facilities are essential if we wish to obtain the kind of inspirational leadership that can interest and stimulate young minds. I do not believe that the Federal Government will or should attempt to dictate such a program, but it should establish generally recognized educational standards, and it should assist in a pump-priming role in the public schools, and also in our colleges and universities. Education in a democracy is the concern of every citizen. The people must insist upon a redirection of emphasis; they should willingly accept their just measure of responsibility for the execution of our educational programs. To all who ask: 'What can I do to help?' my answer is: 'Take active interest in what is being taught, how it is being taught, and by whom'."*

Von Braun wrote his *"Acid Test"* essay in 1958 when the fear of the Soviet military might was at its peak. Now, thirty-seven years later, that fear has disappeared. Instead, we are living under the threat of a *"war of economies,"* with unforeseeable outcome. Had von Braun to write an essay today, he would take the present economic dangers as seriously as he took the military dangers in 1958. Some of his suggested actions would be different today, but his prime argument would be still the same: We need a better educational system!

These words were among the spontaneous public outcries, perhaps the loudest, that followed the unexpected launching of Sputnik. Indeed, statistical figures, eagerly published by the news media, showed that the Soviet school children achieved much better scores in mathematics and science than American youngsters, and that the universities in the Soviet Union graduated more engineers and scientists annually than their counterparts in the United States.

Education had always been a favorite theme for von Braun. He loved to present his ideas whenever an opportunity arose: in private talks, at debating sessions during parent-teacher meetings, in public presentations, by answering questions posed in letters or after speeches. He praised the desire to learn and to know as one of the most distinguished features of human beings.

Invited by the Elliott Committee on Education and Labor to present a statement on education in the post-Sputnik era to the House of Representatives in Washington, D.C., he gave a presentation to that committee on 14 March 1958 [7-6].

At the time of this presentation, modern defense weapons were one of the centerpoints of public debates. Von Braun strongly warned against the trend to consider the existence of these weapons alone as an assurance for the continuation of a secure existence as nation number one, particularly at a time when the technological revolution was sweeping over vast parts of the Earth. To maintain that position among the nations, he considered it mandatory that the United States increase the number of scientific and technical personnel graduating from its schools, and that it offer the highest possible quality of education to students during their formative years.

The federal government, he argued, provides financial assistance to many worthy causes—foreign nations, farmers, ailing industries, the highway system—we should not overlook the most important of them all, the minds of our children. *"If we fail here,"* he said, *"we fail them and ourselves."*

Von Braun offered several thoughts concerning education in the United States:

". . . it is vital that the input of trained manpower in government, industry, research institutions, colleges, public classrooms, and the armed forces will be of sufficient quantity and quality to meet the requirements of the Technical Revolution that we are currently experiencing . . ."

". . . we must recruit more young people into scientific and technical careers . . ."

". . . we must make these careers more attractive to induce more young people to select them . . ."

". . . this involves inspiration, at home as well as in school . . ."

"Our chief reliance must be placed upon the quality of our effort, and the quality of its product," he said, and he warned against the tendency to measure the value of a program in terms of numbers of students, numbers of fellowships, numbers of teachers or numbers of any other factor.

Most important, von Braun felt, is the need to bring parents to understand the impact of science and technology upon this and succeeding generations. *"Once that has been achieved,"* he said, *"parental influence will be felt where it can be of greatest value—in the home, and in the community that governs the schools."*

Von Braun followed the schooling of his own three children with great interest. Not only did he keep track of what they were learning, he also made an effort to supplement what their schools offered by explaining to them details of his own work, plus physics, astronomy, and particularly geography and history, areas of great interest and knowledge for him. In some subjects that had not yet been well developed when he was in school, such as biochemistry and genetics, he read his daughters' schoolbooks, trying to close the gaps existing in his own educational background. He often attended the parent-teacher meetings at his children's schools, and he did not hesitate to speak up at such meetings. *"The most valuable gift we can give a child,"* he used to say, *"is a careful education. This is where society has a prime obligation. To waste the time that a child has to acquire knowledge is an outright sin . . ."*

For him, the time to acquire knowledge never came to an end. During his last weeks in the hospital, he still read book after book, as much as his waning powers would permit.

"Among the many thousands of people whom I met in my life," he said at the time when his illness began to cast its shadows over him, *"there was hardly one who did not know much more than I in at least one field, be it world history, or supersonic aerodynamics, or fly-casting for trout, or celestial mechanics, or repairing an automobile, or searching for black holes, or operating a computer, or welding the tank of a rocket, or flying an airplane, or removing an appendix, or solving differential equations, or soaring in the wave wind, or scuba diving 200 feet down, or planting a flower garden, or growing tomatoes, or just the exquisite art of cooking a square meal . . . Only few things in my life have given me that feeling of supreme happiness that overcomes me when I have the opportunity to learn something I had not known before. To deprive children of the chance to learn is about the meanest crime we can commit toward them . . ."*

3   SPACEFLIGHT—MILITARY OR CIVILIAN?

The eight-part *Collier's* series on man's impending travel into space, leading with *"Man Will Conquer Space Soon,"* published early in 1952, probably deserves the credit for having provided the initial spark that set manned spaceflight projects in motion. A wave of public interest ensued from these articles. The fact that an outpost in space would offer marvelous novel opportunities for observations and activities of all kinds—scientific, utilitarian, and military—became obvious to almost everybody. The question was: Should the development of spaceflight be the objective of a civilian, or of a military, or of a joint program, or even of two separate, parallel programs? Heated debates between protagonists of each of these four possibilities quickly came to life.

The National Advisory Committee for Aeronautics (NACA), established in 1915 by President Woodrow Wilson, decided in 1952 to conduct a study *"Problems associated with unmanned and manned flight at altitudes from 50 miles to infinity"* [7-7]. A first step toward an actual flight system for human space travel was taken by the Air Force in 1956; it resulted in Project Dyna-Soar (from dynamic soaring), an unpowered supersonic glider designed to take astronauts back to Earth after a rocket flight into space.

Recognizing the military potential of orbiting satellites, the Air Force established an ad hoc committee of distinguished scientists in May 1957 to study military implications of space technologies [7-8]. Chaired by Dr. H. Guyford Stever, associate dean of Engineering at MIT, the committee submitted its report to the Air Force on 9 October 1957, five days after the launching of Sputnik, recommending an advanced intercontinental ballistic missile that could be used also as a space booster, and even for a manned mission to the Moon. Another advisory committee, chaired by Edward Teller, and Stever's committee jointly recommended that *"a vigorous space program be established with the immediate goal of landing on the Moon,"* again under Air Force leadership [7-9].

President Eisenhower did not react hastily to the appearance of a Soviet satellite; in fact, he professed that *"one small ball in the air"* did not alarm him one bit [7-10]. However, he upgraded the status of the President's Scientific Advisory Committee (PSAC) to staff rank, and he named Dr. James R. Killian, president of MIT, as his first science adviser.

Later in 1957, Major General Bernard A. Schriever, commander of the Ballistic Missile Division in the Air Force Research and Development Command, had his staff study a five-year plan for the development of a lunar base, but the Department of Defense did not approve the project.

Killian, as chairman of PSAC, submitted a report *"Introduction to Outer Space"* in March 1958 [7-11]. It stated four reasons why the nation should conduct a space program: (1) a compelling urge to explore; (2) defense objectives; (3) national prestige; (4) opportunities for scientific research. However, the White House considered only the first and the fourth reasons to be valid arguments for a national space program. This decision reflected the President's own attitude toward space [7-12].

The members of PSAC shared this restrained philosophy about an American space program throughout the Eisenhower years, and even into the Kennedy Administration. Their view was strongly opposed by the Air Force, the Army, many of the congressional members, industry, scientists, and professional societies, and very particularly by Senate Majority Leader Lyndon B. Johnson who, giving vigorous support to a broad and active space program, urged that space exploration, unmanned and manned, should be made a national objective of high priority.

Debates between the Armed Forces, NACA, the Bureau of the Budget, and presidential advisers about the most desirable course of the nation's evolving space program continued. Von Braun, wishing to stay neutral in these battles, and yet hoping to promote some positive action for the space program, wrote a report *"Proposal for a National Integrated Missile and Space Vehicle Development Program"* [7-13]. It was a proposal for joint action that would give support to military needs as well as to an unfolding program of manned space travel. Specifically, it suggested the development of a large booster rocket with a thrust of 1.5 million pounds (675,000 kg). This proposal found much interest and attention, but the debates continued.

Shortly after its creation in the summer of 1958, NASA established a Special Committee on Space Technology under H. Guyford Stever. Its members included Hugh Dryden, former director of NACA; William H. Pickering, director of the Jet Propulsion Laboratory; James A. Van Allen, professor of physics at the State University of Iowa; and von Braun, technical director of ABMA's Development Operations Division. This committee recommended three major activities: scientific research; advancement of space technology; and development of manned spaceflight for human benefit. The committee's recommendations included the development of a large booster stage, to be built by clustering eight engines of the type that was used by Jupiter, Thor, and Atlas rockets, and also of a new high-thrust engine, to be put on the booster as an upper stage.

For several years, the Air Force Research and Development Command (ARDC) had been engaged in man-in-space studies, under the assertion that *". . . air and space are in truth one single and indivisible field of operation . . ."* The Air Force wished to continue playing an active, possibly even a controlling role in the national space program. However, in February 1957 the secretary of defense had established the Advanced Research Projects Agency (ARPA) on a level above the military services. ARPA was assigned approval rights over all space projects related to the Department of Defense. Although the Air Force obtained authority for its manned spaceflight projects from the Joint Chiefs of Staff, ARPA simply withheld funding approval with the argument that the president did not see a valid military role in space.

The Space Act, signed by President Eisenhower on 29 July 1958, did not spell out clearly who would be responsible for manned spaceflight. Would the newly established agency, NASA, also be responsible for defense-oriented space projects? Even before NASA had come into being, Dryden, as director of NACA, proposed that NACA and the Air Force should jointly work out and conduct a manned space program. However, the Bureau of the Budget was against this proposal.

Attempts to retain a controlling role in the manned spaceflight program were made by the Army as well. Backed by its guided missile development team at ABMA in Huntsville, the Army was in an excellent position to offer existing and proven capabilities for designing, building, testing, and launching large rocket systems. Secretary of the Army Wilbur Brucker, vigorously supported by General Medaris, tried his best to avert an immediate transfer of the von Braun team from the Army to NASA.

As if to give some real substance to this proposal, Medaris initiated an ABMA in-house study of an impressive project that would ultimately serve the armed forces, but would utilize the existing capabilities and experience at ABMA, and also the considerable amount of effort that had already gone into the planning of a large booster rocket suitable for flights to the Moon. The project, called *"Horizon,"* envisioned the build-up of a military outpost on the Moon [7-14]. Medaris masterminded the study; the bulk of the work was carried out by Dr. Hermann H. Koelle and his Future Projects Office staff at ABMA, supported by several Army Technical Services and elements of Army Ordnance. Army Research and Development in Washington, D.C., also contributed; von Braun personally kept some distance from the project.

The final report was submitted to the secretary of defense in June 1959. Before a response was given to the proposal, President Eisenhower decided that he would transfer the von Braun team and the entire Saturn program to NASA. This decision put an end not only to Project Horizon, but also to further attempts on the part of the Army to develop a man-in-space capability.

The Air Force did not want to give up so easily. Early in 1961, it proposed a five-year plan for manned spaceflight developments that included a manned lunar landing by 1967. A part of this plan, the Manned Orbital Laboratory (MOL), was approved by the secretary of the Air Force in 1963, but the project was cancelled by DOD in 1967.

America's spaceflight program—should it be under military, or civilian, or joint, or two separate auspices? Debates went on for years, and proposals for manned space projects from all participants in these debates were submitted well after President Eisenhower had established a civilian space administration, NASA, in August 1958. Neither logic alone, nor attempts of compromises between the competing parties, would lead to a clear-cut decision. Finally, this decision was made by President Kennedy in May 1961 when he brought the manned lunar project to life and assigned it to NASA.

4   ARMY, AIR FORCE, NASA—WHITHER THE ROCKET TEAM?

T. Keith Glennan, NASA's first administrator, recalled the beginnings of the National Aeronautics and Space Administration during an interview in 1986 [7-15]. *"You have to realize first,"* he said, *"that when I was asked to be the administrator I had little or no understanding of, nor any interest in space. I was a member of the National Science Board . . . I had heard of von Braun when he was brought over here and sent out to White Sands, but I had very little knowledge of ABMA, or what it was . . . I had sort of been led to believe by the enthusiasts—including Abe Silverstein, Homer Newell, and others—that we could send up a fairly sizeable satellite, weighing maybe 100 pounds, with rockets that would be available to us. These must have been Redstones and Jupiters, since Thor and Atlas had not flown, as I recall it . . . Now when I looked around to see where the rockets were, they just weren't. There were Wernher's Redstone and its derivative Juno I, and that was about it. It became very apparent to me that we were not going to get anywhere without launch vehicles. The military people were not very cooperative; I guess they wanted to go into the space business by themselves . . . I don't think I had ever met von Braun when I proposed to make an effort to get his team . . . So I went down there [to Huntsville] that fall . . . I met Medaris with his 6 foot 6 bodyguards. He and I never got along . . ."*

Glennan was not successful with his request to have *"a few thousand good ones"* of the ABMA team. The Army did not want to give up its foothold in space. *"I finally backed off and went away,"* he said. The battle was on, and it continued through several skirmishes.

Weeks later, Glennan learned that the Army was going to transfer JPL to NASA. The transfer was handled on the Army's side by Lt. General Lyman L. Lemnitzer, Army Chief of Staff, whom Glennan *". . . got to know as a truly fine gentleman . . . McElroy and I took the paper over to the President to have him sign it . . . Ike signed it, but said: 'I disagree wholeheartedly with the way you are doing it. You should have ABMA and JPL together, Keith.' He added that 'since you have come to the decision, I'll let it go at this'."*

Glennan proved to be a most energetic and successful administrator [of NASA]. *"I sensed that to develop a long-range program,"* he recalled, *"we had to reach a certain level at which the public would have to continue to support us. And that level to me* *would be, at the end of ten years, $3 billion annually . . . When I started at NASA, our budget was something like $315 million . . . our next budget was $615 million, I believe, and the next one was $1.15 billion. That was the budget Mr. Webb inherited and immediately enlarged."*

"During much of 1959, Ike became increasingly concerned that we didn't have launch vehicle capacity enough to get ourselves well into space," Glennan remembered. At that time, the Saturn project was underway at ABMA. *"Ike,"* Glennan said, *"reminded me: 'Keith, we've got to get enough thrust so that we can launch a really large payload up into space.' And I responded: 'I think I can guarantee you that we will have that capability a year earlier if you'll give us another $100 million.' Shortly thereafter, word came back that the President was approving that increase . . ."*

"Was there ever," Glennan was asked, *"any reservation in President Eisenhower's mind about having von Braun play such a prominent part in America's missile and space programs?" "No, none at all. The subject never came up,"* was his answer.

Although Glennan's early attempts to secure the von Braun group for his young NASA ended in failure, there was a great deal of very active cooperation between members of ABMA in Huntsville and the various departments, committees, and working groups at NASA that were involved in advanced planning. When the von Braun team finally joined NASA in 1960, many working contacts, close acquaintances, and even friendships had already been established between NASA members and the newcomers. The transition did not generate any problems.

Cooperation between ABMA and the U.S. Air Force Ballistic Missile Division, based on excellent personal relations between General Schriever and von Braun, had been equally fruitful and efficient since about 1956. During an interview in 1988 [7-16], Schriever remembered: *"We set up a [joint] technical advisory group . . . they had a very good team in Huntsville . . ."* Although the Air Force and ABMA took different management approaches, the joint work proceeded very well. *"We never had any battles internally . . . Von Braun, of course, was a very colorful guy, and very articulate . . . I think he made great contributions that led to the long-range missile and space business . . ."*

"After Sputnik, the whole matter of space was up for grabs," Schriever continued. *"The scientific community, led primarily by the Northeast group—the Boston mafia— did not want to give up space to the military . . . Well, the decision was made in cloistered quarters . . . that NASA would be created. Now the language in the NASA Act made it clear that space would be extremely important for national security, and Eisenhower bought that. But his first words were that space was for peaceful purposes, and that one should not 'militarize' space. Now what does 'militarize' space mean? We had already militarized space, for the Soviets had gone for it from day one."*

Would Schriever have liked in 1958 to have von Braun's group in his organization?

"Oh, sure. Absolutely. I think the Air Force position at the top was that we wanted to take on the challenge of space, recognizing that the potential of space was far greater than just serving the Air Force . . . You can't really quarrel too much with the original NASA bill, because it made clear that national security was a very important considera- tion. As a matter of fact, you could read into the NASA bill that national security had first priority . . . The idea that space was for peaceful purposes caught on with the media, and almost anything I said relating to space being able to support our national security was seen as a contradiction to what the president had said, what the NASA Act said, and so on. Obviously, in the very early stages of spaceflight there was nothing that related to either offensive or defensive considerations. There were only such things as surveillance, communications, and intelligence, all things that any fool could see

would be highly significant to national security. But even wise people were trumpeting 'don't militarize space!' . . . No matter what you say, space is going to be exploited for military purposes . . . I would say that 95 percent of the Soviet space program has been pointed towards military activities. The Soviets picked up from our press the slogan 'don't militarize space,' and now they accuse the United States of doing just that!"

"When the decision was made that we needed a 1,500-mile missile, the IRBM, for deployment in Europe," Schriever said, *"the Army had one design, the Jupiter, and we had the Thor . . . It was finally decided that we would go ahead with both missiles. In order to allocate resources and to assure that the technical requirements of both Thor and Jupiter were met, we created a technical coordination group . . . Those technical meetings went very smoothly . . . I got together with Medaris and von Braun, and we never had any difficulties. There was no rancor except in the mind of Ed [Colonel Edward] Hall, and to a lesser extent some other people. The roles and missions battles had been fought, and it was over with . . . Gavin and I were good friends . . . I admit that I didn't like Medaris much; I just didn't like his style, and I didn't trust him. But I always trusted von Braun and Gavin . . ."*

As the space age began to gain momentum during the spring and summer of 1958, the rocket people at ABMA in Huntsville also began to wonder where they would finally end up—with the Air Force, or with NASA. Personal preferences were split. There was full agreement, though, on two points: First, everyone hoped that the group would be able to continue its work on the development of rockets and spacecraft, possibly with a manned mission to the Moon as the next big project. Second, there was the unequivocal desire that the group could stay together under von Braun's leadership. Good fortune, and the decisions of some wise people, would make both wishes come true.

To some, prospects for productive work and substantial accomplishments looked better under the aegis of the Air Force, simply because the Air Force enjoyed greater public prestige than the almost unknown NASA, and therefore promised more stability in the funding cycles associated with manned spaceflight programs. Others feared that one of the team's most distinct features, its very substantial technical in-house capability that had served the von Braun team so well during the past twenty years, could no longer be brought to bear under Air Force management that would contract all technical work—design, development, engineering, testing, quality assurance—to industry. Ever since he had started building rockets in Germany around 1935, von Braun had strongly believed in a very intimate day-by-day cooperation between the government agency responsible for the project and the industrial contractors expected to build the hardware. The merit of this work philosophy was clearly demonstrated by von Braun's long list of successful projects, successful with respect to technical accomplishments as well as adherence to the predicted time and cost schedules. The Air Force did not rely upon elaborate in-house capabilities, but allowed the contractors far more freedom in technical and managerial decisions.

What were von Braun's personal inclinations? He rarely talked about the pending decision between a military and a civilian future for his group, but he followed very diligently all the statements that were made on both sides, and he kept close personal contact with those who were influential in that decision. Rather than debating the pros and cons of a civilian versus a military environment for the nation's space program, he vigorously pursued a broad effort to develop the concept of a large booster rocket that would evolve through a clustered 1.5 to 1.6 million pound thrust system, based on the existing Jupiter-Atlas-Thor engine, to a 6 to 8 million pound giant that would use several units of the new single-barrel 1.5 million pound engine, the mighty F-1. Although von Braun was very outspoken and definite concerning his technical views, he avoided any trace of animosity. Any one of his potential future superiors would have found him a most cooperative and congenial partner.

5   VON BRAUN'S GROUP TRANSFERS TO NASA

Planning for the large rocket that would take astronauts into space encountered rough sledding during the late 1950s. Around 1955, von Braun had started to make realistic plans for a large booster; beginning in 1958, the Advanced Research Projects Agency (ARPA), mainly under the prodding of Richard B. Canright, provided support for this early work under the title *"Juno V Systems Study,"* and also for subsequent work on upper stages for this booster. At the time when the Army's role in the manned spaceflight program came under debate between the White House, NASA, DOD, the Air Force, and the Army, development work on the powerful engines for first and second stages of the space rocket was well underway at ABMA in Huntsville and at Rocketdyne in California, funded by ARPA, and increasingly also by NASA. The Air Force contributed funds through its contracts for the Atlas-Jupiter-Thor engine.

In parallel to these developments, other events occurred at ABMA. In June 1958 the first Redstone missile developed by the Army-Chrysler team in Huntsville was launched under simulated wartime conditions by combat-ready soldiers. The first American intermediate-range ballistic missile, Jupiter, was developed by the same team during that time period. The first Jupiter delivery was made to the Air Force in August 1958. Also, ABMA began orbiting Earth satellites in 1958.

ARPA's active interest in a powerful rocket, capable of taking astronauts to the Moon, was matched by growing interest in the same objective on the part of the young NASA. Wesley L. Hjornevik, Glennan's assistant; Abraham Hyatt, chief of Launch Vehicles; and Milton Rosen, chief engineer, wrote a report early in 1959 in which they urged the development of Juno V with Centaur or Titan as upper stage. Rosen, in particular, pressed for the next generation, Nova, one configuration of which was to be powered by a cluster of four of the new 1.5 million pound thrust engines, the F-1.

In February 1959, the Department of Defense introduced the name *"Saturn"* for the Juno V rocket system, following a suggestion by von Braun who argued that Saturn was the next planet after Jupiter.

Signals from the White House concerning a manned spaceflight program continued to be negative. When, toward the end of 1958, NASA initiated Project Mercury with the aim of launching an astronaut on a trip into orbit and back to Earth by 1961, White House approval was given only grudgingly. The president's desire not to let this program evolve further was evident. But NASA, being the nation's aeronautics and space administration, felt an obligation to press forward.

In April 1959 a Research Steering Committee on Manned Space Flight was established under Harry J. Goett, director of the NASA-Ames Research Center. It included members of NASA Headquarters, and of all NASA field centers, and it was charged with the task of making plans for NASA's future. However, the climate for such planning was not at all favorable at that time. Opposition to a manned space program, and especially to the Saturn development, persisted not only in the White House, but in at least two more quarters.

The President's Scientific Advisory Committee (PSAC), chaired by Dr. Jerome Wiesner, took a negative standpoint. It reflected an opinion held by numerous scientists who feared that the sciences would be short-changed in the process. Dr. Herbert F. York, director of Research and Engineering in the Department of Defense, expressed the feeling of many military men when he stated in his memorandum of 9 June 1959 that he had decided to cancel the Saturn program because he saw no military justification in the project [7-17]. York's decision had two sources: First, he wished to back the president in his attitude against manned spaceflight; and second, his primary loyalty belonged to the Department of Defense, and he feared that a costly spaceflight program would detract funds from military projects.

Of course, NASA was against York's decision, and so was ARPA. Rosen, Hyatt, and Canright militated for Saturn. In September 1959, Dryden and York jointly chaired a special committee to discuss the situation. Saturn survived, but York strongly recommended that the Saturn project and the entire ABMA should be transferred to NASA, and that NASA should be the funding source for Saturn.

To criticize York for this decision would not be fair. After all, as director of Defense Research and Engineering, his prime responsibility was military defense, and the Saturn rocket would not qualify as a defense weapon.

In his book *Race to Oblivion* [7-18], York discussed the situation of military and civilian space programs during the late 1950s in detail. That situation was confusing. Responsibility for the civilian space program had been assigned to NASA in 1958, while ARPA was responsible for the military space program. And yet, ARPA initiated the Saturn rocket project, and gave continuing support to its development. On the other hand, NASA was charged with administrating the Centaur project, an upper stage with H_2-O_2 engines built by the General Dynamics Corporation for Air Force use. Saturn, the space launcher, was developed by the Army, although the Army had no assigned role in space. ARPA administrated Saturn, although Saturn could not play any military role. NASA was responsible for man-in-space, but it had no authority over the development of space launchers.

Each of the three armed services made its own recommendation: The Air Force wanted to be assigned all military space projects, but not the teams that had worked on these projects in the past. The Navy opted for a military space command, with each of the three services playing an equal role in it. The Army's proposal called for a joint space and missile command, run essentially by Brucker and Medaris, and incorporating the von Braun team. *"None of these proposals was acceptable to anyone beyond those making them,"* York said.

In this clouded situation, York made a simple, but sweeping proposal: Discontinue ARPA's support of large rockets. Assign all military satellite launchers to the Air Force. Assign full responsibility for Saturn to NASA. Transfer the von Braun team to NASA.

York's recommendations were accepted by Dryden and also by McElroy and by the president.

Among those who felt relieved and happy by this agreement was Lyndon B. Johnson, at that time Senate majority leader, who was most anxious to keep the von Braun team together, and to utilize it for the good of the country.

Secretary of the Army Brucker and General Medaris, realizing that the chances of the Army to retain authority over the von Braun group and the Saturn project were dwindling fast, suggested to the Department of Defense in September 1959 that the entire von Braun team, about 4,800 persons, and all their rocket-building facilities should be transferred to NASA. *"Virtually,"* Medaris said [7-19], *"they were offered the whole von Braun team on a silver platter . . ."*

Goett's committee continued unperturbed while Saturn's fate was in limbo. In the course of the committee's deliberations, Dr. George M. Low, at that time director of Spacecraft and Flight Missions in the Office of Manned Space Flight in NASA Headquarters, spoke for most—if not all—of the members when he simply said that a manned lunar landing mission should be the next major goal of NASA. The committee accepted this proposal and, in October 1959, recommended a number of steps towards its implementation; the most important of them was the development of a booster rocket large enough to launch a manned spacecraft for a landing on the Moon and subsequent return to Earth.

That recommendation would not only stabilize, and in a sense legalize, all the work on a large Moon rocket that had been underway at government and contractor facilities for years; it would also make it almost mandatory that von Braun and his large rocket-building team should be transferred to NASA intact. Glennan, facing the formidable task of bringing a full-size lunar landing project to life, agreed. On 14 October 1959 he asked for the transfer from the Army to NASA of von Braun and most of his workforce at ABMA, and of all the rocket-building facilities that would be needed to carry out the Saturn program. One week later, President Eisenhower announced that he had *"decided to transfer, subject to congressional approval, the Army's space team and rocket development facilities to NASA"* [7-20]. On 2 November he said: *"There is a definite need for super boosters for civilian space exploration purposes, both manned and unmanned . . ."* Congress did approve the transfer. Von Braun and 4,519 of his civilian co-workers became members of NASA at the beginning of the new decade. On 15 March 1960, their organization received the proud name NASA—George C. Marshall Space Flight Center (MSFC).

Von Braun and his large team did not leave the Army in a jubilant mood. After all, the Rocket Development Group had grown from 127 to almost 5,000 members during the fifteen years it had been under the Army's control. Many excellent working relations between military and civilian personnel had developed, based on mutual trust and respect. Certainly, there were also situations when the going was a little rough, but the overall result of the symbiosis was very positive: The V-2 launchings, the Redstone rocket, the first American satellite, the Jupiter rocket, more satellites, the first flyby probe to the Moon, the Pershing missile, preparations for the first American astronaut in space, and the beginnings of the Saturn-Apollo project were among the accomplishments achieved under the auspices of the Army, and with the invaluable contributions of countless men wearing the Army uniform [7-20]. Von Braun, and also his team members, always remembered the *"Army years,"* 1945 to 1960, with a feeling of sincere gratitude.

Most of the credit for this successful and enjoyable team work, and particularly for the fact that the rocket group was intact and functional at the time when the Army's direct role in the national space program had to come to an end, is certainly due to Major General Toftoy and Major General Medaris, and, to a very substantial degree, to Lieutenant General James Gavin, Chief of Research and Development of the Army. All three of them proved to be tireless and intrepid fighters not only for the Army's cause, but for the American space program as well. They had strong support in their efforts from Secretary of the Army Wilbur M. Brucker, and—perhaps in a more clandestine way—from Secretary of Defense Neil H. McElroy. The latter had succeeded Secretary of Defense Charles E. Wilson in 1957 after Colonel John C. Nickerson, in a courageous and self-sacrificing but not entirely prudent and clever way, had pointed out some inconsistencies in the decision-making processes at the Department of Defense. Medaris, when discussing the situation years later, added one more positive element in his fight for the team: *". . . and I had the darndest best rocket team on this planet at my disposal . . ."*

Had Medaris not decided in 1958 and 1959 to keep the ABMA group together at all cost as a large, integral rocket team, at least the nucleus of that team would have disintegrated at that time, following the lucrative offers from the fledgling rocket and space industries in the country.

The creation of a national space agency, and the eventual transfer of the von Braun group into it, had become logical steps in a process of evolution that had its beginnings as early as the turn of the century. Many individuals contributed to this evolution, scientists, engineers, dreamers, novelists, visionaries, realists. The most decisive steps during these first fifty years can be attributed to military planners in the German Army, the Soviet military, and the American Army. Events in the United States during the 1958–60 period, when the American space program became the responsibility of NASA, ushered in an era in which the large effort in work and cost required by a comprehensive space program was shouldered by a civilian agency with goals that primarily are serving the peaceful exploration of space.

Changing from a military to a civilian organization was a step that von Braun had anticipated for years. The day when it really occurred was a happy one for him and his team members, particularly for those who, fifteen years earlier, had come from Germany with him. The transfer did not involve any change of location; the group continued to draw the same civil service salaries, and to occupy the same buildings in Huntsville they had been using before. However, von Braun was now the director of a NASA center, with the assignment to develop rocket systems for the peaceful exploration of space. For him, that had been a lifelong dream that now came true. He and his German-born team members felt deeply gratified that their new center was named in honor of the late Secretary of State (former General of the Army) George C. Marshall, of whom President Eisenhower said in his dedication address [7-21]: *"He was a man of war, yet a builder of peace."* Indeed, no other person had done as much as General Marshall to help the European nations, including Germany, find their ways back to a normal existence after the terrible ravages of war. He was the only professional soldier ever to receive the Nobel Peace Prize.

6   A MEMORIAL FOR ROBERT HUTCHINGS GODDARD

Adventurous minds have been dreaming about travel into space throughout history. Toward the end of the last century, four men were born destined to become the real pioneers of spaceflight: Konstantin E. Tsiolkovskii in Russia (1857–1935), Robert H. Goddard in the United States (1882–1945), Robert Esnault-Pelterie in France (1881–1957), and Hermann Oberth, born in the German-speaking portion of Transylvania in Romania, but who lived most of his life in Germany (1894–1989).

Goddard began to think of rockets for spaceflight when he was still a student in high school [7-21]. In 1902, he wrote an article *"The Navigation of Space,"* and sent it to the magazine *Popular Science News*, but the editor would not accept it. As early as 1906, he mentioned in his notebook the possibility of using *"electrified jets"* to propel a rocket between the Earth and a planet. He began detailed studies of liquid-fueled rockets in 1909. Goddard found that the best propellant combination for a high-altitude rocket would be liquid oxygen and liquid hydrogen, a conclusion at which Tsiolkovskii had arrived ten years before, and Oberth, independently, would arrive about ten years later.

In 1914, Goddard applied and received patents for rockets with solid and liquid propellants, for the multistage rocket principle, and for designs of combustion chambers, nozzles, and propellant feed systems. Around the same time, he wrote a paper entitled *"A Method of Reaching Extreme Altitudes"*; he reworked it several times before it was finally published by the Smithsonian Institution in 1919. This was one of the very few essays published during Goddard's lifetime, and even this paper was printed and distributed only in 1,750 copies. One of these copies found its way, through Professor Oberth, into the hands of young Wernher von Braun in 1930. It was the only report by Goddard that von Braun read before the year 1950; some occasional brief notes in newspapers about the *"Moon Professor"* were his only other source of information, but he promptly made Goddard his boyhood hero.

Goddard's *"Smithsonian Paper"* in 1919 had two very diverse effects. First, it aroused the attention, interest, and admiration of some people who were engaged in novel technical developments. Among them were officers of the Navy who gave him a small contract and $2,000 to develop rockets for naval use; and there were his superiors at Clark University who permitted him to continue his experiments under the auspices of the university.

On 3 May 1922, Goddard received a letter—in somewhat clumsy English—from a twenty-eight year old colleague at the University of Heidelberg in Germany [7-22]. The writer was Hermann Oberth:

"Dear Professor Goddard!

Already for many years I work at the problem to pass over the atmosphere of our Earth by means of a rocket. When I was now publishing the result of my examinations and calculations, I learned by the newspaper, that I am not alone in my inquiries and that you, dear Sir, have already done much work at this important sphere. In spite of my efforts, I did not succeed in getting your books about this subject.

Therefore I beg you, dear Sir, to let me have them. At once after coming out of my work I will be honoured to send it to you, for I think that only by common work of the scholars of all nations can be solved this great problem.

With deep respect [signed] *Hermann Oberth."*

Goddard did send a copy of his Smithsonian Paper to Oberth. In turn, Oberth wrote an appendix to his book *The Rocket into Planetary Space* which was in print at that time; in this appendix, he described Goddard's main thoughts and accomplishments not only in some detail, but with great admiration for their originator. Obviously, he was happy to have a brother in arms across the Atlantic whose concepts and results agreed so well with his own.

The second effect resulting from Goddard's 1919 Smithsonian paper was an unexpected, quite negative publicity caused by newspaper articles that ridiculed his allusions to future flights to the Moon. These allegations of absurd fantasies must have hurt him deeply. Goddard had always been a sensitive introvert; he now became a recluse, even a loner, suspicious of others, and unwilling to communicate. Although his restless, super-creative mind flowed over with ideas, he did not publish. His many reports and study papers were just filed away in safes. He was a prolific generator of patents; a total of 214 were granted to him, but they became known publicly only after his death. Unfortunately, he preferred patents to publications. They included double-walled combustion chambers and nozzles to be cooled with the liquid oxidizer or fuel; gyroscopes for stabilization and guidance; jet vanes; fuel pumps; and recovery of burnt-out rockets by parachute.

The 16th of March 1926 was to become a historic date. On that day, a rocket with liquid propellants, probably the first in the history of man, accomplished a flight. Goddard wrote in his diary: *". . . it rose 41 feet, and went 184 feet, in 2.5 seconds, after the lower part of the nozzle had burned off . . ."* [7-21]. This rocket was fueled with kerosene and liquid oxygen.

Robert A. Millikan, the Nobel-Prize-winning physicist at CalTech, wrote to Goddard in 1931, hoping that high-altitude rockets could be used for cosmic ray research. Goddard replied briefly that his research was not yet ready for publication. He also declined repeated invitations by the newly founded American Interplanetary Society (after 1934, American Rocket Society) to become a member. Communicating, exchanging ideas, sharing experiences, and joining forces in a common endeavor just were not Goddard's way of life. *"I do not think it desirable to publish results of the long series of experiments I have undertaken . . .,"* he wrote. The vice president of that society, G. Edward Pendray, later expressed his unhappiness about Goddard's reticence in these words: *"When Robert Goddard in his desert fastness in New Mexico proved uncommunicative, those of us who wanted to do our part in launching the space age turned to what appeared the next best source of light: the Verein für Raumschiffahrt—the Germany Society for Space Travel—in Berlin"* [7-22].

Millikan tried again in 1936 to coax Goddard into an exchange of ideas and results by offering him a more formal cooperative arrangement with CalTech, but again in vain. Guggenheim, who financed both Goddard in New Mexico and rocket work at CalTech, attempted to persuade Goddard to join forces with colleagues in California, but Goddard wished to remain by himself. *"By his secrecy,"* wrote Homer E. Newell [7-23], *"Goddard not only dissipated most of his influence he might have had, he also deprived himself of the engineering expertise that he sorely needed to achieve his dream. The future of rocketry belonged to the team approach—it was, indeed, inextricably tied to the massive funding sources and particular purposes of the national security state . . . Members of the California Institute of Technology Rocket Research Project . . . tried to persuade Goddard to join forces with them. When it was stipulated that a partnership would require mutual disclosure of ideas and projects, Goddard shied away. His reluctance to work openly with others deprived Goddard . . . of the kind of funding support from the military that could have capped his long years of work with their hoped-for fruition. Working alone with extremely limited funds, Goddard could not match the progress being made in German rocketry, which was supported amply by the military during those years."*

In the meantime, some other groups of rocket developers, whose invitations for cooperation Goddard had refuted earlier, were setting up companies in which to conduct their work: Reaction Motors, Inc. in New Jersey, founded in 1941 by members of the American Rocket Society, and the Aerojet Engineering Corporation in California, founded in early 1942. Technical progress in rocketry was thus passing into other hands, becoming linked more and more on the West Coast (at Aerojet) with von Kármán, Frank J. Malina, John W. Parsons, Martin Summerfield, Homer A. Boushey, Jr., and Edward S. Forman, and on the East Coast with Lovell Lawrence, Jr., John Shesta, James H. Wyld, and Hugh Franklin Pierce at Reaction Motors. On 26 September 1945, the WAC Corporal rocket, developed as part of the CalTech Rocket Research Project, reached an altitude of almost 40 nautical miles (70 km). This flight marked the real beginning of U.S. rocketry. The CalTech Rocket Research Project had been reorganized as the Jet Propulsion Laboratory (JPL) in 1944.

A memorable event took place early in 1945. Allied troops in Europe captured parts and even complete units of German V-2 rockets. The material was shipped to the United States; Goddard was requested to help disassemble the monsters, and to analyze their technical mysteries. He wrote an elaborate report on his findings, and he also cited his own patents which covered many of the components he found in the V-2. These patents had been stored, by his own request, unpublished in the archives of the Smithsonian

Institution, so they were unavailable and unknown to the men behind the big German rocket.

Goddard died, following a neck operation, on 10 August 1945, four days before the end of World War II. Only seven weeks later, on 29 September 1945, von Braun arrived in the United States. From the moment on when he realized that he would continue his rocket work in America, von Braun had hoped that he would be able to meet his boyhood hero. How deeply would both men have relished such a meeting!

Von Braun did meet Mrs. Esther Goddard, a most remarkable lady not only because of her exceptional intelligence, but also because of her equally exceptional charm and warmheartedness. She and the entire von Braun family became close and affectionate friends spontaneously when they met for the first time in the early 1950s.

There was another event that brought von Braun in close contact with the world of Goddard. This happened in 1950; von Braun told the story in a long letter to a young West Point cadet who asked him about the relationship between his and Goddard's rocket work [7-24]. After reading Goddard's Smithsonian paper of 1919 as an eighteen-year-old, von Braun wrote, he counted Goddard among his boyhood heroes, though he never saw a Goddard patent before 1950. *"I was not even aware of the fact,"* he said, *"that Goddard had worked in the field so dear to my own heart, liquid-propellant rockets, let alone that even as early as 1926 he had successfully launched the world's first liquid-propellant rocket."*

Von Braun then described how at Fort Bliss in 1950, Lt. Colonel Hamill showed him a large stack of Goddard patents and told him that a lawsuit was going on between the United States Government and the Goddard estate over the question whether the German V-2s brought to the United States at the end of the war, as well as some of the postwar rockets designed in the United States, were infringing upon Goddard patents. If so, the U.S. Government should pay royalties to the Goddard estate.

Hamill asked von Braun to study the Goddard patents and prepare a detailed written assessment. Von Braun's report certified that there were indeed infringements all over the place.

"All the Goddard patents I saw," von Braun further wrote in his letter, *"were classified; they had never been published, even as late as 1950. I was totally unaware of them while in Germany, and even in the United States I saw them for the first time only five years after my arrival, and upon receipt of a secret clearance."*

In concluding his letter, von Braun wrote: *"It might be of interest that (maybe in part as a result of my affirmative report) the lawsuit led to an amicable settlement, under which the U.S. Government paid a generous sum to the Goddard Estate . . ."*

In March 1957, the Worcester Engineering Society celebrated its thirtieth anniversary; von Braun was to be the banquet speaker. In the afternoon of that day, he requested Mrs. Goddard to show him the very place where her husband, thirty-one years before, had launched the world's first liquid-propellant rocket. They found the place on a golf course. In his banquet speech, von Braun said: *"I drove to the launching site this afternoon, and I found it strange that there is no marker or memorial to the great event of Dr. Goddard's first successful launching of a modern rocket. Here, in Worcester, where modern rocketry was born, there should be erected a memorial to this great pioneer"* [7-25].

The following week, von Braun introduced his proposal of a Goddard memorial at a board of directors' meeting of the American Rocket Society. His motion carried without opposing votes. Action began right away. It included a fund-raising campaign which took some time, but in 1960 the memorial was dedicated. Other honors for

Goddard followed. The National Space Club in Washington sponsored an annual Goddard Memorial Dinner, and also a Goddard Memorial Trophy. Symposia are held in his honor. NASA's Goddard Space Flight Center in Greenbelt, Maryland, is named after him.

In 1960, literary essays about Goddard began to appear: Homer A. Boushey, Jr. [7-26], Frederick C. Durant III [7-27], Milton Lehman [7-28], Mitchell R. Sharpe [7-29], Frederick I. Ordway III [1-2], and others wrote about Goddard's life and work. In 1970, Esther C. Goddard and G. Edward Pendray edited *The Papers of Robert H. Goddard*, a work comprising three big volumes [7-21].

Von Braun always held Goddard in highest esteem. The two men were quite different in their ways of attacking the problem of spaceflight and also in the accomplishments they achieved during their lifetimes. But they were driven by the same unbounded passion to explore space and to create the means to travel to the Moon and the planets.

A Goddard Rocket Collection was established in 1959 in Roswell, New Mexico. Dedication ceremonies were held on 25 April of that year; von Braun was the keynote speaker [7-30].

"However belated, the recognition accorded to Dr. Goddard is eminently deserved," von Braun said. *"In the light of what has happened since his untimely death, we can only wonder what might have been if America had realized earlier the implications of his work. I have not the slightest doubt that the United States today would enjoy unchallenged leadership in space exploration had adequate support and recognition been provided to him . . ."* [7-31].

CHAPTER 8

JOURNEY TO THE MOON

1   CAMPAIGNING FOR A MOON PROJECT

Professor Fritz Zwicky, world-renowned astrophysicist at the California Institute of Technology, was a member of the scientists and engineers who interrogated German scientists in Germany immediately after termination of hostilities at the end of World War II. Zwicky was among those who met and questioned von Braun a few days after he had surrendered to American forces in southern Bavaria in May 1945. *"He told us,"* Zwicky recalled in 1946 [8-1], *"that future uses of rockets will include multi-staged manned rockets for use as satellite observation platforms, and that, when the art of rocketry is developed further, it will be possible to travel to other planets, first of all to the Moon."*

Indeed, a journey to the Moon had been on von Braun's mind ever since he read Jules Verne at the age of fourteen. He began writing about rocket-driven spaceships at that time, and during the late 1920s and early 1930s the idea that man should develop technologies to travel to his neighbors in space became almost an obsession with him. He was, of course, not the only enthusiast who believed in rocket trips through space. Nikolai Kibalchich, Konstantin Tsiolkovskii, Nikolai Rynin, Valentin Glushko, Fridrikh Tsander, Jakov Perelman, M. K. Tikhonravov in Russia; Robert H. Goddard, G. Edward Pendray, David Lasser, Ernst Loebell in the United States; Guido von Pirquet in Austria; Hermann Oberth in Romania; Robert Esnault-Pelterie in France; Arthur C. Clarke and P. E. Cleater in The United Kingdom; Hermann Noordung in Austria; Hermann Ganswindt, Willy Ley, Ilse Kuehnel, Johannes Winkler, Walter Hohmann, Max Valier, Reinhold Tilling in Germany—they all shared the dream of a human journey to the Moon, and even to the nearer planets.

During the war years, while he was working on the V-2 guided missile project in Peenemünde, von Braun had to stay quiet about space travel except when he was among his inner-circle colleagues, but he could talk openly about rocket flight into space and lunar journeys as soon as he had arrived in the United States. In January 1947, he spoke to a Rotary Club audience in El Paso, Texas, and showed how a trip to the Moon and beyond might be undertaken.

Von Braun, in contrast to earlier space pioneers, presented not only ideas and some crude sketches, but also sober technical concepts with design drawings and engineering data, and even with a preliminary systems analysis of the entire start-to-finish project.

There were some other space enthusiasts during the early postwar years who also began campaigning for a manned rocket trip to the Moon on the basis of careful technical studies. In 1948, H. E. Ross presented a paper at the annual meeting of the British Interplanetary Society in which he described plans for Earth-orbiting stations, as well as for a manned lunar landing project [8-2]. He even elaborated on a landing technique that used a spacecraft rendezvous in lunar orbit, very similar to the scheme that von Braun presented in his late 1940s Mars study for a landing on the Martian surface, and also to the mode suggested in 1961 by John C. Houbolt for the Saturn-Apollo project (Chapter 8-4).

Jules Verne, in his novel *From the Earth to the Moon*, had astronauts travel to their destination fired from a huge cannon on the Earth's surface. He calculated the required muzzle velocity correctly, about 11 kilometers per second, but he did not elaborate on the landing maneuver or on any technical details of the return trip. Modern planners of journeys to the Moon had to take these aspects seriously. In fact, none of them would have dared to propose a manned lunar expedition without showing convincingly how the Moon travelers would land on the Moon's surface, and how they would return safely to Earth.

A manned round trip to the Moon would consist basically of six major phases: takeoff from Earth, transfer to the Moon, descent to and landing on the lunar surface, takeoff from the Moon, transfer to Earth, descent to and landing on the Earth's surface. These phases might be combined in various ways in order to simplify the project to some extent. In any case, a very powerful booster rocket with a thrust of several million pounds would be needed.

Public debate of a journey to the Moon by human travelers began almost with a bang when *Collier's* magazine began publishing its eight space articles in 1952 (Chapter 5-5). In the lunar articles of the series, their authors described technical facts of a lunar voyage in exciting detail, yet in layman's language, and with realistic pictures, data, and numbers. These essays created the spontaneous awareness of a pending accomplishment, at least a potential accomplishment, of secular dimensions. Their impact was far greater than the editors of *Collier's*, or von Braun and his co-authors, had ever anticipated. All of a sudden, the concept of a manned voyage to the Moon had descended from the eerie realm of dream and fiction to a realistic level of technology and engineering. Almost everybody read or at least heard of the *Collier's* series—and those dealing with an expedition to the Moon in particular. This gave von Braun an excellent platform to launch his campaign for a real lunar program backed by the U.S. Government.

Characteristically, von Braun campaigned simultaneously on three different fronts: the public; congressional leaders; and top players in the national space program. Each of the three would represent a powerful pillar of strength if supportive of the project, but an equally powerful adversary if negatively disposed toward a journey to the Moon.

Knowing instinctively that his greatest asset in this triple campaign was his personal power of persuasion, von Braun established as many direct contacts among government officials, congressional leaders, scientists, high-level members of industry, military officers, and other influential personalities as he could, passionately extolling the reasons why the United States should engage in a manned lunar expedition. It would offer a brilliant opportunity for scientific exploration and research; it would provide an unparalleled stimulus for technological progress; it would be a national accomplishment, entirely peaceful, of the highest order; and it would give the citizens of the United States, and countless people around the world, a mental and spiritual experience as it has occurred only rarely in the course of history.

Von Braun engaged in this personal crusade for a lunar voyage during the early and mid-1950s, at a time when he was deeply entrenched in the Redstone and Jupiter guided missile projects, and in preparations for the Explorer satellite. How he could handle all these projects at the same time will always remain a mystery. After all, that was the time when his three young children demanded—and happily received—much attention, and when he thoroughly enjoyed horseback riding, water skiing, scuba diving, and flying, *"to recharge the batteries,"* as he sometimes said.

From 1950 till 1960, von Braun's position in the Army Ballistic Missile Agency in Huntsville was technical director, Development Operations Division. Once every week, he held a board meeting with forty to fifty of his co-workers where the status of each of the ongoing projects was reported, discussed, and critiqued. His prime projects during that decade were the Redstone and Jupiter missiles. Von Braun followed every technical detail of both projects with greatest care. At all times, he was the one person who had the most complete overall understanding of each project. He made sure that any feeling of uncertainty or doubt on the part of the project managers and engineers would be thoroughly aired while all his staff members were present. No *"soft spot"* would remain undedected and undebated, nor would any uncertainty persist by the time a board meeting came to its close.

Von Braun also used these meetings to keep his co-workers informed of his activities that were aimed at future projects. At least briefly, he described his plans for a Redstone-launched satellite, and his efforts to bring a lunar landing project to life. Actual design studies for these projects could be made in his division only to a very limited extent because of restrictions in his assignments; however, a verbal campaign to develop interest for a lunar project could be conducted easily during his many trips to Washington and other cities, and at his numerous meetings with military, congressional, industrial, NACA, and, from 1958 on, NASA personalities, without stepping over the boundaries set by his assigned work. Fortunately, von Braun's superiors, Major General Holger N. Toftoy in Washington and Major General John Bruce Medaris in Huntsville, were great space enthusiasts in their own rights. They saw the fantastic opportunities open for the United States, and they were willing to give von Braun's duties a broad interpretation.

Most of von Braun's co-workers could see only occasional highlights in the Moon project's colorful history during the 1950s while its fate often dangled on a thin thread. They realized with encouragement that the Air Force became interested in manned spaceflight, but they were disappointed to see the diminishing value that President Eisenhower was willing to ascribe to the conquest of space. They found it difficult to understand that many of the political leaders did not seem to grasp the significance of a great technical accomplishment as an element of peaceful international diplomacy. They were very unhappy about the ill-famed roles and missions decree by Secretary of Defense Charles E. Wilson in 1956 with its unfortunate consequences. At the same time, their hopes were strengthened as it became more and more evident that the technical problems encountered in a lunar landing project would by no means be insurmountable, and that, in effect, work on such a project could be started at any time with excellent prospects for a complete technical success.

During the late 1950s, the *"lunar landing project,"* as it was usually called, resembled a little boat tossed around on a stormy ocean. For years, it was doubtful which course it might eventually sail, or whether it would be shipwrecked before land came in sight. Almost miraculously, it was able to stay afloat, although battered, with torn sails and damaged rudder. Von Braun followed all these events diligently. He was a member of several advisory boards; also, he was often requested to consult or testify for government committees. His most important source of insight was the large number of his friends and acquaintances all over the country with whom he conferred as much as his time permitted. Thus, he succeeded in keeping his hand on the pulse of the fledgling Moon program.

Von Braun's co-workers learned of the project's struggle for life only through his reports, and through sporadic information in the news, trade journals, and occasional communications from Washington. For them, the whole story unfolded only years later when vivid accounts of the Moon project's tortuous path through its infancy began to appear in several books, among them John M. Logsdon, *The Decision to Go to the Moon* [8-3]; Roger E. Bilstein, *Stages to Saturn* [8-4]; and Vernon Van Dyke, *Pride and Power: The Rationale of the Space Program* [8-5].

2   SATURN-APOLLO TAKES SHAPE

Casual observers may think that the project to send astronauts on a lunar round trip came to life quickly and easily: After President Kennedy had decided on 25 May 1961 that this should be done, the big Saturn rocket for Earth launch, the transfer vehicle to the Moon and back to Earth, and the lunar excursion module were built, the astronauts were trained, and the journey to the lunar surface began on 16 July 1969.

It is true that the bulk of the work for the Saturn-Apollo project was carried out during the eight-year span from 1961 till 1969. However, several years of dramatic events preceded that period when the Moon project vacillated between hope and despair, pushed forward by fervent protagonists, held in abeyance by lukewarm hesitators, and objected to by those who considered space travel unnecessary, undesirable, a stunt, a waste of money, a technical impossibility, or just an utter lack of common sense. The situation was aggravated during the late 1950s because even among the protagonists, two opposing factions had developed. The Air Force and its supporters wanted the Moon project under military control, while civilian members of the government, as well as those scientists who were principally in favor of an expedition to the Moon, opted for a NASA-controlled project. Signals from the White House were still less than encouraging.

This uncertain state of the Moon project was a source of much concern for many of the program supporters, but, surprisingly, not for von Braun. He never lost his serene mood and high spirits. To his co-workers, he described positive steps forward in exciting detail, and he reported the delaying tactics as if they were not really relevant. Years later, he confided to friends: *"From about 1956 on, I was convinced that the Moon-landing project would succeed, and after 1958, I had no doubt that it would be assigned to a civilian space agency, and that our team would play a major role in the project. All these ups and downs were merely ripples on the surface."*

What was the source of this unperturbable belief? For von Braun, it was really firm knowledge, rather than only belief. There were probably three sources: first, a profound understanding of human nature, particularly of individuals who occupy highly responsible positions. This ability allowed him to anticipate who would prevail with his views, and who would withdraw when he met with resistance. Second, a keen sense of observing all the other players in the game, coupled with a tremendous memory for technical as well as human details. Third, his very special gift of communication, or rather persuasion while he was communicating. His practice of *"letting others have his way"* opened countless doors for him throughout his life. He was aware of this ability, and he used it profusely! Wherever he traveled, he tried to meet as many people as possible, old friends and new ones. He described, explained, suggested, stimulated, encouraged, pleaded—but always in a pleasant, warmhearted way. With very few exceptions, he always left the desire in the other person to cooperate with him, to support his projects, to pull the same rope, and to be, even indirectly, a member of his team.

There were other reasons, too, why von Braun was optimistic. Many of the people involved in rocket-related work in government offices, the military services, universities, and industry, were true believers in an American space program, and they were eager to help bring a journey to the Moon to life as soon as they saw an opportunity.

Early in 1958, after Secretary of Defense McElroy had established ARPA under Roy M. Johnson, two members of that agency, Richard Canright and David Young, visited von Braun to discuss possible contributions of ARPA to a Moon project. *"We should move forward in discrete steps,"* von Braun suggested to his visitors, *"and develop a large booster in consecutive phases, beginning with the clustering of engines that either exist now, or will be available soon."* Canright then asked: *"How much funding will this require?"*—*"How much do you have?"* von Braun inquired.—*"I'm sorry, a mere 10 million dollars is all I could provide you,"* was Canright's reply. Von Braun's eyes flashed: *"That's wonderful,"* he exclaimed, *"send us the 10 million, and the big project will be on its way!"*

ARPA did send the $10 million. Von Braun and his team members, primarily Hermann H. Koelle and his Future Projects Office, proposed a booster with eight Jupiter engines built by Rocketdyne. Roy Johnson accepted the proposal, and in August 1958 the big booster project was born.

Shortly after this initiation of the Moon rocket project, NASA established the Space Task Group at its Langley Research Center under Robert R. Gilruth, an aeronautical engineer from NACA. The Space Task Group was to develop a spacecraft, the Mercury capsule, for the flight of astronauts into orbit and back. This work developed into the Mercury program, and then into the Gemini program. Later, it led to the Apollo capsule that was used in the manned Moon project. As the program grew quickly in size, the Space Task Group evolved into the Manned Spacecraft Center (from 1973 on, the Johnson Space Center) in Houston, Texas, with Gilruth as its director.

Following a suggestion by H. (Harvey) Julian Allen and further work by Maxime A. Faget, the Space Task Group decided to give the space capsule a conical shape, oriented with the blunt end in the forward direction. The curved bottom of the cone would act as a *"reentry body."* Covered with a surface material that would ablate under the intense heat generated during the capsule's descent through the atmosphere, it would absorb and dissipate most of the capsule's kinetic energy. Finally, the capsule would deploy a parachute and fall gently into the ocean where the Navy would recover capsule and astronaut.

Three Mercury capsules were launched into ballistic trajectories with Redstone rockets, the first with a chimpanzee, Ham, on 31 January 1961; the second on 5 May 1961 with America's first astronaut, Alan B. Shepard; and the third with Virgil I. (Gus) Grissom in July of the same year.

After Ham's, but before Shepard's flight, on 12 April 1961, Soviet Major Yuri A. Gagarin accomplished the first human orbital flight in a Vostok capsule.

Orbital Mercury flights were launched with Atlas rockets. Enos, a chimpanzee, was America's first orbiting astronaut, followed on 20 February 1962 by John H. Glenn who orbited the Earth three times. M. Scott Carpenter, Walter M. Schirra, and L. Gordon Cooper also made orbital flights with Atlas-launched one-man Mercury capsules.

Half a year after Shepard's first space flight in a Redstone-Mercury capsule, plans for the next generation of space capsules, the Gemini spacecraft, were initiated. Launched into orbit with Titan II rockets, they carried two astronauts. After two unmanned orbiting flights, a series of ten manned Gemini flights were undertaken between March 1965 (Grissom and John W. Young) and November 1966 (James A. Lovell and Edward E. Aldrin).

The Gemini program, developed and managed by Gilruth, proved to be a great success. Its purpose was the development of techniques for orbital rendezvous and docking, and for extravehicular activities (EVA). Rendezvous and docking exercises were performed between Titan-launched Gemini capsules and Atlas-launched Agena spacecraft. The program achieved a total of 2,000 man-hours in orbit, and 12 hours of extravehicular work. Problems of adequate positioning of the astronauts during the high-acceleration ascent of the launch rocket, aerodynamic behavior of cone-shaped capsules during their transition from supersonic to subsonic velocities, as well as the functioning of the capsule's ablation-type heat shield, and finally the parachute landing, could be observed and analyzed in detail. As a result, the three-man Apollo capsule could be designed and built on the basis of actual flight data. At the conclusion of the program, NASA was ready to approach the voyage to the Moon with full confidence.

The plea for a lunar landing mission by the Goett committee in October 1959 (Chapter 7-5) certainly was one of the milestones in the history of the Moon project. John M. Logsdon [8-3] wrote: *"Operating pretty much in a political vacuum in terms of policy guidance . . . , NASA planners chose a lunar landing objective fully two years before President Kennedy announced his choice of the lunar landing as a national goal."*

Following the Goett committee's resolve to push for a lunar landing mission, development work on the big booster intensified. A Saturn Vehicle Evaluation Committee was established under Dr. Abraham Silverstein, director of Space Flight Development at NASA. In December 1959, that committee made a far-reaching and also very courageous decision: all upper stages of the Saturn rocket should use liquid hydrogen and liquid oxygen as propellants.

Silverstein could base his hydrogen fuel decision on broad experience gained during a development program for liquid hydrogen-liquid oxygen rocket engines that had been going on for years under his leadership at the NASA-Lewis Research Center in Cleveland, Ohio, in cooperation with industrial contractors, mainly the Pratt & Whitney Aircraft Company. This energetic program led, for example, to the famous RL-10 engine that powered the Centaur stage, and also the upper stage of Saturn I. The second and third stages of Saturn V were propelled by the next generation of liquid hydrogen-oxygen engines, the powerful J-2 with 225,000 pounds (100,000 kilograms) thrust, built at Rocketdyne.

Hydrogen and oxygen would provide a far better performance than any of the conventional propellant combinations, a fact that had been recognized by Tsiolkovskii, Goddard, Oberth, and other rocket pioneers who had studied potential rocket propellants after them.

Liquid hydrogen as a rocket fuel came up in discussions at Peenemünde during the late 1930s. However, the technologies of production and handling of that fuel in large quantities did not exist at that time. Planning for hydrogen-oxygen rocket engines would have been hopelessly premature. Even fifteen years later, when von Braun worked on plans for large space rockets in the United States, he was reluctant to tackle hydrogen rockets. Because of its extreme volatility and its tremendous flammability, liquid hydrogen is far more dangerous to handle than other rocket fuels. While von Braun would have loved to build a hydrogen-oxygen rocket, he was afraid that a mishap during ground operations would be so catastrophic that it could serve a lethal blow to the entire rocket program.

Von Braun always felt that he and his team had to be particularly careful to avoid any accident caused by too much boldness. If the recommendation for a bold advance in technology came from one of his peers, it would have a far broader backing from the start, and the impact of an accident, should it occur, could be borne by more shoulders. When von Braun reported Silverstein's decision to his staff, the first reaction was surprise, but it quickly turned into admiration, fullest concurrence, and a feeling of real gratitude. It is a remarkable fact that during more than twenty-five years of work with enormous quantities of liquid hydrogen, no significant accident during ground handling has occurred in the United States.

As the decade of the 1960s began, three powerful rocket engines were under development at Rocketdyne: an uprated version of the Atlas-Jupiter-Thor engine with 188,000 pounds (83,600 kg) thrust; a new liquid-hydrogen engine, the J-2; and the mighty F-1 engine with 1,500,000 pounds (670,000 kg) thrust. At that time, the configuration of none of the later Saturn vehicles had yet been determined. However, since the propulsion system for any of the future rockets would be its most decisive component, it was appropriate to push the development of the engines as vigorously as possible, and to design the rocket vehicles so that they would match their propulsion systems.

3   PRESIDENTIAL LEADERSHIP

When John F. Kennedy was elected President in 1960, his attitude toward spaceflight was unknown. He probably had not yet arrived at a firm position in his own mind. President Eisenhower, obviously, had not considered a national program for manned space travel to be an especially significant factor in the life and well-being of the country. His view was shared by some of his advisers, including the President's Scientific Advisory Committee (PSAC), and also by the Bureau of the Budget, while others, particularly members of Congress, NASA, the military services, many scientists, and industry, favored a strong governmental support of space activities.

After Eisenhower had signed the National Aeronautics and Space Act in July 1958, it became the legal basis for the creation of NASA, and also of the National Aeronautics and Space Council. The latter was to be chaired by the president. Two standing committees were established, the Senate Committee on Aeronautical and Space Sciences chaired by Lyndon B. Johnson, and the House Committee on Science and Astronautics headed by Overton Brooks. Both committees took a very positive stand for space, recommending a lunar landing before 1968. Although Congress was critical of Eisenhower's restrained attitude, the president remained conservative in his space aspirations; and, in 1960, even expressed the desire to abolish the Space Council. This move was blocked by Johnson [8-3].

An analysis of the goals, and an estimate of the cost, of a Moon landing mission were undertaken by a PSAC ad hoc panel under Dr. Donald Hornig, chemistry professor at Brown University. When the president learned about the price of the Moon project in December 1960, he replied that he was *"not about to hock my jewels"* [8-6], referring to Queen Isabella of Spain when she financed Columbus in his search for a shorter route to the East. *"When they have finished this,"* one of the staff members added to the president's words, *"they want to go on to the planets."*

President Kennedy, after his election on 8 November 1960, decided that he would not abolish the Space Council, and appointed Johnson as chairman. On 21 March 1961, Senator Robert Kerr was named chairman of the Senate Committee on Aeronautics and Space Sciences. He in turn appointed Edward C. Welsh, legislative assistant to Senator Stuart Symington, as executive secretary of the Space Council. Welsh was not only a fervent and active supporter of the Moon project; he also enjoyed high respect from almost everybody involved.

James E. Webb became NASA's new administrator on 20 January 1961, after a very intense search. Should the NASA administrator be chosen for his skill in the administration of scientific programs, as Wiesner had proposed? Or should he be a distinguished scientist himself, as some scientists had suggested? Or should he possess political savvy, as Johnson and Kerr argued? Kennedy, accepting the suggestion of Johnson and Kerr, selected Webb from a slate of more than twenty candidates.

Webb had an unusually diversified background. He had left his mark of distinction as a lawyer, a businessman, a manager of large organizations, an administrator of science and education programs, as a marine aviator, and, under President Truman, as director of the Bureau of the Budget, and also as undersecretary of state. Even Wiesner agreed to this choice. It soon became evident that the President could not have selected a better person.

During the first months of 1961, Kennedy continued to receive differing, and even contradicting, advice from various sources around him [8-3]. When he asked for recommendations how to beat the Soviets in space, PSAC suggested that the Space Council should manage the national space program. Schriever, emphasizing the *"high potential for national security"* of a Moon landing project, suggested to put the Air Force in charge of the national program, while Overton Brooks opted strongly for a civilian program. Wiesner expressed the fear that a large manned space project would divert too many funds from purely scientific space endeavors. Johnson wanted *"general supervision"* over NASA by himself. To top it off, President Eisenhower's persistent warning of the *"military-industrial complex"* was still fresh in Kennedy's mind.

Webb's position was straightforward. He wanted to have a direct working relationship with the president, without interference by the vice president, the armed services, or any committee. Manned spaceflight had been assigned to NASA two years earlier; as NASA administrator, he wished to carry out this assignment as effectively as possible.

In retrospect, Webb's strategy during the initial phase of his new position emerges as a true masterpiece of superior management. First, there was a period of listening, questioning, learning, and debating, without an attempt to formulate his own opinion. He wished to get his hand on the pulse and determine how the space program would best fit into the overall fabric of the new administration. Second, he secured as much future support for the program as possible from individuals, offices, committees, panels, and agencies. Third, he weighed all the different views of a manned spaceflight program that were expressed at that time. Then, he formulated in his own mind a proper course of action as a compromise between a desirable and a feasible space program. Finally, he proposed this course of action to the president.

Webb began his work for NASA on 14 February. Two days later, he renominated Dr. Hugh L. Dryden as deputy administrator. On 24 February, NASA Associate Administrator Dr. Robert C. Seamans, Jr. briefed Webb and Dryden on NASA status and programs. At the very beginning of his appointment at NASA, Webb established a very tight and lasting working relationship with Dryden and Seamans. Next, Webb teamed up with two powerful personalities whose advice and support would be indispensable and even decisive: the secretary of defense, Robert S. McNamara, and the chairman of the Space Science Board of the National Academy of Sciences, Dr. Lloyd Berkner. Both were strong believers in a large space program for America.

Still holding back with personal pronouncements for a manned Moon program, Webb widened his understanding of this bold project, and also of the various space views held by the main players on the national scene. His close contacts with McNamara and Berkner permitted him to keep his distance from the Air Force, and also from some strictly science-oriented committees, both of which did not want to see the responsibility for a large man-in-space program concentrated in NASA's hands. He succeeded in establishing cooperative agreements between NASA and DOD, and also with the Bureau of the Budget, while his grasp of the technical complexities of a Moon landing project grew quickly under the tutoring of his NASA chieftains, particularly George Low, von Braun, Gilruth, and Kurt Debus, assisted by others.

A strong voice of support for the Moon project had come from the National Academy of Sciences' Space Science Board in February 1961. At that time, the board submitted a position paper on *"Man's role in the National Space Program"* which contained the following passages: *"... while the Board stressed the importance [of a manned journey to the Moon] as a scientific goal, it is not unaware of the great importance of other factors [such as] the sense of national leadership emergent from bold and imaginative U.S. space activity ... The members of the Board ... regard man's exploration of the Moon and planets as potentially the greatest inspirational venture of this century, and one in which the whole world can share ..."*

Kennedy could not afford to give much thought to the space program during the opening months of his administration. The mounting crisis in Laos, where the United States faced the problem of giving military support to the pro-American government against communist insurgents, spread its dark clouds over Kennedy's young administration. The president asked that more studies on space matters should be performed; he planned to arrive at decisions in the autumn of 1961, on time for budget preparations for fiscal year 1963.

Two further negative events were to follow soon: On 12 April 1961 the Soviet cosmonaut Major Yuri Aleksejevitch Gagarin, orbiting the Earth in a Vostok capsule, was celebrated around the globe as the world's first man in space, while the United States remained in the background. Hanson W. Baldwin, military correspondent of *The New York Times*, expressed the thoughts that came to the minds of many Americans. He stated that this country's posture in space matters has *"cost the nation heavily in prestige,"* and he concluded that *"... only Presidential emphasis and direction will chart an American pathway to the stars"* [8-7].

Only three days after America's prestige had suffered this blow, on 15 April, the ill-fated invasion of the Bay of Pigs in Cuba began; by 19 April, it had turned into a profound disaster for the non-communist Cubans, and it raised serious doubts about the ability of the United States to deal successfully with political, diplomatic, and military matters.

For Kennedy, the gain of prestige by the Soviets, and the severe prestige loss suffered by his country, must have been a source of grave concern. *"Is there any place we can catch them?"* he asked some of his advisers [8-8]. As Wiesner reported [8-9], he talked to *"hundreds of people"* in an effort to obtain an answer. He felt the need to assert his leadership, restore confidence and pride of the American people for their country, and retain respect for the U.S. Government abroad.

It appears that during April 1961 he came to the conclusion that a manned Moon program would be the best, and perhaps the only available project capable of achieving that goal. However, he still did not decide between Wiesner's proposal against a large Moon program, and Johnson's proposal that was strongly for it. Even Webb was still reluctant to commit himself firmly to a manned lunar landing project. He wanted to ascertain first beyond any doubt that such a big project would have the necessary support from DOD, the scientists, the Bureau of the Budget, and Congress.

On 20 April, Kennedy wrote a memorandum to his vice president [8-10]: *"... I would like to ask you as Chairman of the Space Council to be in charge of making an overall survey of where we stand in space ... Do we have a chance of beating the*

Soviets by putting a laboratory in space, or by a trip around the Moon, or by a rocket to land on the Moon, or by a rocket to go to the Moon and back with a man?" A number of short, but incisive questions followed, ending with the request *"I would appreciate a report on this at the earliest possible moment . . ."*

Johnson was the most consistent and intrepid fighter for a manned Moon landing project, next to von Braun and a few others. His campaign for a strong space program had actually begun within hours after the launch of Sputnik on 4 October 1957 [8-11]. As Senate majority leader, he started inquiries, subcommittees, investigations, hearings, and bills. He buttonholed his colleagues in Congress, made speeches across the country, and prepared the building blocks for a new aggressive space legislation.

Kennedy's request of 20 April gave Johnson a welcome opportunity to make a forceful plea for *"his"* space program. Supported by Welsh, he gathered the latest views on the most desirable space projects from a broad spectrum of sources: NASA, DOD, BOB, AEC, and PSAC [8-12]. The replies of three men to whom Johnson had written personal letters reflected a very vigorous support for a manned Moon project: General Schriever, Admiral Hayward, and von Braun. Schriever, by that time commander of the Air Force Systems Command, urged that this program should be pursued because *". . . we need a major national space program for prestige purposes, . . . [for] national security implications, and because of the need for advancing technology."* Vice Admiral John T. Hayward, deputy chief of Naval Operations for Research and Development, argued that *". . . only the lunar mission makes sense as a means of accelerating the space program,"* but he also pleaded that *". . . practical applications of space technology, . . . such as the use of satellites for navigation, reconnaissance, communications, and weather prediction, not be neglected in any acceleration of the program."*

Johnson had known von Braun from numerous discussions and briefings. His interest in space projects had always been a source of great encouragement for von Braun and his team. Johnson certainly expected, and even counted on von Braun's reply which would contain substantial technical details as well as convincing arguments in favor of a space program as the vice president wished it to come to life.

Von Braun took great care in formulating answers to Kennedy's questions in a long memorandum to Johnson, corroborating his statements with many technical details [8-13]. *"We do not have a good chance of beating the Soviets to a manned 'laboratory in space,'"* he wrote, nor to several other similar achievements; however, *"we have an excellent chance of beating the Soviets to the first landing of a crew on the Moon (including return capability, of course) . . ."*

In concluding, von Braun said: *"I should like to say that in the space race we are competing with a determined opponent whose peacetime economy is on a wartime footing . . ."*

Johnson lost no time answering President Kennedy's questions as soon as he had all the replies to his own inquiries in hand. On the day when he had received von Braun's answer, he wrote a memorandum to the president [8-14]: *"Subject: Evaluation of Space Program."*

"Largely due to their concentrated efforts and their earlier emphasis upon the development of large rocket engines," Johnson wrote, *"the Soviets are ahead of the United States in world prestige attained through impressive technological accomplishments in space . . . The U.S. has greater resources than the USSR for attaining space leadership, but has failed to make the necessary hard decisions, and to marshal those resources to achieve such leadership."*

After a fervent plea for action to establish leadership in space, Johnson wrote: *"We should move forward with a bold program . . ."* As for the specific questions posed in the president's memorandum, he carefully answered some of them in considerable length, others briefly, but to the point. All of his answers reflected von Braun's thoughts closely.

In this memorandum, and particularly in his statements and speeches about the space program at that time, Johnson had an even broader program in mind than von Braun. Besides manned exploration of the Moon, he emphasized such goals as military preparedness, economic stimulation, commercial uses, scientific discoveries, and technological progress. While von Braun absolutely shared this all-encompassing view of spaceflight activities, he stuck to his one-project-at-a-time principle when he proposed immediate action by the president. *"Let's land a man on the Moon . . . [and] put all other elements of our national space program on the back burner,"* he recommended in his memorandum to Johnson. To his co-workers in Huntsville, he would say: *"We must put into one sharp focus what we wish to accomplish. If we propose too many projects at one time, we will achieve nothing."*

Even during this time of determined effort, Webb retained his cautious, albeit very alert attitude. The content of von Braun's memorandum to Vice President Johnson was, of course, well known to him. Intent on retaining the support of the science community, he wrote a letter to Wiesner on 2 May 1961, urging him *"to make sure that this component of solid, and yet imaginative total scientific and technological value is built in . . ."* [8-15].

A most encouraging event happened on 5 May: Commander Alan B. Shepard, as the first American Astronaut, made a 15-minute ballistic rocket flight in a Mercury capsule, launched by one of von Braun's Redstone rockets. This flight provided a much-needed element of assurance to the president, and to others as well, that a human being could safely be trusted to a high-flying rocket.

More meetings, discussions, and debates followed. A large group, including members of NASA, DOD, BOB, and other organizations, set out to write a memorandum to be given to President Kennedy by the vice president. The final form of this memorandum was signed by Webb and McNamara on 8 May [8-16]; it contained the following passages:

"Dramatic achievements in space therefore symbolize the technological power and organizing capacity of a nation. It is for reasons such as this that major achievements in space contribute to national prestige"; and *"We recommend that our National Space Plan include the objective of manned lunar exploration before the end of this decade."*

On 10 May, President Kennedy approved the program as set forth in the Webb-McNamara memorandum. Two weeks later, on 25 May, Kennedy gave his famous speech in Congress on *"Urgent National Needs,"* in which he said: *"Now it is time to take longer strides—time for a great new American enterprise—time for this Nation to take a clearly leading role in space achievement which in many ways may hold the key to our future on Earth . . . ,"* and *"I believe that this Nation should commit itself to achieving the goal, before this decade is out, of landing a man on the Moon and returning him safely to Earth."*

Senator Robert Kerr, who for years had been supporting consistently the fight for a vigorous space program, said: *"This program is one which will enable Americans to meet their destiny"* [8-17], and John Logsdon, professor of political history at George Washington University, wrote: *"The politics of the moment had become linked with the dreams of centuries and the aspirations of a nation, and the result was the identification of space success as a crucial factor in fostering the American national interest"* [8-3].

4   WHICH WAY TO THE MOON?

Detailed plans describing the step-by-step program for the journey to the Moon and back to Earth were not at all firm in the summer of 1961, although a great number of studies concerning this subject had been made during previous years. All these studies agreed on one point: The lunar mission should consist of two major phases; first, transporting the spacecraft with a powerful launch rocket from Earth into an Earth-circling orbit, or at least to orbital altitude, and second, travel of the spacecraft from the vicinity of the Earth to the Moon, and back to Earth.

Transition from the launch phase to the lunar transfer phase, descent to the lunar surface, ascent from the Moon, return trip toward the Earth, and finally landing on the Earth would be a sequence of procedures that followed the launch from Earth. Even before their details were known, it had become obvious that the launch rocket must have the capability of lifting an upper section with a total mass on the order of 220,000 to 260,000 pounds (100 to 120 metric tons) into an Earth orbit, or at least to orbital altitude. This upper section, containing the lunar transfer vehicle, must then be able to dispatch this vehicle toward the Moon and return the astronauts safely to Earth.

The powerful launch rocket, later to be called Saturn V, was the goal of the *"phased development program"* that von Braun had begun to contemplate in 1953, and to discuss with his co-workers from about 1955 on. In 1958, he could start actual development with Dick Canright's initial allocation of $10 million. As the program evolved, it produced the Saturn I and Saturn IB rockets, and finally the Saturn V, whose engine, the F-1, had its origin in an early Air Force contract with Rocketdyne [Chapter 8-5].

The most direct approach to a manned voyage to the Moon and back to Earth would follow a concept in which a huge, five-stage rocket would carry a manned capsule as its top payload. The first three stages, burning in quick sequence, would propel the two upper stages, and the capsule, into the transfer trajectory toward the Moon without stopover in a satellite orbit. Upon arrival in the vicinity of the Moon, the fourth stage would be ignited; it would slow down the approach velocity of the vehicle in such a way that the rocket ship, nozzle first, would gently set down on the lunar surface. The return trip would begin with the firing of the fifth stage, using the burnt-out fourth stage as a launch platform. This stage would propel the payload capsule into the return trajectory. In the vicinity of the Earth, the atmosphere would slow down the payload capsule sufficiently so that it would be able to unfold a parachute and land gently on one of the Earth's oceans.

This *"direct mode"* was the preferred concept of Gilruth's Space Task Group at the NASA Langley Research Center in Virginia. It involved the least complex sequence of space maneuvers, but it would need a launcher almost twice as powerful as Saturn V. That super rocket, tentatively called Nova, existed only as a vague concept on planning papers. If implemented, the Nova rocket would require a completely new set of manufacturing and testing facilities, just because of its enormous size.

Von Braun and his team studied another concept, the Earth orbit rendezvous or EOR mode. That plan provided for the simultaneous launching of two Saturn V rockets. The two vehicles would meet in orbit, each carrying a full payload. One payload would consist of the lunar spacecraft for the roundtrip from Earth orbit to the Moon and back to Earth; the other would be a tanker, ready to fill the empty tanks of the spacecraft in orbit before it began its transfer trip to the Moon. The first stage of the spacecraft, like the third stage in the direct mode, would propel two more stages and the manned capsule toward the Moon. Landing on the Moon and return to Earth would follow a pattern as described for the direct mode.

The main reason why von Braun preferred the EOR mode over the direct mode was the availability of the launch vehicle. Saturn V was an ongoing project at that time. Its development represented a step in rocket technology which was still manageable. Nova, on the other hand, would be the first member of a new generation of launch vehicles, requiring a very considerable extension in time and cost of the entire Moon landing project beyond the limits envisioned when the program began. Landing on the Moon *"before this decade is out,"* as President Kennedy had promised in May 1961, would be out of the question.

There was a second reason why von Braun's preference fell on the EOR mode. For him, the journey to the Moon would not be an end in itself; rather, it would represent but one chapter in the exciting story of man's spacefaring adventures. Unmanned satellites, manned satellites, Earth-to-orbit shuttles, voyages to the Moon, voyages to Mars—it was the beginning of man's reach into space, the transition from *homo terrestris* to *homo spatialis*. Operations in Earth orbit, such as rendezvous maneuvers, transfer of propellants, assembly of space vehicles, and also spacecraft modifications and repair, and particularly rescue operations, should be developed. For von Braun, each spaceflight project was part of an organism that grew and evolved almost like a living system. *"Let's not consider the journey to the Moon as a 'Kilroy was here' affair,"* he would say to his co-workers. *"This project will be a milestone in man's spaceflight enterprise. Each future project will directly benefit from it."*

The Earth orbit rendezvous mode would provide an ideal opportunity, almost without extra cost, to develop Earth orbit operational capabilities. They would at first serve the Moon landing project, and then, for all the future, they would be available as proven technologies for many other projects, including space station support, refueling of spacecraft, deep space mission staging functions, maintenance of scientific and commercial platforms, repair and rescue operations, and assembly of manned space vehicles for Mars expeditions.

Besides the direct and the Earth orbit rendezvous modes, there was the *"lunar orbit rendezvous"* or LOR mode. Under this concept, a single big launch rocket would take off and, after a short stopover in a near-Earth orbit, continue its flight toward the Moon. Three stages would be used for the ascent into Earth orbit; then, the third stage would be restarted to insert the transfer vehicle into the lunar transfer trajectory. That vehicle would consist of three more stages, and the payload system.

That system would contain two capsules built for astronaut occupancy; one of them would land on the Moon, the other would carry the astronauts back to Earth. The first of these three upper stages would put the entire space vehicle into a satellite orbit around the Moon. From there, two stages and the Moon landing capsule would descend toward the lunar surface, landing by braking its speed with retro-rocket thrust. Lunar exploration by the astronauts would begin, while stage number one, including the Earth return capsule, would continue to orbit the Moon.

For return, the third stage, leaving the empty second stage and the lower part of the landing module on the Moon, would take the capsule with the astronauts back into orbit where it would rendezvous with the first stage for the return flight to Earth. Upon reaching the outer fringes of the Earth's atmosphere, the cone-shaped return capsule with the astronauts would separate from the rest of the vehicle. Aerodynamic forces would slow the capsule down sufficiently so that a parachute could be deployed that would take the capsule slowly to the surface of the ocean.

This LOR concept of a lunar journey was not a new idea. Yuri Va. Kondratyuk, a Russian rocket and spaceflight pioneer, described in 1916 how a spacecraft visiting another celestial body could remain in a circular orbit around that body, while only a landing craft, together with an ascent stage, would descend to the surface [8-18]. Twelve years later, in 1928, Kondratyuk published his idea of aerobraking a space vehicle in the Earth's atmosphere when it returned from a space mission [8-19]. Von Braun had proposed both schemes in his book *The Mars Project*. His Mars travelers, leaving their spaceship in a Martian orbit, would use a Martian excursion vehicle for the descent to the surface and return to the orbiting ship. Around the same time, H. E. Ross worked out details for a similar lunar rendezvous scheme, published by the British Interplanetary Society in 1948 [8-2].

Two space planners at the Chance-Vought Corporation, Thomas E. Dolan and Edward Marshall, promoted the lunar rendezvous technique in 1958 [8-20]. Missions of this type were also studied by a group of engineers under the leadership of Clint Brown and William Michael at the NASA Langley Research Center in 1960 [8-21]. In August 1960, another engineer at the Langley Center, Dr. John C. Houbolt, proposed the lunar orbit rendezvous mode for the Saturn-Apollo project [8-22], arguing that this mode would require far less propulsive energy than the other two modes, because the Earth return stage and the reentry capsule need not be taken down to the lunar surface and up again into orbit. He showed that with the LOR mode a lunar landing mission could be accomplished with a single Saturn V launch, while the EOR mode would require two Saturn V rockets plus their rendezvous in orbit, and the direct mode would even necessitate the development of an entirely new Nova super rocket. On 16 May 1961, Houbolt wrote to Seamans and made a passionate plea for the LOR mode.

Earlier that month, Low had stated to Seamans that a manned lunar landing would be feasible with existing technologies, either with a direct flight from Earth to the Moon, or with a spacecraft rendezvous in Earth orbit (EOR). Seamans subsequently established a task group under William Fleming that confirmed Low's statement [8-23].

Perhaps as a result of Houbolt's letter, Seamans on 25 May 1961 established another task group under Bruce Lundin, director of the NASA-Lewis Research Laboratory, that was to study various ways in which a lunar landing could be accomplished [8-24]. By that time, the three possible modes—direct flight from Earth to the lunar surface; Earth orbit rendezvous; and lunar orbit rendezvous—had been joined by a fourth mode, suggested by the Jet Propulsion Laboratory [8-25]. In that proposal, several Saturn rockets would be launched unmanned to the Moon, placing a return vehicle, rocket propellants, and exploration equipment in close proximity of each other on the lunar surface. A return vehicle would be assembled on the Moon from components, erected to its launch position, fueled, and checked out by automatic procedures. When everything was ready for the return flight, an astronaut would be launched from Earth directly to the vicinity of the return vehicle.

The Lundin Committee selected the EOR mode as its first choice [8-26]. Working out a time schedule and funding requirements was assigned by Seamans to another committee under Air Force Colonel Donald H. Heaton on June 20 [8-27].

Feasibility, time schedules, and funding needs were only part of the concerns of government planners. What kind of project would be best from a national standpoint that had to consider NASA and Air Force commonality, defense needs, prestige, and competition with Russian space accomplishments? Seamans conferred with Assistant Secretary of Defense John Rubel, while Webb wrote to McNamara. A joint NASA-DOD study was initiated under Nicholas Golovin in July 1961. However, an accord between Air Force planners and NASA engineers for a unified national program could not be reached. The committee report in the fall of 1961 stated only that EOR should be the preferred concept for a lunar landing mission.

An almost frantic search for the best way to accomplish a Moon landing mission persisted at NASA Headquarters, MSC, and MSFC through most of 1961.

Gilruth and his co-workers, having studied lunar landing missions since 1959, were hesitant to accept the LOR mode because these very complicated maneuvers for the lunar orbit rendezvous had to be executed almost entirely by computer-controlled automatic procedures, largely on the backside of the Moon while spacecraft and earthbound control stations had no contact with each other. Also, Gilruth found that the proponents of the LOR mode had grossly underestimated the complexity, the total mass requirements, and the inherent dangers of that scheme. *"By the way,"* von Braun remembered in 1970 [8-28], *"Max Faget, Houston's key systems man, was probably the most vocal with respect to the inadequacies of the original Houbolt proposal . . . The discrepancy between [this] proposal and the real world is best shown by two figures: Houbolt's fully loaded and fueled lunar excursion module was to weigh a little less than 10,000 pounds. When the spacecraft was actually built a few years later for Apollo 11 that made the first landing on the Moon, it weighed over 30,000 pounds!"*

Von Braun did not wish to give up the rescue possibility of the near-Earth rendezvous maneuver, and he also emphasized the great value of the development of an Earth orbit rendezvous technology for many future space projects. Avoiding an exclusive stand for the EOR mode, he urged further analytical studies of the different modes.

Members of the Marshall Center and of Gilruth's Space Task Group (STG) established close working relations for this purpose early in 1960. There were frequent meetings at the *"working level,"* when STG engineers expressed surprise at the fact that this level included von Braun personally! Indeed, von Braun involved himself very deeply in all technical discussions. He was always more polite toward STG members than toward his own co-workers at MSFC, but when it came to his relentless drive for highest quality of work, from early planning all the way to the finished product, he made no distinction between men from MSFC and from STG, or between employees from government and from industry. This had been his personal pattern for forty-five years. However, most of those who joined him in working level meetings are likely to share the feeling of the violin player who said of his symphony orchestra conductor Maestro Toscanini: *"He was a tough task master, but he made me play my violin better than I would ever have thought I could play it!"*

In November 1960, the Space Task Group was raised to the status of a full-fledged NASA Center, the Manned Spacecraft Center (MSC), later to be named Johnson Space Center after Vice President Lyndon B. Johnson. This move was not only natural in view of the gigantic task Gilruth faced after accepting his share in the Moon landing project; it also provided, from a management and administrative standpoint, the proper balance between von Braun's launch rocket group and Gilruth's lunar vehicle group. In the summer of 1962, MSC moved from the NASA Langley Research Center, Virginia, to Houston, Texas, where proper facilities for the fast-growing Center had been built.

All through 1960 and much of 1961, MSC favored the direct mode for the journey to the Moon, while MSFC gave preference to the Earth-orbit rendezvous mode. Members of NASA Headquarters, among them D. Brainerd Holmes, Nicolas E. Golovin, Milton Rosen, and presidential adviser Jerome Wiesner, also opted for the EOR mode. In July 1961, MSC and MSFC established several work panels, after considerable prodding by von Braun's deputy Eberhard Rees, to address the mounting problems of matching the launch phase with the lunar transfer phase. Later that year, Gilruth suggested the development of *"a launch vehicle with sufficient performance and reliability to carry out the lunar landing mission using the direct approach . . ."* [8-29]. Both the LOR and the EOR modes, he feared, would not guarantee sufficient *"mission reliability and flight safety,"* and he expressed the suspicion that rendezvous modes were proposed only *"to avoid the difficulty of developing a reliable Nova class launch vehicle,"* a suspicion that definitely contained an element of truth.

While the exchange of opposing views between MSC and MSFC persisted through 1961, Houbolt crusaded for the lunar rendezvous mode, with the main argument that this mode would require the least amount of propulsive power to transport man to the Moon's surface and back to Earth. This claim was certainly correct. However, its proponents, in the view of its opponents, did not give enough weight to the very complex rendezvous and alignment problems far away from Earth, some of them occurring behind the Moon. Demands to be met by the flight computers would be really exorbitant, and so would be the task of providing contingencies for this complicated sequence of events, i.e., emergency actions and solutions in case something should go wrong during flight.

This divergence of opinions led to an enormous number of studies and reports. As Seamans remarked several years later [8-30], no other question in the entire spaceflight program was ever studied and debated to such an extent. Approximately one million man-hours were expended in an effort to find out which way to the Moon would be the best. In June 1961, the Fleming Committee determined that the direct mode should be chosen; however, this suggestion did not bring the problem closer to a consensus either. While work on the Saturn program, as well as on the Atlas-Agena and the Titan-Gemini programs for the development of rendezvous techniques, progressed very nicely during 1961 and 1962, work on the actual flight to the Moon could not start because the scheme of how to get there had not been decided.

Saturn I achieved its maiden flight on 27 October 1961. This was the first of a string of ten successful Saturn I launchings.

An important event happened on 1 November 1961: NASA established the Office of Associate Administrator for Manned Space Flight under D. Brainerd Holmes. Shortly after assuming responsibility for the Moon landing program, Holmes instituted the Management Council with representatives from several Headquarters offices, MSC, MSFC, and the Launch Operations Directorate in Florida (later named Kennedy Space Center, KSC). The Council members met regularly to discuss, debate, and resolve pending problems, a much needed management function that quickly proved very beneficial to the Saturn-Apollo project.

In an effort to settle the question how the lunar landing should be achieved, Holmes asked Milton Rosen, his director of Launch Vehicles and Propulsion, in November 1961 to study this question with an appropriate working group. After much analyzing and debating, the Rosen group cast its vote for the EOR mode [8-31].

During the autumn of 1961, the lunar mission mode question dominated the thinking of project planners at NASA Headquarters and at the field centers; it led to countless presentations and debates, some of them quite heated. *"There was a tremendous tension between NASA Centers,"* said Dr. Joseph F. (Joe) Shea who worked for Holmes in headquarters at that time. Ludie Richard and Joseph (Joe) DeFries were among the main spokesmen at MSFC, while Charles W. (Chuck) Mathews and Charles Frick campaigned for MSC. John H. Disher, head of Advanced Manned Systems at NASA, remembered those times twenty-five years later [9-39]: *"This polarization was really strong, complicated by some personal animosities . . . Von Braun was conciliatory and was willing to give in for the best of the program . . . Bob Gilruth—I can't say that he had a similar bent."*

Silverstein held on to the direct mode. *"Incidentally,"* Seamans said in 1986, *"Abe Silverstein to this very day does not think that the LOR was a good idea."*

One day late in 1961, von Braun came back from another lunar mode meeting. *"There is a new twist,"* he told his associates. *"Bob Gilruth has begun to drop his concerns regarding the need for a totally computer-controlled rendezvous operation on the rear side of the Moon. Apparently, the computer people at IBM have made tremendous progress. Bob is now quite comfortable with the LOR mode."* From that time on, von Braun was less ardent in his plea for the EOR mode. On the other hand, he lost no opportunity to emphasize the urgent need for realistic design data for the lunar mode system. *"The weight figures John [Houbolt] presents are totally inadequate,"* he said. Indeed, Houbolt assumed an unpressurized lunar excursion module; the astronauts would have to remain clothed in their pressurized suits for the whole time from descending to the Moon until, three and one half days later, they would ascend and dock with the orbiting transfer vehicle. Also, there was no allowance for safety measures, contingencies, redundancy, and other elements of systems design that were most important, and even decisive, in the view of space mission designers. On 15 November 1961, Houbolt wrote to Seamans: *"Give us the go-ahead, . . . and we will put man on the moon in very short order!"* [8-33]. George Low in the NASA Office of Manned Space Flight had become convinced by that time that LOR would be the best mode. Gilruth and his team followed suit by the end of 1961. In Washington, Wiesner, Golovin, and Holmes held fast to EOR, while Rosen's working group now considered the direct mode the best, based on a vaguely defined Nova launch vehicle. *"If a rendezvous mode must be chosen,"* they wrote, *"then EOR is still preferable to LOR"* [8-4; 8-25].

Gilruth's swing to the LOR mode was understandable in the light of the remarkable progress achieved in the area of guidance and control computers for automatic flight maneuvers. After he had convinced himself that the Saturn V would be capable of transporting a lunar transfer vehicle and a lunar excursion module that would be much heavier than what Houbolt had originally presented, he and his center gave formal support to Houbolt's lunar orbit rendezvous mode in January 1962. In his justification, he said: *". . . one spacecraft could be designed specifically for lunar landing and take-off, while the other could be designed for flying to and from the Moon, and specifically for re-entry and Earth landing. As an additional bonus, this allows the tremendous industrial job to be divided between two major contractors . . ."* [8-3; 8-25]. These were convincing arguments indeed.

In spite of Gilruth's definite stand for the LOR, Holmes stated in January 1962 that *". . . the EOR is the working mode"* for the lunar project. Attempting to better understand the arguments of Gilruth at MSC and von Braun at MSFC, he sent Shea, Chief of his Systems Engineering Office, to both centers for clarification. Shea realized that each center knew relatively little of the other center's viewpoints, so he made a wise decision: Each center had to write a technical assessment of the other center's preferred mode [8-34].

Shortly after the members of MSC had decided to accept the LOR mode, von Braun one morning came to his usual board meeting, sat down on his chair, and said with the most carefree smile on his face: *"I have come to the conclusion that we should choose John Houbolt's lunar orbit rendezvous mode for our Moon project."*

He had fully expected, of course, that a storm would break loose among his co-workers who, after all, had worked and fought with him for many months to make the

EOR the accepted mode. The storm did break loose. *"Have you forgotten all your good arguments about the rescue capability? Do you realize how dangerously complex the rendezvous maneuvers will be in lunar orbit, more than 300,000 kilometers away from Earth, even behind the Moon? Are we going to give up the opportunity of developing an Earth orbit staging capability with Saturn V rockets?"*

In typical von Braun fashion, he let the storm rage for a while. Then he presented his arguments. They were, as usual, carefully and wisely chosen, compelling in their logic, and absolutely convincing. *"You see,"* he began, *"we have lost already so much time with our debating and quarreling. One fourth of this decade is already gone. In the remaining time, we can hope to achieve only [that mode which] requires the least amount of time. This will be the LOR scheme, because the flight testing program for that concept will be shorter than the flight testing programs that would be needed for either of the other two modes . . . It is true that the LOR mode will require a whole gamut of very sophisticated guidance and control maneuvers, including a critical rendezvous operation in lunar orbit . . . We will need mighty good computers . . ."*

Von Braun, keeping Kennedy's words *"before this decade is out"* in mind, became restless. *"We just cannot afford to continue in this state of limbo. While we talk and talk, the decade is ticking off. Had we been permitted to develop the EOR mode after the president had given the green light for the Moon project, we could have made it by 1969. It is too late now. We better forget, for the time being, the rescue capability in Earth orbit, and the development of a Saturn rendezvous and Earth orbit staging technology. Let's rally our forces behind John Houbolt's LOR mode, and let us put our best and total effort into this project. Bob Gilruth is already backing the LOR mode."*

There was another reason why von Braun felt encouraged to accept the LOR mode. *"The fact that neither MSC nor MSFC did originally propose or even support the LOR mode is an extra bonus in this decision. It was Langley's, and in fact John Houbolt's idea and crusade. There need not be any priority complex nor 'not-invented-here' syndrome either at MSC or at MSFC. Believe me, accepting the LOR mode will present us with our only chance to reach the Moon in this decade!"*

Von Braun's board members believed him. There were no further opposing views. Giving full credit to Houbolt, von Braun accepted the LOR mode as the one he and his team would fully support. After having indicated his concurrence with the LOR mode to members of MSC in April, he announced his decision formally in June 1962.

Neither Holmes, von Braun's boss in Washington, nor Wiesner were ready to give up the EOR mode, or even the direct mode. They were convinced that the two main arguments for the EOR mode, rescue capability and the development of techniques for staging and refueling of large rocket systems in Earth orbit, had unquestionable validity, and that an extra effort would be in order to make the Earth orbit rendezvous the accepted mode. Finally, under joint prodding by Gilruth and von Braun, Holmes gave in and backed the LOR mode. On 11 July, NASA officially concurred in the choice of the LOR mode. Wiesner and his President's Scientific Advisory Committee, and also Golovin, continued to express their doubts concerning the lunar rendezvous.

President Kennedy visited the Marshall Center on 11 September 1962. When he saw the plans and the first components of the gigantic Saturn V rocket, and also the huge test stands and all the other facilities for fabricating and testing, he exclaimed: *"That is wonderful! If I could only show all this to the people in Congress!"* Later, von Braun explained the flight schedule for the journey to the Moon, describing also the lunar orbit rendezvous mode. *"I understand Dr. Wiesner does not quite agree with this mode,"* the president interjected. Wiesner, the president's science adviser, replied: *"Yes, that's right. I believe that the direct mode is better."* Von Braun immediately found himself engulfed in a lively debate. Under normal conditions, without the president, his entourage of dignitaries, and the watchful eyes and ears of all the people from the news media, he would have relished this debate, defending his decision for the LOR mode. Wiesner believed that with a little saving here and there, and with less conservative safety margins, a direct-mode journey could be accomplished with only one Saturn V vehicle. Von Braun could have proven quickly that Wiesner's assumptions were too optimistic, and that his proposed plan would not be technically feasible. However, such a debate would have made Wiesner a loser in front of the president, his staff, and the press corps. This would have been extremely unfortunate and unwise. Von Braun became tense and nervous, talking in polite generalities. The president must have read the danger signal in von Braun's eyes. He quickly changed the subject and moved on.

Webb's definite and final approval of the LOR mode on 7 November 1962 cleared the way to the Moon. Von Braun's MSFC would provide the Saturn V launcher, complete with its all-inertial guidance system. Gilruth's MSC would develop the transfer stage, the lunar excursion module, and the reentry vehicle. The guidance, control, and navigation system for the three spacecraft would be developed under the auspices of Dr. Charles Stark Draper at the Massachusetts Institute of Technology (MIT). For the transition from launch rocket to lunar spacecraft, both MSFC's and MIT's guidance systems would join forces and share responsibilities.

The seven years between Webb's decision and the landing of Apollo 11 in Mare Tranquilitatis were filled not only with extremely hard work, but also with dramatic and even tragic events. For von Braun, the first three or four years of this period were the happiest in his life.

5   SATURNS, MOON SHIPS, REENTRY VEHICLES

An expedition to the Moon would consist of two major phases: the launch system that lifts the complete expeditionary force, with all its necessary equipment and the astronauts, away from the Earth's surface, and into the lunar transfer trajectory; and the spaceship that transports the astronauts on their 250,000 mile (400,000 km) trip to the Moon, lands them on the lunar surface, accommodates them while they walk and live on the Moon, and finally brings them back to their home planet.

The first phase of this gigantic project, Saturn, was the responsibility of von Braun's group in Huntsville. Responsibility for the second phase, Apollo, was in the hands of Gilruth and his group in Houston. NASA Administrator Webb and his staff of directors would be responsible for overall program direction. Theirs was primarily a management job, while Gilruth and von Braun were the focal points of creative action.

Awe-inspiring as all these tasks were, Gilruth's part was more complex, more difficult, more novel and unprecedented than von Braun's. He had to reach more deeply into the unknown regions of technology and science. The astronauts would be exposed to more critical and dangerous situations, and over a longer time period, during Gilruth's project phase than during von Braun's.

On the other hand, the violent rocket forces that were at work during ascent, the enormous stresses to which all components of the huge Saturn rocket would be exposed, the countless bolts and welds that had to hold the system together, the hundreds of valves, the thousands of switches, sensors, actuators, control lights and instruments whose proper functioning was indispensable for a successful flight—all of these parts of the launch rocket represented an aggregate of potential danger that was probably not smaller than the risk factor with which the space vehicle engineers had to cope.

Gilruth's career began at the National Advisory Committee for Aeronautics (NACA). *"I was an expert in the field of high-speed aerodynamics . . . out in the Mojave desert,"* he recalled in 1988 [8-35]. *"I was in the flight research section where we flew airplanes . . . I had read one of Wernher's articles in* Collier's, *and that got me interested . . . but I couldn't conceive of building a program such as he described . . . however, Wernher was a great salesman, he was absolutely superb. And he was very, very clever and forthright, and he always believed what he was saying . . ."*

Was there any early rocket and space work at NACA? Gilruth headed the Pilotless Aircraft Research Division at the Langley Research Center during the 1950s, and there was a need to test airplane models at transonic and supersonic speeds. *"There weren't any wind tunnels to do that in those days,"* Gilruth said, *"so we flew hundreds of rocket-powered airplane models from Wallops Island. That's how I got into the rocket business. The whole business of thinking about going to the Moon got started as a result of Shepard's suborbital Mercury flight on 5 May 1961,"* Gilruth remembered. *"We had done some preliminary thinking before Shepard, but I never thought we would do anything about going to the Moon back then . . . it was the President [Kennedy] who really got us started."*

NACA became NASA on 12 October 1958. At that time, the Space Task Group (STG) was established under the direction of Gilruth. It quickly grew to a size of 600 members. When von Braun was virtually alone in actively planning manned expeditions to the Moon, he expected to be in charge of astronaut selection and training as well as developing the lunar spacecraft itself. However, these functions were assigned to the newly created Space Task Group at the request of Gilruth. Though not happy with the ruling, von Braun accepted the decision without further debate. When STG was elevated to the Manned Spacecraft Center (MSC) in November 1960, von Braun and his deputy Eberhard Rees strongly supported the complete equality in status of the MSC and their own Marshall Center.

Gilruth's first assignment was *"to put a man in orbit."* Project Mercury resulted, with the suborbital flights of Shepard and Grissom in 1961, and the Earth-orbiting satellite flights of Glenn, Carpenter, Schirra, and Cooper in 1962 and 1963. After these one-man flights, Project Gemini followed with seven two-men orbital flights in 1965 and 1966, and a total of 2,000 man-hours in space. During the summer of 1962, MSC moved to Houston, Texas; in 1973, it was renamed Johnson Space Center (JSC).

Von Braun's MSFC and Gilruth's MSC were bound together by a joint project of fantastic dimensions. As teams, they were quite different. Von Braun's group had grown systematically over a period of twenty years; its core still contained some of the Peenemünde rocketeers who started building rockets before World War II. At any time during that period, the group had at least one specific major project to work on: the V-2, Redstone, Jupiter, Junos I and II, and the Saturn series—and each of these projects was an important milestone in the evolution of large, precision-guided rockets. Von Braun had always insisted in participating personally in every detail of each of his projects. His leadership was all-encompassing. Richard W. Cook, for many years von Braun's highly respected director of administration in Huntsville, remarked years after von Braun had left his Huntsville team: *"Wernher did not allow any one of his team members to acquire a color of his own . . ."* In contrast, Gilruth did allow many of his team members to acquire bright colors of their own: Charles A. Berry, Maxime A. Faget, Charles Frick, Caldwell C. Johnson, Ken Kleinknecht, Christopher C. Kraft, Eugene F.

Kranz, George M. Low, Charles W. Mathews, Joseph F. Shea, Sigurd A. Sjoberg, Donald K. Slayton, Robert F. Thompson, Walter C. Williams.

Most of the STG members had worked in aeronautical research and development work before. Now, in the lunar project, they were confronted with a variety of different projects that had to be developed concurrently: a Moon ship with propulsion systems; guidance, control, and navigation systems; life support systems; separation and docking capabilities; provisions for extra-vehicular activities; communication systems; a lunar descent and ascent system that would be capable of taking the astronauts gently down to the lunar surface, accommodating them during their stay on the Moon, and taking them up again to the orbiting spacecraft; and an Earth return vehicle that would enable the astronauts to reenter the atmosphere, to descend without overheating their capsule interior, and finally to come to rest softly on a watery surface. Above all, a number of astronauts for repeated journeys to the Moon had to be selected, trained, checked out, and prepared for their flights.

"All this is relatively straight forward," Gilruth said. *"But the real problems begin when you think of all the contingencies for which we have to be prepared, the 'what if' situations. What will you do in mid-space if a diode fails, or a valve gets stuck, or a battery loses power, or the water recovery system quits working, or a rocket engine does not reignite, or a computer garbles its commands, or the ground station and the spacecraft cannot talk to each other? We must be prepared somehow for all these eventualities . . ."*

Von Braun's product, the launch system, and Gilruth's product, the spaceships, would have to fit together perfectly, not only with their external configurations, but with their functions, their power systems, their testing and checkout procedures, their rescue provisions, and their communication and data systems, at least during the period of flight preparation, checkout, launch, ascent to orbit, and injection into the lunar transfer trajectory.

How did the Gilruth group and the von Braun group work together?

There were enough critics who predicted that *"this whole thing will never work."*

And yet, this whole thing worked. There was an artful management system that linked NASA Headquarters offices, MSC, MSFC, and launch operations in Florida, described in the next chapter. But beyond the management functions, there was the human element, without which even the best management system would be meaningless.

Gilruth, in retrospect, said [8-35]: *"We did not get along all that well initially. He [von Braun] was all out for his outfit in Huntsville, and he really wanted to get hold of the spacecraft business which I was in charge of. He would have liked to have the astronauts, too, and I wasn't about to give them to him. After a while he accepted the fact that we were going to run the astronaut program from Houston. Later, we would send astronauts down to talk with Wernher and his people. We had our differences, but long before the business was over we had become quite good friends . . . Once we got going, Wernher and I would agree on most things."*

Were there any reservations on MSC's part at having to associate with former wartime Germans?

"No, not at all," was Gilruth's reply. *"Once we got to know them, we liked them. [Kurt] Debus was a nice guy; he was very competent at running [launch operations at] the Cape. Eberhard [Rees], he's the salt of the Earth. And Wernher—those three were the ones I knew and worked with as they were on the Management Council . . . You're bound to have competition. If you don't have tension between outfits, they're no good . . . I could talk to Wernher much better than I could talk to Brainerd [Holmes] . . ."*

Von Braun, surely, would have assessed his relations with Gilruth in similar terms. At first, he was sometimes unhappy about MSC's slow start in the joint efforts, but he soon developed a high respect for Gilruth's engineering talents, and for his very sound, careful, and yet aggressive approach to all engineering problems. What von Braun would have praised most in his colleague would probably have been the unerring steadfastness with which he directed MSC's vast program through all the problems, pitfalls and difficulties that came up during these eleven years of the joint Saturn-Apollo program.

Had von Braun been asked who, in his opinion, deserves the highest credit for the success of the Moon project, he would have named President Kennedy first; without him, the program would not have come to life. But among the thousands of others who made decisive contributions to Saturn-Apollo, his first choice would certainly have been Gilruth.

The first member of the Saturn family, later to be called Saturn I, was powered by eight Atlas-Jupiter-Thor-type engines. The first Saturn I launch took place on 27 October 1961. Three Saturn I vehicles were launched as single-stage rockets, with water filled into the upper tanks to simulate the mass distribution of a three-stage rocket. During the second and third Saturn I launches, the water ballast tanks were ripped open by explosive charges near the peak altitudes of the trajectories (Project Highwater). The release of 114 metric tons (30,000 gallons) of water at an altitude of 105 kilometers (320,000 feet) resulted in the sudden appearance of a white spherical cloud, beautifully visible from the ground, with a relative size about equal to the image of the full Moon. It provided an opportunity to study effects of such clouds upon radio signal transmission to and from rockets.

From the fourth Saturn I on, each rocket had two stages; the second stage was propelled by a cluster of six liquid hydrogen-oxygen engines (RL-10) that had been developed for the Centaur project by the Pratt & Whitney Aircraft Company in cooperation with the NASA Lewis Research Center.

The Saturn I program's main objective was to develop the technique of multi-engine clustering, with all the related problems of handling large systems during assembly, checkout, testing, and launching. Saturn I launchings also tested stage separation techniques, components of the inertial guidance system, and communication links that were to be used on later Saturn flights. Eight of the ten Saturn I vehicles were built at the Marshall Space Flight Center in Huntsville; the remaining two were manufactured under contract by the Chrysler Corporation.

Saturn V's three stages would be powered by two new engines, the kerosene-oxygen first stage F-1, and the hydrogen-oxygen upper stage J-2. Although every component and every assembly was subjected to as much testing as possible on the ground, there were some functions that could not be tested on Earth-bound test stands, such as engine ignition or stage separation under conditions of weightlessness. Similarly, Gilruth could not ground-test the complicated maneuvers to be carried out by the different parts of the Moon vehicle. Von Braun's and Gilruth's needs were satisfied by a rocket vehicle, later to be named Saturn IB, that was big and powerful enough to allow testing of the J-2 engine, of the various modules of the Moon vehicle, and of components of the guidance and control systems for the Saturn V and the Apollo Moon ship.

Saturn IB, in its first stage, again used a cluster of eight engines. The second stage was powered by one of the new J-2 engines. The first four Saturn IBs, launched between February 1966 and January 1968, were unmanned. They tested Apollo's command and service module (CSM) combination, the guidance and navigation systems, the reentry capsule of the CSM, the lunar module (LM) with its descent and ascent engines, and other components. The next Saturn IB, launched on 11 October 1968, was manned; testing the operational capabilities of the CSM, it was given the designation Apollo 7. Three further Saturn IBs were launched during 1973 as part of the Skylab program, while the last Saturn IB, on 15 July 1975, conducted a manned rendezvous and docking mission with the Soviet spacecraft Soyuz during the Apollo-Soyuz Test Project.

In parallel to these Saturn I and IB flights, Gilruth's group carried out a very active flight test program with the two-men Gemini capsule, part of it in cooperation with MSFC. Boosted into orbit by Titan II rockets, Gemini spacecraft practiced rendezvous maneuvers with unmanned Agena spacecraft, docking, extra-vehicular activities, and controlled reentry. Ten Gemini flights were made between March 1965 and November 1966.

Conceptual design studies for the big Saturn rocket that was to launch the lunar expedition had been underway in von Braun's Future Projects Office under Hermann Koelle since 1960. The C-5 rocket, as it was called at that time, was configured with four F-1 engines in the first stage, for a total thrust of 6 million pounds (2,720 tons). That design, however, did not satisfy at least two rocket men: Milton Rosen, director of Launch Vehicles and Propulsion in NASA's Office of Manned Space Flight, and von Braun. Koelle shared their opinion.

The projected weights of the lunar transfer vehicle and the lunar landing vehicle, which had to be injected together into their lunar trajectory by the big Saturn rocket, kept growing as their conceptual designs at the Manned Spacecraft Center progressed. This meant an increasing demand on the carrying capability of the launch rocket. One day, as von Braun looked at the drawings of the first stage of the rocket, he pointed at the empty space between the four engines and said: *"Doesn't this big hole just cry for a fifth engine?"* [8-36].

Rosen had pleaded for a fifth engine since March 1961 [8-37]. Responding to this double-barreled request, NASA Headquarters approved the five-engine first stage in December of that year.

After this decision, planning for the big Moon rocket proceeded quickly, and von Braun's MSFC team laid the groundwork for the manufacturing of the stages. Procurement activities were very carefully and strictly controlled by NASA Headquarters under Webb's personal supervision. The launch rocket was to have five J-2 hydrogen-oxygen engines in the second stage, and one such engine in the third stage. Both the F-1 and the J-2 engines were already under development at that time at the Rocketdyne Division of North American Aviation in Canoga Park, California. The Boeing Company in Seattle was given a contract in December 1961 to build the first stage. Developing and manufacturing the second stage, S II, was contracted to North American Aviation in September 1961. The rocket's third stage, S IVB, would be similar to the second stage of Saturn IB, already under development at the Douglas Aircraft Company in Huntington Beach in California; Douglas received a contract in December 1961 to develop and manufacture the S IVB stage. The Instrument Unit, containing all the guidance and control, data system, flight computer, and telemetry equipment, including a three-axis gyro-stabilized platform, was developed and built by MSFC under the supervision of Hans Fichtner, with the IBM Corporation as subcontractor. MSFC was also responsible for the overall systems engineering of the Moon rocket, later (February 1963) to be called Saturn V.

Besides the big launch rocket and the composite lunar transfer and landing vehicle, a comprehensive facility was needed to assemble the huge Moon rocket, to set it up on a launch pad, to tank it and make final tests, to position it very precisely in the desired launch direction, and then to launch it toward its lunar target.

Launch facilities for von Braun's first rocket project in the United States, the Redstone, had been established in 1950 at Cape Canaveral in Florida where the Air Force had been launching rockets before. Kurt Debus, in charge of V-2 static testing at Peenemünde, became director of the Missile Firing Laboratory; he took up residence in Cocoa Beach south of Cape Canaveral, together with his deputy, Hans Gruene, and other members of Huntsville's Guided Missile Development Division. Their number grew quickly, and so did the launch facilities; they were ready for the first Redstone launching in 1953. Sixteen years later, they had grown into a huge array of launch pads, storage and checkout hangars, assembly buildings, shops, and other buildings, from where NASA's, the Air Force's, and some of the Navy's rockets were launched routinely.

A report, describing the dramatic history of the rocket launch center—NASA's part was later named the Kennedy Space Center—was written by Rocco A. Petrone [8-38]. A West Point graduate, Petrone joined von Braun's team in September 1952. Assigned to Debus's Missile Firing Laboratory in Florida, he developed launch pads and launch control stations (blockhouses) for the Redstone and Jupiter missiles that were shipped to Cape Canaveral for launching. Later, Petrone became Apollo program manager, and from 1966 to 1969, he was director of Launch Operations. His responsibilities included supervision of the construction of the gigantic VAB (Vertical Assembly Building, later called the Vehicle Assembly Building), of the *"crawler"* that carried the Saturn rockets in a vertical position from the VAB to the launch pad, and of two identical launch pads, Pad 39 A and Pad 39 B, with provisions for fuel and oxidizer tanking, mechanical and electric checkout, and launch.

After the first Moon landing mission, Saturn-Apollo 11, in July 1969, Petrone became director of the Apollo program at NASA Headquarters. Petrone recalled the early times at Cape Canaveral in 1989 [8-39]. *"I cannot overemphasize the extremely close relationship required between Huntsville and Florida. There were many times when I would have nightmares concerning a possible breakdown in the technical interfaces between the flight systems controlled by Huntsville and the ground systems in Florida . . . Interfaces were much more intricate and involved with the launch vehicle at Huntsville than with the spacecraft at Houston . . . Marshall had the largest accumulation of technical talent ever gathered for this endeavor . . . I had greatly admired the experienced and proven team in Huntsville in 1952, and it came into full flower for the Apollo program."*

Rocket components of that magnitude had never been built before. New methods for manufacturing and testing had to be developed. Existing companies even did not have hangars large enough. During the autumn of 1961, NASA took over the Michoud Ordnance plant near New Orleans where the Chrysler Corporation was going to manufacture the first stage of Saturn I, and Boeing the first stage of Saturn V. NASA also acquired land in Hancock County, Mississippi, and built firing test stands for the first and second stages of Saturn V. The first firing tests of the Saturn V first stage were made at MSFC in Huntsville where large test stands had been built under Karl Heimburg's guidance during the early 1960s.

About 90 percent of the total budget for the Saturn vehicle program went directly to industrial contractors. Very close working relationships between the companies and MSFC personnel developed quickly. At first, this tight elbow-to-elbow cooperation between industrial and government personnel was not always appreciated by the companies. Later, however, company members admitted that the close alliance with MSFC from the start on had been extremely helpful; problems could be worked out together as soon as they arose [8-40]. Rosen, head of the Launch Vehicle Office at NASA Headquarters, noted: *"All the expertise behind the V-2, Redstone, Jupiter, and Saturn I went into the [Saturn V work] at Boeing"* [8-41]. A detailed description of this highly complex history of Saturn V's development program, and of its many problems, crises, and accomplishments, was given by Roger E. Bilstein in his book *Stages to Saturn* [8-4].

Another, very different test facility resulted from an idea that von Braun began to promote during the mid-1950s: a huge water tank, big enough to accommodate even large components of space structures that would have to be handled and serviced by astronauts under the conditions of near weightlessness in space. Submerging such systems, balanced with appendages for neutral buoyancy, and equipping the *"simulated"* astronauts with diving gear, would create neutral buoyancy conditions that would be similar, at least in some respects, to conditions in space. Handling a component of a spacecraft that has its normal mass and inertia, but virtually no weight, could be practiced in this manner.

This idea met with much criticism from higher-ups who did not see any value in such exercises, but von Braun finally prevailed. The tank was built, and it proved to be one of the most useful test facilities in the space program. Besides many engineers and technicians, all the astronauts practiced in the tank. Von Braun personally spent many fruitful and pleasant hours underwater, playing astronaut. The Manned Spacecraft Center (later, Johnson Space Center) in Houston, realizing the great usefulness of the neutral buoyancy tank, also built such a facility, only bigger (being in Texas!) than the one in Huntsville.

As the Saturn program began to come to life, von Braun asked his Space Sciences Laboratory (the former Research Projects Laboratory) to make an estimate of the number and severity of meteoroid hits that a spacecraft in orbit or on a lunar journey would have to expect. It turned out that existing observational data on meteoroids in the desired size and frequency range were not only very meager, but also inconsistent. If reliable data was needed, new measurements would have to be made. A young physicist in the Space Sciences Laboratory, Dr. Charles A. (Chuck) Lundquist, suggested that large-area meteoroid sensors be flown on a satellite as large as the available two-stage Saturn I rocket could carry. The Pegasus project resulted, built by the Fairchild Corporation under contract to the Marshall Center; Dr. William G. Johnson was project manager. Three similar satellites were put in orbit in February, May, and July 1965; each had a sensor area of about 135 square meters (1,460 square feet).

All three Pegasus launches were successful. Assumed meteoroid impact numbers proved to be far too high; fears of disabling meteoroid hits on spacecraft as planned at that time were unwarranted. Even for the Skylab with its relatively thin skin, developed and built during the early 1970s, the probability of a dangerous meteoroid hit during its anticipated lifetime would be so low that a *"meteoroid bumper,"* to be attached to the outside of Skylab, was not recommended by the Space Sciences Laboratory. Von Braun, yielding to the desires of the designers who had already designed and built a meteoroid bumper, decided that it should be flown anyway.

When Skylab, during its launch in 1973, ascended through the atmosphere, the airflow tore part of the bumper shield off. Severe damage to Skylab resulted, including loss of one of its two solar power panels, and part of its heat protection. Very elaborate repair and rescue operations in orbit succeeded in saving the Skylab space station and its mission (Chapter 12-3).

Techniques for this rescue operation, which included the deployment, through a narrow airlock, of an umbrella-like sunshield, were tried out in lengthy practicing operations in Marshall's neutral buoyancy tank. Probably the rescue of Skylab, and its restoration to a satisfactory operational status, would not have succeeded without this underwater facility.

Among the many novel problems that confronted the Saturn designers and engineers was the question of the behavior of metallic structures exposed to the very low temperature of liquid hydrogen. The danger of embrittlement of metals and metallic alloys under this influence had been known for some time, at least as a potential danger. A lengthy *"liquid hydrogen embrittlement"* study and test program was initiated at MSFC, pioneered by Wolfgang H. Steurer, Karl Pschera, Rudolf H. Schlidt, Robert J. Schwinghamer, and others. The program continued successfully under the leadership of William R. Lucas with substantial cooperation from industrial companies.

Perhaps the most critical problem in the manufacturing of the huge tanks needed for Saturn V was the welding of the various tank segments. Again, MSFC had to pioneer new methods and techniques. Werner Kuers and his co-workers, together with the Saturn stage contractors, developed the proper welding and weld-testing methods, as described in detail by Bilstein [8-4]. The success of the Saturn program proves that satisfactory solutions were found for all these problems.

Initiation of the lunar project necessitated dramatic expansions of the Marshall Center's capabilities for manufacturing, assembly, and testing of large rocket systems. MSFC, under Webb's directive, decided in 1961 to build and test the first few vehicles of the Saturn I type, and at least individual stages of the Saturn IB and the Saturn V types, on its own premises in Huntsville. At the same time, again with strong Headquarters support, MSFC made plans to establish a production and test facility for Saturn stages at the Michoud Ordnance plant in Louisiana, not far from New Orleans. That plant, built on the site of a former sugar plantation and refinery, had been acquired by the federal government during World War II. First, Liberty ships were fabricated there; later, the buildings were used for the production of airplanes and tank engines. With a ceiling height of 35 feet (10.5 meters) and an area of 43 acres (17.4 hectares) under one roof, and with direct access to the Gulf of Mexico, that was an almost ideal place to manufacture Saturn stages.

Together with several hundred civil service employees from MSFC, a few thousand Chrysler, Boeing, General Electric, North American Aviation, and other contractors manufactured the first stages of the Saturn IB and the Saturn V rocket vehicles, taking the Huntsville-manufactured stages as prototypes. Welding the huge, thin-walled aluminum tank units for the stages presented a particular challenge; no similar work had ever been done before. Through very intense and successful joint efforts between government employees and contractors, TIG (tungsten inert gas) welding methods were developed, and X-ray testing procedures were introduced, which proved to be entirely adequate. The welding seams of one big Saturn stage covered a total length of 10 kilometers, and each centimeter of the seams was carefully X-rayed!

Two test stand facilities for the Moon rocket were eventually built, one in Huntsville, and one at the Mississippi Test Facility (MTF) on the Pearl River in Hancock County near Bay St. Louis, Mississippi. Several small communities had to be relocated when the huge MTF was built by the U.S. Army Corps of Engineers. The first static firing test of a Saturn V second stage at MTF took place in 1966. A year later, the first Saturn V first stage was tested on the big S-IC test stand at MTF. The Huntsville stand had even two test positions. It was ready for the first static test of a complete Saturn S-IC stage in 1965. Each of these two test stands contained the largest concentration of concrete in its state.

At each of the two big outside facilities, the Michoud Assembly Facility (MAF) and the Mississippi Test Facility, work was assisted and supported by a large computer installation at Slidell in Louisiana.

Government-industry teams at MSFC in Huntsville, at MAF, MTF, and Slidell, and also at Cape Canaveral in Florida worked well; rapid progress of the Moon project was the result. This demonstrated the validity of Marshall's principle of government-industry teams. However, these arrangements soon caused heated labor disputes. Trade unions claimed that much of the work being done by center employees was the prerogative of union workers. Strikes ensued, and the Saturn project suffered dangerous delays. Flare-ups occurred first at the Launch Operations Directorate at Cape Canaveral where launch pads for the Saturn rockets had to be built. Debus, director of the Launch Operations Directorate, and von Braun argued that rocket work underway at NASA is predominantly of a research and development nature, rather than routine construction, and that it cannot be simply assigned to construction contractors.

Finally, Secretary of Labor James P. Mitchell appointed a committee to clarify the differences. After lengthy discussions, compromises were found, and the work could proceed. More labor disputes occurred at NASA centers, including Huntsville, following reduction-in-force orders that had to be imposed by NASA Headquarters. In 1962, work on Saturn test stands in Huntsville came to a halt because of strikes by the electricians' union. Von Braun, deeply upset by the interruption of work, argued that the dispute caused the U.S. space program to trail further behind that of the Soviet Union. President Kennedy's Labor Committee warned that the strike threatened the national interest, and the *Huntsville Times* newspaper accused the strikers of irresponsibility and greed, claiming that one electrician earned more than von Braun [8-42]. Finally, MSFC obtained a federal injunction, and the electricians resumed their work.

Labor disputes were not the only roadblocks that NASA, including the Marshall Center, encountered on their way to the Moon. The early 1960s were a time of grievous racial unrest in the South. Webb was particularly concerned about the dangers this could mean for the space program. He implored von Braun to make every effort to hire qualified blacks into MSFC's labor force.

Von Braun did indeed make every effort to comply with the government's urgent request to avoid any trace of racism. While Governor George C. Wallace stood in the doorway of the University of Alabama in Tuscaloosa, blocking the entrance for black students in defiance of federal orders, and vowing *"segregation forever,"* Huntsville displayed a far more progressive attitude. Desegregation proceeded smoothly in Huntsville. Civil rights leaders saw little reason to campaign in the city. Then, in 1963, racist attitudes flared up again in central and south Alabama. Attorney General Robert Kennedy put pressure on Vice President Lyndon B. Johnson, who put pressure on Webb, and he in turn put pressure on von Braun, demanding more response to equal employment principles. Von Braun promptly established an early version of an affirmative action initiative, working closely with contractors in the city. They formed the Association of Huntsville Area Contractors (AHAC), with Milton K. Cummings at Brown Engineering as spokesman. AHAC not only recommended hiring more black employees, but also *"significant financial contributions to aid black schools and training programs for blacks, and more responsibility concerning housing, education, and the availability of private and public facilities"* [8-43]. In an attempt to interest the president of Huntsville's predominantly black A&M College, Dr. Richard D. Morrison, in technical work under NASA contracts, von Braun visited him and described to him the opportunities for research contracts. Unfortunately, the visit was not successful. Von Braun then sent his chief scientist to Morrison, for the same purpose. *"You know,"* the president said, *"we are an agricultural college. What I'm trying to do is make better farmers. If I can teach my students how they can get better crops from their land, I have done my job. This new-fangled technology at the Marshall Center is not for us."*

During later years, Morrison's successors took a different stance. Several fine research contracts were set up between the A&M University and the Marshall Center, among them studies of crystal growth under the weightless conditions of orbital flight.

On 8 December 1964, von Braun gave a talk to the Huntsville Chamber of Commerce. *"I think,"* he said, *"we should all admit this fact: Alabama's image is marred by civil rights incidents and statements."* Huntsville's businessmen, he urged, should help improve Huntsville's facilities for education, transportation, and recreation, and they should give support to *"those less fortunate families who are bypassed by the big space and missile boom"* [8-44]. *The New York Times* correspondent Ben A. Franklin, with reference to this and other talks, called von Braun *"one of the most outspoken and persistent spokesmen for moderation and racial reconciliation in the South"* [8-45].

Alabama Governor Wallace visited Huntsville on 8 June 1965 to attend a Saturn test firing, and to hear addresses by Webb and von Braun. *"Let's shed the shackles of the past,"* von Braun urged, and Webb stated that *"the size and importance of our operations in Alabama require us to add our support to the efforts of forward-looking and fair-minded leaders of the State"* [8-46]. Later that day, during a more light-hearted chat, von Braun asked Wallace whether he wouldn't like to be the first person to step on the Moon. *"Well,"* Wallace replied, *"better not. You fellows might not bring me back to Earth after you got me up there."*

"From MSC's viewpoint," Gilruth remarked later, *"the year from June 1961 until June 1962 was the year of decisions."* Webb, Dryden, and Seamans had just begun their work in NASA Headquarters. Project Mercury got underway. The Launch Operations Center at Cape Canaveral was established. The members of the Manned Spacecraft Center settled in their new home in Houston, Texas. Work on the Apollo guidance and navigation system began at the Draper Laboratory at MIT in Cambridge. The lunar orbit mode (LOR) was chosen for the Moon project. The basic designs of the command module, CM, the service module, SM, and the lunar landing and ascent module, LM, were firmed up. In NASA Headquarters, Holmes was appointed director of the Office of Manned Space Flight. He established the monthly Management Council meetings between himself, Gilruth, von Braun, and Debus, director of the Launch Operations Center; these meetings proved extremely valuable in the further course of the Saturn-Apollo program. That name was given to the Moon project in the summer of 1961.

The conical shapes of the Mercury, Gemini, and Apollo reentry capsules with convex front areas covered by ablative heat shields, originally proposed by H. Allen at the Ames Research Center, were chosen among different shapes, including pointed and winged bodies.

By the end of 1962, the overall concept of the lunar journey had been firmly established [8-4].

The three-stage Saturn V rocket would carry the *"moonship"* as payload. This composite spacecraft consisted—beginning at the top of the assembly—of the command module, CM, a conical, very strong structure. It accommodated three astronauts on couches; their life support system; guidance, control, and navigation equipment; thrusters for attitude control; a lateral hatch for ingress, egress, and extra-vehicular activities; a docking mechanism at its tip; and a parachute.

Next, there was the service module, SM, of cylindrical shape, with the transfer propulsion engine and its storable, self-igniting propellants. The service module contained an attitude control system; three fuel cells and their tanks with liquid oxygen and liquid hydrogen for electric power; oxygen and water for the astronauts; and other subsystems.

The next component was the lunar module, LM, consisting of two major parts: the descent stage with descent engine and its storable propellants, and four landing legs; and the far more complex ascent stage with the ascent engine and its storable propellants, a pressurized compartment for the crew with life support system, egress and ingress hatch, attitude control system, communication system, docking hatch, and rendezvous facilities. The LM, with all its marvelous mechanical and electric systems, was an odd-looking creature; Jim McDivitt, astronaut on Saturn V's first flight with a manned LM, remarked: *"It sure flies better than it looks"* [8-47]. Each of the last three Apollo moonships also carried a lunar roving vehicle, compactly folded and attached to the descent stage.

Stages 1, 2, and 3 of the Saturn V launch rocket would burn in quick succession; the third stage with the moonship as payload would reach orbit about 8½ minutes after take-off. A brief stopover in orbit would provide a last opportunity for checking the major systems, and for taking the correct aim for insertion into the lunar transfer trajectory. A second burn of the third stage of almost 6 minutes duration would give the moonship its required velocity and direction for the transfer; then, the burnt-out third stage would separate and continue its uncontrolled flight to the lunar surface on its own.

A complicated maneuver would then be performed by the combined command and service module (CSM): it would separate from the lunar module, move a short distance away, turn around by 180 degrees, rendezvous again with the lunar module, whose cocoon petals had just opened, and attach the tip of the command module to the docking hatch of the LM. Moving now backward, the CSM would pull the LM out of its protective shroud. With docking achieved, the astronauts would be able to move back and forth between CM and LM, thus increasing their living space and their comfort considerably. In this arrangement, they would make the 3½ day cruise to the Moon.

After arrival in the lunar orbit, the LM with two astronauts on board would separate from the orbiting CSM, descend to the Moon, and land on its surface after slowing down with the thrust force of the descent engine. The third astronaut would remain onboard the orbiting CSM. For ascent, the ascent stage would ignite its engine, using the descent stage as launch pad. Arriving near the orbiting CSM, the ascent stage would rendezvous and dock. Crew and equipment would transfer into the command module, and the empty ascent stage would be pushed away.

The service module engine would now inject the combined CSM into a return trajectory to Earth. Both modules would remain together until shortly before reaching the Earth's atmosphere. At that time, they would separate, and the command module would make its fiery descent through the atmosphere, finally opening its parachute and splashing down into the ocean near a waiting recovery ship.

D. Brainerd Holmes had been head of NASA's Office of Manned Space Flight since November 1961. Seamans, after some realignment of headquarters functions, appointed Holmes as deputy associate administrator in October 1962, but in June 1963 Holmes left NASA and returned to private industry.

The Office of Manned Space Flight remained without a director until September 1963 when Webb appointed Dr. George E. Mueller as associate administrator for Manned Space Flight. *"I started out in vacuum tubes and what became semiconductors at the Bell Laboratories,"* Mueller remembered [8-48]. *"I didn't get interested in space per se until I went to work for what was at that time Ramo-Wooldridge, which later became Space Technology Laboratories . . . I took over first the electrical labs at Ramo-Wooldridge and then became their chief scientist . . ."* Later, Mueller's work included space projects, such as Pioneer, and guided missile projects for the Air Force.

A few months after Mueller had joined NASA, he announced to von Braun and his group at MSFC that all Saturn Vs, from the very first launch on, will be launched in *"all up"* fashion, meaning complete three-stage rockets, even with activated payload components. This was a directive, not a suggestion. It came as a shock to the rocket people at MSFC who had been used, through many years of rocket development work, to a carefully planned step-by-step build-up of component testing that would finally, after many partial tests, end up with a complete systems test. Mueller presented his arguments, but they met with heated counterarguments by von Braun and his men. *"Partial tests will not be really valid,"* Mueller argued, *"because a component behaves quite differently when tested as a separate unit."* This did not convince his counterparts. *"We just don't have the time to go through your lengthy test program,"* he said. *"Remember, 1969 is the date for the lunar landing!"* Again, he found no support. Finally, he insisted: *"Now look, fellows. You are the most experienced group of rocketeers in the world. You know how to do things. You have twenty-five years of learning from your mistakes behind you; you do not make further mistakes. I know that you can do it in all-up fashion! I have fullest confidence in you. Let's do it! In the first launch of the Saturn V program, we will launch the big three-stage rocket, with the command and service modules on top, in one piece!"*

That did it. *"It sounded reckless, but Mueller's reasoning was impeccable,"* von Braun said later. The first Saturn V was launched in one piece, with three live stages and the command and service modules on top, on 9 November 1967. Mueller's optimism was fully borne out; the launch was a success.

During the following eight years, a total of thirteen Saturn Vs were launched, each of them in all-up fashion. Every launch was successful. Dr. William R. Lucas, director of MSFC from 1973 till 1986, stated in retrospect [8-49]: *"An early press release openly stated that because of the complexity of the system and the tremendous advancement in technology required, program officials fully expected that half of the ten Saturn Is launched would fail. None did. Neither did any Saturn IB, nor did any Saturn V—and there were thirty-two Saturn launches in all . . ."** Von Braun, in 1975, remarked: *"As it happened, all but two of the manned Apollo-Saturns lifted off within tiny fractions of a second of being precisely on time. One was held for weather, and the other had to be held because of a faulty diode in the ground support equipment"* [8-50].

Although the launchings of the Saturn V rockets were successful, their behavior in flight revealed several critical shortcomings that had to be ironed out. First, there was the sloshing problem. The huge quantities of fuel and oxidizer, contained in tanks with diameters of 10 meters (33 feet), showed the tendency to move and slosh whenever there was a lateral movement of the rocket, producing strong forces in almost every direction. Fortunately, this problem could be solved by applying *"slosh baffles"* to the inner walls of the tanks.

The first Saturn V launch, besides several component tests, had to test the reentry capabilities of the command module at velocities equal to those the capsule would encounter during its return from the Moon. While it achieved this test, the rocket showed some obnoxious lengthwise oscillations, called *"Pogo effect"* in the rocket vernacular. The second Saturn V, carrying a heavier payload than its predecessor, achieved the expected trajectory; however, it experienced very violent Pogo oscillations during ascent. Also, one of the five J-2 engines in the second stage shut off prematurely; a second J-2 engine followed. The single engine in the third stage, programmed to re-ignite some time after its normal cutoff, failed to re-ignite.

This problem caused much concern. MSFC and its contractors responded with an all-out troubleshooting and error analysis effort. The trouble was found in a ruptured ½ inch tube through which liquid hydrogen was channeled to the igniter system. This

---

*The last Saturn V flight toward the Moon (Apollo 17) occurred in December 1972, and another Saturn V launched Skylab in May 1973. The last Saturn IB, taking American astronauts to a rendezvous with their Russian colleagues in the Apollo-Soyuz mission, was launched in July 1975.

tube contained short pieces of flexible bellows. During ground tests, the cold surface of the bellows would condense water from the surrounding air, freeze it, and thus stiffen the bellows and protect them during vibrations. Under space conditions, there is no ice to protect the bellows. Vibrating heavily during ascent, they broke. Hydrogen pressure in the engines sank, and engines in the second stage shut off. The same happened in the third stage. Replacement of the bellows by pieces of pipe with elbows solved that problem.

The violent Pogo shaking originated from a near-coincidence of the natural frequency of the rocket system and the frequency of an oscillation caused by the coupling of the flow of propellants through the feed pipes, and the buildup of pressure in the combustion chambers. This problem was solved by including a *"damper,"* actually an extra volume, filled with helium gas, in the oxygen line.

Troubleshooting, fixing, and testing activities ran high during 1967 and 1968 at MSFC and the Saturn V contractors. On 21 December 1968, the third Saturn V was ready for launch, with Frank Borman, James A. Lovell, Jr., and William A. Anders on board. The flight was a complete success: no engine cutoff, no sloshing, no Pogo effect, no problems with the command and service module. On Christmas eve, the little capsule with the three spacefarers circumnavigated the Moon, after they had wished the people on Earth *". . . good night, good luck, a merry Christmas, and God bless all of you— all of you on the good Earth."*

Brilliant as this accomplishment was, the path leading to it had not been without tragedy.

After the success of the first four unmanned Saturn IB flights in 1965 and 1966, which checked out components for the lunar missions, a test flight with a manned command module was planned for February 1967. The complete Saturn IB rocket was placed on its launch pad in January, and systematic checkout work began, mixed with some last-minute changes in the complicated command module. On 27 January, a test of the closed capsule, with the astronauts aboard, was conducted. An electric short between two live wires occurred which ignited the insulation. The capsule at that time was filled with pure oxygen at a little more than atmospheric pressure. Much of the command module's equipment contained combustible materials; they burned violently, and after a few seconds the interior of the module was a charred mess. The three astronauts, Virgil I. Grissom, Edward H. White, II, and Roger B. Chaffee, died instantly.

Within hours after the tragic accident, Webb met with the president and asked him to let NASA, and Webb personally, remain in charge of all the many actions that would ensue: investigate the causes of the accident, determine the best course of action, recognize the errors that undoubtedly had been made, eliminate all possible future causes for similar accidents, make the necessary technical and managerial changes including personnel changes, formulate statements for publication, and try to keep the time period that would be lost for the Moon project as short as possible.

NASA personnel would be better prepared than anybody else to analyze and judge the accident, Webb argued, and to initiate the proper steps to keep the impact on the whole program within manageable limits. The president agreed.

Webb nominated an investigation board that determined the causes of the accident and the major factors that had contributed to the dangerous situation. In April, Webb asked Low, Gilruth's deputy at MSC, to take on the task of rebuilding the Apollo capsule. That choice was strongly supported by *"everybody in the NASA hierarchy between me and the President,"* as Low said later [8-51]; certainly, Webb could not have made a better choice.

Low established a Configuration Control Board and conducted an extremely thorough review of the entire command module. *"We considered 1697 changes; 1341 were approved,"* Low remembered. Over a period of 18 months, no fewer than 150,000 Americans worked around the clock to effect the changes. Rebuilding and qualifying much of the original command module, they perfected *"two of the most magnificent flying machines yet devised, the command and service module, and the lunar module"* [8-51]. One and one half years later, a new command module was ready on the launch pad; it took its Apollo 8 mission passengers around the Moon during that unforgettable Christmas night in 1968.

Shock and grief over the tragic loss of three astronauts ran deep throughout the nation, shared in many parts of the world. Von Braun sent a handwritten letter of sympathy to his colleague and friend Gilruth.

6   MANAGING A GIANT PROGRAM

President Kennedy's initiation of Saturn-Apollo immediately led to a tremendous growth of activities inside NASA. The magnitude and diversity of the program required a large number of subprojects to be started almost simultaneously. Many of them, after being conceived and defined as part of the total program, would at first remain relatively independent, but later would have to converge toward the overall project plan in a fully coordinated manner. This process was familiar from previous projects; however, in scope and magnitude Saturn-Apollo surpassed any previous effort by a wide margin.

For NASA Headquarters, the onslaught of program management activities became overwhelming. Seamans, as general manager of the agency, tried heroically to stay on top of the avalanche, and to maintain a management function that reached from the very top deeply into the inner workings of each of the three field centers. In addition to the Moon project, NASA at that time had a number of other space projects of various sizes under development, and Headquarters had to lead ten different field centers. In view of the flood of management problems, including all the decisions needed to keep the huge NASA system going, Seamans had no other choice than to establish more and more management offices at headquarters, each of them responsible for one or more of the many different subprojects that made up the entire NASA program. Each of these numerous management offices reported to him.

By far the largest and most important of these management offices was the Manned Space Flight Office under Associate Administrator D. Brainerd Holmes. Gilruth, von Braun, and Debus, as center directors, reported directly to Seamans; as directors in the Saturn-Apollo project, they reported to Holmes. However, for each center there were also a number of headquarters project offices to which the project offices at the centers had to report. This management structure may have looked all right on paper; however, although each of the participants put forth his best efforts to make the system work, difficulties began to mount quickly. There was no formal, and only little actual, coordination among the numerous headquarters project offices; but, each of them demanded from the centers an ever-growing number of presentations, reports, debates, and reviews. The center directors, besides working directly with Holmes's office, had to coordinate the project offices in Washington and their own project offices, and also to keep Seamans informed of the background of those problems requiring top-level decisions. This complex management structure was far too time-consuming to be effective. Seamans, with management responsibility for all the NASA field centers and all their diversified programs, faced a task that was simply too broad to be solvable.

Holmes had become director of the Office of Manned Space Flight on 1 November 1961. *"On my first visit to Huntsville,"* he recalled [8-52], *"I had the impression that they were not going to stand for any nonsense from the bureaucrats in Washington . . . I enjoyed the group and thought they were competent and experienced . . . Von Braun certainly did manage his people . . . I developed a very high regard for him and a considerable personal fondness."*

Did Holmes ever have any negative feelings of working with a group of German nationals who in the fairly recent past had been enemies of the United States?

"No," was his answer, *"I thought they were an absolutely tremendous asset. They were unequalled in the launch vehicle business. I recall Kurt Debus expressing disdain for the Air Force's way of cutting corners in their launch operations at Cape Canaveral. They* [the Germans] *were meticulous in everything they did. From time to time, I did note a few ethnic comments . . . but this was seldom and minor. Except for that, as far as I could see, everybody in the NASA and DOD communities welcomed them as team members. I think they wanted very much to be good Americans and worked very hard to do a good job."*

Before Holmes began his work at NASA, he was interviewed by Webb, Dryden, and Seamans. *"They wanted me to reorganize manned spaceflight activities which had been under Abe Silverstein, and rather narrow in scope. They wanted me to try to pull together the rocket people down at Huntsville, and the Langley people [i.e., Gilruth's Space Task Group] . . . One of the first things I did was form a Management Council that met periodically in Washington."* This innovation proved most useful. *"It provided cohesiveness to an organization that was very disparate, and whose elements were not always talking to each other,"* Holmes said.

"Cooperation between the Manned Spacecraft Center and the Marshall Center," Holmes explained, *"was accomplished by strong project leadership in Washington, coupled with the full support of each of the center directors, largely . . . through the monthly Management Council meetings. There, we decided the major issues and the course of the program. It was really very good after the first few months."*

The Moon project meant a change in the life-style of von Braun's Marshall Center. For twenty-five years, the von Braun team had been a rather self-contained rocket development group. There had always been a large amount of joint work with industry and with universities, but program management activities never needed as much attention as technical development, systems engineering, quality assurance, testing, manufacturing, and launching.

Saturn-Apollo, by its sheer size and complexity, brought a new dimension to the art and technology of rocket-building. It caused a quantum jump in its evolution, and it meant a big step for von Braun in the conduct of his work. He took it in stride, embracing the new situation with force and enthusiasm. He changed the organization of his center to accommodate the new responsibilities, explained the need for the changes to his associates, and very carefully defined and delineated duties, responsibilities, and authorities under the new system. *"Our rocket team has today become more than ever a managerial group,"* he remarked, and on 16 August 1962 he wrote a *"MSFC Management Policy Statement #1"* [8-53] that set the new course.

"In the past," von Braun wrote, *"such a paper was needless. Our organization was compact and unified in the accomplishment of a single major project, with management of the project carried out at the very top of the organization. This situation no longer prevails . . ."*

The substantial increase of the organization, and its responsibility for several major projects, required the modification of its management structure. Von Braun decided to create *"project offices"*; their responsibilities, in contrast to those of the existing technical divisions, were spelled out in von Braun's management policy statement. Division directors as well as the heads of project offices, it said, were to report directly to him.

Technical divisions were responsible for all efforts related to the planning, development, building, and testing of the components and systems belonging to a project. To assure maintenance of a high level of technical competence, members of the technical divisions had to keep their hands dirty by actively performing work on projects.

Project offices had to direct, coordinate, and budget all project-related efforts of the technical divisions as well as the contractors. Technical support in depth, as required by the project offices, were to be provided by the technical divisions.

Von Braun's policy directive was the appropriate response to a situation of which Bill H. Sneed, head of the Program Control Center in the Saturn V Program Office, said many years later [8-54]: *"It had become necessary to focus technical and programmatic management responsibility for the various projects in the cognizant project offices . . ."*

Holmes's regular Management Council meetings in Washington, and von Braun's internal restructuring of the Marshall Center, were very significant contributions to the gradual formation of a management structure adequate for the conduct of the huge Saturn-Apollo project.

While Holmes was busy forging a super-team out of the von Braun, Gilruth, and Debus teams, and as he came to grips with the details of the manned mission to the Moon, he had to cope with some adverse forces from another direction. *"All the while,"* he recalled [8-52], *"we had Jerry Wiesner over at the White House throwing rocks at the whole thing. He made it very difficult for us; but, I don't think it was entirely Jerry . . ."* Dr. Nicholas E. (Nick) Golovin, serving under Wiesner on the President's Science Advisory Committee, shared Wiesner's views. *"Now,"* Holmes said, *"I don't say they weren't sincere. But they were always saying, 'Don't do it this way, do it that way'. And those contrary ideas probably came from Nick. Generally, I would say that Jerry or Nick were against almost everything we were trying to do."*

Holmes left NASA in the summer of 1963 and returned to industry. *"I think my greatest contribution was forming a team, and getting the people involved to work together. During these two years, we established every development contract for Apollo as well as for Gemini. We also established all of the facilities contracts. Establishing a launch center directorate at Cape Kennedy [formerly Cape Canaveral] was very important. I had to use charm and arm twisting to get von Braun to release Debus to become center director . . . I thought that was a very good thing to have happen."*

Did Holmes feel comfortable working with von Braun? *"Yes, very much so. He was loyal and very smart . . . George Low is also high on my list. He was very conscientious, as was the German group. I think they respected one another . . . He first had to overcome some negative feelings from Huntsville because of his previous association with the Gilruth people, but he soon was respected by all of von Braun's people, and particularly by Wernher himself."*

Indeed, Low enjoyed highest respect among the Huntsville people. Von Braun often praised Low's brilliant technical talents, his sound judgment, and his fairness. The fact that tensions between the Manned Spacecraft Center and the Marshall Center subsided almost completely during the later years of the Saturn-Apollo program was due in a substantial part to Low's personal influence. He put the focus on technical issues and on efficient cooperation. Being an excellent engineer himself, he managed to keep mutual discussions concentrated on the purely technical problems and on the efforts to resolve them. He was a hard driver for accomplishment, but at the same time he spread soothing oil on a rough sea. His contributions to the success of the Moon project, direct and indirect, were most significant, perhaps even decisive. It was a grievous tragedy that these excellent relations, and the fond feelings between Low and the von Braun team, particularly von Braun himself, did not continue when Low, after Dr. Thomas O. Paine's resignation in September 1970, became acting administrator of NASA, and, in March 1971, deputy administrator under Dr. James C. Fletcher (Chapter 11).

After Holmes's departure from NASA in June 1963, the Office of Manned Space Flight remained without a director until September. This time of interregnum was a hardship for the Moon project, for Webb and Seamans at headquarters as well as for Gilruth, von Braun, and Debus at the field centers. In September 1963, Webb appointed Dr. George E. Mueller as associate administrator for Manned Space Flight (Chapter 8-5).

Twenty-five years later, Mueller reminisced [8-48]: *"I'll never forget my first visit to Huntsville as the newly appointed associate administrator for Manned Space Flight. We had a dinner that evening, and Eberhard Rees gave the welcoming address. Wernher and Eberhard were a great team. Wernher was the outgoing one, Eberhard the practical one. Wernher was an exceptionally fine engineer as well as being a foresighted individual . . . Houston [i.e., the Manned Spacecraft Center] was a little more reluctant to give up its sovereignty, but eventually they, too, became cooperative."*

Rees, introducing Mueller, talked about the difficulty of proving or disproving the correctness of an idea that sounds perfectly logical, but is not readily verifiable. To illustrate his point, he told the old story of the alligators in the New York underground sewer system. New Yorkers vacationing in Florida, so the story goes, bring their children at home baby alligators that can be bought cheaply at Florida roadside stores. The youngsters are enchanted and allow the cute pets to monopolize the family bathtub. After a few days, Mom or Pop wishes to take a bath. Under pressure, junior, who has lost interest in the alligator anyway, throws the poor thing into the commode and flushes it into oblivion. Arriving in New York's gigantic underground sewer network, the alligator finds food from the many restaurant disposals, and it meets countless other alligators of varying sizes that had met with the same fate before. *"That means,"* Rees said, painting a really grotesque scene, *"that underground New York is teeming with hordes of alligators. Now, George, would you please prove or disprove this statement."*

"Eberhard," Mueller said, *"I cannot comment on your horror story. In fact, I have not come here tonight to prove or disprove anything, but to improve a few things. That's what I intend to do. Let's go to work!"*

Thus began a relationship of intense work between Mueller, the von Braun team, Gilruth's Manned Spacecraft Center, and Debus's Launch Operations Center in Florida that was to culminate, six years later, in the landing of Apollo 11 on the Moon.

Throughout the summer and fall of 1963, the plight of the Saturn-Apollo center directors increased. *"Our headquarters-center relations have become so terribly complicated,"* von Braun remarked to his associates, *"it is almost impossible to obtain a guideline, let alone a decision."* Not long after Mueller had come aboard, von Braun, fully supported by Gilruth and Debus, made a proposal—in fact, a strong plea—to Webb. *"Put a man in charge solely of the Saturn-Apollo program,"* he said, *"and place him between Dr. Seamans and the three of us. We will be happy to accept him as our boss. This will greatly simplify life for all of us, and it will make our program manageable."*

Webb agreed. Mueller became the absolute focal point of the Moon project. In the course of building up his office structure for this new assignment, he hired Air Force Major General Samuel C. Phillips as director, Apollo Program. He also arranged for Air Force Colonel Edmund O'Connor to assume the newly created position of director of

Industrial Operations within von Braun's organization at MSFC, a position and function that Phillips had strongly recommended.

This restructuring of the Saturn-Apollo organization proved to be very fortunate. The new program managers, Mueller, Phillips, and O'Connor, soon enjoyed highest respect at the field centers and at headquarters alike. They devoted their efforts exclusively to the Moon project, providing the active and ever-present leadership which the three field centers wanted and needed, and that contributed substantially to the success of the Saturn-Apollo program. Von Braun's relationship with the three new-comers was excellent. This does not mean, though, that von Braun and Mueller always saw completely eye-to-eye; there were honest disagreements, but they were always debated in a spirit of fairness and cooperation until a mutually acceptable solution to the problem could be found.

Establishment of an Office of Manned Space Flight under Mueller, an Apollo Pro-gram Office under Phillips, and an Industrial Operations Office under O'Connor had far-reaching consequences. It resulted in very close NASA Headquarter-center rela-tions, with daily telephone conversations, and with complete visibility of all program proceedings for every element of the huge Saturn V project. Also, it put much-needed emphasis on the managerial aspects of the program, in addition to the emphasis on technical excellence of all the components of the Moon rocket.

Seamans remembered the restructuring of the Saturn-Apollo program in an interview in 1986 [8-55]:

"On the actual running of the manned spaceflight program, what we had done at the very beginning and for a couple of years was to have all the center directors report to me as the general manager, and have the program offices at headquarters view the centers somewhat as contractors . . . This was a difficult arrangement, although it was probably a good thing to do for a while. I remember a meeting—it might have been at Langley Research Center, but certainly one of the centers—when there was pretty close to an uprising among some of the center directors. They felt that what we were doing was difficult and awkward, and recommended that we establish direct lines of responsibility with the program offices. Wernher was one of the articulate leaders in this. Mr. Webb was really quite upset about it. I think it was the last time that we had the senior people from the centers and the many program offices all together . . . Jim Webb did not like surprises, if you want to call it that, but I think the time had come for Wernher and Bob Gilruth and eventually Kurt Debus to work first with Brainerd Holmes and then George Mueller directly . . ."

Mueller recalled an extra little twist in the process of introducing the new Saturn-Apollo management structure. *"After the first couple of meetings,"* he said in that interview in 1986, *"when it was pointed out to me that the centers were independent empires, I learned that all they wanted from us in headquarters was money. I told them that that was not the way it was going to run . . . We sat and worked our way through as to how we were going to operate. And Wernher was the first to accept it. No, not really— it was Kurt Debus, for he was not sufficiently bound up in the internal politics at that time . . . Wernher turned out to be one of the strongest supporters . . ."* Actually, what Mueller had been told about the *"money from headquarters"* sounded a little different in its original version. Von Braun was sometimes quoted with the statement: *"All we need is a rich uncle in Washington who sends the money, but does not interfere with our work."* He really did make statements like this, even repeatedly. However, it was always part of a more elaborate statement. If quoted out of context, it creates a wrong impression. *"We need a strong and determined leadership in Washington,"* he used to say, *"that assumes authority over the field centers and makes decisions when they are needed. Also, our leaders in Washington should do the alley fighting that seems to be unavoidable in a government-managed program as large and as complex as ours. However, headquarters should not wish to be actively involved in every small technical detail of our daily work; field centers are well prepared and equipped to handle these problems by themselves. In fact, besides the strong leadership that sets the goal and the pace, and makes decisions between options and also between field centers when the need arises, we just need a rich uncle in Washington . . ."*

Heart and soul of the Saturn V effort at MSFC was the Saturn V Program Office, headed by Arthur Rudolph. His background in rocketry was almost legendary; he was a co-worker of famous Max Valier who lost his life in a rocket explosion in 1930; in 1931, he built and operated a liquid-propellant, liquid-cooled rocket engine for the German Army; in 1933, he joined young Wernher von Braun at the rocket testing ground Kummersdorf, and he remained a member of von Braun's team until he retired from NASA, and from rocket work, in January 1969.

As Saturn V program manager, Rudolph maintained two organizational lines to Mueller's headquarter office: one through O'Connor and von Braun at MSFC, the other one through Phillips at headquarters. All of Rudolph's major offices on the Saturn V level had counterparts in Phillips's office, the so-called GEM-boxes (George E. Mueller's initials), with daily coordination by telephone. Sneed's Program Control Center was one of these Saturn V offices. In parallel to these management-oriented offices, there were the technically oriented project offices, one for each Saturn stage, for the instrument unit, and for ground support equipment. These offices developed and maintained an exceedingly tight relationship with the contractors. The passwords were *"contractor penetration,"* and *"government-industry teams."* Work of these offices was strongly supported by the existing technical laboratories at MSFC under the Directorate of Science and Engineering. Von Braun insisted from the beginning of the Saturn V program on very close working relationships between Saturn program management, Saturn contractors, and MSFC technical laboratories.

Not all contractors at first liked this close monitoring, and even surveillance of their work by government people. However, the positive consequences of this intimate cooperation became so obvious that the *"MSFC style"* or *"Arsenal concept,"* as it was called in contrast to the Air Forces *"loose rein"* approach, was not only accepted but appreciated by contractors.

Visibility and instant access to every phase of Saturn V management was provided through Sneed's Program Control Center, an impressive management tool that lived up to the demands of the task on hand. In 1965, Webb toured the facility; after briefings by Rudolph and Sneed, he exclaimed: *"I saw here . . . one of the most sophisticated forms of organized human effort that I have ever seen anywhere!"* [8-56]. At Webb's urging, large numbers of executives from government and from American and foreign industries were given *"guided tours"* through Rudolph's Saturn Program Office during the ensuing years. When Rudolph retired from NASA in 1969, Colonel Lee B. James became his successor as Saturn V program manager. James had been manager of the Saturn I and Saturn IB projects from 1963 to 1967, and deputy director of the Apollo program at NASA Headquarters from 1967 to 1968. He retired from NASA in April 1971.

Management of the Saturn V program was MSFC's major activity during the 1960s. Concurrently, the Moon-going part of the project—the command and service module, and the lunar module, both with accommodations for the astronauts—approached its completion at the Manned Spacecraft Center (renamed Johnson Space Center in 1973) in Houston, and the huge facilities came to life which were needed at Cape Canaveral (named Kennedy Space Center in 1964), for the final assembly, checkout, and launching of the Saturn-Apollo system. Mueller and Phillips were responsible for all segments and phases of the Moon Project. For Webb and Seamans, Saturn-Apollo was but one portion of the total NASA program that included unmanned space flight projects, space science projects, technology projects, applications projects, and—the first A in NASA's logo—exciting projects in aeronautics.

From the very beginning of his tenure at NASA, Administrator Webb was held in highest regard not only in his own organization, but by other government agencies, by the Congress, and particularly by industry. The latter's respect, it must be noted, was derived from awe rather than pure admiration, as can be appreciated from a statement by von Braun: *"The uniquely tight procurement procedures introduced by NASA Administrator Jim Webb made it possible to acquire billions of dollars' worth of exotic hardware and facilities without overrunning initial cost estimates, and without the slightest hint of procurement irregularities"* [8-57].

Progress and problems of the gigantic Saturn-Apollo effort were assessed at the Management Council, consisting of Mueller, von Braun, Gilruth, and Debus; the four of them met in Washington every four weeks. The council was, in fact, the nerve center of the Moon landing project.

The efforts, struggles, and triumphs of NASA's top managers in the course of the Moon project were told in an essay by Seamans and Ordway, entitled *"The Apollo Tradition—An Object Lesson for the Management of Large-scale Technological Endeavors,"* published in 1977 [8-40]. Excerpts follow:

"The undertaking of the Apollo lunar exploration program involved one of the major technological endeavors in the history of civilization. In terms of financial, manpower, and other resources, as well as the time allowed for its completion, Apollo had no parallel as far as a single, goal-oriented effort is concerned: it was unique."

Seamans introduced the phased planning concept, a systematic approach to the progressive planning activities required during an evolving project. This concept turned out to be most helpful for the Saturn-Apollo program. NASA, therefore, retained it as a management tool not only throughout the Saturn-Apollo program, but for all future projects as well.

Essential to the phased project planning concept is a sequence of four major activities, each ending with a decision, in the course of the life of the project:

Phase A: Analytical studies as required to establish the overall feasibility of the specific project. Several different approaches may be studied and compared at this stage.

Phase B: Engineering analysis, and 'breadboarding' of components, to determine the best approach to be followed among several feasible approaches.

Phase C: Detailed definition of project features, including preliminary design. Development of the necessary supporting data, and of a firm plan for project development and operation.

Phase D: Final design, hardware development, and manufacturing. Operations to achieve project objectives.

As each project passed through these various activity steps, managers could define, at early dates, the large numbers of emerging tasks or work packages in terms of objectives, performance, manpower requirements, time schedules, priorities, and relationships of each to all the others.

"This meant," Seamans and Ordway wrote, *"that resource estimates could be refined, as well as estimates of the time needed for completion. In other words, forward planning was a continuous iterative process . . . The management of Apollo relied heavily on effective communications, and on the rapid generation of technical and*

management information. Both . . . are key factors in the success of any large-scale enterprise. Government and industrial experience had long ago demonstrated that a large percentage of management problems is due to breakdowns in the rapid flow of information."

A key element in the Saturn-Apollo management structure was the relationship between NASA and its industrial contractors. For many years, von Braun and his associates had firmly adhered to the conviction that in joint government-industry projects that involve the development of novel technologies, the two partners must in fact form a team together, with a continuous two-way flow of information, and with active support and help from the government whenever a need arises. Webb and Seamans fully shared these convictions.

"The agency also realized," Seamans and Ordway continued, *"that its contractors often had to solve problems on the frontiers of human experience. Consequently, it was important to work jointly, as partners, and not expect the industrial teams to take unfair risks . . ."*

In fact, NASA was much more interested in encouraging contractors to admit their errors, and in offering help to quickly correct them, than in blaming contractors for deficiencies. This philosophy of mutual understanding and help contributed immeasurably to the creation of a NASA-industry spirit of highly efficient teamwork.

All possible steps were taken to ascertain that no project manager, no individual, no office, no committee, no organizational element of any kind ever became isolated from the main stream of events. NASA wished to be sure that no problems or difficulties arising anywhere in the NASA-contractor system were ignored or glossed over. A continual cross-feeding of ideas took place at countless interfaces and checkpoints. By working in such an open atmosphere, it was reasoned, the chances of anything going wrong would be considerably reduced.

When Webb took the oath of office in 1961, he stated that his *"purpose will be to work toward creating an environment within which NASA could be as innovative in the management of its program as it was in aeronautics and space science."* At another occasion [8-57], he said: *"The exploration of space is a great adventure. We are all privileged to be allowed to contribute. That privilege carries with it the responsibility of effective management in the national interest."*

Seamans and Ordway concluded their essay on Saturn-Apollo management on a sad note, written four years after the last Apollo astronauts had returned from the Moon:

"Apollo, and its immediate—and closely related—successor Skylab, taught NASA the valuable lesson that today's triumphs do not automatically signal support for tomorrow's follow-on ventures. Almost as amazing, to many observers, as the success of these two programs was the failure of a large-scale, post-Apollo manned spaceflight effort to gel in their aftermath. The attempt to build major new missions failed . . . Support for large-scale scientific and technical endeavors must involve a preponderance of the public . . . Citizens must view the effort as worthy of their tax dollars if support is to last for extended periods."

What was the primary reason why the public failed to provide support for a new great space endeavor during the early 1970s?

Webb, Seamans, Dryden, Mueller, Gilruth, and von Braun were no longer members of the space program. The president was not interested. There was no longer a voice speaking up for a spaceflight endeavor that would make the citizens and their representatives in Congress aware of the opportunity and the challenge to retain the leading position among spacefaring nations, to enjoy the admiration and respect of other nations, to continue to provide almost unlimited fields for scientific research, to embrace and use space exploration as the driving force for technical innovations, to let the space program work as a stimulus for the young generation to learn and acquire knowledge, and to fill the minds of the American people with enthusiasm for search and discovery.

7   RIVALRY AND COOPERATION IN THE SPACE FAMILY

There can be no doubt that effective management is the most important premise for the success of a project of the magnitude and complexity of the Saturn-Apollo mission to the Moon, once its technical feasibility has been assured. The premise for effective management, in turn, requires the closest possible cooperation between the various segments of the project organization.

Tension between the elements of NASA during the Saturn-Apollo project is sometimes quoted as a prominent problem that haunted the endeavor. Mueller said during an interview in 1986 [8-58] that *"the science people felt that manned spaceflight was taking all their money away from them. They had been arguing with the President's Science Advisory Committee, with the Space Science Board, and with everybody else . . . They were saying 'Let's go back to doing real science and not play around with these men who are just mucking things up . . .' All this was exacerbated by Houston's wanting to stop flying because of the risk in using man to do science on the Moon . . ."*

There was tension also between the Manned Space Flight groups. John H. Disher, at that time in charge of Advanced Manned Systems at NASA Headquarters, recalled [8-59] that during the early years of the Moon program *"polarization between NASA centers was really strong, complicated by some personal animosities between Silverstein and von Braun, and to some degree between Gilruth and von Braun. So the interfaces across the launch vehicle, flight missions, and spacecraft activities were pretty abrupt."* Could von Braun's wartime past have been the reason for this? *"No,"* Disher said, *"I never heard it mentioned. But there were plain human jealousies . . ."*

Shea, who worked for Holmes in Washington in 1962 when the question of the best mission profile for the journey to the Moon was still unsettled, remembered twenty-five years later [8-60]: *"There was, at the time, tremendous tension between the NASA centers. Gilruth and the people at the Manned Spacecraft Center really resented von Braun, because he had the presence and the press, and many thought he ran the program. There was a real jealousy going on . . . I always felt von Braun kept it under control, that he didn't abuse the situation . . . At the Manned Space Flight Management meetings, von Braun would be making a pitch, or Rees would be making a pitch, and there was just no warmth at all . . . But, von Braun was always the gentleman. Always. He was not the one who had the problem . . ."*

How did Mueller and von Braun work together? *"George and Wernher got along perfectly,"* Disher recalled, *"just perfectly. They were simply 'sympatico,' a great team."*

Mueller's Apollo program director, Phillips, commented [8-61] on von Braun's role in the greater Saturn-Apollo team: *". . . after weeks and months of interaction, Wernher and I became close friends. And we remained so . . . He turned into a good team player; he was very effective in carrying his views in a discussion of alternatives, and in making his own position felt and heard. But once the person in authority made a decision and said 'Here's what we are going to do,' he was very quick to embrace that decision, and to counsel his people on how they were going to work . . . Probably the teamwork within his organization was best. Well, it's hard to say it was best for it was good in all quarters. But I never had a single moment of problem with the Marshall Space Flight Center. Their teamwork, cooperation, enthusiasm, and energy of partici-pation were outstanding . . .".*

On Phillips's suggestion, the Marshall Center established an Industrial Operations department, as a counterpart to its Science and Engineering Department. Its first director was Robert Young from Aerojet. *"As far as I know,"* Phillips said, *"he worked very, very effectively with Wernher and Eberhard, Weidner, and the many other people—Arthur Rudolph heading up the Saturn V office, Lee B. James the Saturn IB office, and Leland F. Belew the engines office . . ."* Colonel (later Brigadier General) Edmund F. O'Connor replaced Young when the latter returned to industry. *"Ed O'Connor did a fine job and related very effectively with Wernher . . . I felt it important to implement an organized and structured approach to program planning and control. Again, the Huntsville organization responded very effectively to that. The individual who was most instrumental [in Huntsville's very active response to those aspects of management] is Bill H. Sneed . . ."*

Around 1964, von Braun had become very well known in this country and abroad. He had been on the front covers of both *Time* and *Life* magazines, was speaking and writing regularly in the public arena, and by many was felt to be the space program's most visible and vocal spokesman. Was there any antipathy at NASA Headquarters because of this, perhaps coupled with German wartime history?

"No," was Phillips's answer, *"not at the headquarters level. I don't remember finding any antipathy, but I did observe—what's the right word—there were obvious frictions with Bob Gilruth, and I think those frictions probably had their beginnings in debates on how to carry out the lunar mission . . . There, again, once the decision was made, Wernher directed his organization very effectively to support the decision. There was no friction or belief that Wernher and his people were trying to fight for some older agenda. None of that. The only frictions I ever observed probably had their origins in jealousy—and I guess that's natural . . ."*

Phillips had been an Air Force officer since 1940. Serving as a fighter pilot in World War II, he flew out of England. *"I was introduced to the V-2 on the receiving end,"* he remembered. *"I had also escorted, in our fighter group, bombers in making bombing raids on Peenemünde . . ."*

What was Seamans' attitude toward the von Braun team? Did he feel comfortable working with it during the Apollo years?— *"Yes, very much so,"* Seamans said in 1986 [8-55], *"and I had the feeling that 'the Germans' felt comfortable with me. From my very first visit at the Marshall Center, I had nothing but great respect for the technical capabilities of that team . . . During the Apollo years, Wernher and his team became better and better known in the United States . . . They did their work extremely well . . ."*

How does Gilruth remember the Saturn-Apollo years, and the cooperation be-tween his and von Braun's group?

"It was a good team under Holmes," he said [8-35]. *"I remember that after our meetings we would have dinner, and before the dinner we would have a few cocktails. Those informal sessions broke down a lot of barriers . . . Mueller was a very hard-nosed guy. Some of the things he did were good, and some were not. Our problem was to embrace the good ones and get him to change the poor ones."* Did he and Wernher work closely together on common issues?— *"Yes, we worked together . . . After Wernher and I had been working at NASA for some years, we understood each other, and we didn't have any real problems . . . Brainerd had a lot of good things. But neither [Mueller nor Holmes] were flight people; they did not come up through the hard knocks*

of having systems fail . . . Seamans was a lot more open-minded than Brainerd and Mueller . . . I had been working with [flying machines] all my professional life, and Wernher had, too. That makes a big difference . . ."

"Wernher was ahead of America during the war years. It was his V-2s that got us into the space business. He was the guy that started us going. If he hadn't been around, it would have taken more years before we would have gone into space."

How would von Braun describe the joint tribulations and triumphs of the journey to the Moon?

An observer attending meetings at von Braun's Marshall Center would have realized that opinions in Huntsville were sometimes at variance with opinions held at Gilruth's Manned Spacecraft Center, but he would never have heard words of personal criticism of members of NASA Headquarters, or of another center, either from von Braun, or from one of his associates. Von Braun never spoke badly about another person, and he did not tolerate such words from his team members. If someone began to criticize a colleague who was not a member of the Marshall Center, von Braun cut him off with a sharp rebuke.

"There was a job to do, and we knew that it would remain undone unless we did it together," he would say. *"Tension between Houston and Huntsville? Well, I would rather call it different views held by different centers, as long as we didn't have all the facts in hand. Whenever you let active people with creative minds loose on a project, you will have a whole assortment of different views, and everybody is ready to fight for his own conviction. That is human nature. But this is the time when serious studies have to start, when different options must be compared on the basis of their face values, their merits not only as technical systems, but as budget items, as pacing elements in a tight time schedule, as safety risks, as potential bridges into the future. As soon as such detailed studies are made, opposing views have a tendency to lose their uniqueness, their decisive advantage, their absolute superiority, and proponents of different schemes begin to have their views converge. We have observed this process time and again during the past thirty years. By the time the Moon project approached its maturity, the three Saturn-Apollo centers, Houston, Huntsville, and Cape Kennedy, had really become one greater lunar project team . . ."*

8   MANAGING THE MARSHALL CENTER

Center directors were faced with two basic kinds of management activities. First, they had to manage the technical development of projects within prescribed performance specifications, budget constraints, manpower limitations, and time schedules. Second, they had to manage the smooth and efficient cooperation of thousands of their employees with each other, and also with contractors, colleagues from other centers, headquarters offices, and scientific institutions. How did von Braun approach and solve these innumerable, diversified, and often very complex management tasks? What kind of a manager was he?

Judgments by persons who had contact with von Braun in management situations vary between *"he was a brilliant manager"* [8-62] to *"he was not a manager in the classical sense, but he had no problems with management"* [8-61]. Both of these statements are correct in principle. Those who commented on von Braun's management style, and who were qualified, through their own work, to pass such judgments, agree on some basic points: Von Braun *"did his work extremely well"* [8-30]; he was always absolutely loyal to his superiors; he made every effort to be a good team player within an existing organization; he was always on top of his assigned projects.

This characterization reflects von Braun's management style during the period from 1950 to 1970 while he worked on Redstone, Jupiter, Pershing, Saturn, and Skylab. Eberhard Rees, von Braun's deputy and confidant since 1939, and his successor as MSFC director from 1970 to 1972, made this observation [8-63]: *"Von Braun always worked best when he had a strong boss. In fact, he was happiest under his three strongest bosses, General Dornberger in Peenemünde, General Medaris at the Army Ballistic Missile Agency in Huntsville, and Mr. Webb at NASA Headquarters during the Saturn-Apollo project."* In each case, von Braun formed an ideal two-men work team with his boss. He provided the ideas, the project plans, the engineering, the scheduling, the well-organized and highly motivated work force, the convincing arguments, and the public relations, while the boss provided the leadership necessary to keep the program alive within the framework of the government, to make decisions when several options were available, and to establish a workable balance between von Braun's team and other teams that participated in the program.

"He was just a skillful manager," this is how some people try to size up von Braun. Yes, he was a skillful manager, but he was far more. Not only was he one of the most sparkling and creative minds of his time; he was also a motivator, a maker and mover, and an achiever who held on to his dreams until they had become real-life accomplishments. *"Any project as big as a huge space rocket is a many-splendored thing,"* von Braun used to say, and he added some good advice to prospective project managers. *"Before comprehensive planning can begin, the feasibility of the project must be assured in several different areas. First, of course, it must be compatible with the basic laws of nature, for example, the conservation of energy. Second, it must be doable as an engineering achievement, without a need for novel inventions, basic breakthroughs, or magic materials. Third, its cost to completion must remain within the limits of what the Bureau of the Budget can be expected to approve. Then, very importantly, the project must have a well-defined goal with so much public appeal that the taxpayers back up, and even stimulate their congressional representatives in their support of the project. Finally, the president, very personally, must be in favor of the project. We Americans may at times be quite critical of our president, but we still listen to the signals coming from the White House. If the president believes and publicly states that a certain accomplishment will be good for the country, the majority of his voters will follow his lead . . ."*

Von Braun talked little about management, but he lived it. For him, management functions were the tissues that kept the framework of an organism together. This organism consisted of the basic idea for a project; the work force of technicians, engineers, scientists, and administrators; the supporters providing the funds; the customers who would benefit from the project; the peers who had to approve of the project; and, finally, the public that had to be in favor of the project. Neglect of any of these elements would make the project suffer.

It has been said that von Braun's greatest asset that helped him achieve his successes was his charisma, his great personal charm. Certainly, these attractive characteristics worked wonders in obtaining the cooperation and loyalty of all his co-workers, with negligible exceptions; but this would not have been possible had his charming smile not been backed up by unusual intelligence, knowledge, and talent to grasp the essence of many different kinds of problems—technical, scientific, managerial, administrative, political, even psychological. One simply felt secure under his guidance.

The management structure of von Braun's organization reflected his belief in simplicity, efficiency, and flexibility. *"We will always need a number of basic skills,"* he used to say, so he established permanent laboratories for rocket engine testing, mechanical structures, aero-astrodynamics, guidance and control, computer systems, quality assurance, space sciences, and some others, all backed up by the necessary workshops. These permanent laboratories formed the horizontal elements of his management matrix. Then, there was a need for project offices that could develop and manage specific projects. A project officer or project manager was responsible for all the requirements of the one project assigned to him, so he needed access to several laboratories simultaneously. The project offices, therefore, formed the vertical elements of the management matrix. Each project office element intersected with each laboratory, and vice versa. In this way, direct access between any two elements was assured. Bureaucratic entanglements were reduced to a minimum; every activity could be located easily; cross communication was quick and efficient, as well as communication to and from the top. Overall control of center activities became manageable.

How did von Braun actually control the daily center activities? He used a surprisingly simple, but extremely effective tool, the weekly notes. Each of about thirty-five of the top engineers, managers, and scientists in the center wrote a one-page summary of his work, his progress, his failures, and his problems that he had encountered during the week. Those thirty-five pages were submitted to von Braun each Friday. By Tuesday morning, von Braun had read all of them, and had written his comments, suggestions, and directives on the margins. Then, each note was copied thirty-five times, and each of the writers received not only his own annotated page back, but also the annotated pages of all his colleagues.

Every week, these notes gave von Braun a comprehensive picture of the status of each project, of each laboratory, and of each office enabling him to interact with each element of his organization. They also gave each of his thirty-five top men immediate access to all ongoing activities, and to von Braun's reactions and decisions. No other management procedure could have equaled the weekly notes as a communicator, an alert system, a promoter of genuine team spirit.

Von Braun expected his project managers primarily to be good engineers. They would have to follow all technical details of their projects with great care and to spot immediately any technical weaknesses that might crop up. Such problems had to be brought to the attention of everyone who was even remotely involved in that project. The manager was expected to make every conceivable effort to solve the problem, and to remove any possible doubt in the health of his project. If he needed help, he was to ask for it. Von Braun himself was frequently the best source of advice and help.

Managers of contracts with industry were held to the same rules. In fact, they were to form a work team between contractor personnel and their own men that was jointly responsible for the quality of work. To assure this quality, von Braun's organization always included a powerful and well-staffed quality assurance laboratory that had to sign off on every essential part of a project before it was accepted for inclusion in a flight system. Not only the function, but even the mere existence of the quality assurance laboratory as a prominent and influential element of the organization resulted in a high level of reliability of the Marshall Center's products. Each of the laboratories made an effort to achieve high quality before submitting a product to Quality Assurance for critical testing. A substantial part of the credit for the high quality record of von Braun's projects from the early 1950s to the early 1970s is due to the relentless, but still very cooperative drive for quality of the center's director of Quality Assurance, Dieter Grau.

On von Braun's fiftieth birthday, in 1962, some of his co-workers presented him with a volume of papers reflecting work that was underway at his center [8-64]. At that time, the Saturn-Apollo project was in full swing. The foreword to this book described in some detail the management practices at the Marshall Center, and the personal role von Braun played as the top manager. *"This careful and conscientious organization of the engineering phase of a project,"* the foreword stated, *"makes it relatively easy to establish and maintain realistic time schedules. It may not be surprising, therefore, that the completion dates of von Braun's projects generally coincide well with the promised dates. Or rather, schedules are established so that they can be promised with a clear conscience."*

With this sober approach to scheduling and costing, von Braun must have been an exception among program managers, as demonstrated by a remark from the late Dr. Donald Quarles, assistant secretary of defense, who chaired an investigating committee for missile projects during the late 1950s. After hearing von Braun's presentation, Quarles said: *"What you have shown me here gives me an excellent impression of sound engineering and planning; but, fellows, . . . I must tell you one thing: you are very poor promisers!"*

When von Braun was asked for his advice on how to manage a large group of engineers working on a technical project, his answer comprised a package of simple, sober principles—most of them age-old truths—which sound so easy, and yet are practiced so rarely. *"Make sure that you start out with a good, sound, logical concept for your project, with a well-defined goal,"* he would say. *"See to it that each of your men knows the goal, and does not lose sight of it. Break the project down into packages, and assign responsibilities to individuals. Let everybody know that 'responsibility' means working toward the goal, recognizing problems, and solving them! Establish and maintain communication channels throughout the total project structure. Be sure that there are no gaps in the project organization, and no unnecessary overlaps either. Conduct frequent review meetings so that every part of the project remains visible to each of the project engineers. Encourage your men to bring up their problems, to discuss their concerns, and to ask their questions. The head of the project should always be thoroughly informed about the project to the extent that he recognizes an approaching crisis before it strikes. In fact, his intimate familiarity with all the details of the project should always surpass that of everybody else. Maintain as much personal contact with your people as possible, at least with your project engineers and project managers."*

"Of course," he would sometimes add, *"you can expect to motivate your co-workers only when you are thoroughly motivated yourself. Remember the credo of the medieval horsemen: 'Throw your heart across the ditch, and your horse will follow!'"*

"I have always been blessed with excellent co-workers," he used to say. Besides a number of associates who had absolved their apprenticeship in Peenemünde, there was a growing number of young men and women who joined the team from about 1950 on, among them highly talented engineers and scientists. During the Saturn-Apollo years, 1961 to 1970, von Braun had excellent managers and administrators among his close associates. Harry H. Gorman, Edmund F. O'Connor, Lee B. James, Bill H. Sneed, Robert E. Lindstrom, Leland F. Belew, Richard Cook were pillars of the von Braun team in Huntsville. *"But,"* von Braun noted, *"the best management capability would be powerless if it did not have the strong, unwaivering support from the very top."* Major General Toftoy provided this support during von Braun's first years in America, and so did his successor as von Braun's superior, Major General Medaris. As commander of first the Army Ballistic Missile Agency and subsequently the Army Ordnance Missile

Command in Huntsville from 1956 to 1960, he superimposed a military management structure over von Braun's civilian structure, probably the only way how he could keep the Army's guided missile development program alive during those stormy times.

There was some good advice Medaris offered to the young managers under his command: *"Always give clear assignments to your men. Nobody can march to the tune of an uncertain trumpet!—Follow up on your assignments. Make sure that they are carried out. Don't allow any alibis!—Obstacles in your way are no reason for a cheap excuse. Obstacles are here to be overcome!—Establish guidelines that enable you to measure success and failure of your men. Always be available to make a decision, if this is what your men need. Never make a decision before you have all those facts in hand that you need in order to decide, but don't hesitate with a decision as soon as you have all those facts together!"*

Medaris often quoted another golden rule of management: *"Leadership is a two-way street,"* he used to say. *"You want your men to be loyal to you, so you better be loyal to them. You want them to trust you, so you better trust them. You want them to stand behind you, so you better stand behind them—regardless!"*

Von Braun was a team builder, a team leader, a team accomplisher. There was a team around him ever since his high school days on the island of Spiekeroog when, at the age of sixteen, he built and operated an astronomical observatory with his school mates in their spare time. During each of the two peaks of his career, when the A-4 rocket in Peenemünde began its test flights, and when American astronauts landed on the Moon, there were about 10,000 men and women who proudly counted themselves as members of the von Braun team. And yet, *"team"* is not sufficient to express the relationship between von Braun and all of those who, directly or indirectly, worked for him. It would be more correct to speak of a symbiosis, a naturally grown organism. Von Braun provided the *vis vitae* that gave this organism its tremendous vitality. At the same time, he set the goals and gave directions, he assigned tasks and responsibilities, and he checked the progress. He stimulated and encouraged, he warned of overzealous steps and stopped futile approaches. At all times during a project, he was easily the best informed team member as far as project status was concerned.

Gilruth, quite certainly, was a better engineer than von Braun. Homer Newell, Herbert Friedman, John Naugle, Frank McDonald were far better scientists. Krafft Ehricke was more productive than von Braun in proposing innumerable spaceflight projects. Webb was an unequalled administrator. Von Braun would have been the first to give fullest credit to each of these men for superior accomplishments; and, in fact, he often and most generously did. However, none of them would have come near the singular achievement with which von Braun is credited: building a team of engineers, scientists, and administrators and, while generating considerable government and public support, leading his team in the development of precision rockets from the first tentative flight tests in 1934 to the giant Saturn V that launched Apollo astronauts on their lunar journey barely thirty-five years later. Besides his outstanding capabilities in technology and program management, he had the charisma of the real leader. Most felt that to work for him was a privilege. Yielding to his wishes never meant a loss of face; it gave the feeling of reassurance, of receiving his help and support whenever needed, of being solidly integrated in the team.

For von Braun, his rocket team was one element in his crusade for space. He conceived the development of spaceflight as a broad, even an international effort of mankind, a step in human evolution rather than only the doings of a limited group of individuals. From the very beginning of his career, he tried to involve as many engineers and scientists at industry and universities as he possibly could.

Close cooperation between companies and the von Braun team developed, joint working groups were formed. Von Braun felt proud when a visitor to his laboratories once remarked: *"I knew that there were people of four different kinds working together, industry, Army, universities, and von Braun team, but they were so closely integrated in their work that it was impossible to tell who was working for whom, all of them just worked for the joint project . . ."*

This close cooperation between von Braun's government team and industrial companies served also two more immediate purposes. First, it resulted in the timely initiation of development work at cost figures far below the cost levels of comparable independent industry activities, because a wealth of experience and know-how was available in the government teams at no extra cost. Second, when a contract with industry began, it enabled the government to define precisely what the contractor should produce, how and what should be tested, at what stage of perfection the product would be acceptable, and what cost level could be considered reasonable.

Industry did not always like this *"help"* from government specialists, at least initially. On the other hand, von Braun and his men often received high praise from industry for their assistance and cooperative spirit.

The undisputed master of government contracting and cost controlling of large projects, Webb, who steered NASA and its contractors so successfully through the demanding times of the Saturn-Apollo project, wholeheartedly supported von Braun's endeavor to retain this close working relationship with his contractors. *"We have found,"* he said [8-65], *"that we must be able to speak and understand the language of those on whom we rely, to know as much as they do about the problems they are dealing with, to check and supplement their work in our own laboratories, and, in some cases, to help untangle snarled situations . . ."*

Webb's deputy at that time, Seamans, described NASA's situation with these words [8-40]: *"More than 90 cents out of every NASA dollar earmarked for space flight were spent on contracts. At NASA's peak in the mid-1960s, some 20,000 industrial units were at work, most of them on the Saturn launch vehicles and their Apollo payloads. They included approximately 2,000 prime contractors and an additional 18,000 sub-contractors . . . NASA sought to work side by side with its contractors on a peer basis, to be involved with them technically as well as in an overseer sense from the beginning of a procurement through the delivery of a flight-ready article. In other words, NASA desired to develop a far more intimate role with its contractors than simply receiving reports on their progress at arm's length . . ."*

It is an irony of fate that von Braun sometimes met with criticism from younger colleagues who asserted that *"the von Braun people wanted to do everything in their own shops, not letting others participate in the building of rockets . . . those people would have loved to launch the big Saturn-Apollo rockets from the backyard of the Marshall Space Flight Center in Huntsville, if they had been permitted . . ."* [11]. Around 1965, NASA counted 34,000 employees. The number of contractor employees working under NASA contracts at that time was 377,000. Besides the 20,000 American contractors, 200 universities and 80 foreign nations contributed to the Moon project.

"In reflecting on the Apollo program," Webb wrote in 1975 [8-66], *"I am overwhelmed at the sheer magnitude of the task and the temerity of its undertaking . . . It is a tribute to the innate good sense of our citizens that enough of a consensus was obtained to see the effort through to success."*

Fletcher wrote at the same time [8-67]: *"No nation ever demonstrated its aspirations and abilities as dramatically as did the United States when it landed the first men on the Moon . . ."*

9   THE EAGLE HAS LANDED—WHAT NEXT?

Man's epic journey to the Moon has been described many times, perhaps best in *Apollo Expeditions to the Moon* edited by Edgar Cortright [8-68] in which seventeen of the main actors in the heroic drama tell their own stories.

On the evening before the launch of Apollo 11, the first Moon landing mission, there was a little get-together in Titusville near Cape Kennedy with NASA officials, dignitaries from the U.S. Government and foreign governments, rocket pioneer Hermann Oberth and other rocket oldtimers, and members of the news media. Von Braun was his usual self, beaming with optimism, and radiating his proverbial joy of life—although he was a little more tense than usual. He left the party early to go back to the mission control center, but not before Norman Mailer and some other journalists had interviewed him. *"Of course it will be a success,"* he said.

Meanwhile, astronauts Neil A. Armstrong, Michael Collins, and Edwin E. Aldrin Jr. slept toward the most exciting day in their lives. All three had been in space before. Armstrong said later: *"As we ascended in the elevator to the top of the Saturn on the morning of 16 July 1969, we knew that hundreds of thousands of Americans had given their best effort to give us this chance. Now it was time for us to give our best."*

About one million visitors had come to the Cape to see the Moon rocket go off, and perhaps a similar number of people lined the highways and roads near Cocoa Beach, Melbourne, Cocoa, Titusville, and other places from which the ascent of the big rocket and its vapor trail could be observed. There stood the Moon rocket on its launch pad, brilliant white against the blue sky, motionless, but ready to blast off, pointing toward space as if it wanted to say: Here is our future, let's go! When the flames of *"first stage ignition"* appeared at the bottom of the mighty Saturn, a roaring sound of jubilation broke loose, but it was soon totally overpowered by the sound of five F-1 engines that produced a thrust of 7.5 million pounds (3,400 metric tons). It lifted the giant rocket as gracefully as an egret would rise from a Florida pond.

Three and one half days later, there was a voice from the Moon: *"The Eagle has landed"*, and then: *"That's one small step for a man . . . one giant leap for mankind."*

More triumphant flights followed, and there was the heartbreaking accident of Apollo 13 on 13 April 1970 that almost cost the lives of three young astronauts, John L. Swigert, Jr., Fred W. Haise, Jr., and James A. Lovell, Jr. Almost miraculously, they could return to *"a lovely, lovely planet"* [8-69], using the lunar module as a *"lifeboat."* Saturn-Apollo 17 in December 1972, the last flight to the Moon, was the most successful of the six lunar missions from a scientific standpoint. It helped clarify the Moon's nature, and also its evolution through astronomical times. It is now certain, as astronaut Harrison H. Schmitt noted, that Earth and Moon *"were formed about 4.6 billion years ago in about the same part of the youthful solar system."*

"The Apollo program, was it worth it?" Dr. Paul D. Lowman, Jr., asked in 1975 [8-70]. As a scientist who participated in planning and analyzing Apollo missions, he argued convincingly that it indeed was.

Six journeys to the Moon, and later 513 man-days on the orbiting Skylab space station—they made us feel at home in space, but they did far more: They awakened us to the fact that our primary home in space is a small planet circling an average star, a planet with a beautiful surface and a thin layer of breathable air, locked in a tenuous balance that provides support for living beings. This balance must be protected and preserved if life in the long run is to continue.

Von Braun again and again expressed this fundamental thought. Space should be explored because we want to know more about this universe, he said. Our Earth is part of it, and from our viewpoint even its most important part, but it is still a part of a greater world. We should learn and know as much as we can about this greater world. Only profound knowledge will enable us to understand our Earth sufficiently to appreciate its unique beauty, and to become aware of our responsibility to keep it in a shape that permits life to continue here. Knowledge has become the prime mover of our human evolution, and the basis of our continuing well-being on Earth. Regardless where destiny will lead us, we will need all the knowledge about our Earth, about our neighbors in space, and about ourselves to cope with the challenges that are awaiting us. When we reach out for the Moon and the planets, we just do what our destiny makes us do.

Few events in recent history have found as much enthusiastic response around the world as the landing of astronauts on the Moon. It was a source of immense pride for the United States, and particularly for those hundreds of thousands of people in NASA, at scientific organizations, in industry, and in the government who felt that they had played some active role in this superb accomplishment. *"We had this magnificent triumph, and the entire world was applauding,"* NASA Administrator Paine recalled sixteen years later [8-71].

Those individuals within NASA who had been involved most directly in the Saturn-Apollo program were now confronted with the burning question: What next?

By the end of the 1960s, a large variety of technical capabilities for future unmanned and manned space projects had been developed and even demonstrated under real-life conditions. Choosing the most desirable program for the nation on the basis of these capabilities would be the privilege and responsibility of the president.

To help him make the best possible selection from the broad spectrum of available choices, President Nixon on 13 February 1969, five months before the first Moon landing, appointed a Space Task Group chaired by Vice President Spiro T. Agnew. The Task Group was to submit *"A Coordinated Space Program for the Future,"* along with a suggested budget. The proposed space program should include *"a very bold option that would get us an initial landing on Mars . . ."* [8-72]. Members of this Space Task Group were the science adviser to the president, Dr. Lee A. DuBridge; the administrator of NASA, Dr. Thomas O. Paine; and, as a representative of the Defense Department, Secretary of the Air Force Dr. Robert C. Seamans, Jr. The group also included as observers the under secretary of state for Political Affairs, U. Alexis Johnson; the chairman of the Atomic Energy Commission, Dr. Glenn T. Seaborg; and the director of the Bureau of the Budget, Robert P. Mayo.

The Space Task Group listened to numerous presentations by members of NASA Headquarters and field centers, industrial companies, and universities, and finally submitted its recommendations for a future national space program to the president. It was a marvelous program, embracing almost all the projects of planetary exploration and space research that could be envisioned at that time.

Was it the answer to the question: What next?

There was no shortage of optimists who would have been quick to suggest *"Let's go to Mars!"* No other project could have had more appeal to von Braun. However, his answer to that question was the result of his sense for realism, rather than of his hopes and dreams.

"We were extremely fortunate," he said after the successful flight of Apollo 11, *"that the president as well as the great public supported the Moon project wholeheartedly, so much, in fact, that our government—and that includes the Bureau of the Budget—could afford to stand firmly behind the project from beginning to end."*

Von Braun talked frequently about *"after Apollo"* space projects, in his own inner circles as well as in numerous discussions with members of Congress, industry, and the news media. In essence, he said and emphasized what space people had pointed out for thirty years, and even longer, namely, that the development of spaceflight will eventually result in tremendous benefits for mankind in many essential ways, spiritually, technically, scientifically, educationally, culturally, economically, politically. The Moon landing was a great spiritual experience around the world. It was a technical, and also a political success, and it was a great gift to many scientists. It must be proven now, he contended, that spaceflight will provide all these other benefits the space enthusiasts have promised.

Following the Saturn-Apollo project, he recommended that the various kinds of commercial and industrial uses of orbital flight should now be developed, including communication, television programs, weather service, intelligence information, earth resources, crop surveys, fishing operations, timber management. The unique advantages of spaceborne observatories for astronomy, cosmic ray physics, plasma physics, and the physics of Sun-Earth relations, should be recognized and used to a far greater extent.

Vigorous programs should also be initiated to use the weightlessness in orbit for the production of materials in space that cannot be produced with equal quality on Earth. We still know very little about such possibilities, he said, but we should expect that an environmental change as profound as the elimination of gravitational forces from the processing chambers will open the doors for technical and scientific processes of which we have only very little knowledge today.

Von Braun used to say that we now have a transportation system for heavy loads complete and ready, flight-proven in six Moon landings and half a dozen other spaceflights, and even paid in full. He believed that for the next twenty years, there was no need to develop another launch system. Saturn could take care even of our manned spaceflight requirements, and together with Atlas, Titan, Delta, Scout, and other existing launch systems, all our needs could be met. He explained that the production lines to manufacture these vehicles existed, and also the crews to build, test, and launch them. All of them have demonstrated high levels of reliability. He said we had to show that spaceflight is useful, and even profitable, for people on Earth, and in fact, space projects should begin to pay for themselves. *"We have benefitted tremendously,"* von Braun would insist, *"from the willingness of the people to become enthusiastic about spaceflight as a new frontier, as a high adventure, as an accomplishment that bolsters national pride and prestige. We must begin now to think of people as taxpayers. We have been promising for years that spaceflight will lead to benefits for all mankind, and that includes material benefits.*

"While devoting our main effort to the task of making spaceflight a wellspring of all these earthly benefits," he argued, *"we can develop our future space systems at a comfortable pace, without running the risk of a period of 'down time' in our spaceflight activities. Among these future space projects will be a space shuttle with two fully recoverable stages; a permanently occupied space station in orbit; a vigorous program of unmanned solar system exploration; and, as our next real highlight in space, a manned expedition to Mars."*

"As an immediate goal," von Braun often remarked, *"we should modify parts of the Saturn vehicle system in such a way that they provide us with a habitat in space, a baby space station, so to speak. That station will give us an opportunity of finding out in a low-risk and low-cost way, and at an early time, what we really wish to do in space during the next twenty years. Besides, this will give our country the chance to stay at the forefront of space technology and space accomplishments. A two-stage Saturn is*

capable of launching a heavy structure into orbit with the external contours of the third Saturn V stage, fashioned from the hydrogen and oxygen tanks, and outfitted internally as a comfortable habitat and laboratory in which astronauts will be able to live and work for extended periods of time."

Also, he said, we should develop and build a *"rapid transit"* vehicle for a modest payload that would be able to take materials, or supplies, or scientific instruments, or satellites, or space probes, or even human passengers into a low Earth orbit, or from orbit back to Earth. The latter would also represent a much-needed orbital rescue vehicle for stranded or sick astronauts. Those systems, von Braun argued, should be built for immediate use. Besides their applications to the work at hand, they would serve as forerunners of a more elaborate orbiting space station, and of a larger Earth-to-orbit roundtrip vehicle, that would be developed later after we had acquired enough knowledge and experience regarding the work programs we will wish to carry out in orbit.

If our well-working Saturn program were discontinued now, he contended, and if we put all our space eggs into a new and different basket that is even not yet developed, we would face tremendous expenditures in dollars and in time for which we would not be able to show tangible returns soon. We would even not be in a position to define, in terms understandable to the taxpaying laymen, what kind of benefits we expect to reap eventually. Therefore, let's utilize to the fullest extent what we have developed, built, and paid during the past twelve years, and let us demonstrate now step by step what our spaceflight capability can do for all of us. Eventually, we should begin to develop, at a rate which our national budget can bear, a fully recoverable space shuttle that will provide us, together with the rapid transit system, with a launch capability that does not force us to throw away each launcher after its ascent.

Dreams of a journey to Mars must have been a background melody in von Braun's never-resting mind since the 1920s. When the Saturn-Apollo project neared its completion, the sounds became louder. For the transfer stage from Earth orbit to Mars orbit, von Braun even played with the possibility of a nuclear rocket (Chapter 7-1). Besides optimists who expressed confidence in the bright future of nuclear-heated rocket propulsion systems, there were others who took a more restrained view. Based on the projected performance figures of the nuclear optimists, von Braun showed that a manned expedition to Mars could be carried out by starting the journey with two Saturn V rockets that would transport two nuclear transfer stages, their hydrogen propellant, and all the other gear and equipment from the ground into a near-Earth staging orbit. From there, the nuclear transfer stages would take the expedition, including the astronauts, to Mars, and back to Earth. Should a nuclear engine not become available, the expedition could be accomplished with chemical transfer stages. In this case, the journey would have to start with five or six Saturn V rockets.

Nuclear energy can also be used for space propulsion in the form of a power source for an electric propulsion system. Proposals and design studies for such systems have been made since the late 1940s. Although such systems represent efficient and versatile propulsion units for a variety of unmanned and manned space missions, and although numerous models of electric thrusters have been thoroughly tested on the ground, and even in orbit, with very promising results, von Braun did not include electric spacecraft in his advanced space mission studies. He never offered any technical arguments against electric propulsion; he just preferred the brief and violent burst of chemical or nuclear-thermal rockets to the long-time, gentle thrust force of an electric rocket, although the total propulsive impulse delivered by an electric rocket on a deep space mission is several times higher than that of a chemical or nuclear-thermal rocket of equal initial mass and payload. It must be said, though, that von Braun's view on that point was not shared by all of his co-workers, nor by numerous other colleagues in the United States and abroad.

A manned mission to Mars would certainly have been the crowning event in von Braun's life. The reason why he mentioned it only rarely during the late 1960s was his conviction that the space program should, after the Moon mission, demonstrate its *"benefits for all mankind"* by providing a variety of useful applications of space activities. Once the usefulness of space travel and space exploration has been broadly accepted, he argued, the public will be ready to support a great new adventure in space, such as the journey to Mars. *"Right now,"* he said early in 1969, *"it will be wise to emphasize in our advanced space program planning projects of immediate usefulness, and to keep the manned Mars mission on the back burner . . ."* One reason for this restraint was Project Viking, an unmanned mission to Mars whose planning phase had begun in 1967. Two landing craft were scheduled for launch in 1975, and for arrival on the Martian surface in 1976. That mission would provide a wealth of new information about our neighbor planet, possibly with profound consequences not only for technical details of a manned expedition, but also for the public's readiness to support a journey to Mars with human explorers aboard.

The other two major space projects that occupied prominent places in the planning efforts during the late 1960s, the *"orbital workshop"*—actually a first modest space station—and a shuttle vehicle that would provide rapid two-way transportation between Earth and orbit at low cost, would directly benefit the broad utilization effort. The orbital workshop, in particular, had been a von Braun pet project for many years. *"We will certainly have large space stations later,"* he often said, *"but we should first find out what we will use them for, how they should be equipped, and what roles man should play there. If we had to design a large and very costly space station now, we would really be groping in the dark. Orbiting workshops, built from empty Saturn tanks and launched with two-stage Saturns, would be ideal testing grounds. We really should build the large space station after we have gained more knowledge and experience with orbiting workshops."*

Mueller, as associate director for Manned Space Flight and the overall project officer for the Saturn-Apollo program, was a strong supporter of both projects, but with main emphasis on the shuttle. In fact, he considered the shuttle to be NASA's most important development effort after Saturn-Apollo, suggesting even that the shuttle should carry out all those low-orbit space launchings which at that time were accomplished with a variety of rocket launchers, including Scout, Delta, Atlas, Titan, Saturn I, and Saturn IB. With this broad role for the shuttle, its conceptual design grew quickly in size and complexity. Members of the Johnson Space Center in Houston enthusiastically embraced the new initiative, opting for a large two-stage system with full recoverability of both stages. Von Braun suggested a smaller shuttle system that would be less costly, less complicated, and less demanding with respect to development time, testing requirements, and cost. It could be launched at shorter intervals, and it would be better suited to support the efforts of space scientists who wanted to have frequent low-cost opportunities to carry out their space experiments. Also, a simpler shuttle would be available sooner than a complicated two-stage shuttle.

Plans and preparations for several scientific space projects were underway at that time, among them a large space telescope, later to be called the Hubble Space Telescope; Voyager missions to Jupiter, Saturn, Uranus, and Neptune; several solar exploration projects; and the Viking lander missions to Mars. For all believers in spaceflight, 1969 was a year not only of splendid accomplishments, but also of great hopes for the future.

Rather than continue with the flow of events in late 1969 and early 1970, the next chapter will describe von Braun's life and work as director of the Marshall Center in Huntsville during the decade from 1960 to 1970.

In retrospect, it is obvious that the Saturn-Apollo mission to the Moon was the supreme accomplishment among NASA's projects. It was certainly the highlight in von Braun's life. In spite of his tremendous workload, he was mostly relaxed and in good spirits. He enjoyed excellent working relations not only with his immediate co-workers, but also with his superiors in NASA Headquarters, with most of his colleagues at the field centers, with the astronauts, and with the universities and the industrial companies involved in the Saturn-Apollo project. He was a highly valued presenter and interpreter of space matters in Congress. He followed the development of all phases of the gigantic Saturn-Apollo project in as much detail as he possibly could, and he was certainly that person in the entire program who had the most comprehensive knowledge of all its aspects and ramifications.

Von Braun's friends were often amazed when they realized that in the middle of this breathtaking pace he still found time for his hobbies, for traveling, flying, and scuba diving, for family outings on his Tennessee river boat, for writing and speech-making. He really lived his life *"full bore,"* as he used to say.

CHAPTER 9

THE HUMAN SIDE OF A SPACEMAN

1 A MAN OF STRIKING APPEARANCE

Most visitors who met von Braun for the first time, and then commented on their impressions, gave almost identical descriptions: a man of strong build, with broad shoulders and a firm, sincere handshake . . . a personality that radiates great human warmth while showing impressive knowledge . . . with his blond hair, blue eyes, easy movements and boyish smile, he gives the image of perfect balance of body and mind, born to succeed in whatever he undertakes . . . in short, a man of striking appearance.

Dornberger remembers his first contacts with the twenty-year old von Braun during his inconspicuous visits at the Raketenflugplatz (rocket test field) near Rein-ickendorf [1]: *"This young, tall, fair-haired student with the broad, massive chin immediately caught my attention through his skillful approach to practical work on the teststand, and at the same time through his astounding theoretical knowledge . . ."*

Many years later, journalist Bernd Ruland interviewed von Braun [9-1]. *"I met many prominent people during my long career as a journalist,"* he wrote, *"but none of them was so open-minded, so youthfully easy-going and unconventional, so natural and straightforward as this man who combined technical genius and unusual organiza-tional talent in one fascinating personality . . ."*

When von Braun talked, his words flowed easily and swiftly, but he carefully selected each of them, and he had the ability of keeping those to whom he spoke glued to his lips, neither talking over their heads, nor down to them, nor boring them with unnecessary detail. *"Perhaps one of the greatest of his many assets,"* his friend Erik Bergaust wrote [9-2], *"is the famous von Braun charm. He has all the qualities of a young boy."* Another friend, Frederick C. Durant III, recalled: *"When he participated in a meeting, his confidence and enthusiasm pervaded the room."*

Bonnie Holmes, his secretary for twenty years, remembered: *"Even when he had to call a meeting on some dismal situation, and everybody entered the conference room with sinister looks and a drooping head, it didn't take more than five minutes before a ringing laughter would emerge from the room . . ."*

When von Braun spoke to a group of people, each individual felt personally addressed. He always talked in a voice loud and distinct enough for everyone to follow him. Convinced that he had something essential to say, he wished to be clearly understood by everybody.

A few years after his arrival in the United States, von Braun's ability to express himself in English was such that his American colleagues had no difficulty at all in understanding him. Some said that his German tongue was still quite noticeable, others felt that they couldn't tell any difference between his and the average native's language. His rich vocabulary, and particularly his ability to spice his talks with colorful idioms, were frequently praised. When von Braun was exclusively among former Germans, he always talked German, flawlessly even thirty years after he had left Germany. As soon as a non-German was near, he immediately switched to English, and he insisted that everybody else do the same.

"When you talk to von Braun," a colleague once remarked, *"he looks straight in your face, eager to catch every word you say. But most of the time, he talks. His presence, his immediacy, his total engagement always dominate the scene. There is no feeling of absent-mindedness on his part. When you begin to talk about something that does not interest him, he quickly takes over and leads the conversation into another direction. Sometimes, this can be frustrating, if you wanted to present an idea to him, or ask his opinion on something, and he was just not interested . . ."*

Von Braun's physical strength became apparent at numerous occasions. When he and some associates visited a laboratory or a teststand, his questions and debates would frequently continue far beyond the comfort limits of his associates. He would go from room to room, up stairs and through narrow passages, always inquiring, listening, suggesting, playing with valves and switches, and immersing himself fully in the problems of his hosts. *"He can really wear you out,"* was a remark not unusual among his companions. Von Braun, by no means unaware of this fact, expressed the same thought in a more cynical way. *"A boss,"* he sometimes said, *"is a man who develops ulcers in the stomachs of his co-workers."*

His physical stamina showed even more when he indulged in one of his favorite sports, scuba diving. An excellent swimmer since his boyhood days, he loved the water. Arthur C. Clarke had introduced him to the art and science—and passion—of diving with an aqualung, and he quickly became an afficionado and expert. Whenever he was near the seaside during a business trip, he used every available weekend to gather some colleagues and friends, to don a set of rented diving gear, and to jump in. One of his associates, James S. Farrior, remembered a diving trip to the Florida Keys. *"That's when I realized for the first time the unlimited energy he possesses,"* he said. *"Wernher swam around every rock and poked into every crevice, and he did not cease until the last tank on our boat was empty. Everybody else had long since stretched out on the deck, totally exhausted . . ."* Bergaust [9-3] reported a little anecdote that Farrior had told him, reminiscing about that Florida Key trip: *"Wernher,"* Farrior said to von Braun, *"I hate to tarnish your image, but I have to state that you don't do everything well. After a fine dinner of the fish we had speared, it fell to your and my lot to do the dishes. You are, without doubt, the most awful dishwasher I have ever seen, bar none!"*

On another occasion, von Braun and some associates rented a boat, diving gear, and a guide in Long Beach, California, and headed for the crisp waters off the coast of Santa Catalina Island. The underwater scenery was marvelous: beds of green kelp, swaying in the tidal waves, with brilliant red California goldfish and other colorful creatures in between; with rocks and moray eels and large sea bass, and with lots of fun and excitement. Von Braun was as happy as a young boy. All his California friends had their wet suits, and von Braun had borrowed one from another friend. His two associates from Huntsville, Gerhard Heller and Ernst Stuhlinger, had none; after an hour of diving in the sparkling 58 degree F (14½ degree C) water, they felt the cold creeping up. Von Braun was indomitable. *"Let's go now to that reef,"* he would say. *"Now, we want to explore that bay,"* and he insisted that everybody share his excitement and enthusiasm. *"Have you seen that big crab underneath that rock? Did you go around that corner, there's a school of several thousand fish!—Try to get that abalone shell from over there!"* Well, the afternoon stretched into the early evening. Hours later, the Alabama travelers arrived back in Huntsville. Hertha Heller and Irmgard Stuhlinger met their husbands at the airport. *"When they arrived,"* the wives commented later, *"they were still shivering all over, and their lips had a distinctly bluish tint!"*

Another exciting underwater adventure waited for von Braun and his diving companions in the Exuma chain of islands in the Bahamas. James P. Lewis and his wife from upstate New York had invited them and some other friends for the trip on their 78-foot yacht Searcher. The Exuma islands sit like the spillway of a dam between the Atlantic and the Caribbean. Tremendous volumes of water, warm and comfortable, rush back and forth between the islands as the tides rise and fall. Divers can easily cover a mile in fifteen minutes near the bottom without any effort, just watching the fantastic abundance of tropical fish, corals, big shells, lobsters, gigantic rays, groupers, barracudas, and occasional hammerhead sharks—hoping that one of the yacht's Boston Whalers would be close when they surfaced. *"Shooting the rapids,"* von Braun called this fabulous experience, and his excitement found no end.

Von Braun's love for diving, as Bergaust remarked, won him several wonderful new friends, among them Ed Link, developer of the famous Link Pilot Trainer, and pioneer of underwater diving technology; John H. Perry, Jr., who designed and built the four-man submarine Deep Diver; and Walter Cronkite, CBS's unforgettable anchor man. Cronkite once wrote von Braun a birthday card: *"I hold a secret admiration for a man whose life has been devoted to getting to the stars, and whose hobby is getting to the bottom of a lagoon . . ."*

Flying was another passion of von Braun. Over the years, he acquired all classes of pilot's licenses available to nonmilitary pilots, private and commercial. He made most of his business trips by NASA airplane. Government regulations demanded that two professional pilots were on the plane, but whenever von Braun was aboard, one of the pilots sat in the passenger compartment while von Braun occupied the left-hand seat. Even after long and exhausting meeting days in Washington, when his associates on the flight back to Huntsville dozed off wearily in their seats, von Braun sat in the cockpit and flew the plane to Alabama through the night, often through bad weather, like a seasoned pro.

"Wernher, do you play golf?" he was sometimes asked. *"No,"* was the prompt answer, *"it would be far too dangerous."*—*"Dangerous? How can you say that?"*—*"Well, you see, if I started to play golf, I wanted to do it right, and to learn how to play like an expert. That would take a great deal of my time, most of what I need for this rocket and space business, for flying and scuba diving, for boating and water skiing, for reading and writing, and, perhaps most important, for my family. Don't you see how dangerous it would be if I started to play golf?"*

Von Braun's striking appearance was fully matched by his ever-working, sparkling mind. There were no dull moments for him, nor for those who shared some occasional off-duty hours with him. The same words that Saul Pet [9-4] wrote about Franklin D. Roosevelt could be said about von Braun: *"Through a thousand competing pressures and details, he appeared imperturbably on top of life."* He had a remarkable gift to leave the problems of his office behind and to enjoy the leisure of an hour or two at an airport, in the dining hall of a hotel, or even during a brief walk on a beach. There were always some colleagues or friends around whom he would invariably engage in an animated talk in which, of course, he would do the talking and the others would listen, only rarely interrupting him with a question or a quip. Frequently, the conversation would begin with a question, and von Braun would answer at great length, drawing an almost infinite supply of knowledge out of his fabulous memory. He loved to share his knowledge with others. Even the process of formulating sentences, of choosing words, of sprinkling idioms into his talk gave him unconcealed pleasure. The subjects of these talks were of great variety. While future exploits of spaceflight, manned journeys to Mars, or commercial activities in satellite orbits figured prominently in these conversations, he could also give dramatic accounts of hunting and fishing trips in Norway, or of travels over the Antarctic ice cap.

General Medaris once remarked: *"One could have the most lively conversation with von Braun for hours, and still would not be able to guess what his profession was."*

He would talk with equal fervor about education in the United States, or the legacy of the Moon project. *"Apollo 8,"* von Braun might say, *"taking its astronauts farther away than any other human being had ever been, was a brilliant technical success for all who helped design, build, and launch it. But even more important than the technical achievements of this mission are these beautiful pictures of mother Earth that Borman, Anders, and Lovell brought back. They showed our home planet as a sparkling jewel within endless black space, and they were seen by more than a billion people. Our atmosphere, which sustains the lives of all living beings, is just an extremely thin pellicule covering the Earth's surface. Nobody who sees a picture like this can fail to realize that our earthly abode is exceedingly precious, just because it is so extremely delicate and fragile. How vulnerable must it be to any kind of abuse! How easily could this intricate balance of energies, matter, and forces, which enabled life to evolve on Earth, be thrown into disarray, making the Earth's surface unsuited for the sustenance of life as we know and like it. I am sure that these fabulous pictures of our Earth will make all of us aware of our duties to keep our Earth clean, to avoid all sorts of abuse and unnecessary waste, and to help maintain it for countless future generations of people, animals, and plants . . ."*

Another theme he loved to talk about was the way in which philosophers of various times and countries have been trying to understand man's place in this world. He did this in a fashion that might not have fully satisfied a devoted student of philosophy, but which translated the ethereal substance of this profound question into the sober, precise, logical language of *homo technicus*. There can be no doubt that von Braun was aware of the positive impression his *"striking appearance"*—physical and mental— made on almost everyone with whom he came in contact. He received attention, recognition, and compliments in profusion, but he accepted all these amiable reactions modestly, and even with self-effacing replies, always pointing to the thousands and thousands of others who helped him achieve his successes. He was happy to see that people thought so well of him; this was for him like the sunshine on a beautiful day, something one accepts with joy and gratitude, but without complacency.

2   SCIENTIST, ENGINEER, MANAGER, OR . . . ?

Was von Braun a scientist, or an engineer, or a manager? None of these designations would fully fit the nature of his personality. His monumental mind contained elements not only of a scientist, an engineer, and a manager, but also of a philosopher, a humanitarian, a politician, a diplomat, a down-to-Earth realist, and a high-flying visionary for whom life in space appeared almost as natural as life on Earth. He was the hard-driving boss, relentless in his demand for perfect achievement, and he was also the warm-hearted and compassionate friend in whose presence everyone felt good. On rare occasions, he could be so grumpy that it was advisable not to stay close to him.

Each of his many talents had a touch of genius that captivated those who crossed paths with him. In every sense of the word, he was a leader—a leader of the gang of boys at his school on the island of Spiekeroog, the leader at the Raketenflugplatz Reinickendorf, the leader of his giant development project at Peenemünde, the leader on the road that led mankind from Earth into space.

It has been said that a scientist wants to know, an engineer wants to do, and a manager wants to know that somebody does. Scientists ask questions of nature, von Braun asked questions of people. He wanted to know, but he was too impetuous and impatient to be a scientist. He did ask questions, but he wanted immediate answers. He had an incredible thirst for knowledge, but it had to be knowledge that could be absorbed easily and quickly. *"Define for me the nature of a virus, please,"* he once asked a young scientist on his staff. *"But do it in three sentences. Don't give me a lengthy dissertation!"* The young man tried his best: *"A virus is the smallest entity of living organisms we know of, without cellular nucleus and metabolism. Viruses multiply only inside living cells; outside, they assume an inert mode of existence, something like a crystal. Viruses cause various diseases . . ."* At that moment, von Braun's patience had run out. *"Stop it, that's enough,"* he said, but he recorded and kept this concise description of a virus in his memory, together with innumerable other facts about scientific subjects, ready at any time to be played back with high fidelity.

One day, von Braun came back from a brief vacation. *"Did you have a good time?"* his co-workers asked. *"Yes,"* he said, *"I got a hold of my daughter's schoolbook on biology, and I read it from cover to cover."* And then, he described in his dramatic, but precise and factual way the story of DNA and the miraculous double helix, of heredity and gene-splicing, of evolution and the dangers of genetic damage by nuclear radiation.

At another time, during a boating afternoon on the Tennessee River, von Braun talked about a book by George Gamow he had read. It explained the happenings in the universe during the first seconds and minutes after the Big Bang. The amount of detail he remembered from the book was amazing, and so was his ability to piece all these minute facts together into a grandiose story of the birth pangs of stars and galaxies.

For von Braun, science was a revelation. It allowed him a glimpse at the inner workings of nature, and it fortified his feeling of being comfortably at home in this universe. He was an avid reader of articles and books about the results of scientific research, and he delighted in telling others what he had read in his precise, lively language. Whenever he had the chance of meeting a scientist at a convention, an observatory, or even socially, he overwhelmed him or her with questions; he impressed many scientists with his knowledge, his quick grasp, his agility of mind, and his astounding capability of formulating precisely what he wanted to know.

In his speeches, he often talked about science and research, and he left no doubt that he considered scientific work one of the noblest activities of man. The fact that his work as a developer of spaceflight provided scientists all over the world with a fabulous opportunity for research and exploration was a continuous source of joy for him. He was hesitant, though, to provide active support to science-oriented projects within his own center. When members of his Space Sciences Laboratory, particularly James A. Downey, in 1963 began to propose a family of satellites for the study of cosmic rays, X rays, and gamma rays, later to be called High Energy Astronomical Observatory or HEAO, he showed some interest, but he wished *"not to press the issue too hard"* because the main effort of the center should be focused on the Saturn-Apollo project.

A similar situation existed for the large space telescope, later to be named Hubble Space Telescope. As early as 1923, Hermann Oberth had written in his book *The Rocket into Planetary Space* that satellite orbits will be ideal locations for astronomical telescopes. Space telescope projects were proposed and vigorously pursued from the astronomer's standpoint by Lyman Spitzer at Princeton University, and by other astronomers. Members of von Braun's center began around 1964 to study the flight mechanical aspects of space telescopes, and they suggested that a telescope project should be included in the center's program. Von Braun was interested in this project and encouraged further studies, but he wished the effort to be limited to modest paper studies so that the main project at that time, Saturn-Apollo, would not suffer from such *"secondary projects."*

Studies on both projects, HEAO and the then unnamed space telescope, continued at the Marshall Center, but both became full-fledged development projects only in 1971 under von Braun's successor, Eberhard Rees, after most of the work on Saturn-Apollo had been completed.

Reading papers and books on scientific subjects was a delightful pastime for von Braun which he permitted himself only rarely. It was the *"sugarcoating on my carrot cake,"* as he put it. He also kept an active interest in the content and progress of scientific research work at other places that might possibly profit from spaceborne facilities. During the early 1960s, he became intrigued with possibilities of solar research using satellites. He bought a dozen copies of astrophysicist K. O. Kiepenheuer's book *Our Sun*, distributed them among his senior staff members, and declared them *"recommended reading"* for each of his directors. A decade later, Skylab, developed under Marshall's management, was in orbit, carrying a substantial array of sensors and telescopes for solar research.

Von Braun believed in a strict concentration of his and his center's efforts on development projects, one project at a time. He did not wish any project of scientific research to acquire the *"critical mass"* needed to give it identity, to make it productive, and to have it earn recognition by peers. This attitude imposed severe restrictions on the projects that could be pursued in the Marshall Center's Space Sciences Laboratory; only projects *"in direct support of the Saturn program"* were acceptable. Restricting the center's efforts to one project at a time, against strong temptations, was courageous and probably wise, but it did not make everyone of von Braun's co-workers happy. However, this self-imposed restriction was probably one of the reasons why von Braun's team was so successful with its large spaceflight projects.

An exception to this rule was the Explorer 1 satellite, but this was almost a by-product of the Redstone and Jupiter projects, falling as a ripe fruit from the tree. After this brilliant success, von Braun decided not to pursue the building and launching of satellites much further, but rather to concentrate on the Saturn-Apollo program. Further minor exceptions were some short-time projects, such as the high-altitude testing of rocket-launched atomic bombs in the Pacific in 1958, the Pioneer 4 flyby of the Moon in 1959, the ballistic flight of the chimpanzee Ham in 1961, and the first high-altitude rocket flight of an astronaut, Alan Shepard, in 1961. Two larger projects that were assigned to the Marshall Center, but failed to evolve into successful projects because they did not enjoy sufficient support from the center director, were the Agena and the Centaur upper stage projects (Chapter 9-4).*

One project that owed its life-giving spark to von Braun, but then suffered from his unwillingness to engage in more than one project at a time, was electric space propulsion. Remembering that Hermann Oberth had proposed an *"electric rocket"* in the early 1920s, von Braun stimulated one of his staff members to study electric propulsion systems in 1947. Experimental work began in 1957 with a Marshall Center contract at Electro-Optical Systems under Dr. Abraham Zarem. In the same year, the NASA Lewis Research Center also started a program of electric propulsion work; JPL followed later. By the mid-1960s, electric propulsion technology had reached a state of development that warranted the initiation of a program aiming at electrically propelled rocket stages for deep space missions. However, von Braun chose to abide by the one-

---

*Both projects proved to be very successful upper stages in a number of later space missions.

project-at-a-time rule, and to keep the Marshall Center's role in electric propulsion development on a very low and inconspicuous level of continuing paper studies.

Several years later, Marshall Center Director William R. Lucas decided to seek approval for a full-fledged development project of a solar-electric propulsion system (SEPS). However, by that time the shuttle effort was in full swing, resulting in severe funding constraints for other projects. Very likely, deep-space spacecraft will not be propelled by American-made electric propulsion systems for many years to come.

By the time the Saturn-Apollo program approached its end, a relaxation of the strict one-project rule at the Marshall Center became possible, and even appropriate. Von Braun's successors, first Rees and then Lucas, allowed the research-minded members of the Space Sciences Laboratory more free rein, and a series of noteworthy research programs developed at the Marshall Center, among them studies in solar, infrared, gamma ray, and X-ray astronomy, and also work in magnetospheric physics, solar-terrestrial relations, cryogenics, superconductivity, materials processing, protein research, and solid state physics.

While von Braun did not support or even permit substantial research projects to be pursued at his center independent of the immediate needs of ongoing development work, he encouraged small-scale scientific activities throughout his organization. He even insisted that besides the Space Sciences Laboratory, each of the numerous center laboratories should also have the opportunity, and the funding, to indulge in some pet projects of a scientific nature *"to sweeten the diet of their daily drudgery."*

Many visitors came to the Marshall Center through the years. Von Braun was always happy to have guests, to chat with them, to explain his programs, and to describe his progress. With most of them, he struck it rich from the first moment on. His great natural charm, his ability to explain his programs, his wit, his amiable politeness never failed to impress those who came to see him. He intuitively knew how much he had to explain to make his visitors understand the problem without boring them with too much detail. Among his visitors, there were members of NASA Headquarters, representatives and senators from Congress, high officers from the Pentagon, directors from industry and from government organizations, vice presidents and presidents, and even princes and kings.

Surprisingly, von Braun was less at ease when he addressed scientists. The reason is not clear. He had an unlimited admiration for the gigantic edifice of knowledge that the work of scientists had built over the centuries, and he was happy to be able, through his work, to open a few gates for the acquisition of more knowledge. On the other hand, he knew quite well that some scientists, totally engulfed in their own studies, were critical of the space program as a *"gigantic money sink"* for the sake of some *"circus stunts."*

Even among those scientists who were eager to utilize the ability of big rockets to transport their instruments into space, and who, quite generally, happily accepted the wave of enthusiasm for space exploration that began to permeate the country during the late 1950s, some remained quite reserved regarding the person of von Braun. *"We had people on the scientific side,"* Herbert Friedman said in an interview in 1990 [9-5], *"who were effective [as promoters of spaceflight]. Lloyd Berkner was a very effective spokesman. And Jim Webb, when he became head of NASA, was also very effective. He established the university centers, and in that way gave space science a big boost. Von Braun was outside the picture of most scientists . . . When he tried to insert science in his talks before public forums he often made some 'boo-boos.' He was obviously not a trained scientist; his forté was engineering, and even there it was more his leadership, and his ability to organize the group that stood out, rather than the details of the technology for which we remember other members of the team primarily . . . We may appreciate him better in the long run when we attempt to send humans to Mars. I believe his concepts of artificial gravity will be essential . . ."*

There were other occasions when von Braun made mistakes. He often told a little story in a conversation to emphasize a point. Sometimes, when he was under time pressure, he shortened and even fragmented the story so that it did not make sense, much to his embarrassment when he saw his words in print the next day.

Some scientists erroneously believed that von Braun claimed to be a scientist. Von Braun never made this claim, but he was sensitive to allegations that questioned his motives or his sincerity. His primary goal was the development of precision rockets for travel through interplanetary space, and he saw a host of benefits for mankind flowing from this work, among them brilliant opportunities for scientific space research, if scientists would only grasp these golden opportunities and put their instruments aboard the space vehicles.

This, however, may not be so easy. Scientists will often request that the spacecraft be designed in a way that special features of an experiment can be accommodated. However, engineers and project managers, not too familiar with scientific methods and procedures, may find it difficult to understand the arguments of scientists. Is it surprising that impetuous von Braun sometimes felt uneasy in this situation? He preferred a community of engineers and project managers to a *"community"* that consisted of a number of brilliant, yet quite independent minds, a community that was very impressive as an accumulation of knowledge, but relatively incoherent with respect to project planning and management.

When von Braun was chosen *"Man of the Year in Science"* by the Associated Press, he showed great surprise. *"Why should they choose me?"* he asked. *"I am not a scientist! I am only a beneficiary of science,"* he said, but he certainly was also a great benefactor for science.

While von Braun hoped and wished that scientists would utilize the new tool of rocket flight to extend their field of action into space, he never really campaigned for a science project. Some of his associates did, but the most they could hope for from the boss was quiet toleration. To those science projects which were brought into the Marshall Center's programs and carried through to a successful achievement during the late 1950s and the 1960s, von Braun never gave the same careful, continuing attention that he gave to rocket projects and Skylab. The difference showed in the Explorer projects that followed Explorer 1; in the Pegasus project that measured meteoroid impacts; in the High Energy Astronomical Observatory (HEAO) satellite program; in the solar astronomy projects on Skylab; and in the Hubble Space Telescope project that was pioneered by Lyman Spitzer and other astronomers in the 1950s, started as an engineering study project at the Marshall Center in the 1960s and was assigned to Marshall as a development project by Jesse Mitchell at NASA Headquarters in 1971.

Considering von Braun's genuine interest in the results of scientific research, and his continuing desire to support the work of space scientists by providing the tools for their work, it is difficult to understand his tendency to keep a certain distance from scientists working with the rockets and spacecraft that he developed. Many of von Braun's staff members took the same arm's length stance when they worked with scientists. Fortunately, others—among them Richard Cook, James T. Shepherd, Leland F. Belew, Fridtjof A. Speer, James A. Downey—met their colleagues from the science camp with understanding and the desire to cooperate. During the 1970s and 1980s, the Marshall Center became the cradle of several very successful space projects with primarily scientific objectives. A visitor who toured the Space Sciences Laboratory in 1988 commented later: *"The science program at the Marshall Center is one of the best kept secrets of NASA."*

If von Braun was not a scientist, was he an engineer? In one sense, yes, even a great one; in another sense, not really. During a joyful and spirited evening party at von Braun's residence, Maria von Braun told her guests how she had just fixed a broken picture frame by drilling a hole and driving a screw into the wood. *"Do you have a drill?"* von Braun asked, full of surprise. *"Oh yes,"* Maria answered, *"I have an electric hand drill, and a whole box full of other tools, and I even use them quite frequently."*— *"I did not know that,"* von Braun replied, but Maria said: *"It makes no difference, Wernher, because you would not know how to operate the drill anyway, and you would certainly hurt yourself,"* and she continued to her guests: *"Wernher is so brilliant, but when a nail must be driven into the wall, he always calls me. He does not go beyond replacing a fuse, occasionally."*

And yet, von Braun unquestionably deserves to be called an engineering genius. Unbothered by the little details of around-the-house technology, he set his mind on the rocket-powered spaceship as a boy of fourteen, and he kept it there for the next fifty years, leaving in his wake such engineering marvels as the V-2, the Redstone, the Explorer, the Jupiter, the Pershing, the Saturn family, and the Skylab.

In all these projects, von Braun proved to be an engineer in mind and at heart. Frank Williams, a member and later director of von Braun's Future Projects Office, remembered [9-6]: *"Von Braun would come down and literally pore over the drawing boards with you, and look at the performance and check the engineering work . . . When the Saturn V design was being established, von Braun was in the forefront, immersing himself in the whole vehicle: structures, systems, and missions . . ."*

As Konrad Dannenberg, one of von Braun's veteran project managers, recalled [9-7], von Braun *"would talk as easily with the 'top brass' as with the 'tin benders' . . . He would solicit advice and suggestions from workers in the shops, taking into account the realities of fabrication and manufacture as the design evolved . . . In this way, von Braun avoided the pitfalls of having top-level managers making critical decisions among themselves, and arriving at assumptions about fabrication that might not approach reality."*

Von Braun's real forté was the engineering development of rocket systems. All the major components of the V-2, the Redstone, the Jupiter, the Saturn family, and Skylab not only show the handwriting of their initiator; a number of their basic features are directly based on von Braun's ideas and suggestions. He spent untold hours in the design rooms, the laboratories, the workshops, the assembly hangars, and on the test stands where his rockets came into existence. His most decisive contributions to rocket technology were made during the 1930s when the A-series of rockets, culminating in the A-4, was developed at Reinickendorf, Kummersdorf, and Peenemünde. Subsystems developed during that time included rocket motors, gyro-stabilized guidance platforms, attitude control systems, burning cutoff devices, servo motors, and test stands. Certainly, he was not the handyman type who fixes everything around the house and the family car, but he influenced and penetrated the design of his rockets to such a degree that they became the most reliable rocket systems ever.

It may be obvious that von Braun did not meet the classical description of a program manager or program administrator according to the definitions of the Harvard Business school, nor could he have been compared with one of the giants of scientific programs, such as Arnold Sommerfeld in physics, or Ludwig Prandtl or Theodore von Kármán in aerodynamics. Instead of a billion-dollar-a-year corporation, or an illustrious academic research program, his goal was the creation of technical systems that would enable man to travel into space. He established and adhered to some basic principles of project work which became the characteristic hallmark of von Braun projects. Here are some of his well known credos:

1. The person to whom the development and management of a project has been entrusted must always be absolutely on top of his project as far as objective, schedules, status, and upcoming problems are concerned. As soon as the slightest doubts arise about the health of the project, the boss must be informed. The project manager must be fully accountable for everything that happens in his project.

2. A project manager has *"to keep his hands dirty"* by spending a substantial portion of his time in the laboratories and workshops, and on the teststands, where his project comes to life.

3. The project manager must maintain an unrestricted flow of information at all times throughout his project organization, up and down. Any impending or actual failure must be investigated, analyzed, and corrected to the point that no further reason for concern remains.

4. A system developed and built for space use must be assembled, tested, and checked out as a complete unit on the ground as thoroughly as this is possible under one-g conditions. Assembly and checkout procedures that need to be carried out in space should be held to an absolute minimum.

5. A project should start out with a carefully defined objective, and the project should be optimized for that objective. Attempts to build *"multipurpose"* space systems, capable of accommodating numerous different functions with different requirements, should be avoided.

6. Product integrity and quality cannot be managed into a system; they must be designed and engineered into it!

7. The relationship between contractors and project personnel is a two-way street. Contractors must be considered as partners, and in fact as team members. This close integration of contractors into the project work force will not amount to a control of contractors, but to a sharing of knowledge and experience, and of the burden of responsibility.

To those of his co-workers who, under the strain of their assignments, began to show signs of disappointment or frustration, he had some down-to-Earth admonishment:

"Let's stop lamenting and start doing!"

"This life is not a bed of roses!"

"Don't think that the world owes you a living. It does not!"

"Nobody can pull a rabbit out of a hat unless somebody has put it in first!"

"I've learned to use the word "impossible" with caution."

"Man muss sich verschenken können!—you should be willing to give of yourself!"

(The original German version sounds far more elegant than its translation.)

Von Braun sometimes quoted Admiral Hyman Rickover, the father of the nuclear submarine. *"When Rickover was asked how in the world he found those fabulous managers who helped him build the* Nautilus, *he answered: 'I don't hire any managers at all; I hire darned good engineers, and when I know them real well, I select some and make managers out of them!'"*

Chapter (8-6) is devoted to the management aspects of space programs. Could von Braun be called a manager? This would not quite do justice to the facts. People who knew von Braun well from joint work would agree on a statement with which Lee B. James characterized von Braun [9-10]: *"You may not be able to describe him in terms of standard management formulae, but he certainly was doing a fantastic job in managing his projects, and his people!"*

James had become a member of General Medaris's staff in Huntsville in 1956. From 1960 on, after retiring from the Army as a colonel, he continued working in von Braun's team as project manager for Saturn I and IB, then as deputy director of the Apollo program under General Phillips at NASA Headquarters, then again at the Marshall Center as deputy program manager for Saturn V under Arthur Rudolph. After Rudolph's retirement in 1969, James became program manager for Saturn V. During all these years, his working relationship with von Braun was extremely close.

"Part of his genius was his great ability to recognize and use very talented people," James said. *"In management he was just outstanding . . . His charisma turned everyone on . . . He had vision, audacity, and he produced! . . . His handling of the Jupiter program was superb . . . He was respected and admired everywhere . . .*

"Saturn V went through many technical problems," James added, *"but they were not our real problems . . . The Washington staff and the Houston staff came from the same places and started with good mutual support . . . Even the people at the Cape were pretty much Houston people. The interfaces were my biggest problems . . . Also, there was some unhappiness, including mine, with NASA Headquarters and the rest of the world thinking there was no one in our entire space program but astronauts . . . What astronauts want, astronauts get . . . At that time, there was a lot of tension between the elements of NASA . . . the science people felt that manned spaceflight was taking all their money away from them . . . there were heated debates sometime . . . It was most remarkable how von Braun kept his balance in all that turmoil, his optimism, his cooperative spirit toward all those different factions, his determination to forge ahead . . . he certainly was not a manager in the conventional sense—he was far more!"*

Success on the scale of von Braun's cannot be attributed to a single cause. In von Braun's life, a variety of circumstances worked together in a most fortunate combination: His hereditary background, formed by a long line of aristocratic ancestors who distinguished themselves as high government officials, university professors, military officers, and diplomats; his upbringing in a family where the traditional values of a harmonious family life ranked first; his early exposure to persons of outstanding accomplishments; his encounters with people of great influence and power who recognized, needed, and accepted his talents. When von Braun heard remarks about his fantastic successes, he often said: *"Well, I was just extremely lucky!"* However, in the long run luck comes only to those who earn it. Von Braun's ability to learn, to understand, to correlate, to memorize, and to retrieve from his vast memory was superb, but so was his desire to utilize all of these extraordinary talents with a degree of determination and purpose that matched the abundance of his gifts.

3   JUDGMENTS OF SUPERIORS

Long before von Braun assumed leadership over his first little rocket team, his teacher at the Hermann Lietz school on the island of Spiekeroog wrote to his parents about their fifteen-year-old son: *"Wernher is a genius. You can be proud of him! He will do great things."*

Von Braun became a civilian employee of the German Army in 1932. The head of the Ballistics Section in Army Ordnance, Colonel (later General) Karl Becker, held two doctorates and a professorship in science and engineering. He was considered the prime authority on ballistics at that time.

Becker was convinced that the technology of guided rockets would not make any progress unless it was based on sound and comprehensive scientific analyses. He urged von Braun in 1932 to go back to the university and earn a Ph.D. degree. *"First of all,"* he said, *"you have to round off your education."* He granted him continuation of his employment as a civilian with the Army, while he worked on his thesis. In the summer of 1932, von Braun enrolled at the Friedrich-Wilhelm-Universität in Berlin. In April 1934 he received a doctor's degree for his thesis *"Combustion Phenomena in Liquid-Propellant Rocket Engines."* The study dealt with all the essential components and problems of a rocket motor: propellant chemistry, injection nozzles, heat transfer, combustion pressure and temperature, expansion nozzle geometry, cooling jacket design. Von Braun's thesis adviser was Dr. Erich Schumann; among his teachers at the university were the Nobel Prize laureates Erwin Schroedinger, Max von Laue, and Walter Nernst.

Von Braun's supervisor at the Army Ordnance Ballistic and Ammunition Department, Lt. Colonel Wolfram Ritter von Horstig, had to assess his capabilities in 1936; he wrote [9-9]:

"Von Braun is a young, very active physicist with sound and useful technical ideas whose realization he attacks with great determination . . . he skillfully utilizes his co-workers according to their specific knowledge. This is one of his remarkable abilities . . . With his outstanding talents in many different fields as well as his very profound knowledge and capability in physics, he is able to solve even extremely difficult technical problems in the development of rockets . . . He shows particular skill in negotiations with industry that often are quite difficult . . . He is a model for his co-workers . . . In private life, he is a very lively, good-natured, popular fellow, always ready to help or to share a joke. In all contacts with superiors, he is open-minded, natural, and very tactful . . . It may be said with certainty that he will achieve outstanding things in his specialty, the broad field of rocketry . . ."

Among von Braun's many superiors during his professional career, Major General (Dr.) Walter Dornberger stands out as the one with whom he had a longer, closer, more intense, and more crucial association than with any of the others. When their joint work began in 1932, Dornberger was already a rocket man. He was the only one of von Braun's superiors who had acquired substantial knowledge and experience in rocketry before he met von Braun. Dornberger was firmly, even passionately convinced that rockets would play a decisive role in the future fates and fortunes of mankind.

Their association ended in Peenemünde in 1945. At that time, the first long-range guided rocket, the A-4 or V-2, had come to life. Looking back over these thirteen years, Dornberger said: *"We opened the gates, and we did start out on the way to the future . . ."*

The work that lay ahead in 1932 was formidable. Dornberger took an active part in every technical detail of the gradual evolution of the modern rocket, but he did far more. He steered and guided von Braun's budding rocket team through a maze of man-made obstacles: disbelief, neglect, and suppression by higher government officials; severe rivalries between military departments; jealousies, ambitions, and unbelievable intrigues on the part of the Nazi regime; and mounting pressures—physical, mental, and spiritual—caused by the miseries of war.

Dornberger was thirty-seven years old, and von Braun was twenty, when they joined their forces and their dreams. *"From the beginning,"* Dornberger wrote in his book on Peenemünde and the V-2 in 1958 [1], *"we wanted to open the gates to the infinite reaches of space . . . our final goal stood clearly before us . . . We did not intend to build just a weapon with which this war could be brought quickly to its end . . . we did not try to do this, nor could we ever have achieved it . . . The A-4 was only an intermediate phase . . ."*

"Von Braun," he wrote, *"always overflowed with ideas, with dreams of grandiose projects . . . How often did I have to slow him down, and to pour water into his sparkling wine . . . He had a fantastic gift to ingest a mountain of scientific facts,*

technical reports, arguments from discussions, and observations at companies, and to sort out only those details which were important for our project . . . All the rest, he threw overboard and quickly forgot . . . Never did any fight, or any persistent difference of opinion, cast a shadow on our relationship. There was complete mutual acceptance and appreciation; we always fully supported each other."

On the occasion of von Braun's fiftieth birthday, Dornberger wrote [8-64]: *"His personal contributions to all fields of modern rocketry and spaceflight are innumerable, decisive, guiding, leading, and more or less willingly accepted by most of his peers . . . From his early days he wanted to go into space, and to explore the planets and the universe. His military work in Peenemünde was only a necessary step in this direction. The conquest of space by man was, and remains, his goal . . ."*

Even before the war had come to its end in Germany, a good fortune made another remarkable soldier cross von Braun's path: Colonel (later Major General) Holger N. (*"Ludi"*) Toftoy. The story of Toftoy's involvement in the search for the German rocketeers was told in Chapter 3-7. In May 1945, after Toftoy had become Chief of the Rocket Branch in the Research and Development Division of Army Ordnance, he made a strong plea that German rocket scientists be brought to the United States; on 23 July, he was ordered to organize this move under the code name *"Project Overcast"*—later renamed *"Project Paperclip."*

"I have certainly felt right along that I have been fortunate to have had this opportunity . . ." Toftoy said at a later time [9-11]. *"I felt this specialized group would do the country a lot of good . . ."*

Toftoy had orchestrated the search for the rocket people, and the negotiations with the War Department and the secretary of state for their eventual transfer to the United States, mostly from Paris and from Washington. In August 1945, he met with von Braun and a number of his associates in Witzenhausen near Kassel where many of the former Peenemünders and their families had found a temporary place to stay.

"The first thing Toftoy did," von Braun remembered, *"when he met with us and saw the situation of the families, most of whom had come to Witzenhausen as refugees from all parts of Germany, was to order a generous supply of milk for the youngsters and the babies. Next, he met with some of us in a little schoolhouse and discussed with us the possibility of contracts to continue our work in the United States"* (Chapter 3-9).

Von Braun and six associates arrived in the United States in September 1945. A few weeks later, in Fort Bliss, Texas, von Braun suffered from a liver ailment and had to go to the Beaumont Hospital for treatment. *"I was happily surprised,"* von Braun said later, *"when Colonel Toftoy came from Washington to visit me, just to see how I was doing . . . For several hours, we talked about plans for the future . . ."* In 1948, Toftoy said: *". . . it is possible that this generation will see huge rocket ships carrying passengers that can circle the Moon and return to Earth safely . . ."*

For twelve years, General Toftoy was a staunch supporter, a mentor and protector, and a warm-hearted friend of the German rocketeers. On 15 April 1955, when the first forty of the Germans and their families became citizens of the United States, Toftoy addressed *"his"* new Americans: *"I met you ten years ago almost to the day in a crowded schoolhouse in Germany. I urged you to come to this country and help us in our missile program. I promised you no future—but today my and your highest hopes have been realized. I want to congratulate you from my heart on all you have achieved, on this great team of rocket engineers and scientists you have built up during these ten years . . . I am sure that the future holds even greater things for you . . ."* [9-12].

Toftoy appointed Major James P. Hamill as commander of the Army post in Fort Bliss, Texas, where the Germans were stationed. A military staff of officers and enlisted men, and a contingent of engineers from the General Electric Company, together with the German Paperclip alien residents, made up the Suboffice Rocket (Chapter 4).

For Hamill, these were unusual circumstances, to say the least. *"None of my military books,"* he remarked to the Germans much later, *"gave me any hint on how to manage a group as diverse as what I had around me."*

Hamill was an authoritative commander, but an atmosphere of genuine trust did not develop between him and his Germans during the years in Fort Bliss. Only after Hamill had moved to the Pentagon and the Germans to Huntsville in 1950 did the relations become relaxed. Hamill reminisced on many joint endeavors and accomplishments, and he told his rocketeers how proud he was of all of them. *"You are unusual people,"* he said at an oldtimers' reunion in Huntsville around 1954. *"It took me some time, and quite an effort, to understand you. Maybe the reason is my strictly military upbringing . . . I consider it my good fortune that I was privileged to be your commander for almost five years. These were certainly the most exciting years of my career."*

"I can only say," Hamill recalled in 1969 [9-13], *"that this group was screened, guarded, and observed more closely than any group as yet in the history of our country . . . The men were absolutely loyal, not only to the United States in general, but also to all the military departments. I never saw a team that worked so hard, and so enthusiastically! Colonel Toftoy one day asked for plans of a large rocket that he wanted to show to the General Staff . . . We received the request only one day before the presentation was to take place. The Germans worked without interruption the whole day, and through the following night. At seven o'clock in the morning, the drawings and data sheets were complete, and I could take them to Toftoy . . . Looking back over these years, I am really glad we made it together,"* Hamill said, and his Paperclippers agreed wholeheartedly.

Major General John Bruce Medaris became commander of the Army Ballistic Missile Agency (ABMA) at Redstone Arsenal on 1 February 1956. Von Braun's Development Operations Division, with 1,700 civilian and 350 military members, was to be a part of Medaris' command.

Medaris met von Braun the first time in 1954. *"As chief of the Ammunition Branch in Washington,"* he recalled in 1989 [9-14], *"I had gone to Redstone in connection with some ammunition problems . . . we sort of sparked each other right off the bat . . . Right from the beginning, we were very close."*

A few years later, during a luncheon talk, the General remembered his beginnings as a *"missile man"*: *"I met a most unusual kind of man, and he had an exciting team around him. In fact, I felt an immediate challenge to take charge of that group, and to lead it to great accomplishments."* Medaris did take charge of the von Braun team and integrated it into a greater Army team that eventually, as the U.S. Army Ordnance Missile Command (AOMC), included ABMA, Redstone Arsenal, the Jet Propulsion Laboratory, and White Sands Proving Ground with a total complement of 25,000 people. *"During my first official contacts with von Braun and his group of top-level scientists and engineers,"* Medaris wrote in his book *Countdown for Decision* [7-19], *"we came to understand each other very quickly . . . I was struck from the start by their self-discipline and persistence . . . They also had no fear or hesitancy about admitting mistakes—a sure sign of good leadership and high morale.*

At that time, von Braun's Redstone missile was ready for deployment, and his Jupiter approached completion. Simultaneously, the Thor missile, almost identical in performance to Jupiter, was developed under Air Force management, and a bitter feud was brewing between Air Force and Army over the question which of the two services should be in charge of guided missiles. The Army was in danger of losing this battle when General Medaris took command. Von Braun was very happy about his new boss. *"Our survival as a rocket-building team is at stake,"* he said. *"Only a tough fighter in command of the Army Ballistic Missile Agency has a chance to keep it alive, and General Medaris is such a man!"*

The von Braun team did stay alive, and Jupiter was completed. This reflects not only the outstanding abilities of Medaris, but also the excellent working relationship between him and von Braun throughout the time of their association. One of Medaris' aides once revealed a little secret: *"Each of them believes that he has the other one fully under control, and each of them thinks that the other one harbors the same conviction . . ."*

Thirty years later, at eighty-seven, Medaris told his rocketeers: *"Wernher and I were about the most perfect possible match between two men who wish to pursue great projects together . . . He called me 'boss,' but I am sure that I was as much under his guidance as he may have been under mine . . . My life was so much richer because his path crossed mine . . ."*

Medaris was von Braun's last superior in a strictly military organization. In 1960, von Braun's team became a member of NASA, and Dr. T. Keith Glennan, NASA's administrator, became von Braun's new boss. During those years, NASA had to build up its manpower and management structure, its programs, its funding resources, its relations with other segments of the government, its very identity. The administrator could not develop and maintain the same close relationship of day-by-day interactions with his field centers that von Braun had enjoyed with Dornberger and Medaris. And yet, Glennan and von Braun always were on excellent terms; they enjoyed a productive and congenial relationship.

Recalling the early 1960s, Glennan said in 1986 [9-15]: *"Von Braun ran a truly great show. He was a fine and effective salesman on the Hill. However, when we brought in General Ostrander and assigned the completion of the Agena and Centaur stages to von Braun's Marshall Center, Wernher never fully accepted these assignments. His objective was Saturn I and Saturn V. We finally had to assign . . . Centaur to the Lewis Research Center."* He continued: *"I don't remember ever hearing any of von Braun's team speak German. They became an integral part of the Huntsville community, actively participating in civic and educational affairs probably more than their counterpart Americans . . . Wernher was one of the most exciting, far out, blue sky space cadets—but one of the most conservative engineers I ever knew."*

For James E. Webb, taking the helm of NASA at a time when a manned expedition to the Moon began to assume realistic dimensions (Chapter 8-3) must have been an almost irresistible challenge. He eagerly absorbed the technical briefings, and he quickly acquired considerable fluency in the scientific and technical matters that constituted the space program in the 1960s. Typical for him, he kept abreast of technical developments and problems by carefully observing the debates of engineers and managers, rather than by reading reports.

Von Braun greatly enjoyed discussions with Webb, and this feeling seems to have been mutual. They complemented each other, but each of them took a very lively interest in the other's activities. Webb was an absolutely tireless talker; *"trying to talk to Mr. Webb is like trying to take a sip of water out of a wide-open fire hydrant,"* a frustrated counterpart once said. However, Webb liked to keep a measured distance from his associates in NASA, just to retain his freedom of action. Exceptions to this rule were the other two members of his triumvirate; whenever Webb talked about a decision he had reached, he said: *"Dr. Dryden, Dr. Seamans, and I . . ."*

It soon became obvious that Webb sought and trusted von Braun's judgment, that he was impressed by his cautious approach to technical problems, and that he made good use of von Braun's ability to talk to members of Congress. In particular, Webb liked von Braun's careful step-by-step approach in technical developments; each new step was taken only after the previous one had been secured. He also approved of von Braun's effort to bring spaceflight to the public by expounding its great potential for useful spinoffs, for stimulation of technical progress and scientific research, and for providing a source of spiritual excitement for millions of people around the globe.

There were also situations in which Webb, the down-to-Earth administrator, did not quite see eye-to-eye with von Braun, the space pioneer. *"He was very careful to make sure that the rockets would fly (no small accomplishment!),"* Webb said, *"but he was very impatient with paperwork . . . He had a tendency to step outside of NASA procedures—in order to get work done . . . Also, he tried to do more at his Marshall Center than what his due share within NASA would be . . . On the other hand, he had an ability to meet a difficult problem under very difficult conditions that was most remarkable . . . He also made all of us adhere to a very high engineering standard . . ."* [9-16].

There was still another area where Webb imposed his leadership upon von Braun. During that same interview in 1985, he remembered what Dr. Dryden, Dr. Seamans, and he were saying to von Braun back in the sixties: *"You can't do it that way, you have got to do it this way because you are a part of NASA. NASA is a bigger program than the manned program, it's bigger than the work done in any one center . . ."*

In 1967, Webb began urging von Braun to give scientists more recognition as participants in the manned spaceflight program; in particular, he strongly suggested that von Braun establish a formal position for a kind of chief scientist, visible and accessible to the world outside MSFC, that would act as a two-way bridge between von Braun's center management and those numerous places of scientific endeavor that were eager to use man's ability to travel into space for the benefit of scientific research and exploration. Von Braun then established the position of associate center director for science and appointed the director of his Space Sciences Laboratory, Stuhlinger, as head of the new office. Stuhlinger's deputy in Space Sciences Laboratory, Gerhard B. Heller, became director of the laboratory. Dr. George C. Bucher became Stuhlinger's deputy in his new position.

As NASA's administrator, Webb's main concerns were (1) to secure continuing political support for NASA's programs, and (2) to produce technical results of highest quality. In both areas, von Braun made decisive contributions. With his proven ability to generate support from the public, from industry, from Congress, and from the White House, he was Webb's best horse in the stable. Von Braun's technical achievements as director of MSFC, likewise, were generously recognized and frequently praised by Webb. Von Braun, in turn, considered Webb *"one of the greatest blessings NASA has ever experienced."*

Webb retired from NASA in 1968, a year before the first landing on the Moon on 20 July 1969. One reason for his leaving was probably the fact that the Saturn-Apollo program, with all its industrial contracts, was well underway and on a stable course. A large follow-on program presenting a similar challenge to an administrator of Webb's stature was not in sight.

There may have been a second reason. As an administrator of superior qualifications, with vast experience in public service, he felt that an entity such as NASA could remain a well-functioning organization only if it was built and organized in a way that would make its successful operations independent of the individual personalities that happened to be available at any given time. But then he realized that bringing such an organization to life would be a task whose magnitude far exceeded the amount of effort he was willing to expend during the remainder of his professional life, so he *"turned in his uniform"* and returned to private life.

Almost twenty years later, Webb reminisced on the old times [9-16], but there was a slight undertone of sadness in his words. *"You have to remember that von Braun was Mr. Interplanetary Travel . . . He was known well by a lot of people, where people like myself were not known."*

Webb was probably correct. People around the world are always more impressed by individuals who accomplish great feats in exploration, by the pioneers and crusaders, than by the administrators, regardless how brilliant they may be. But for many thousands who helped build the machines that took men to the Moon, Webb will always be *"one of the greatest blessings NASA has ever experienced."*

How does Dr. Robert C. Seamans remember von Braun?

"My first real impression," he recalled in 1986 [9-17], *"came in September 1960 when I visited the Marshall Center . . . the laboratory directors were in the conference room . . . It was interesting to see what happened when von Braun entered the room. He clearly had everybody's absolute and total respect . . . From my very first visit at Marshall, I had nothing but great respect for the technical capability of that team, and for their ability to face up to design and other difficulties when they appeared, and to fix them . . . Clearly, Wernher and the Marshall people were very closely knit. But they tended to feel their way cautiously in any other kind of relationship . . . Congress would swoon every time [von Braun] appeared. But Wernher didn't have much impact on the Budget people, who were pretty hard-boiled . . . Von Braun and his people preferred a hands-on operation . . . They did their work extremely well . . ."*

How did von Braun accept broad NASA management strategies?

"I would say that he worked with us very astutely . . . I felt very comfortable with Wernher. Remember, I came from working with Doc Draper [Dr. Charles Stark Draper, head of the Lincoln Laboratory for Guidance Systems at MIT] who was widely respected, and he always liked the hands-on development process . . . My background, I always felt, was very compatible with that of Marshall . . . The real test came with Centaur. The Marshall group hated the business of working through the Air Force, and General Dynamics was doing a miserable job on the Centaur. Clearly, something had to be done. Finally, Wernher came to us and said that they were going to cancel the project. We were more than a little surprised, and immediately transferred Centaur to the Lewis Research Center. Of course, Abe Silverstein was delighted to show that Marshall wasn't that good and that they, the Lewis Center, could run the program. For many reasons, Wernher and Abe Silverstein didn't always hit it off . . ."

"Let me add that had we not had the German team, it would have been almost impossible to have gone to the Moon. To put together the Saturn V and have it work so flawlessly was a tremendous achievement . . . I doubt anybody else can be singled out who is equivalent to Wernher . . ."

How would von Braun judge his trio of superiors in Washington, Webb, Seamans, and Dryden?

When von Braun was praised for his brilliant achievements in the Saturn program, he rarely missed the opportunity to say that his team had been fortunate to work, live, and thrive under the singularly effective leadership of an impressive triumvirate in Washington, Jim Webb, Bob Seamans, and Hugh Dryden—a brilliant administrator, a masterful engineer, and a distinguished scientist. They provided leadership for NASA, as well as stability for the projects, and they even sent the money! Each of them was a powerful leader in his own right, but together they represented a joint authority that stood as a solid rock at the top of the huge NASA organization. Dryden died in 1966. Webb as well as Seamans retired from NASA in 1968. None of them was there when NASA entered into a critical phase in 1970.

D. Brainerd Holmes, on a recommendation to Webb by Seamans, was appointed director of the Office of Manned Space Flight in NASA Headquarters on 1 November 1961. During an interview in August 1988 [9-18], he recalled:

"Before I met von Braun, I thought of him as a person who had been over-publicized by the U.S. Army. With more exposure to him, I found him to possess a great deal of charm and ability, and I could understand why the Army had used him as a showpiece for its space effort . . . On knowing him, I almost immediately liked him; I liked his directness . . ."

"Von Braun was an accomplished politician and a great salesman. And that's not a negative statement. You have to give and take when you deal with politicians, and von Braun was very skillful at it . . . At the same time, he was one of the warmest persons I can think of . . ."

Holmes and Webb were two very different persons. *"I never got along very well with Webb. I felt he was a consummate politician with almost no understanding of the technical side of things . . . However, if I had been more mature, I would have understood how a politician thinks, and I would have been able to get along with him alright. I think that, overall, Webb did a very good job . . . He once said to me: 'You know, you don't know one bit about politics. It's all compromise.' And he was right. Now, von Braun, he was able to work with Webb. He knew how to conceal his feelings if told to do things he didn't like. He always handled himself very well, I thought, socially, testifying, or directing his people."*

What, in Holmes' view, were von Braun's shortcomings?

"I don't think he was a particularly fastidious manager . . . He was able, however, to attract people like Rees who ran the shop. One of the great problems with some leaders is that they don't know how to pick the right people to help them. But von Braun was excellent at that, so it's difficult to find weaknesses . . . I never saw any indication that he ever suffered from Potomac Fever, or let his publicity go to his head. I never felt his judgment was marred just because he was subject to praise or got his picture in the paper . . . I think von Braun's letter [to Vice President Johnson] had a strong influence on President Kennedy's decision . . . there was no one else out there like von Braun; he was a unique person . . . I think he did a lot for America."

George E. Mueller, Associate Administrator for Manned Space Flight from September 1963 to December 1969, met von Braun for the first time in 1958 at the Cape when Mueller, working for the Ramo-Wooldridge Corporation (later Space Technology Laboratories) under Air Force auspices, was proposing a ground station network with three 200-foot dishes around the globe to keep track of lunar probes. At that time, NASA tried to keep the Air Force from moving into the space program.

Von Braun impressed Mueller as *"very self-confident, very intelligent; a very outgoing person,"* as he recalled in an interview in 1986 [9-19]. *"We had been in competition with Wernher in getting Pioneer off; at that time, we were neck-to-neck with him. I had a great deal of respect for Wernher in that first encounter."*

After Mueller had joined NASA, his relations with von Braun became very close. They conversed by telephone almost daily. *"I got the center directors and their key people together,"* Mueller recalled, *"and we sat and worked our way through as to how we were going to operate . . . Wernher turned out to be one of the strongest supporters . . ."*

As the Saturn-Apollo program neared its first flight tests, the question of a follow-up program after the Moon-landing adventure arose not only within NASA, but also at the highest levels of the government (Chapter 8-9). The list of possible projects was impressive: A permanent lunar station, a shuttle for two-way Earth-to-orbit transportation, a permanent station in Earth orbit, and a manned expedition to Mars with nuclear rocket engines.

Mueller, enthusiastic for spaceflight and encouraged by the fine progress of the Saturn-Apollo program, saw a brilliant future in space, and wished to pursue all of these projects in one huge, far-reaching, long-range space program. *"We looked at a number of possible goals,"* he said, *"that might serve the same purpose as Apollo did—the landing on the Moon within a decade. And we came up with the conclusion—Wernher and I did, together . . . that we should propose the manned Mars exploration mission . . . And that is how that long-range program developed . . . Wernher was taking the lead in the shuttle while Houston was looking at creative alternatives. Max Faget, for example, came out with the straight-wing approach. We were never able to sustain the idea that this was the approach that ought to be taken . . . Marshall did play a very strong role in the Skylab program, and Wernher was one of the leaders in that project; many of the creative ideas there were due to him and to his team . . ."*

In a joint planning effort, Mueller, the Marshall Center, and the Manned Spacecraft Center in Houston put together an elaborate program plan. It was a spaceman's dream, beginning with Skylab, and evolving through advanced Earth orbiting workshops to a space station, while in several parallel projects a large shuttle with two recoverable stages would be developed, replacing all the existing launch vehicles, and reducing the launch cost to a minimal fraction of then current costs; a permanent outpost on the Moon would come into existence, as well as a manned mission to Mars, propelled by nuclear rockets. At the same time, huge optical telescopes for Earth orbit, and radio telescopes for the backside of the Moon would be planned. Satellites taking closer and closer looks at the Earth would also be developed and several unmanned planetary missions would be started.

Prospects for the future looked really exciting. Von Braun reported about this program plan from time to time to his associates. However, he did not talk with his usual enthusiasm. The deep-seated confidence that normally radiated from his presentations on future projects was missing. The plan was just too optimistic, too grandiose.

In 1969, shortly after the first landing on the Moon, another event began to take shape. *"I thought it would be important in the post-Apollo era,"* Mueller said, *"to have some of the strength of the centers moved into headquarters, because I could see [a tendency] to reestablish the centers as independent operating units. So I suggested to Wernher that if we were going to make this long-range plan effective, we were going to need him and Bob Gilruth at headquarters. Wernher, like the good trooper that he was, agreed to do that. But Gilruth wasn't about to leave Houston. I guess he was getting close to retirement, and in any event did not move . . . But things really got caught up in [Vice President Spiro] Agnew's getting involved in the Maryland affair [acceptance of illegal monetary contribution]. Otherwise, things might have been different . . ."*

Mueller left NASA in December 1969, after the second Apollo landing, and returned to industry. *"I was done with Apollo,"* he explained [9-19]. *"I didn't want to make another ten-year commitment. And, anyway, I had some kids who had to be educated, and I had to earn some money!"*

Air Force Major General Samuel C. Phillips was assigned for duty as Apollo program director at NASA Headquarters in Mueller's Manned Space Flight Office in January 1964. He brought with him a vast experience in government-industry contracting from his positions in the Air Material Command, the Air Research and Development

Command, and the Air Force Systems Command. Among other projects, he was involved in the Thor and Minuteman missile projects. In 1943, as a young fighter pilot, he escorted bombers out of England on bombing raids on Peenemünde.

"By the time I met Wernher," he said during an interview in 1988 [9-20], *"I was prepared to dislike the man; in fact, I was fully prepared to dislike him because of the obvious backgrounds that both of us had. At the same time, I was prepared to figure out what was needed in order to be able to work effectively with him . . . Interestingly enough, during weeks and then months of interaction, Wernher and I became close friends. And remained so . . ."*

In his Wernher von Braun Memorial Lecture on 28 January 1988 at the National Air and Space Museum in Washington [9-21], Phillips said: *"Over many years, he and I became very close friends as well as working associates . . . Wernher always had an agenda. I don't think I ever saw him either on or off the job when he was not trying to sell me on some idea! He never ran out of ideas. He was an idea-a-minute man. [Also,] and probably more important, he had the rare gift of giving his undivided attention to whomever he was talking to. He could make a person feel personally important to him, and that his or her ideas were of great value. He did this no matter how great a crisis he might be involved in at the moment. My wife says that she always felt like Wernher had been waiting all day just to talk to her. He was certainly a very friendly person."* Phillips also recalled [9-20] that von Braun was very effective in carrying his view in a discussion, and making his own position felt and heard. *"But once the person in authority,"* he noted, *"made a decision and said: 'Here's what we are going to do,' he was very quick to embrace that decision, and to counsel his people on how they were going to work."*

Upon Phillips's recommendation, von Braun established an Industrial Operations office at Marshall. The first person to head this office was Bob Young from Aerojet. *"He worked very, very effectively with Wernher and Eberhard, Weidner, and many other people—Arthur Rudolph heading up the Saturn V office, Lee James on the Saturn IB, and Lee Belew for engines,"* Phillips said.

Later, Colonel Edmund F. O'Connor succeeded Young. *"As far as I know,"* Phillips noted, *"Ed O'Connor did a fine job and related very effectively with Wernher."*

How would Phillips assess von Braun's role in the space program? *"I will answer the question somewhat differently today, in January 1988, than I would have some years back. In the early years, I probably shared the feeling . . . of a lot of people, that American engineering and American industry were completely capable of designing, developing, building, and operating all the kinds of vehicles that would have been required for a lunar landing without the German input . . . I've thought about it in recent years, and I am not so sure that it is really so . . . When I think of the Saturn V, which was done so well under Wernher's direction, and which obviously was essential to the lunar mission—you couldn't have gone to the Moon without it—I am not sure today that we could have built it without the ingenuity of Wernher and his team . . ."*

Dr. Thomas O. Paine joined NASA in February 1968, as deputy administrator to Webb, upon the recommendation of President Johnson. He became administrator when Webb left NASA later that year.

Paine and von Braun *"struck it rich"* right from the beginning. Realizing that NASA was heading for a time of decision around 1970 when Saturn-Apollo would go through its climax and a new goal in space would have to be established, Paine counted heavily on von Braun's ability to help chart the future course of the nation's space program, and to incite the public's interest and enthusiasm for that program, as well as the willingness of the U.S. Government to accept it as a national undertaking.

In 1969, the future was still full of promise. During his von Braun Memorial Lecture on 29 January 1987, Paine recalled asking von Braun *"to come up to Washington and head up a new planning group within NASA to look out to the future, and to advise both NASA and also the Congress and the White House as to where we should be going in space. And Wernher gave up the directorship of the Marshall Space Flight Center and came on up and put his shoulder to the wheel, and he and I worked as hard as we could, trying to make it come out right."*

A very close working relationship between Paine and von Braun developed quickly. *"It was because I had such great respect for von Braun's vision that I said: 'It's time that NASA established a strong, visionary type of planning operation',"* Paine recalled in an interview in 1985 [9-22]. *"I felt that with his help, we could together work to develop a stronger NASA program."*

"I must confess," Paine said, *"that there were some strong voices in NASA saying that this was not a wise move, and there was an equally strong feeling that the way to use Wernher and his team was to keep them down in some place like Huntsville a little bit under wraps. We at headquarters would work with the White House and on the Hill, and not rake up all the V-2 memories. I had to very carefully consider that view, for there were some very wise people whose opinions I respected . . ."*

"However, it seemed to me that there were very few people in the world who had a track record of predicting the future . . . But Wernher had consistently, decade after decade, come up with thoughts on what was going to be important and, more to the point, what could be made to happen . . . The transition of von Braun to headquarters was smoother than I expected, especially when I consider all the negatives I had encountered and had overridden when I made the decision to bring him up from Huntsville. The reason is that Wernher himself was a much smoother person . . ."

Paine was von Braun's first superior during his long career under whom he did not work on a real project with hardware development, testing, and launching, but only on proposals, plans, and hopes.

In his Von Braun Memorial Lecture in 1987, Paine told a delightful anecdote about young von Braun. The fact that he chose and told this little story shows better than many words the high esteem and affection in which Paine had always held him.

As a young boy, so the story goes, von Braun got passionately interested in rocketry. He bought a number of firework rockets, the biggest that he could find in Berlin, and attached them to the rear end of his little cart. He had devised a fuse arrangement that would light them all simultaneously, and he sat in the cart with the steering pointed right straight down the street while his brother Magnus stroke a match and lit the fuse. A few seconds later, there was a bang and a big pile of debris and broken windows, and the police came and everything else, and young Wernher was remanded into the custody of the Minister of Agriculture (who was, of course, his father). Years later, Magnus was asked by the daughter of his elder brother Sigismund: *"Uncle Magnus, why aren't you as famous as Uncle Wernher?"* he said: *"Because after that had happened with the rocket cart, I didn't do it again, but Uncle Wernher did it again the following week!"*—*"There is a moral there, I think,"* Paine added.

Dale D. Myers worked at North American Aviation from 1943 to 1970 when he became associate administrator for Manned Space Flight at NASA Headquarters in Washington. He left NASA in 1974 and returned to North American as vice president of Rockwell International and president of North American Aviation. From 1977 to 1979, he served as under secretary of the Department of Energy. He returned to NASA as deputy administrator in October 1986, and in April 1989 he became acting administrator. Dale Myers retired from NASA in mid-May of the same year. In December, 1989 he reminisced about von Braun during an interview [9-23].

"I didn't know him at all until the period of the Apollo command module

development, when he would come in [to North American] for meetings on the [second stage of the Saturn V rocket] S-2.

"My first real awareness of Wernher was when I received the microfiche data that came over from Germany after World War II . . . So, I learned of his technical ability and his technical management capability during that time . . . I had the image of a guy who had great vision and great technical competence to have been able to make something like this happen [the V-2 development]. I couldn't imagine how the Nazi system worked at all; and, I had to give him a tremendous amount of credit for being able to push forward ideas of the nature that he was involved in. It was pretty amazing . . ."

"I [joined NASA in 1970], just in time for Apollo 13. I was head of Manned Space Flight, and Wernher von Braun, Bob Gilruth, and Kurt Debus reported to my office . . . I found him a man of great vision and competence, and the ability to choose good people to work with—all the things that make a guy an outstanding technical manager . . . There were sensitivities with Bob Gilruth. Wernher and Bob had some strong words from time to time; but, I think, they respected one another. I don't think there was anything but the greatest respect. I used to see that sense of mission in the flight readiness reviews that we would have when we would bring the center directors and the top technical people together to discuss the readiness of the Saturn V launch vehicle and the command module and the lunar module . . . At those meetings there could be strains, but they were clearly technical; there was no concern about the personal outcome of an argument. The focus was on what had to be done right for that particular flight."

How, in retrospect, does Myers assess von Braun's contributions to spaceflight? *"I would put him very close to the top, and I'll tell you why. He was the one who continued to push large programs and technologies, the development of new capabilities, all the activities that led up to the Saturn V and the studies of Nova and the big 260-inch solid rocket motors. He wasn't necessarily the guy who started everything, but it was his inputs into NASA, his vision, that created that level of technology. I wish we had Wernher von Braun with us today . . ."*

"We were good friends. I felt very badly about the things that were happening [during the early 1970s], and I think that strained our relationship, but I always felt we were close friends. I was not always able to get the things done that he thought ought to be done, and we had arguments about that, but I think in general we related very closely. I had a very warm feeling for him . . ."

Did Myers ever hear any mutterings at the headquarters level about the United States having brought von Braun and his team over from Germany after the war, and elevating him to such a prominent position within NASA? [9-28].

"Never. By the time he became a part of NASA I think the NASA people felt that he and his German associates had so much to offer that the matter never came up. Perhaps they felt that he had done his penitence down there at White Sands! It never really was an issue. Of course, later there was the issue of Arthur Rudolph, which was just awful . . ."

Dr. James C. Fletcher was president of the University of Utah when he was nominated NASA administrator by President Nixon in March 1971. In 1952, reading von Braun's articles about space exploration in *Collier's* magazine, he said to his co-workers in a systems analysis group he was heading at that time: *"Hey, look at these articles! This is where we ought to go! This will interest all of us—scientists, astronomers, physicists, aeronautical engineers!"*

During an interview in 1985 [9-24], Fletcher recalled this story, adding that *"Those articles really impressed my group and made the members get interested in space. Wernher and Willy Ley—they were the two guys I remember. So I knew of von Braun through his writings before I got involved in the ICBM [intercontinental ballistic missile] program."*

Four years later, in 1956, Fletcher visited Redstone Arsenal and met von Braun personally. *"We were down there to learn how he did things. I had two or three people with me with whom I was working, trying to get the ICBM program moving ahead . . . It was clear that von Braun's team really knew what it was doing! Our relationship was strictly professional, and there was of course competition—they [the Redstone/ABMA group] had the Jupiter, and we [the Air Force] had the Thor . . . and there was the argument over roles and missions. I remember Bennie Schriever and Bruce Medaris fighting over the matter . . ."*

After another fifteen years, in 1971, Fletcher was the head of NASA, succeeding Thomas O. Paine as administrator. George Low, who had come to headquarters from the Houston Center in 1969, was deputy administrator. The Moon landing program was in full swing at that time, but President Nixon *"had mixed feelings about the space program. He wanted to cut back on it."* Fletcher had to preside over this most unpleasant process. *"Our job was to balance the manned and unmanned activities in terms of available funding. Von Braun, who had moved to headquarters in 1970, called this exercise 'moving peaks along a curve,' because the funding would always peak up somewhere in the future, and those peaks kept moving further into the future. We felt we came up with a sensible program, and Wernher had a lot to do with it . . . George Low was in favor of central planning. But there was the matter of competition between Houston and Huntsville, and Wernher represented the Huntsville group. And that was a good thing, for we did not have too many people at headquarters who did. Dale Myers and others were more sympathetic to Houston and their ways of doing things. So it was a good thing Wernher was there to balance things off."*

While von Braun was director of a large NASA field installation, he was to a great extent insulated from the daily political and administrative give-and-take characteristic of headquarters operations. When he transferred to NASA Headquarters, however, von Braun was no longer lord and master of thousands of loyal subjects and had to face what occasionally amounted to simple jealousy! *"Some of the headquarters people certainly resented him,"* recalls Fletcher. *"I was from the outside . . . and said: 'Oh boy, what an asset!' But there was antipathy towards Wernher coming up. And that persisted to the end, and that may have been one reason why he decided not to stay with the program."*

As for von Braun's influence over the ultimate configuration of the shuttle, *"It's hard to say,"* in Fletcher's opinion, *"because it was a team effort. He was always worried about size and weight, and he gradually came to the conclusion that we could not have a completely reusable shuttle because of costs involved. I think he was satisfied with the way it turned out, and because some of his work had caused us to come to the conclusion we eventually arrived at . . ."*

"He was often frustrated as he had to move the peaks along his curves . . . He had collected a remarkable team down there [in Huntsville]. But we made use of his assets, for example, his ability to write and speak about space, and he was certainly our best representative on the Hill. He was very articulate, very practical, and a good advocate."

Von Braun often mentioned his enjoyable and pleasant relationship with Fletcher. These feelings certainly were reciprocal. Fletcher praised von Braun's willingness to accept the restraints imposed upon the space program without visible signs of displeasure, and von Braun was happy to find in Fletcher a counterpart who always took time for a strategic discussion.

Both liked occasional jovial joking. Returning from Cape Canaveral to Washington one day with a group of colleagues on the NASA airplane, the travelers enjoyed a drink.

Von Braun had his usual martini; Fletcher, as a devout Mormon, had milk. *"Too bad, Jim,"* von Braun said, *"that your faith does not allow you more than a glass of milk—cheers!"* Fletcher's reply was prompt: *"Too bad, Wernher, that your faith does not allow you more than one wife—cheers!"*

Edward G. Uhl, chairman of the board, president, and chief executive officer of Fairchild Industries, was von Braun's last superior during his long career. *"This is my boss,"* von Braun would proudly say, but beyond *"the boss"* Uhl was probably the closest and most respected friend von Braun ever had. It was a friendship on a one-to-one basis, with a man who in his own professional life had worked his way up to a top position in the world of business.

"I had known von Braun," Uhl said in an interview in 1985 [9-25], *"since the time he came to the United States back in 1945 . . . I was in the Ordnance Special Projects Section [in White Sands where] Colonel Harold Turner built that huge rocket test stand . . . and that's where I met Wernher . . . We kept in running contact with each other over the years. When I first came to Fairchild . . . we got involved with him in the Pegasus micrometeoroid spacecraft project . . . from time to time I would say to him: 'I don't know what your future with NASA is, and what you expect to do in the future. If you ever want to leave, please think of us at Fairchild. We would really like to have you in our company . . . The seed was planted a long time ago."*

Later, in 1970 and 1971, *"when NASA began to plan the shuttle program and after Paine had left, there was a lot of work going on as to how the shuttle should be developed. And there was some serious difference of opinion. And it was about that time that Wernher called me one day and asked if I would come into Washington to have lunch. So, off I went . . . We talked for some time . . .*

"He would be the senior technical person at corporate headquarters. He would have supervision over all our corporate technical work. Frankly, I was a little apprehensive as he was such a star, and I was afraid he would come in and be a prima donna. Well, when he came in it was just as easy as you can imagine. He was like the Pied Piper—everyone liked to follow him. So there really was not a ripple, and we were able to lift the technical horizon of Fairchild . . . Wernher could open doors like nobody else . . . I think he was very sensitive to not exploiting his name too much; he did so very judiciously. He had a great loyalty to the company, and he made a real difference to Fairchild." More of von Braun's work at Fairchild will be described in Chapter 12.

How did, in turn, von Braun judge his superiors?

Each of them was quite different from the others, but for von Braun all of them had one feature in common: They invariably enjoyed von Braun's unwavering loyalty. Every phase of his work was a common endeavor with the boss. He never made a less than respectful remark about a superior to his associates, nor did he tolerate others in his team to make negative remarks about a superior.

When he was asked how he was enjoying work with his boss, he always said: *"It could not be better, we have excellent working relations."* He continuously kept his superior fully apprised of the status of all his activities, every success and every failure.

This does not mean that there were no occasional differences of opinion, even profound ones. However, von Braun always laid all his thoughts openly on the table, and he debated his views with complete openness until a joint decision could be found. From then on, that joint decision was the law of the land, and he defended it as if it had been his own opinion from the beginning.

Even in such heartbreaking decisions as the termination of the Skylab program, or the scuttling of Saturn V, von Braun tried to explain the decisions to his team members by pointing out the adverse circumstances that made such decisions necessary. He just did not want any shadow to fall on the image of his superiors.

4 ... AND OF COLLEAGUES AND OTHERS

Conrad Hilton, founder of the worldwide hotel chain, began his memoirs with words of sincere gratitude to all those who helped him accomplish his life's work. Had von Braun ever written an autobiography, he would have begun with similar words. For him, spaceflight was a team effort and a team success. *"The lone inventor who works in his garage and surprises the world one day when he opens the doors and rolls out his Moon rocket has no place in this business,"* he said long before the possibility of spaceflight had become a subject of public interest and debate.

The team not only included those engineers, technicians, scientists, and project managers who were members of his immediate organization, but also those large numbers of men and women who gave support and substance to his projects as industrial leaders, government officials, politicians, reporters, journalists, writers. One reason why he never even planned to write his memoirs was, as he put it, *"the sheer impossibility of naming the thousands and thousands of individuals who constituted the team, and who rightfully would expect to read their names and accomplishments in an account of the team's work."*

How would these members of the greater team, and also those many others who had their own projects, but came in contact with von Braun through their work as colleagues or peers—sometimes as competitors—view von Braun?

Statements, memories, anecdotes, recollections from people whose lives he touched, and who had personal contacts with him, are almost legion. By far the greatest portion of them are very positive: *"He was a genius in many fields . . . he was the warmest person I ever met . . . he was absolutely unique . . . he made me perform at my very best . . . he had a sure feeling for what would be politically feasible . . . his engineering talent was fabulous . . . he could explain the most complex situation so that everybody could understand it . . . he was a reporter's dream . . . how could he excel in so many different things, and still have not more time on his hand than any ordinary person . . . he simply made you feel good . . ."*

Then, there were other comments, critical ones, although very rare. Typically, they came from people who had never worked with or for von Braun, and even did not know him personally, but still wished to pass judgment on him: *"He is arrogant . . . he does not listen to others . . . he has a gigantic ego . . . he did not develop his rockets with his own team . . . he was Hitler's willing tool . . . he was a Nazi megalomaniac . . ."*

There were situations in which von Braun worked on one part of a project, while a colleague, with his team, was responsible for another part, such as in the Explorer 1 or the Saturn-Apollo.

Dr. William H. Pickering, head of the Jet Propulsion Laboratory team that worked with the von Braun team on Explorer 1, said in 1986 [9-26]: *". . . we worked very well together, right up to the launching . . . ,"* and: *"Wernher's charisma was very, very effective. He is the only person I have ever seen go to a congressional committee meeting and have the congressmen all come down and shake his hand . . ."*

Gilruth's and von Braun's mutual feelings were not always entirely positive. However, in the course of the joint Saturn-Apollo program, the two men came to know and respect each other. *"Yes, we worked together . . ."* Gilruth said [8-35]. *"It was a good team under [D. Brainerd] Holmes . . . Wernher and I were kindred spirits . . ."*

Then there were those colleagues and peers who had their own fields of responsibility within the space program, but depended on von Braun for supporting work. Sometimes, a colleague had to ask von Braun to take drastic measures in order to correct a situation in a joint work program that developed management problems in von Braun's organization. John H. Disher, deputy director of the Apollo Applications

Program and the NASA Headquarters program manager for the Marshall-managed Skylab program, recalled [8-32] how von Braun had appointed a member of his personal staff as Skylab program manager. *"That man was a good guy,"* Disher said, *"but he turned out to be a disaster as far as running a center program was concerned. He just didn't work out at all . . . I said: 'I'd like to have Lee [Leland F.] Belew'. George [Mueller] and Wernher got together, and after some arm twisting, Leland agreed . . . He turned out to be a great manager, and he undid the mistakes made earlier by his predecessor . . ."*

Disher—as many others in similar situations—greatly appreciated von Braun's prompt action for the benefit of a project. Experiences like this certainly contributed to the positive feelings of many colleagues toward von Braun. Disher, who had known von Braun from many years of joint work, said: *"He is a giant in the field of spaceflight, one of four or five people most responsible for making possible our goal of landing man on the Moon . . . [As an early space pioneer] Wernher stood almost by himself . . . He really stood alone . . . space exploration per se was not very saleable before Sputnik . . ."*

When von Braun's group joined NASA in 1960 and became the George C. Marshall Space Flight Center (MSFC), Air Force Major General Donald R. Ostrander, head of the Launch Vehicle Office at NASA, assigned responsibility for all NASA launch vehicles, except Scout, to MSFC. Von Braun, in addition to having to restructure his organization from an Army installation into a civilian NASA organization, found himself responsible for the management of a gamut of major projects: Redstone-Mercury; Juno II; Agena B (upper stage for Thor and Atlas); Saturn C-1, C-2, and C-5 (later to become Saturn I, Saturn IB, and Saturn V); the 1,500,000 pound (680 ton) thrust F-1 rocket engine; and, last not least, the Centaur stage.

Centaur had been proposed as a second stage for the Atlas rocket by the General Dynamics Corporation in 1956. It was to be powered by hydrogen-oxygen engines (later to be named RL-10), under development at Pratt & Whitney since 1955. In November 1958, General Dynamics received a contract from the Department of Defense's Advanced Research Projects Agency to develop that stage.

A successful program to develop hydrogen-oxygen rocket motors had been conducted at the Lewis Flight Propulsion Laboratory by Dr. Abraham Silverstein throughout the 1950s, providing a solid technical background for Pratt and Whitney's work. Test firings of the RL-10 engine began at Pratt & Whitney in August 1959. At that time, studies were underway at von Braun's organization to use RL-10 engines also for the second stage of the Saturn I rocket.

As the design of the Centaur stage proceeded at General Dynamics, its weight went up, and the payload capability of the Atlas-Centaur rocket went down. *"General Dynamics was doing a miserable job,"* Seamans said (Chapter 9-3).

After NASA project management of Centaur had been assigned to MSFC in 1960, Friedrich Duerr became project officer. In spite of his and his group's great efforts, there was not much progress. *"Centaur went to Huntsville and got into a lot of trouble,"* Edgar M. Cortright, Newell's deputy, said during an interview in 1988 [9-27]. He suspected—rightfully—that von Braun did not give the Centaur his full attention and support. Indeed, von Braun suggested that the Centaur stage project should be discontinued, and that RL-10 engines, or even Agena engines, should be used for the second stage of Saturn I. Those combinations would offer considerably greater payload capabilities than Atlas-Centaur.

However, Newell and Cortright felt that so much effort and money had already been spent on Centaur that the project should be kept alive. They subsequently extended the deadline for its completion, reduced the payload requirements considerably, and transferred the Centaur project to Silverstein's Lewis Research Center.

"It was obvious," Cortright continued, *"that Huntsville did not have much interest in Centaur . . . Wernher said to me: 'You know, you are really on the wrong launch vehicle . . . what you should do is put an Agena on the Saturn I . . .' They were always extremely responsive, and showed that this would be a very capable launch vehicle that would give us a much better payload than we would get on an Atlas Centaur. But, it would cost more money . . . We had a very gentlemanly meeting, as one usually did [with the von Braun group]."* Surveyor 1 was launched on an Atlas-Centaur on 30 May 1966, with reduced payload. It landed on the Moon on 2 June. A number of further successful space launchings with Atlas-Centaur and Titan-Centaur rockets followed this first Surveyor.

"One meeting with Wernher stands out in my mind, and that was the decision to go ahead with the shuttle . . . Tom Paine called the meeting . . . All the center directors were there; I was a center director by then at Langley . . . George had just finished quoting a $7 billion total pricetag for the shuttle, and a cost of a pound in orbit that was impossible—something like $10 a pound! We said, no way; and we emphasized the point that we were going to eat up the agency with the shuttle budget, and that the space science and other programs would just go down the tubes . . . Then Bob Gilruth stated that it was a choice between a space station and a shuttle . . . Wernher spoke eloquently for the shuttle . . . I always felt that Wernher sensed what was going to go. He was very supportive of George Mueller. And remember, George would play Marshall and Johnson against each other. He had a way of getting his way, in any event . . . Tom Paine then called for a vote. If I recall correctly, if there were eighteen people at that meeting, fifteen of them voted for the space station, with three votes cast for the shuttle . . . George, Wernher, and Tom. So we did the shuttle!"

How did Wernher get along with Abe Silverstein and Bob Gilruth?

"I never heard a rude word between Wernher and Abe or Gilruth," Cortright said. *"They may have held different views. I know that Abe respected Wernher, and Wernher respected Abe . . . I remember Abe telling me one day that the best rocket engine man in the world was at Marshall . . ."*

Years after Silverstein had retired from NASA, and von Braun had died, Silverstein remarked to one of von Braun's old team members: *"You guys in Huntsville always thought that I was against you. That simply is not so. I always respected you. In fact, ever since the von Braun team faded out of NASA, something essential has been missing in the space program . . ."* [9-28].

When the United States imported foreign wartime technology and the personnel associated with it, Silverstein recalled [9-29], *"I felt very comfortable with that; I thought that was the right thing to do."*

When Silverstein suggested the exclusive use of hydrogen-oxygen engines on all upper stages of Atlas, Titan, and Saturn rockets (Chapter 8-2), von Braun and his people in Huntsville admired Silverstein for his courageous promotion of this new technology. Von Braun, who had long been interested in liquid hydrogen rocket motors, had been hesitant in the past to recommend hydrogen rocket engines for fear that an accident might occur that would endanger the entire rocket and space program. Did Silverstein recall von Braun's reservations?

"I never quite knew why he didn't support the idea. The calculations were fairly clear . . . back in 1957, in my shop we started the contract with North American Aviation/Rocketdyne for the construction of the F-1 engine . . . for a heavy lift vehicle. Optimization calculations for upper stages showed very clearly the gains to be made with hydrogen engines."

Late in 1959, *"we sat down in our committee,"* Silverstein recalled, *"and during the meeting, which went on for about a week, the Huntsville group initially was against the liquid hydrogen concept . . . One of its members would revise and redo the calculations . . . He tried to convince his boss, but he didn't . . . Finally, on the last day of the meeting, as he kept pushing against hydrogen, von Braun told him to shut up!—'Abe's right!', he said."*

Many discussions took place between Silverstein and the von Braun group, dealing with a variety of aspects of spaceflight. They were always substantial, von Braun appreciated them and took them seriously. And yet, there was an atmosphere of tension in these discussions, at least on von Braun's part. The feeling came up among von Braun's associates that Silverstein was against the von Braun group on general principles. That was quite unfortunate, because at that time von Braun and his co-workers considered Silverstein as the best rocket man in NASA Headquarters, and they would much rather have seen a brother-in-arms in him than an antagonist. Does Silverstein have any recollection of that situation?

"There is no basis for that feeling . . . I don't have the least idea in the world why those feelings occurred . . . We got along very nicely. I had a great deal of respect for von Braun's capability. He was a wonderful leader . . . There was no problem at all. When the Apollo flight was completed, I sent him a congratulatory letter attributing the success of the flight in large measure to his rocket. And he sent me a nice note back thanking me for my help."

"I thought [von Braun's group] made a magnificent contribution. People like Rees and others working around von Braun did a tremendous job. Their rockets were really very fine pieces of mechanical engineering. The wonderful thing was that the success rate was so high. So I have nothing but the greatest respect for that team . . . There was Willi Mrazek, I thought he was splendid. And of course the launch team was very good, too."

What does Silverstein think, in retrospect, of von Braun's transfer to NASA Headquarters in 1970?

"Really, it was a waste of his effort, a waste of his talent. He was best with his team, which worked beautifully."

Did Silverstein ever hear, during his period at NASA, any complaints that von Braun and his team had been brought over here, and that he occupied such a high position?

"Never, never! The Apollo job was so tough that we needed all the help that we could get. Bob Gilruth and I went to Keith Glennan [in 1958] and told him: 'We've got to get von Braun into the program!'"

Could von Braun have heard these warmhearted, noble words with which Silverstein remembered their joint work, he would have been profoundly happy. Had he ever written down his own memories, he would have been no less admiring of Silverstein's accomplishments.

John Naugle, for many years NASA associate administrator for Space Sciences and Applications (OSSA), had numerous contacts with von Braun, beginning in 1946 when Naugle, as a young physicist at the Naval Research Laboratory, took part in the test launchings of V-2s at White Sands Proving Ground. Close working relationships began during the early 1960s when OSSA held regular meetings with the center directors, when *"we were faced with the problem as to how you get the centers to respond, how do you really work with them . . . ,"* as Naugle recalled during an interview in March 1986 [9-30].

"I had thought of [von Braun] as an arrogant, aristocratic person" before I actually met him, Naugle said. *"I was quite surprised to find him a very decent person . . . Wernher was a very sensible individual, and he understood what the public reaction was. At first, when he arrived in Washington [in 1970], I thought I might find*

him to be an opponent of the space science program. But I found him very sympathetic, and generally we shared the same view as to what the agency should do. Prior to the time Wernher arrived, there had been some fierce battles between Ed Cortright and Homer Newell on the one side, and Webb and Seamans on the other side . . . At that time, Seamans and Webb were looking for ways to use the Saturn V and Saturn I capabilities. You recall that there was an effort to try to put Voyager on Saturn— Voyager ultimately became Viking [the Mars lander]. The idea was to stack up two Mars landers on top of one Saturn V. Wernher fought very hard for that program, Newell and Cortright opposed it, preferring more and smaller missions on Atlas-Centaur or Titan-Centaur vehicles." (The Voyager noted here was of a different design from that of the later two Voyager outer planet space probes.)

After von Braun had joined Paine at headquarters in 1970, there were frequent close contacts between von Braun and Naugle and their organizations (Chapter 11). Naugle and his family also had personal contacts with the von Braun family. *"I found von Braun and his wife—despite coming from the German aristocracy—to be very warm human beings,"* Naugle said. *"I recall a summer study up at Woods Hole, and Wernher and his wife and son were there. I had my family with me, and my son organized a fishing trip, and Wernher went along with his son, also. Apparently, his son did a lot of fishing and was quite successful, because I can remember Maria in the evening complaining of being a fish wife, cleaning all those fish he had caught. I had two daughters—teenagers at the time—who had listened to Tom Lehrer [and what he said] about Wernher von Braun. They were very critical and nasty and snotty about him, and wondered why I was associated with such a person. Well, the evening before our fishing expedition, he came by our little cottage. And my daughters took a look at him and went into a giggly panic . . . He talked to my daughters, and by the time he left our cottage, the girls had completely turned around. That's the way he was."*

How did the scientists at NASA view von Braun?

"There was a mixture of feelings. Remember back in the late 1950s when Jim Van Allen and Bill Pickering teamed up with Wernher? Their Explorer triumph left a residual feeling of good will on the part of many scientists. When Apollo came along and it had the number one priority and all the resources were put into it, there was a lot of jealousy on the part of scientists and a fair amount of unhappiness because we were not doing too much science on the Moon. But that tended to be focused on Houston, and not so much on Marshall. Then there was the reaction of some scientists to the myth of Wernher as opposed to him as a human being."

Did opinions change much when he came to Washington?

"I think many people, including myself, changed their views of von Braun when he came to Washington. Scientists found him much more knowledgeable about space science, and much more supportive of it, than they had expected. Wernher gained a great deal of respect and empathy at headquarters although he did not really succeed at what he came up [from Huntsville] to do."

What was the relationship between von Braun and Homer Newell?

"My recollection is that they were not close . . . There was a difference in personalities. Homer was an austere, proper New Englander, and Wernher was a much warmer, friendlier person . . . Newell had been doing the agency planning, Paine was unhappy with his work, and he brought Wernher in to replace Newell in that role. There was certainly no love lost between them . . ."

Von Braun, true to his character, often noted during his stay in Washington that he enjoys an *"excellent relationship"* with Newell, and that he greatly appreciates this opportunity of being associated with such an eminent scientist.

Michael Collins, Apollo 11 astronaut who circled the Moon in the command and service module while Neil Armstrong and Buzz Aldrin made the very first landing on the lunar surface, remembered his contacts with von Braun during an interview in May 1987 [9-31]:

"My first meeting of any substance with von Braun was a design review in Huntsville of the Apollo command and service module . . . I remember being very much impressed by his ability to go through the circuitry and describe what he thought were shortcomings. One of the things—had it been pursued further, that might have prevented the accident of Apollo 13—was this: In the service module, there were two oxygen supply tanks, and thus there was redundancy for the command module's oxygen supply. Von Braun pointed out during the meeting that the lines from the two tanks came very close together [mutually endangering each other in case of a rupture]. Of course, that may have been what happened to Apollo 13 when one of the oxygen tanks exploded. It broke the line leading from the second tank, and thereby both tanks were lost. It's something I will always remember. Von Braun . . . immediately spotted this, [but] no one ever did anything about it."

What was Collins's impression of von Braun before he met him?

"I think I probably had an image of a person more obsessed with machines and organization, rather than the warm human being that I later knew him to be . . . I found him to be a warm human being . . . As a professional, I think one of his great assets was to throw aside all the structure and all the bureaucracy and just listen to people and talk to people . . . Which brings up an interesting point, and that is the [space shuttle] Challenger explosion . . . certainly, a lot of the fault was laid within the Huntsville organization . . . There has been the tendency among some to say: 'Oh, yes, that attitude goes back to the original Germans who were very Teutonic and autocratic and too formal.' I hope that people don't reach that conclusion, because I think it would be a great mistake. When von Braun was director there in Huntsville, the lines of communication were open . . . They listened to individual engineers and the little guy, and I think von Braun always had a good exchange with the people in Washington . . . So I cannot really imagine a sort of siege mentality . . . during von Braun's tenure . . . I always remember von Braun as extremely friendly and outgoing. I think that was one of the things that set him apart from most other people. He was not only a superb engineer, but also a public relations man's dream. He was good in both arenas, and that's rare. Very rare."

Frederick C. Durant III had frequent professional, and continuing close personal contacts with von Braun, beginning in 1951. He remembered an event in the summer of 1952 after the *Collier's* space articles had come out [6-6]: *"He had to give a talk at Johns Hopkins [University] . . . after dinner, we took off together for the auditorium . . . We found the roads blocked, and people streaming in to hear Wernher . . . There was an enormous response! The impact of the Collier's articles had made him a celebrity . . ."* Back then, did Durant ever sense any negative feelings about von Braun and his team who, after all, in the fairly recent past had been our enemies?

"Absolutely not; there were none . . ." Durant did mention, though, that not everybody was positively inclined toward von Braun personally. *"One of the problems facing von Braun was simple jealousy. [Theodore] Von Kármán did not like him, nor did some academics . . ."* On the other hand, *". . . no one seemed to object that the United States was using German technology. Of course, by then there was the Cold War, and we were closely involved with Britain in trying to contain developments in Eastern Europe. Also, of course, the British had their Germans at Farnborough, and they had*

conducted those V-2 firings at Cuxhaven . . . I had the feeling that people were excited at the potential of spaceflight . . ."

"The team in Huntsville was absolutely unique. When the American-born members of that team outnumbered the Germans 10 to 1, and later even 70 to 1, the team spirit was still there . . . Wernher had charisma and leadership quality. And he was so damned good technically. Yet many people did not understand him . . . I would explain that Wernher was a modest individual who was always looking out for the common good. He didn't leave you with the feeling that he was arrogant. I feel that von Braun was one of the greatest men I have ever met . . . Wernher's greatness was to point out the feasibility of spaceflight, and the way how to achieve it. He knew better than anyone that its time had come during the postwar period. And one of his greatnesses was the ability to communicate that fact. And another one was his ability to lead the design of the vehicles that would make spaceflight possible, and then go ahead and build them, through his program management at Huntsville . . . Wernher was the right person at the right time . . ."

Rocco A. Petrone, working at Cape Canaveral in Florida from 1952 to 1969, often expressed his admiration for von Braun. *"My first impressions of Wernher von Braun,"* he said in 1989 [8-39], *"were of an experienced, practical, extremely communicative individual who also was capable of dreams and visions that made him unique . . . He had his feet on the ground, but his head in the clouds . . . I recognized that in many ways Wernher belonged 'to the world.' As the years passed, my opinion of him only grew deeper and fonder . . . Von Braun opened up new frontiers that will challenge mankind for centuries to come . . . I remember him best for 'keeping the torch burning' during the dark times of the 1950s before the Russians woke us up from our sleep with Sputnik—which did not have to happen if our authorities had only listened to Wernher."*

Dr. Richard W. Porter deserves a very special place in the history of the von Braun team. Chapter 3-7 described his almost superhuman efforts in contacting and rounding up the Peenemünders, widely dispersed over war-torn Germany, during and after the waning days of World War II, sharing their miseries as displaced persons with no housing and virtually no food, outfoxing senseless orders and decisions by incompetent local commanders, and, finally, helping form the nucleus of a joint rocket and guided missile development organization in the United States.

Porter had known of von Braun and his work before war's end; he met the man for the first time in Garmisch, Bavaria, in May 1945.

"They had arrived with 13 freight cars from the Nordhausen area," Porter recalled during an interview in May 1989 [9-32]. *"Well, we were all pretty suspicious of each other . . . Von Braun was reserved, but he didn't refuse to answer . . ."*

What were Porter's first impressions of the man? *"Very good; I always liked him and got along well with him. And what I liked most was that he knew his business. Everything he said to me made sense."* Later, when plans were made to take about 125 of the Peenemünders to the United States, Porter and von Braun, and also Colonel Toftoy, had to select those men.

"First of all," Porter recalled, *"we had to know where and who the people were. I was amazed at von Braun's ability to tell me exactly what such and such a man could do, what his strengths and weaknesses were, and so on. He knew his people individually. He knew at least 600 people well enough to tell you what they could do. My greatest admiration for the guy was this ability."*

Beginning in the fall of 1945, Peenemünders began to arrive at Fort Bliss; even before year's end, assembly of the V-2 parts at White Sands Proving Ground had started, and test firings soon followed. Porter brought in about 120 engineers, technicians, and administrative people from General Electric. "Pappy" (L. V.) White was his representative, but he came regularly to see the progress, and keep the joint work going. *"We got along fine with the Germans,"* he remembered. *"We used to have great parties. After the first successful V-2 flight we went to the beer joint in the Organ Mountains half way from Las Cruces to White Sands. There was a lot of beer. And comraderie. And poetry from all over. And plenty of speeches . . . They were all very happy and felt things were working out well, and that we were doing a good job."*

Were there any anti-German feelings expressed? *"I never encountered a bit. It was amazing. Our crew stayed there until the move to the Alabama area"* [in April 1950].

Herbert Friedman, one of the finest long-time space scientists who in his later years became president of the U.S. Academy of Sciences, talked about his contacts with von Braun at an interview in 1990 [9-43]; see also Chapters 4-4 and 9-4.

"I didn't get to know him until the mid-1950s, and all through the 1960s. He would appear on committees on which I also served. He would meet with the Space Science Board occasionally and would always push the goal of man-in-space. He was totally serious about sending men to Mars. I thought it was way, way out. It was something that was far beyond my horizons. [Apollo] was a big stretch from anything we had experienced up to that time. We thought it was a terrible gamble. Of course, in principle the technology was there to make it work."

Friedman's recollections of von Braun's personality are probably typical of the picture most space scientists had of von Braun during the 1960s:

"He was an affable person with a friendly personality. He certainly had the capability to charm people. On the other hand, many of us resented him because he would appear [at meetings] . . . and monopolize the stage. He was always followed by media people, and he could disrupt a meeting very thoroughly just by being there . . . I was put off by his public image."

Indeed, von Braun had a way with Congress. Many observers, members of Congress and others, commented on this fact.

Dr. Glen P. Wilson, staff member of Lyndon B. Johnson's Senate Aeronautical and Space Sciences Committee, said during an interview in 1989 [9-33]: *"Von Braun, a witness before that committee . . . , was a charismatic man in more ways than one. He was a superb witness. He knew how to answer the questions that the senators were asking, and to anticipate what it was they were trying to discover . . . he understood in great detail the importance of the staff . . . he knew that getting knowledge into the staff was probably as important as his testimony before the senators . . . I remember many occasions when he would see me and come over, and we would start talking, and he would tell me about some of the latest developments. It was a good, shrewd move on his part. But it wasn't phony; it was real . . ."*

How did the senators themselves regard him as a witness? *"He was a very popular, credible witness. The senators had an implicit trust in him, just as they had in Hugh Dryden. When von Braun told those folks, look, we can go to the Moon or Mars or whatever, they would believe him. He was very popular, very much so. We had the best attendance at our meetings when it was announced that von Braun was going to be a witness. Von Braun was simply a superstar, and not just because of his genius, but because he went out of his way to make himself available to the people who needed the information."*

Don Fuqua served twelve terms in the House, representing Florida's Second

Congressional District. He was chairman on a number of committees dealing with science, technology, space, energy, and government operations. Von Braun, throughout his professional work in the United States, made contacts with politicians who had, or could have, some influence on the government's attitude toward space. Among those who soon developed close and very friendly relations with von Braun were Congressman George P. Miller, chairman of the House Committee on Science and Astronautics; Congressman Olin E. (Tiger) Teague, chairman of the House Subcommittee on Manned Space Flight; and Don Fuqua.

"I remember having dinner with Wernher and Eberhard Rees in Huntsville in 1963," Fuqua said during an interview in September 1987 [9-34]. *"From then on for several times a year we would go there, and also von Braun would be testifying here in Washington . . . It was an important learning experience . . . von Braun was a very fascinating person. He was very exciting to be around, to talk to. And he always had time to talk to you, and to answer your questions . . . he liked to talk about the benefits of space . . . I became a very good friend of Wernher . . . He was certainly one of the best salesmen that NASA had. Jim Webb was a great salesman, but Jim was looked upon more as a professional bureaucrat, and he was very good . . . Wernher had the credibility, the respect, and he was the type of person that members would come to see and want to meet. He was a man of great competence, and he succeeded. He was a great person in explaining things to lay people in a way that they could understand. That was one of his greatest attributes beyond being a genius. And while he could explain things in a very understandable way to the public, he never talked down to people . . ."*

Did Fuqua recall any of his colleagues on the Hill criticizing the German team at Redstone?

"No, never. The feeling was, we're glad to have them on our side . . ."

"I think Wernher at a very crucial time provided the impetus that we needed—and the vision we needed. He was a great spokesman for the space program to get public support behind it . . . We had a lot of bright people—the Bob Gilruths and Hugh Drydens, and I don't want to take any credit away from them—but I feel that von Braun was a catalyst at that time to get the program moving. Not only did he get public support during the Eisenhower Administration, but he had vision, and he was a great persuader and worked tirelessly. If he had been a politician instead of a scientist, he would have been a hell of a good politician!"

Almost everybody who had some working contact with von Braun became impressed by his personality and quickly developed a liking, even a personal fondness for him. However, there were exceptions. In some cases, there was a tactful mutual avoidance; rarely, the lack of empathy became manifest during open debates.

Milton Rosen, developer of the Viking high-altitude research rocket during the late 1940s, established contact with von Braun in 1946. During an interview in 1988 [4-5], Rosen recalled his early debates with von Braun, and also his interactions with the von Braun team during the Saturn program (Chapters 4-4 and 8-5). Agreements on technical issues were sometimes difficult to reach, sometimes just impossible. While Rosen would remain adamant, von Braun's patience would run out; Rosen accused von Braun of having blind spots, von Braun accused Rosen of having a closed mind. While discussions would often lead to divergent opinions, *"they were always interesting, and they would help clarify our own standpoint,"* as one of von Braun's associates remembered.

Rosen was very critical in 1952 when von Braun's *Collier's* articles were published.

"I can hardly conceive of anything," he wrote [9-35], *"that would do more harm to this country's defense effort, and to the cause of spaceflight itself"* than to embark upon one of *"the fantastic projects for a spaceship that have been proposed in the last few years."* A note in support of Rosen's attitude came from Arthur C. Clarke [9-36]: *"You will read a number of criticisms of von Braun's 'satellite or bust' propaganda in the* Journal [of the British Interplanetry Society] *shortly. Our view is definitely on Rosen's side, but we suspect that von Braun is really trying to drum up public support and may not believe everything he advocates!"*

Von Braun's *Collier's* articles did not advocate that a Moon or Mars ship as described should be built immediately. They merely showed that available technology would make travel into space possible, but von Braun often emphasized that the actual development of spaceflight will be a long, complex process along an evolutionary route that would lead through many intermediate steps and accomplishments—a fact that was borne out during the twenty years of rocketry and spaceflight development culminating in Apollo and Skylab that followed the *Collier's* articles.

Ten years after Rosen's first meeting with von Braun, he was chief engineer in the Vanguard satellite project. It was an extremely ambitious project, and the chief engineer found himself in a constant battle with the intricacies of a three-stage rocket of marginal performance, most of whose components and subsystems were novel developments. He faced the additional burden of a superimposed high-level Navy management structure that often tried to influence purely technical decisions.

When the Vanguard project began to have failures, Rosen's colleagues at the Marshall Center repeatedly offered their help, but none of these offers were accepted. There was much sympathy for Rosen. Von Braun took the opportunity at several occasions to praise him and his team publicly for their fine work and their exemplary devotion. For a sophisticated rocket system like the three-stage Vanguard, the time for completion of the project that the engineers had at their disposal was simply too short.

On 17 March 1958, the Vanguard team's tireless efforts were rewarded by a first success; a 3¼ pound (1.5 kilogram) satellite reached orbit. Von Braun sent a telegram to Rosen: *"My heartiest congratulations to you and the personnel of Project Vanguard. You have my profound admiration for the initiative, pluck, and faith which were rewarded by today's launching."*

When Rosen was director of Launch Vehicles at NASA Headquarters during the Saturn-Apollo project, there were frequent debates about the Saturn rockets between him and von Braun's Marshall Center. Many led to agreements, but some ended with opposing views. Sometimes, there was even the impression that Rosen relished the latter more than the former! Von Braun's standpoint had always been that a technical decision for or against a particular system must not be made on the merit of one factor only, such as efficiency, but that other factors, such as reliability, existing experience, availability of components, relation to other systems, usefulness for other projects, development time, possibility of testing, cost, and others should also be taken into account. Being a visionary who wanted to promote spaceflight as vigorously as possible, but also a perfectionist for technical quality and adherence to promised schedules, he had numerous criteria that he was determined to meet. For Rosen, von Braun was too far out in one direction, and too conservative in the other. *"For all the bragging he did about spaceflight, when it came to the engineering of his own rockets, his men had a hell of a time getting him to take risks,"* Rosen said in 1988 [4-5]; von Braun's men would never have confirmed that statement!

At least part of Rosen's occasional critical attitude toward von Braun's projects may have resulted from the fact that Rosen, although basically a development engineer with a creative mind and with some practical rocket work to his credit, was forced to limit his activities to a desk job at NASA Headquarters, while von Braun was in the enviable position of directing a huge field center with a number of exciting hardware projects.

Rosen was certainly an excellent engineer. As long as he argued as an engineer, relations with the Huntsville people were pleasant, even amiable. When he tried to overrule conclusions those people had reached after decades in successful rocket work, things could become tense. As the Saturn-Apollo project neared its completion, relations between him and the Huntsville people became much smoother. Recollections of divergent views began to fade out, giving room to memories from a period of thirty years of joint endeavors to make rockets and spaceflight a firm possession of people on Earth.

Reminiscences of Dr. Fred L. Whipple, director of the Smithsonian Institution's Astrophysical Observatory in Cambridge, Massachusetts, are of special interest because Whipple was the only real scientist with whom von Braun had, at least at intervals, a friend-to-friend relationship.

"I knew him by reputation," Whipple said during an interview in 1986 [5-21], *"and I was not surprised in any way when I met him [in 1951]. He was a very vigorous person, and extremely devoted to his subject. Yes, I was delighted to meet him because I felt that he was the man who was going to put us into space. We became good friends."*

Did von Braun feel uncomfortable with scientists, or they with him? *"It's quite simple,"* Whipple said. *"Wernher was an engineer, not a scientist in the eyes of scientists. An engineer is an engineer and not a scientist, a very respectable profession, but not regarded a scientist by the fraternity. Many of my colleagues realized that he was a top-notch engineer, but otherwise were not interested."*

How did astronomers react to von Braun's promotion of spaceflight in the 1950s? *"I was part of a very small minority who got interested in it. Later, when the astronomical community realized that it was possible to send instruments into space, they were aghast at the cost. For the price of one of these rockets you could build a telescope. Most astronomers didn't then realize that they were comparing apples and muffins; you couldn't compare telescopes in space with telescopes on the ground . . . There were a few, Lyman Spitzer, for example . . . [and] Arthur C. Clarke; they had the clearest vision of what might happen in space. Very few working astronomers did . . . It was not until the late 1960s that astronomers began to realize the potential of a telescope out in space . . . Gerard Kuiper, Bob [Charles R.] O'Dell and others got more and more enthusiastic—but that was around 1970, not in the early 1950s."*

Did most astronomers look upon von Braun as somewhat of a showman?

"Well, he was a showman. That is how you sell ideas. It's like Carl Sagan today. Not very many . . . have appreciated what von Braun has been doing for science by publicizing it. I think they are a bit jealous. In those early days, conservative astronomers felt that space travel was a bit far out . . ."

Carl Sagan was one of the persons for whom von Braun felt great admiration. He avidly read Sagan's essays and books, and he recommended his co-workers to do the same. *"Carl is a brilliant communicator with the public,"* he would say, *"taking a strong and convincing stand for space exploration. He keeps the fire burning, and he has a great way of conveying the challenge of scientific exploration to a huge audience. He is so successful in creating an awareness of man's need for space exploration also among those whom the engineers will never reach . . ."*

Sagan, on his part, expressed admiration for the big rockets that von Braun brought to life, and also for the Huntsville team and its many contractors that built and launched those rockets, opening roadways into space for exploration and science.

However, the close and warm relationship that the von Braun group enjoyed with so many others did not develop between Sagan and the von Braun team. It seems that Sagan always retained some reservations about von Braun because he had accepted the support of the German Reichswehr in 1931 and 1932 when he wanted to develop the modern precision rocket as a means to explore outer space, while the Army wished to develop such a rocket as a weapon. Ten years later, Hitler discovered and began to support the Peenemünde rocket as a *"vengeance weapon."* A scientist, and, in fact, every decent person, Sagan argued along with a large number of scientists, should refuse to work on projects that may have the potential of military applications. Rockets, satellites, and spacecraft, he felt, should have been developed, built, and operated solely for peaceful purposes, without any connections to the military.

In an essay prepared specifically for this biography at the request of the authors, Sagan described his feelings about von Braun [9-37].

"Wernher von Braun played an absolutely central role in the history of rocketry and in the development of spaceflight—equally on the inspirational as on the technological side. This is very much in the tradition of the earlier spaceflight pioneers, Konstantin Tsiolkovsky and Robert Goddard. The key event that convinced me, personally, that spaceflight would happen in my generation was the 1948 two-stage launch of a WAC corporal aboard a von Braun-designed V-2 which reached an altitude (I seem to remember) of about 250 miles. His Colliers *articles and his popular books— especially the* Conquest of the Moon *and* The Exploration of Mars*—were influential in shaping my teenage views about the feasibility and nature of interplanetary flight. Much later, his* "Mars Project" *fell into my hands, and I'm sure affected my later views on Martian exploration.*

"On the other hand, and I hope [the authors] will do justice to this side of von Braun in [their] book, I found many things deeply disturbing about his career—his willingness to work for the Wehrmacht and the SS, to accept a commission in the SS, to brief Hitler and Himmler, and to use slave labor in the production of V-2s. I am bothered by such reminiscences of his student days as those by Constantine Generales (published in the JBIS*, as I recall), about spinning mice in a homemade centrifuge in his university rooms until the walls were splattered with mouse blood. His casual attitude toward the use of V-2s to commit random mayhem and murder in England (*"we aimed at the Moon, but hit London instead"*) is a kind of quintessence of the socially irresponsible technologist, and Tom Lehrer's song about von Braun, in my view, hits the mark (*'When the rockets go up/ Who cares where they come down?/ That's not my department/ Says Wernher von Braun'*).*

"The von Braun team was brought to America to fight the Cold War, and I remember noting with amazement the ease with which he and his colleagues negotiated the transition from compliance to the Nazis to red-blooded Americans. I found von Braun's mastery of American English and his comparatively indetectable German accent remarkable, considering his age at the time he emigrated to the United States.

One of the lessons I have learned from his career is the responsibility of the scientist or engineer to hold back and even, if necessary, to refuse to participate in technological developments—no matter how 'sweet'—when the auspices or objectives are sufficiently sinister. Von Braun helped me to understand how to respond to Star Wars (a case, by the way, where nearly 10,000 American scientists and engineers have signed a pledge to refuse to work on it, and to refuse to accept any money for any purpose from the Strategic Defense Initiative Organization).

"I spent time with von Braun on perhaps ten or twelve occasions—some scientific and technical meetings, including the old American Rocket Society in the 1950s;

National Academy of Sciences Space Science Board meetings and summer studies; at NASA Headquarters, toward the end of his life; and once or twice privately. I remember meeting him on a lonely runway in, I think, Langley, Virginia, where he flew his piston-engine airplane in himself. The subject of that meeting was maintaining the Saturn V assembly line so we could send really large payloads to Mars. I wish we could have been able to succeed there, but we failed. We could really use a heavylift vehicle of the Saturn V class today for going to Mars.

"There were many von Brauns. I remember the von Braun with silver hair, striking good looks and an all-American 'r' (all lips and no uvula), passionately and effectively describing the mechanics of a Mars mission. I can remember his marveling at the 'dead stick' landing mode of the early shuttle design. But I also remember the film of him lecturing to the Air Command and Staff College at Maxwell Air Force Base in the 1950s, when he was perfectly happy to use military arguments—including specious scenarios on how important it was to put nuclear weapons in orbit, guided every inch of the way to their target by men in space stations. He was willing to use nearly any argument and accept any sponsorship as long as it could get us into space. I think he went too far.

"I remember asking von Braun in a meeting at Woods Hole, Massachusetts, what he felt was the most compelling argument for human flight to other worlds. His answer was that people were like birds, swallowing the fruit, and wherever they alight, excreting the pits. He put this in somewhat more direct terms, but it is an inelegant metaphor at best. I was surprised that someone who had spent his entire life advocating spaceflight did not have a better explanation of his quest. Unlike many space technologists, von Braun understood the scientific value of spaceflight very well—although he mentioned nothing about it in answering the question I just mentioned. But in the technology itself, and in organizing and maintaining high quality and extremely effective technical teams, von Braun was unsurpassed. The modern rocket, which he pioneered, will prove to be either the means of mass annihilation through a global thermonuclear war or the means that will carry us to the planets and the stars. This dread ambiguity, which faces us today, is central to the life of Wernher von Braun."

Sagan is correct: This *"dread ambiguity"* was central to von Braun's life, at least from 1932 on. Those who knew him well were aware how much this ambiguity disturbed him, although he talked about it only rarely. Tom Lehrer's song about von Braun certainly does not hit the mark. Throughout his life, von Braun was deeply concerned about where his rockets would *"come down."* He had his full share of mental anguish, along with all those who follow their destiny to be creative as scientists and engineers, and who must realize that they have no control over the fate their brainchildren will meet in the hands of those who use them for their own purposes.

The story about the birds is surprising. By saying this, and using these words, von Braun certainly made a mistake. Had one of his friends been there, he would have come to his rescue. It was one of the errors von Braun sometimes made, garbling up some thoughts which normally would make sense. He sometimes talked about *"birds dropping plant seeds"* when he described how life on Earth spreads over newly created areas, such as islands, lava flows, or land slides. Also, he often talked most eloquently and convincingly about the many reasons why we should travel to other worlds. Sagan obviously caught von Braun at an instant when he was careless with his words and even his logic. This incident shows what von Braun's associates had known all along: As a human being, von Braun was not always as careful as when he developed his rockets.

How would von Braun's immediate co-workers have agreed with these statements by superiors, colleagues, and friends, most of them quite positive, some of them critical?

"After less than half an hour, I was absolutely fascinated by him, and that impression has not left me ever since" said Dr. Adolf K. Thiel, who met von Braun for the first time in 1937, and then worked with him for fifteen years. Most, perhaps all of von Braun's close co-workers would underwrite this statement. They proved their feeling by remaining faithful team members for as long as the team existed, some of them for more than thirty years. Only very few of those who had joined von Braun left the team, either because they wanted to earn more money, or because they wished to pursue a specific professional career, or for health reasons. Thiel was one of them, becoming senior vice president at Thompson-Ramo-Wooldridge.

While the men and women who shared not only the successes and triumphs, but also the daily drudgery and frustrations with von Braun, would judge him positively, they would add a little extra here and there, not to change the total image, but to show that von Braun was not only a genius, but also a human being.

When von Braun interacted with others, he usually kept himself under iron control, even while he was at leisure. Whatever he did, he wanted to do it perfectly, and he wished to leave a perfect impression. Thus, for example, he hated to lose an argument. If he was not certain that he would win, but still wished to give it a try, he encouraged one of his associates to present the idea. He would give it eloquent support, but if it did not take hold, he could easily dissociate himself and leave the lost cause to the associate.

Traveling with von Braun had two aspects. First, it would afford his companion the opportunity of being close to him for hours or even days with numerous chances to discuss technical work. Also, with von Braun's great pleasure in just talking, one would have a chance to learn about his thoughts about the space program at large, or his views on the political situation, or his interpretation of history, or his newest readings in science journals, or almost any area through which his overactive mind might be roaming. It was always a great experience just to hear him talk.

Then, there was a second aspect, well known to his close co-workers of whose continuing unlimited loyalty he could be certain. They occasionally experienced a more down-to-Earth von Braun, sometimes just a case of utter forgetfulness, sometimes a little worse.

Lee B. James, at that time Saturn V project manager, remembers [9-38]: *"There were funny moments. After borrowing a quarter at the Los Angeles Airport one day, he asked me to watch his bags while he made a telephone call. With so much on his mind, I never saw him again that day . . ."* Another associate, director of one of his laboratories, remembers a story that happened in Washington during the 1960s. Von Braun and he had planned to visit first a company and then NASA Headquarters together; they had come to Washington separately and stayed in different hotels. They met the evening before to make plans for the next day. *"Let's meet at eight o'clock sharp at 13th and E Streets,"* von Braun said, *"without suitcases. We pick these up at our hotels when we are ready to go to the airport. First, we will take a cab to the company; then, we will go to NASA; then, I'll see that fellow who wants to write an article on Saturn, you can go with me there; then, we will pick up our suitcases at the hotels and take a cab to the airport. At some time in between, we'll grab a bite to eat in some cafeteria. Now, please, be on time tomorrow morning! I don't want to wait at a street corner during rush hour!"*

Next morning, his associate was at the corner five minutes before eight. No von Braun. The rush hour was tremendous. At nine fifteen, von Braun appeared, with briefcase and suitcase. No *"good morning,"* no apology, no explanation, only a curt *"here, why don't you take the suitcase; I'll take the briefcase. Let's go."* Von Braun was in a terrible mood. There was silence in the cab. When they met with the company people, von Braun came back to his usual self, vocal and persuasive, charming, full of jokes—

everybody felt good. Von Braun talked much longer than his schedule would have permitted. Then they took a cab to NASA. Riding in the cab, von Braun talked and talked; then he said: *"Look, it's so late already, I'll skip that fellow with the Saturn article, and we will proceed to the airport right after our NASA meeting."*—*"But I have to pick up my suitcase at the hotel, as we had planned last night,"* his associate said. That remark turned von Braun completely around. *"Now look,"* he said, *"you are only a burden for me when we are traveling together. We better part our ways. Why don't you do your thing, and I'll do mine."* When the cab stopped, he took his briefcase and suitcase and left, while his associate proceeded to pay the cab driver.

Such little glitches must have been his way of compensating for all these disappointments and frustrations that confronted him every day, building up steam pressure. Sometimes, the safety valve just opened.

The morning hours never were to von Braun's liking. *"I'm convinced,"* he used to say, *"that none of the important achievements in human history were accomplished before ten thirty or eleven in the morning!"*

If there was, during a business trip, an early joint breakfast with von Braun, two things were the rule: first, he would be at least half an hour late; and second, he would be in a bad mood and should not be engaged in a conversation. In fact, his experienced fellow travelers would see to it that the morning newspaper was on the table next to his coffee cup; that would spare them an unpleasant beginning of an otherwise successful and enjoyable day.

Fortunately, occasions when von Braun dropped his self-control were rare and brief. Most of those who met him never experienced any such case; they would hardly believe that something like this could ever happen.

On countless instances, von Braun had charming, warmhearted, sincere words, spoken or written, for a co-worker, congratulating him on an award, or thanking him for a substantial contribution to a project, or admonishing him to take a little rest, or wishing him good luck for an impending operation, or congratulating him and his wife on a newborn baby, or imploring him to end his bachelorhood and find himself a wife, or consoling him after a mishap in his work, or encouraging him when he faced a particularly tough problem.

Again and again, von Braun showed that he believed in the necessity of a healthy balance between work and play, and he often tried to persuade his co-workers to accept the same philosophy. One day in the early 1950s, while Maria von Braun was visiting her parents in Germany, he and two of his associates, Friedrich and Ruth von Saurma, planned to rent a Cessna airplane, fly to the Gulf coast, and spend a leisurely weekend on the beach. The plane had four seats, so they invited their colleague Stuhlinger to join them. *"That's a brilliant idea,"* was the reply, *"and I really appreciate your invitation, but I have so much work to do; I just cannot afford to take off for an entire weekend."* But von Braun knew better: *"Come on. I bet you, mankind will not reach the Moon one hour later because you come with us, rather than spending this weekend over your books. Come and join us! We'll let you pilot the plane!"*—Of course, Stuhlinger joined them, he piloted the plane, and the four of them spent a most delightful weekend flying, swimming, beach combing, and having fun.

One question came up frequently when von Braun's personality, his work, his influence on rocketry and spaceflight, and his role in the American space program were discussed: Would there have been travel to the Moon without von Braun and his team?

The answers to this question were remarkably uniform: eventually, yes; but not so soon. At least some, probably many years later. Von Braun's own answer was, in essence, the same. *"Man did travel to the Moon,"* he would say, *"because it is his destiny, not because I wanted it. A little less poetically, you might say: because he has it in his genes. All I did was help others do what they wanted to do anyway, what destiny made them want to do. I consider myself extremely fortunate for having had the privilege of contributing to this project. If I had not been there, I do not doubt that someone else would have stood up to rally the forces and lead the crusade, perhaps at another place and at another time, but he would have come. Traveling to the Moon was simply in the cards for mankind. Of course, there are many material advantages accruing from a project of this kind, but the ultimate motive for traveling to the Moon is irrational."*

5   VOICES OF CRITICISM

"He was such a charmer, you will hardly find anybody who has anything negative to say about him," was a frequent comment when the authors tried to round out von Braun's image by comments that would show flaws in his work or his personality. And yet, there were voices of criticism. They came from different sources, and for different reasons.

There were (and still are) people who did not know von Braun personally, and who never worked in the American or any other space program, but who saw in von Braun an exponent of all the evils of the Hitler regime. Their attitude is characterized by a statement of Rep. John D. Dingell, Democrat of Detroit, quoted by the *El Paso Times* in its July 1, 1947 issue. Calling the Army's leaders *"nuts"* for bringing over the German rocket specialists, he added: *"I have never thought that we were so poor mentally in this country that we have to go and import those Nazi killers to help us prepare for the defense of our country. A German is a Nazi, and a Nazi is a German. The terms are synonymous."*

Then, there were a few individuals who knew von Braun well as colleagues. Wishing to pursue their own ideas in contrast to suggestions offered by von Braun, they found all kinds of blind spots and fallacies in von Braun's arguments. Milton Rosen [4-5; 9-35] was probably the most outspoken representative of such critics (Chapters 4-4, 9-4).

A source of recurrent criticism during the first years of the Saturn-Apollo project was the sister center of von Braun's Marshall Center, the Manned Spacecraft Center in Houston. The two centers were quite different in their histories, traditions, and management structures, and also in their approaches to engineering tasks, their working arrangements with contractors, and their ways of assigning responsibilities. Differences of opinion of the center directors, even friction and hard feelings, were unavoidable. Criticism was mutual. Homer E. Newell wrote in 1979 [9-53]: *"The Marshall Center reflected the background and personality of its leader, Wernher von Braun, and his team of German rocket experts. Bold, with a bulldog determination, undaunted by the sheer magnitude of a project like Saturn, they could hardly be deterred by request or by command from their plotted course . . . The Manned Spacecraft Center developed an arrogance born of unbounded self-confidence and possession of a leading role in the nation's number one space project . . ."* Von Braun rarely complained as to how Houston handled technical and managerial problems associated with the joint project; and he always refrained from direct personal criticism. As the Saturn-Apollo project progressed, criticism between the two centers subsided more and more. By the time the flights to the Moon began, Gilruth and von Braun had become sincere friends, and the initial criticism had changed into mutual trust and admiration (Chapter 9-4).

That change from a preconceived—and negative—notion to a feeling of solid friendship, taking place soon after personal contacts and working relationships had been established, was a typical occurrence during von Braun's life in the United States. Phillips [9-20], Naugle [9-30], and others described their experiences in becoming close friends of von Braun once they had come to know him personally.

Was there criticism of von Braun within his own center? Very little, but there was some. Every once in a while, a new face would show up in von Braun's immediate vicinity, a newcomer to the team. While he was practically unknown to his colleagues, von Braun would entrust him with his fullest confidence, installing him as a kind of personal aide, listening to his advice, and giving him preference and even authority over long-time, seasoned team members, although the man did not have much to offer in the way of experience, knowledge, or talent—only complete devotion to the boss. These cases, fortunately quite rare and short-lived, could lead to some headaches among von Braun's co-workers. *"He has such a fabulously sure judgment for almost everything,"* they would say, *"but sometimes there seems to be a lapse . . ."*

There was one area of criticism which had deeper roots, and which deserves closer scrutiny. It goes back to the age-old adage of *"engineers versus scientists."* Von Braun was not spared his share in occasional flare-ups of this dilemma, but the problem was not limited to von Braun and his team, nor is it limited to the era during which he was at work.

On many occasions, von Braun not only professed, but actually proved a burning interest in science, at least in astronomy, and also in modern biology, particularly genetics. He read about the results of scientific research as much as he could. If his path crossed that of a distinguished scientist, his curious inquiries were endless. He was enormously proud that his rockets and spacecraft would open doorways for scientific exploration into regions not otherwise accessible. Von Braun's positive attitude toward science did not fail to result in much recognition and praise from outsiders.

However, not everybody fully shared in these accolades. Problems became manifest in two areas: in science-oriented activities within the Marshall Center, and in Marshall-assigned projects that included science payloads.

Within the Marshall Center, von Braun did not wish to have scientists pursue purely scientific studies, even if they had been specifically tailored to rocket and spacecraft projects underway at Marshall, such as, for example, cosmic ray studies. Practically all work undertaken at the Research Projects Laboratory (later named Space Sciences Laboratory) had to be in support of the mainline projects; during the 1960s, these were Saturn and Skylab. Real science projects came into their own at Marshall only under von Braun's successors (Chapter 9-2).

With regard to Marshall-assigned projects with science payloads, Newell, in his book *Beyond the Atmosphere* [4-10], wrote: *"The effort to superimpose the Juno space science launchings and the Centaur launch vehicle development [for scientific payloads] on the Marshall team, when Saturn represented its real aspiration, simply did not work out. The Juno launchings had to be canceled after a string of dismal failures, which space science managers at headquarters felt were caused [among other reasons] by a general disinterest in the objectives of space science as the scientists saw them . . ."*

Similar problems surfaced when project management of Skylab with its rich science program was assigned to the Marshall Center.

As Skylab planning progressed during the mid-60s, the unique research opportunities presented by the large facility for a wide variety of studies were seized upon by a growing number of scientists at universities and research centers. Being confronted with this flood of would-be scientific experimenters on their spacecraft, the engineers at Marshall almost panicked. Members of von Braun's Space Sciences Laboratory tried their best to help explain and understand, to mediate, and to build two-way bridges between the scientists on the outside and the engineers on the inside. Von Braun, quite in contrast to his usual determination to penetrate deeply into all the technical and managerial details of a project, kept his distance from the scientists. The situation is illustrated by a remark made by Richard Tousey, solar physics scientist at the Naval Research Laboratory, the most active and successful of all Skylab scientists: *"We cannot reach von Braun,"* he said, *"he is always stonewalled by his engineers who do not care for the needs of us scientists."* Other scientists sometimes expressed the desire to meet with von Braun on a one-to-one basis, without his protective bodyguard of engineers around him, to explain their scientific goals and their experiments, and to ask him to bring about a closer contact between the Skylab engineers and the scientists. Had von Braun shown the same personal interest in the work of the Skylab scientists that he always showed for the results of science in general, he could have helped allay the early plight of these scientists substantially. A decisive improvement occurred in 1966 when Leland F. Belew, previously manager of rocket engine development at Marshall, was appointed program manager for Skylab. He listened to the needs of the scientists, and he followed up with proper actions. He worked well with his counterparts at Headquarters, particularly Charles W. [Chuck] Mathews and William C. [Bill] Schneider. Another step of improvement came in 1968 when Newell, chief scientist at NASA Headquarters, took a hand in organizing and overseeing the total scientific effort within the Skylab program.

Skylab, in spite of severe damage incurred during ascent when part of the thermal insulation and one solar panel were torn off, became a brilliant success for the engineers as well as for the eighty-odd scientists who had their experiments aboard. During the later phases of project preparation, and particularly during the many months while Skylab was in orbit, engineers and scientists worked very well together. The project had become a learning opportunity of the highest order for both sides, Marshall engineers and outside scientists. Both had learned their lessons and were not only ready, but eager to apply what they had learned to the follow-up projects, Skylab II and Skylab III, which were under preparation at the time when Skylab I reaped its rich harvest. These projects doubtlessly would have become further outstanding successes for science as well as for space engineering. Tragically, NASA decided in 1973 to discontinue the entire Skylab program.

6   *"THE LADY I WORK FOR"*

"What you see here," von Braun sometimes said to visitors, pointing to an organization chart of his Marshall Center, *"are the people who work for me, about 7,200 in all. Let me now introduce to you the person for whom I work, my real boss. Here she is, Mrs. Bonnie G. Holmes. By her job title, she is a secretary. But that is a misnomer. She is not a secretary; she is a phenomenon. While I am running the center, she is running me. I would not dare making any major decision before having it checked out with her first. Her common sense is absolutely reliable, her memory almost limitless, with an access time approaching that of a modern computer. Her capacity for work seems to have no bounds. Even at times of crises, she never panics. When I need her, she is always ready to accept whatever I ask her to do. She is always friendly, smiling, at ease. If she has to tell me that I am going to make a mistake, she does it in such a conciliatory way that I just*

have to agree with her. Really, if anybody around here should deserve a monument, it would be Bonnie."

Bonnie Holmes was not only the ideal executive secretary for von Braun, she was also ideal for those who had to see von Braun for a decision, and who did not succeed in penetrating the wall of work that surrounded him most of the time to the point of complete inaccessibility. *"Be here at 2:35 this afternoon, and I'll get you in,"* she would say, and she would do it!

How Bonnie Holmes managed her mountain of office duties, and at the same time had a wonderful family, worked as a member of the church council, played a prominent role in the rural community of Vinemont near Huntsville where she and her family lived, and met everyone who crossed her way with an amiable smile—nobody really knows. *"I guess I just thrive on work,"* she said. *"I always enjoy whatever I'm doing, even washing dishes and canning fruit!"*

In October 1951, she applied for a secretarial position at Redstone Arsenal in Huntsville. A few months later, she read in *Collier's* magazine an article *"Crossing the Last Frontier,"* written by von Braun. *"I was intrigued by the story itself,"* she recalled in an interview in 1986 [9-39], *"and also by the way he presented it, telling how scientists and engineers now know how to build a space station that would be a long step in uniting mankind, and how, within the next ten or fifteen years, there will be man-made satellites that could be a great force for world peace.*

"You can imagine my surprise when, a few weeks later, I received a phone call, telling me that Dr. von Braun was looking for a secretary . . . and that I was . . . selected to go for an interview . . . When I got there, I was a little disappointed because Dr. von Braun was not there . . . he was on leave because Mrs. von Braun was having their second child . . . So, I was interviewed by Charles Davidson . . . A little later, I could not believe my good fortune when I was told that I had been selected for the position . . . Starting in May 1952, I worked for both Dr. von Braun and his deputy, Dr. Eberhard Rees. Thus began the most wonderful career a girl could have . . .

"I studied the organization chart to learn who was where. Heads of the Staff Offices and the Laboratories were constantly in and out of Dr. von Braun's office, so I learned them rather quickly . . . I first had some difficulty understanding them because of their accents, and learning to pronounce their names . . . But everyone was very patient and understanding, and I soon grew to like them all very much . . . It wasn't long until I was working solely for Dr. von Braun because of his increasing workload. Although the work was very interesting, I must admit that it was more difficult than anything I had ever done. I think the most difficult thing, however, was adjusting to Dr. von Braun's work habits. He always took work home with him, and he must have worked late into the night because he brought in a briefcase loaded with action items for me each morning. He arrived a little later than the other employees, but he also stayed later . . . Before too long, the long days became rather routine, and I found that we could get more work accomplished after the phone stopped ringing and things became quiet . . . He was a good teacher; he gave concise, but explicit instructions. He wrote notes on all the mail and reports that he read. From these notes and from his dictation of letters and memoranda, I soon learned how he wanted things done, how he felt about many aspects of his work, and how he would respond to many questions . . . He left the office management and administrative matters up to me . . . he told me to take care of anything that I felt I could do in his absence . . . I would prepare a briefing sheet for Dr. von Braun on requests and actions taken so that he was aware of what had transpired during his absence . . .

"Dr. von Braun was a well-balanced person, very much in control. I think he became most upset when there was disharmony within the organization, and he was afraid this might hamper work progress. He was very good, however, with settling disputes or misunderstandings among the employees, and he could get things back on an even keel.

Having to pose for photographs, and to take time out . . . to do more public relations type things, upset him a bit. He realized this was important, but I think that sometimes he felt like he was wasting valuable time. There were two things I remember that made him rather tense: First, there were the requests from congressional offices for him to make speeches. Dr. von Braun was admired by almost everyone on Capitol Hill. People soon learned that the surest way to get Dr. von Braun to make a speech was to get their respective congressmen to call him personally. Knowing that he needed the support of all these congressmen to keep the programs going, made it difficult for him to say 'no.' This pressure, which they probably did not realize at the time, added quite a strain on him because of all the travel required, and also the subsequent long hours at the office in order to keep up with his work. Second, he became upset when he was singled out for an honor that he felt should go to the whole team. It bothered him quite a lot to be so much in the news and singled out, knowing that he would hurt other people on the team who should have been recognized. For this reason, he would say when he accepted awards or honors that he accepted on behalf of the whole team.

"There were many problems that he approached with concern; among them was maintaining good working relations between personnel in the different laboratories and offices; trying to settle arguments when someone thought another person was overstepping into his responsibilities; establishing good rapport with the top officials in the companies with whom we had contracts; gaining their confidence and respect so that there could be mutual understanding of what was involved and what he expected out of them for the betterment of the programs."

Were there ever signs of frustration?

"Sometimes. For the most part, however, he was an optimist. There were a few times I remember when he was disappointed; once when the Jupiter C was scheduled to launch the Explorer 1 satellite, and he was required to go to Washington to be ready to meet the press when the satellite was in orbit. He really wanted to go to the Cape to be present for the launch. But when the satellite was safely in orbit, I think his excitement overshadowed the disappointment . . . He showed signs of frustration on occasion when his travels kept him away from his family so much, particularly when his children were small, and he had to leave Mrs. von Braun to cope on her own.

"There were other times of frustration when he couldn't do all that he wanted to do. There were never enough hours in the day for him. He worked very hard and expected others around him to do the same. I think no one minded because he inspired them to do their very best."

Did Bonnie Holmes maintain contact with von Braun after he had gone to Washington?

"Yes. As you can imagine, after having worked for someone of Dr. von Braun's caliber for almost twenty years, you don't sever the relationship immediately. By then, he and his family seemed to be an extension of my own family. I watched his children grow up at the same time my own children were growing up. Maria and her children are still close friends of mine . . . His secretaries in Washington, Julie Kertes at [NASA] Headquarters, then Pat Webb and Kayren Governale at Fairchild, called me many times with questions and messages from Dr. von Braun. He himself called me from time to time. He came to Huntsville on the occasion of the opening and dedication of the

*Von Braun Civic Center; when Maria wasn't able to make the trip with him to Alabama
for the opening ceremonies, he asked me to go with him, and I did."*

Would she remember any particular story that happened in the front office while
she was von Braun's secretary?

*"One morning, Dr. von Braun brought in a freshly laundered short-sleeve shirt
with the instructions that I mail it to Astronaut John Glenn in Houston. On the previous
day, when the 'Original 7' were on tour with Dr. von Braun, he got a bit warm in his suit
and long-sleeve shirt, so John Glenn offered him the short-sleeve shirt he had in his
attaché case; Dr. von Braun promptly accepted the offer, and he wore Glenn's shirt for
the rest of the day. Mrs. von Braun had laundered it that night.*

*"Dr. von Braun often introduced me to visitors as 'the lady I work for.' The most
enthusiastic reaction to this introduction came from Mrs. Esther Peterson who visited us
in 1965 at the time when she was special assistant to President Johnson and assistant
secretary of labor . . ."*

7   *"MEET MY FRIENDS . . ."*

In von Braun's world, friendship was a part of the very fabric of life. There were
hundreds of people on six continents, each of whom he would have introduced happily
with the words: *"Meet a dear friend of mine . . ."* Being close to others, sharing with
them a spirited conversation, a joke, a drink, or joining them for a boat ride, a duck
hunt, an afternoon on water skis, a flight in the cockpit of a jet plane, a campfire evening,
a scuba diving adventure along a coral reef, a ride on a husky-drawn sled across the
snow fields of Antarctica—he was always eager to share his exuberant joy of life with
somebody. Certainly, he would always do most of the talking, but he would present his
thoughts with such convincing charm that his partners couldn't but agree with what he
said. He included the other person so fully in his thinking and feeling of the moment
that the impression of a personal closeness would often result.

There were many occasions when von Braun made new friends: after public
speeches, at presentations in government offices, at industrial companies, in parent-
teacher meetings. A visit to the doctor's office, or to the income tax adviser would often
end up with a personal friendship. Von Braun made friends at symposia and congresses,
as a result of letters written to him, even at the boat dock and in automobile repair
shops. When von Braun left Huntsville in 1970 and moved to Washington, he gave his
vintage Mercedes as a personal gift to the man who had serviced the car during
previous years, Wolfgang Fricke.

There was hardly a city that von Braun touched during his many travels where he
did not have friends. If he had a stopover of a few hours at an airport, his secretary
would make arrangements so that a friend would wait for him at the gate and spend the
stopover time with him. One hour was good enough for a martini or a quick lunch; with
two hours at his disposal, he would persuade the friend to take him on a sightseeing
tour. The precious time would be filled with animated talking, joking, and laughing. All
travel sleepiness would be forgotten, and the two would have the happiest time
together. Back on the airplane, von Braun would immerse himself again in the study of
project proposals and test reports, or he would simply doze off.

Among the large number of men and women whom von Braun would have called
friends, there were a few whom he had met in the early days, long before he was *"the
boss."* One of them, Klaus Riedel, was working on the Mirak rocket at the Raketen-

flugplatz Reinickendorf in 1930 when von Braun, as an eighteen-year old student, joined that seven-man group of rocket and spaceflight enthusiasts.

Two years later, after von Braun had been transferred to the Army's rocket development group at Kummersdorf, Dornberger hired for that group two young men who had been working with rockets at the Heylandt Company, Walter Riedel and Arthur Rudolph. At that time, Rudolph had already developed, built, and statically fired his first rocket engine, a liquid-fueled, jacket-cooled motor that burned alcohol and liquid oxygen for 60 seconds and developed 300 kg of thrust. Both of these newcomers quickly became close friends of von Braun, and they remained so, together with Klaus Riedel, when von Braun became technical director of the Army's rocket development program. When the Peenemünde project began in 1937, Klaus Riedel became director of the Test Laboratory, Arthur Rudolph director of the Development and Fabrication Laboratory, and Walter Riedel, who soon acquired the nickname Papa Riedel because he took such fatherly care of his subordinates, became director of the Technical Design Office and at the same time von Braun's deputy.

Klaus Riedel lost his life in an automobile accident in 1944. Papa Riedel participated in Operation Backfire, the test launching of a number of A-4 rockets in Great Britain, and became a British citizen in 1957. He died in 1968. Arthur Rudolph went to the United States with von Braun in 1945 and remained one of von Braun's closest co-workers until his retirement early in 1969. For the previous six years, he had been project manager for the Saturn V rocket that launched the Apollo capsules to the Moon.

In addition to these early friendships with rocket colleagues, a close personal friendship began in 1930 between von Braun and Constantine D. J. Generales from Athens, Greece, who studied medicine in Zurich, Switzerland, while von Braun studied physics at the Eidgenössische Technische Hochschule in Zurich. Generales later settled in New York as a doctor of internal medicine. The von Brauns named their son, Peter Constantine, in honor of this lifelong friend.

A very special kind of friendship existed between Dornberger and von Braun. When they met at the Raketenflugplatz Reinickendorf in 1931, there must have been instant mutual admiration. At that time, von Braun, nineteen, was a student of physics and *"a rocket enthusiast of surprising theoretical knowledge,"* as Dornberger later remembered. Captain Dornberger, thirty-six, had been in charge of the Army's rocket development for two years. As it turned out, the two men could hardly have been a better match for the gigantic task that lay in store for them, the development of the long-range, precision-guided rocket.

Von Braun felt fortunate to work for a man who also believed in the great future of rockets and space flight, but whose thoughts had had seventeen more years than his own to mature, and who also was a member of the powerful and wealthy organization of the German Army. Both men were firmly determined to drive the development of rocketry forward toward the distant goal of interplanetary travel.

Dornberger, who was von Braun's superior from 1932 till the end of the war, tells of his good fortune in having von Braun as a co-worker, companion, and friend in his book *Peenemünde* [1]. Von Braun, in turn, held Dornberger in unlimited respect for his total commitment to the cause of rocketry, for his straightforwardness, his tremendous capacity for work, his wise counsel, and particularly for his personal courage. He often said: *"I owe Dr. Dornberger the better part of my success in life."*

Although the difference in age washed out as the years passed, von Braun retained his deep respect for the man who, always faithful to his beliefs, succeeded in piloting the A-4 project through the rough seas of Nazi-dominated, war-shattered Germany. Dornberger continued to admire von Braun for his ability to assemble and to stimulate a work force of several thousand people for a technical development of unprecedented complexity. The degree of mutual dependence, but also of mutual trust and personal attachment between the two exceeded the bounds of normal friendship. Their encounter in 1931 may be the most decisive single factor that led to the development of spaceflight in our time.

After the war, Dornberger went first to England for interrogations. Later in 1945, he went to the United States as a consultant for the Air Force, and then joined the Bell Aircraft Company in Buffalo, New York, as a vice president. He retired in 1960 and made his home in Chapala, Mexico, from where he kept lively contacts with many of his former associates, particularly with von Braun and Rees. He died during a visit to Germany in 1980.

Hermann Oberth was a dear friend of von Braun, and much more. *"I owe him the guiding star in my life,"* von Braun said. In 1930, Willy Ley, another highly respected friend of von Braun and his passionate co-believer in space travel, introduced the two to each other in Berlin. *"I am only a student and cannot offer you anything but my spare time and my enthusiasm. Isn't there something I can do to help you?"* the eighteen-year-old said. *"Come right over,"* Professor Oberth replied . . .

On Oberth's seventieth birthday in 1964, von Braun wrote: *"You were the ideal guide who helped me, as a young student of engineering, make my first contacts with the theoretical and practical problems of rocket technology, and who guided my enthusiastic dreams about the exploration of outer space into those channels which finally made the dreams come true. I am deeply aware of the decisive role that your revolutionary ideas have played in the realization of our space flight projects in the past, and will undoubtedly play in the future as we penetrate deeper and deeper into space . . ."* [9-40]. On the occasion of Oberth's seventy-fifth birthday, von Braun said: *"For all times, Hermann Oberth will be celebrated as the prophet of spaceflight . . ."* [9-41].

Oberth never spared words when he had an opportunity to praise his former protege and lifetime friend: *"He represents a new type of scientist: scholar, engineer, and manager . . . His success is based on his genius as well as on his energetic drive, but no less on his human qualities . . ."* [9-42]. There were times, though, when Oberth felt differently. Shortly after Peenemünde had been established, von Braun invited him to participate as a consultant, thus providing professional security during the wartime period. When hostilities came to an end, the United States Army offered von Braun and selected members of his team contracts to continue rocket development at Fort Bliss and White Sands. Those who were chosen to go to America represented a nucleus of a team that could facilitate technology transfer on the basis of laboratory, shop, and test stand work the men had carried out in Peenemünde before and during World War II.

Oberth was not a professional Peenemünde engineer; he was a visionary genius, a far-out planner, a prophet of the space age to come, but neither a team leader nor a team member. Not being offered a contract to work in the United States must have hurt him deeply, and he came to believe that this was caused solely by von Braun who feared that he—Oberth—would overshadow him in America. Oberth's unhappiness grew when he encountered difficulties in finding employment in Germany during the immediate postwar years, and he shared his feelings with old rocket friends Eugen Sänger and Willy Ley in letters [9-42]. Once von Braun was installed in Huntsville and again director of a large rocket development team, he invited Oberth to join him again as a consultant, and all previous bitterness was forgotten. Oberth died in 1989.

In 1939, von Braun met an enthusiastic young man at a soaring plane symposium in Darmstadt, Ernst A. Steinhoff. Von Braun invited him to attend a static rocket engine firing test in Peenemünde. Under the impact of this awesome experience, Steinhoff spontaneously implored Dornberger: *"Please, give me a job, I want to stay!"* He did stay, and he soon was the director of the department for electronics, measuring instruments, guidance, and control, charging off almost like a rocket himself. His youthful optimism occasionally even tempted him to *corriger la fortune*—to correct the course of fortune. Von Braun and Steinhoff got along splendidly, even though von Braun sometimes had to reduce Steinhoff's high-flying plans to reasonable dimensions. Their friendship had something of the luster and happy exuberance of boyhood pals.

Steinhoff persuaded many of his former colleagues at the Technical University of Darmstadt to join the Peenemünde works. His department therefore acquired the nickname *"Little Darmstadt,"* not without causing occasional chagrin to other department members who had studied at other universities and therefore did not carry the trademark *"Darmstadt"* on their lapels, a distinction that sometimes seemed to be required to make the grade in Peenemünde.

One of the early team members with whom von Braun developed a close friendship was Dr. Herbert Axster. A patent lawyer in Berlin, he served as a reservist in the Army with the rank of lieutenant colonel during the war. Dornberger appointed him chief of his military staff in Peenemünde. *"Colonel Axster,"* one of von Braun's staff members later said, *"was one of the few high-ranking military officers with whom a sensible dialogue on technical matters was possible."*

It was particularly during the later years of the war when Axster often was at the focal point of tensions between the SS and the Peenemünde group. His diplomatic skill and his courage enabled him more than once to defuse a situation that had become dangerously hot.

In Fort Bliss, Axster's experience with legal matters was invaluable during the time when the transfer of the von Braun group into the Army structure had to be organized. There was no precedent for such a transfer. At first, the Peenemünders had no legal status; Axster conducted the necessary negotiations and saw to it that each member of Project Paperclip was given at least a rudimentary contract that spelled out some basic responsibilities and rights.

Von Braun was happy to have a partner who took care of all these countless administrative and legal issues that needed almost daily attention and decisions, and he gave Axster a free hand and his fullest confidence. Axster, in turn, relished this closeness to the boss, and at the same time also to Major Hamill, the military commander. This put him into a distinctly privileged position within the group, and he began to assume more and more authority over the team. Many of the team members became concerned when they realized that von Braun was losing contact with his co-workers, and even with his commanding officer. Von Braun soon began to share this concern. After some heart-to-heart conversations with team members, he loosened his very close ties with Axster, and became again the sole and unrestricted leader of the team. Axster was asked to return to Germany in the early 1950s.

Von Braun not only enjoyed working for a strong boss; he needed one to perform at his best, and he knew it. *"I owe a special debt of gratitude to Providence,"* he sometimes said, *"for giving me a series of strong bosses. They varied considerably in their personalities, but each of them just came at a time when his particular characteristics were needed most."*

Right after the war, Colonel Toftoy assumed command and sponsorship over von Braun and his 126 Peenemünders. He became a fatherly friend to the group, and he held his protective hands over it during the early postwar years when the men from

Germany underwent their transformation from former enemies to members of the Army Ordnance missile team, and to citizens of their new country.

Von Braun always had a strong sense of loyalty toward his superiors, Dornberger in Peenemünde, Toftoy, Hamill, Medaris, Webb, Holmes, Myers, Mueller, Seamans, Paine, Low, Fletcher, and Uhl in the United States. Among those to whom he felt attached as a friend beyond his usual sense of loyalty was D. Brainerd Holmes, director of Manned Space Flight since 1961. Holmes, like von Braun, was a man of strong opinions and unwavering determination. Both of them loved sophisticated arguments, but in matching their sharp wits they became trusting friends. When, during the early years of the Saturn-Apollo project, tensions between the Houston Center and the Marshall Center began to develop over roles and missions, Holmes established the Senior Management Council in which he and the elders of both centers would *sit down and reason together*" in true Lyndon B. Johnson fashion. In the process, the two center directors, Gilruth and von Braun, became good friends.

Von Braun's relationship with most of his own team members was always a little different from that with outside colleagues who did not directly work for him. Although he obviously enjoyed being with team members at social gatherings, on weekend boating trips, and during extended travel, he would never drop the last vestige of authority during these contacts, in contrast to his associations with friends who were not members of his team. There, he was only a friend, a companion, a buddy, and nothing else; for them, he wished to be a completely detached person.

Von Braun felt very close to all his team members. And yet, it was not a relationship in the sense of simple friendship. He was always the supreme leader, a fact that he never mentioned, but everybody felt. The relationship was too formal, too respectful to be called a friendship. Von Braun did not steer the relationship knowingly into that direction; however, it was probably fortunate that this fine dividing line between von Braun and his team members, this invisible curtain of respect and dignity, remained intact throughout the years while he was the leader of the team. The existence of this imponderable barrier was one of the reasons for the unparalleled team stability which began, at least for some team members, in the early 1930s and lasted until von Braun left his team in 1970 to join NASA Headquarters in Washington.

Several years after the Peenemünders had arrived in the United States, restrictions on traveling and outside contacts were gradually lifted. Von Braun was eager to meet others who shared his glowing enthusiasm for rockets and spaceflight; he found them at a number of places, particularly in the American Rocket Society, the British Interplanetary Society, and the International Astronautical Federation. He became a regular contributor and frequent speaker for these organizations, many of whose members became his good friends. Some of these friendships remained active to the very end of his life. Frederick C. Durant III, Navy pilot during the war, engineer, author, president of the International Astronautical Federation from 1953 to 1956, and co-initiator and organizer of Project Orbiter which led to America's first satellite, Explorer 1 (Chapter 6-1), was instrumental, perhaps decisive in helping von Braun bring his early satellite ideas to life and to success. He also became one of von Braun's most faithful friends and companions for leisure hours and social gatherings. He introduced von Braun to many of the key persons in early American rocketry and space planning, and he helped him, as a newcomer, adjust to the attitudes, proprieties, and codes that should be observed in his new country. Durant deserves much personal credit for von Braun's quick and successful adjustment to the American way of life.

Carsbie C. Adams, the young hospital administrator from Atlanta, who shared von Braun's love for flying and for traveling, also belonged to the inner circle of von Braun's friends. *"Von Braun had been invited to go to Sidney in Australia to give some university lectures,"* Adams remembered in 1989 [9-43], *"and asked me to go with him . . . so I suggested [that we] just circle the globe . . . that's how it started . . . In Delhi, Wernher had a good friend, Krishan Mathur, an industrialist, who gave us a car and a driver . . . We visited three temples to Muhammed, Sikh, and Buddha . . . von Braun behaved just like the natives, sitting on the floor with his arms stretched out, and then bowed over and put his head on the floor . . . he always acted in conformity with the people around him . . .*

"We flew to Kathmandu in a DC-3 . . . It was a particularly tragic time for there were hundreds of Tibetan refugees who had crossed the mountains into Kathmandu . . . It was so tragic that Wernher and I decided that we had to do something . . . we worked through our Nepalese guide and arranged to give some cash . . . That was one side of von Braun that many people never recognized . . . He had enormous compassion for others who were in difficulties . . ."

Another inner circle friend of von Braun who shared his love for flying, traveling, and hunting was Erik Bergaust, journalist, book author, outdoorsman and aerospace enthusiast, and von Braun's big game hunting companion in Norway, Canada, and Alaska (Chapter 9-7 and 9-9). Bergaust wrote a very personal biography about von Braun [9-44].

Frederick I. Ordway III, astronautical researcher, historian, and author had been close to von Braun and his family for about twenty-five years, many of them as a professional associate of his in Huntsville. They wrote several books together [9-45]: *Careers in Astronautics and Rocketry* (1962); *History of Rocketry and Space Travel* (1966, 1969; and 1979); *The Rockets' Red Glare* (1976); and *New Worlds: Discoveries from Our Solar System* (1979). The last book was published after von Braun's death.

Ordway's contacts with von Braun originated in the American Rocket Society (ARS). *"Having been a member of the ARS continuously since January 1941 when I was thirteen years old,"* Ordway remembers, *"I learned about him as soon as his name began to appear in the ARS journals."* This would have been around 1947. In 1952, the Hayden Planetarium staged the Second Symposium on Space Travel. On that occasion, Ordway met von Braun for the first time; while there, he also met Milton Rosen, Willy Ley, Fritz Haber, Fred Whipple, George O. Smith, and other pioneers of rocketry.

Presentations that von Braun prepared for the International Astronautical Congresses in Paris (1950), London (1951), Stuttgart (1952), Zurich (1953), and Innsbruck (1954) were published in the *Astronautica Acta*. The United States was represented by von Braun on the editorial board of this journal, and by Ordway on its advisory board. This work provided a continuous linkage between von Braun and Ordway, and an opportunity for frequent meetings. At the Innsbruck congress in 1954, Ordway met Stuhlinger for the first time and heard him present a paper on *"Possibilities of Electric Space Ship Propulsion."*

"During an evening in October 1956," Ordway recalls, *"von Braun briefed me on the Jupiter program, on a troop-carrying rocket concept in which General Medaris was deeply interested, and on the satellite project for the International Geophysical Year for which the Navy and Army were in competition."*

Ordway was a member of the von Braun team from 1959 through 1964 following several years of close association in a consulting contractor capacity. Later, he joined the faculty of the University of Alabama in Huntsville, and then the Department of Energy in Washington. He maintained close personal and professional ties with von Braun until the end of his life.

One of von Braun's first new friends he met in England after the war was Arthur C.

Clarke, the great novelist and prophet of spaceflight, who found in von Braun a true comrade when it came to visionary dreaming. Their mutual enthusiasm for exploration included the world of the oceans. *"One day,"* Clarke remembered in 1988 [9-46], *"at Fred Durant's house, just before going to the Great Barrier Reef [near Australia], I brainwashed him to take up scuba diving,"* a sport for which von Braun quickly became a true afficionado. When Clarke wrote a book on *Challenge of the Sea*, von Braun wrote the introduction.

Von Braun's friendship with astronomer Fred Whipple dates back to the time when the *Collier's* articles on space exploration were written, around 1952. Von Braun's and Whipple's common ground was not only the love for astronomy, but also the fervent belief that satellites should be built, and that many astronomical observations can be made from space far better than from the Earth's surface. *"We became good friends,"* Whipple recalled in 1986 [9-47]; and yet, there was always a trace of a thin sheet of cellophane that separated von Braun from all the scientists with whom he came in contact, including Whipple, although Whipple certainly approached the status of close friend of von Braun more than any other scientist.

As the space program picked up momentum after Sputnik, more and more congressional committees visited the Marshall Center. Von Braun enjoyed these visits; they allowed him to talk about his projects with people of considerable influence. Several lasting friendships resulted from these briefings. Don Fuqua, one of Florida's congressional representatives, must have truly appreciated and enjoyed those exchanges with the space people. *"It was a very fascinating thing,"* he remembered in 1988 [9-34], *"I became a very good friend of Wernher."* That feeling was certainly mutual; von Braun always spoke of Congressman Fuqua with great respect and affection.

Among von Braun's friends in whose company he always felt completely at ease was Dr. James R. Maxfield, Jr., oncology specialist and director of the Maxfield Clinic in Dallas, Texas. Maxfield was a true Texan, full of impressive vitality and exuberant joy of life. Von Braun enjoyed flying and hunting trips with him, and he also received medical checkups for his pilot's license at the Maxfield Clinic. It was during a physical examination at the clinic in 1972 when the first indications of a developing kidney tumor were found (Chapter 13).

One of the closest personal friendships von Braun ever had began in 1945 during the V-2 test launchings at White Sands. A young engineer in the Ordnance Special Projects Section, Edward G. Uhl, met von Braun while he helped build a rocket engine test stand for the Army (Chapter 9-3). The two men must have developed instantly a genuine liking for each other. They stayed in contact, and their professional paths crossed again when the Martin Company in Orlando, Florida, which Uhl had joined, built the Pershing missile that had been developed under the auspices of von Braun's group at Redstone Arsenal.

Later, Uhl moved to Fairchild Industries where the Pegasus micrometeoroid satellite, initiated and developed at von Braun's Marshall Center, was built. Around that time, Uhl told von Braun to think of Fairchild if he ever plans to leave NASA. In 1972, von Braun joined Fairchild Industries as vice president for engineering; his main assignment was *"to put into place at Fairchild a strategic planning activity"* (Chapter 12-1). On several occasions, Uhl and von Braun enjoyed hunting trips together. Also, they traveled together extensively in connection with Fairchild's efforts to introduce communication satellites in India, in the Near East, in South America, and in Alaska.

When von Braun's illness began to cast its shadow over his life, Uhl did everything in his power to ease his plight. He visited him at home and in the hospital in Alexandria.

"Whenever I went to see him, I felt I would be there for perhaps fifteen minutes, but when I got ready to leave, he said: 'No, please stay. I want to talk to you.'" Next to his own family, Ed Uhl was probably von Braun's closest friend during his later years.

8   SPACEMEN IN ANTARCTICA

Members of von Braun's Space Sciences Laboratory, in their effort to support the Saturn-Apollo project with knowledge and experience available from Earth-bound exploration projects of a similar nature, established contact with the National Science Foundation's [NSF] Antarctic Research Program around 1964. A lively exchange of data about exploration programs ensued; factual data were presented by the Antarctic explorers, and planning data were offered by the space people. Along with the discussions, a feeling of friendship quickly developed between the polar explorers and some of von Braun's associates.

One day, Philip M. Smith, director of field planning in the Office of Antarctic Programs in the NSF, asked Stuhlinger: *"Why don't you guys come and see us down yonder; you could learn far more rapidly what it means to pursue a research project in a beautiful but thoroughly hostile environment!"* That was a once-in-a-lifetime opportunity that just could not be declined. At Christmastime in 1966, four happy spacemen turned their sights fully to this Earth and traveled south: Gilruth and Faget from the Manned Spacecraft Center in Houston, and von Braun and Stuhlinger from the Marshall Center in Huntsville.

In Christchurch, New Zealand, the staging area for the U.S. Antarctic program, they met Smith and other members of the program, and received a set of warm clothing and other equipment for the Antarctic adventure. The next morning, the four travelers, and a number of other people connected with the Antarctic program, boarded a Lockheed Constellation and flew straight south. They were all huddled together in the huge hold of the airplane between crates, tarpaulins, and bundles destined for Antarctica. Soon after the southern tip of New Zealand had disappeared from sight, von Braun vanished. A little later, the copilot came back from the cockpit, sat down between the others, leaned back, closed his eyes, and mused: *"This will be a very restful flight for me. Your friend sits in the righthand seat. In fact, the pilot will also get some relief. Your friend flies the airplane. He even flies her well, I must say!"* Nine hours later, when the McMurdo Sound on the Antarctic continent came in sight, von Braun appeared again, smiling happily, and the copilot woke up and left. *"I always wanted to fly a Constellation,"* von Braun said, *"it's a lot of fun!"*

The space people spent a fabulous week on the Antarctic continent, which was filled with unforgettable impressions and adventures. Von Braun was as happy and excited as a young boy. He wanted to see and to know every detail of the land, of the research projects, of the countless support functions, of the daily problems. His questions would never end. When they flew to other stations in one of the huge LC-130 turboprop transport planes, or in a sleek helicopter, von Braun would invariably change places with the copilot. Wherever they went, he would overwhelm the scientists, the technicians, the engineers, the pilots, the support people, the administrative officers with his insatiable thirst for knowledge.

After their return, von Braun wrote a report about his impressions [9-48]. For him, and also for his three colleagues, the primary purpose of their trip to Antarctica was to find out how their Antarctic colleagues managed to plan, organize, prepare, and execute a great project of research and exploration far away from any home base, and under unusual environmental conditions. Although vastly different in cost, complexity, and total effort, the missions to Antarctica and to the Moon have a number of problems in common. Experiences gathered by the Antarctic mission planners and explorers would be of substantial value to those who had to prepare the first expedition to the Moon.

In 1966, when the spacemen made their landfall on the Antarctic continent, exploration had already been going on there for more than fifty years. Changes in methods of exploration could be seen everywhere, mostly based on progress in technologies. For example, as von Braun wrote, *"the oldest stations on Antarctica were nailed together on the site. The most modern ones we saw were completely prefabricated and pre-equipped in the United States before they were flown directly to their present locations. Electrical gear and plumbing in these prefabricated huts was installed and checked out, and even the pinup girls seemed to have been pasted to the living room walls before air shipment . . . Space people should learn from this: Prepare your station equipment with all details as completely as you can in the convenience of a well-equipped manufacturing plant on Earth before you ship it out into the cold! This should be a golden rule also for those who have to make plans for a station in a satellite orbit . . ."*

For the four space people from up north, this week in Antarctica was a time of most intense learning, but also a time filled with fun, and with fascinating human experiences. There are no political boundaries on the Antarctic continent; the spacemen met scientists from a dozen countries, including the Soviet Union, and all were like members of one big family. Without exception, the scientists were strongly motivated to pursue their work, and to accept happily all the hardships of life in Antarctica. Enlisted men in the Navy, assigned to Antarctica to carry out the numerous support functions, were not always blessed with the same high degree of motivation.

One day, von Braun and Stuhlinger took a stroll through *"downtown McMurdo,"* a stretch of sand and pebbles lined with barracks that house McMurdo's population of about 1,000 in summer, and 200 in winter. They entered a mess hall where the Navy men spent their free hours, and sat down at a table with two sailors, a young one and an older one. Both of them held their heads low; obviously, they were in sad states of mind. *"What's the matter with you guys? Is it not great to be in Antarctica?"* von Braun asked. *"You see,"* the young sailor said, *"I got married last fall, and a week later they shipped me down to this godforsaken place. I wish I were up north with my young wife."*— *"That's sad indeed,"* von Braun replied. *"I can fully understand why you should be so miserable. But what's the matter with you?"* he asked the older one. *"You see,"* he said, *"I'm a married man. I have been here for a year. Now they want to ship me back home. I don't want to go, I want to stay here. At home, I have to live with my wife. I don't want to go up north. It's so wonderfully quiet down here."* Von Braun, always trying to find a pragmatic solution to a problem, suggested: *"Couldn't the two of you just switch places, you go home, and you stay here?"*—They looked at him with startled expressions, half in bewilderment, half in pity. *"Sir,"* the older man said, *"has any one of you two guys ever been in the Navy?"*

When the spacemen visited Pole Station at the geographic South Pole, dug out as a maze of rooms and tunnels several meters under the ice, one of the *"natives"* at the station said jokingly: *"If you want to be real Pole travelers, you have to run around the polar flag pole in bathing trunks at midnight tonight!"*—He may not have been serious about it, but von Braun was. At a quarter to twelve that night—the Sun was still up, of course, as it is supposed to be at the South Pole in January—von Braun became restive. *"Midnight is approaching,"* he said. *"Let's put on our bathing trunks and run around the flag pole!"* So they first took a very hot shower that supplied them with some extra heat energy; then they put on their shoes, and since they had left their swim suits at home, they wrapped towels around their midriffs, and then they ran out into the snow at an air temperature of about −28 degrees C (−18 degrees F). They threw snowballs at each other, rolled in the snow, had their pictures taken, and felt great. After about fifteen minutes, the cold began to creep up on them. They ran back to the steam bath, and soon afterwards enjoyed again the full thermal protection of the Pole Station which is comfortably heated by oil burners. One of the *"natives"* noticed that only two of the four space people from up north had gone through the polar snow bath adventure, von Braun and Stuhlinger. *"Huntsville did it again!"* he exclaimed.

The Pole travelers tried every one of a dozen different means of transportation, from huge airplanes through helicopters, tracked vehicles, sno-cats, powerwagons, motor toboggans, gnats, to old-fashioned dog sleds. They traveled to a radio experiment laboratory with a 34 kilometers (21 miles) long dipole antenna laid out on the snow, and to the 18 kilometers (11 miles) distant Byrd Station. Riding on a powerful Thiokol Trackmaster, each of the four was invited to take the driver's seat for a few kilometers. That was great fun; the best driver, unquestionably, was Bob Gilruth, he charged off like a seasoned polar explorer! They learned that in extremely rough terrain, man on his feet is still by far the best and most reliable mode of locomotion, at least over short distances.

Riding on a dog sled at Scott Base, the New Zealand Station on Ross Island, was a delightful experience. The strength, manageability, and mobility of the dogs is unbelievable. They are very friendly and gentle toward humans, but rough among themselves. The dog team leader stands on the runners at the rear end of the sled, guiding the dogs by shouting the original Eskimo commands. Each sled can accommodate two passengers, so there were two sleds, a *"Houston"* sled and a *"Huntsville"* sled. As they dashed over the limitless snow fields of Ross Island, von Braun, of course, sat in the front seat of the Huntsville sled. After a short while, he asked the team leader to stop, got off his seat, and suggested that Stuhlinger should now sit in front. The journey was most enjoyable, but Stuhlinger soon realized why von Braun had been so magnanimous: the dogs have the (very practical) habit of relieving themselves while they are running at full speed. Their bushy, overactive tails generate a fine mist which is acutely felt by the man in the front seat, while the person behind him has the benefit of an efficient spray shield.

A deeply moving experience was the visit to Cape Evans on Ross Island where Captain Robert Scott erected a supply and shelter hut in 1909. This hut is well preserved. Ice masses that had accumulated inside the wooden building were removed in the early 1960s by a volunteer party of New Zealanders in an effort to restore the cabin to its original state of 1911 when Scott left it for his ill-fated journey to the Pole. Many of the stores of food, material, tools, newspapers, books, clothing, and equipment for chemical and geophysical laboratory work are still in fairly good condition. It was a touching thought of being so close to the lives and work, and to the hopes and sufferings of those heroic men. Equally impressive was the fact that this hut, as a historic shrine of immeasurable value, was then open to Antarctic visitors, without a fence or guard, and even without *"Don't . . ."* signs, and did not show any marks of souvenir hunters and name carvers—certainly a convincing testimony to the wonderful spirit that permeated the entire Antarctic continent.

9   *"WHAT I BELIEVE"*

Among the many projects that von Braun led to success, the most demanding and impressive was the Saturn V rocket that launched astronauts on their way to the Moon. It made a dream come true that had been alive in his mind ever since he wrote, as a young boy: *"There is no doubt that one day, man will be able to travel to the Moon, and to walk on its surface . . ."*

The Moon project had taken shape under the hands and brains of many thousands of craftsmen, engineers, scientists, technicians, organizers, and managers, each of whom had his part not only in the accomplishment, but also in the worries, and in the responsibility for the ultimate success. And yet, it was von Braun who, in the morning hours of that fateful 16 July 1969, had to give the final answer to the question: *"Are we ready to launch?"*

Implicitly, that simple question stood for innumerable other questions. Did nobody make a mistake in all these countless calculations? Will all these myriads of electric and mechanical gadgets work properly? Is there no leakage in this jungle of pipes and valves? Are all computers programmed correctly? Will all these powerful hydraulic systems function as they should? Has no error been made in the timing of those hundreds of events which all depend mutually upon each other? Have all possible contingencies been taken into consideration? What has to be done first if something goes wrong? Do we have maximum safety for the astronauts in case of a system failure?

Although von Braun would never have accepted the notion that the Saturn-Apollo project was *"his"* project, he knew that he would be the first to be criticized in case disaster struck. After a successful flight, there would be many to share the praise. After a failure, the word would be: *"Wernher, it was your foolish idea to begin with!"* He also knew that the entire development of spaceflight, in which he believed so fervently, would suffer a severe setback in case of a tragedy in space. This knowledge must have weighed heavily on his mind in the moment when he had to give the final go-ahead signal for the Saturn launch. Surely, the responsibility was shared by several of von Braun's colleagues and friends, particularly by Gilruth whose Manned Spacecraft Center was responsible for the lunar transfer and return stages, the lunar landing and take-off system, the landing capsule, and the accommodations for the astronauts. When the moment of launch approached and the final question of launch readiness was asked, both men answered with an unqualified *"yes."*

A week later, when the astronauts were safely back on Earth, a reporter wanted to know: *"Dr. von Braun, what did you think after you had given your final 'yes' a week ago?"*—*"I quietly said the Lord's prayer,"* was his answer.

He could have done many other things, for example, anxiously wait for the first confirmation from the astronauts that everything aboard was all right; or, think of all the thousands of parts and instruments—many of them furnished by the lowest bidder!—that had to work properly; or, pin his eyes on the countless meters in the control room that indicated the status of the flight systems; or, implore the Lord that he may let this one succeed . . . however, his prayer was simply: *"Thy will be done."*

It would have been true to his nature if he had added: *"You gave me this love for exploration and adventure and spaceflight, and also this gift to transform the dreams into reality. I have lived and worked as one little part of Your boundless creation. If we succeed with this journey to the Moon, it will be to Your glory. If we don't, it is Your will. As far as I am concerned, I have used all the talents You have put into me, and I have done my very best . . ."*

Whether these thoughts actually came to his mind at that moment, nobody will ever know.

Those who had known von Braun before the late 1950s may have been surprised by his answer. Throughout his younger years, von Braun did not show signs of religious devotion, or even an interest in things related to the church or to biblical teachings. In fact, he was known to his friends as a *"merry heathen" (fröhlicher Heide)*. Those who knew him through the 1960s and 1970s noticed during these years that a new element began to surface in his conversations, and also in his speeches and his writings: a growing interest in religious thought.

It is possible that the seeds for this interest had existed in von Braun's mind subconsciously. After all, he had been brought up in a tradition-rich aristocratic family whose line of ancestry can be traced back to the year 1285, and whose members included prominent officials of the church. Young Wernher received a very careful education not only in the usual scholastic subjects, but also in art, music, classical literature, and religion. Very likely, what von Braun sought in his later years was not a consolation of the soul, or a moral strengthening, or a road to salvation, or a relief from the feeling of guilt—it was the quest for a synthesis of these seemingly divergent forces that rule the course of the world: The need for material subsistence, the drive for power, the urge for knowledge, the technical evolution, the struggles in the name of religious faith. He had delved deeper into the world of engineering and science, and he had become more familiar with economical problems, diplomatic activities, educational systems, even military planning, than most other people; now he wished to round off his view of the world by integrating also the basic elements of religious thought into this far-reaching concept of our earthly existence.

An avid reader since his boyhood, von Braun not only devoured the books written by Jules Verne and Hermann Oberth, but also those by Johann Wolfgang von Goethe, Friedrich von Schiller, and Immanuel Kant. It was particularly the latter who played a decisive role in the development of von Braun's religious thinking. Here he found the bridge between the visible world around us, which never ceased to impress him most profoundly, and some invisible world from which, as he was convinced, must come the master plan for this marvelous system of natural laws and orderly evolution.

From the mid-1960s on, von Braun occasionally talked about his religious thoughts. He sometimes shared his views on religion with his traveling companions. *"How do you feel about this, does it make sense to you?"* he might ask. However, he would not wait for a response; in true von Braun fashion, he would give the answer himself, always well-formulated and exhaustive. He had come to the conclusion that the world of technology—which for him began with toy rockets and eventually embraced manned voyages to the Moon and the planets—and the world of science—which gave us these fantastic insights into the atoms and the stars, and even into the mysteries of live organisms—must somehow fit into the design of a greater system in which our human destiny, too, finds its place and its meaning.

"Dr. von Braun, do you believe in God?" As von Braun's publicity grew, there were more and more occasions when he was asked this age-old question. His answer was always prompt and to the point: *"Yes, absolutely!"* And then, he would begin to talk in his characteristic von Braun style, with perfect grammar and syntax, letting his carefully chosen words flow like a sparkling mountain stream, while he described his religious convictions with an almost disarming simplicity.

He was neither embarrassed nor annoyed by this question. He even seemed grateful for the opportunity to formulate and describe the elements of his religious belief. In essence, he said what Goethe had his Faust say to Gretchen: *"Who may say, I believe in him, or I do not believe in him? Does he not embrace and sustain you, me, himself?"*

"It seems to me that your question is irrelevant," von Braun would say. *"It is so obvious that we live in a world in which a fantastic amount of logic, of rational lawfulness, is at work. We are aware of a large number of laws of physics and chemistry and biology which, by their mutual interdependence, make nature work as if it were following a grandiose plan from its earliest beginnings to the farthest reaches of its future destiny. To me, it would be incomprehensible that there should be such a gigantic master plan without a master planner behind it. This master planner is He whom we call the Creator of the Universe . . . One cannot be exposed to the law and order of the universe without concluding that there must be a Divine intent behind it all."*

"For me," he would continue, *"there is no real contradiction between the world of science and the world of religion. The two are dealing with two different things, but they are not in conflict with each other. Theologians are trying to describe the Creator; scientists are trying to describe His creation. Science and religion are not antagonists; on the contrary, they are sisters . . . While, through science, man tries to harness the forces of nature around him, through religion he tries to harness the forces of nature within him . . ."* [9-49].

Sir Bernard Lovell, in his book *Astronomer by Chance* [9-50], argues that *"science and theology must not be viewed as mutually exclusive forms of human behavior. Rather, they should be harmonized to provide a self-consistent view of reality . . . Science lacks an ethical basis and fails to speak to much we humans experience . . ."*

Von Braun expressed the same basic thought a little differently: *"Science itself has no moral dimension; it is neither good nor evil. We must apply our own moral yardstick to judge its ethical value."*

"Man has this fabulous ability to learn, to understand, to correlate, and to create," von Braun wrote. *"He has the capability to make nature his servant. His freedom in making decisions is almost fearsome . . . Science has taught us one most important lesson about God that we should never forget: We have learned that God does not interfere in the free order of life and nature which He created. If we do not accept this, we must abandon the entire concept of freedom . . ."*

Erik Bergaust, science writer, author, and outdoors man par excellence, met von Braun in 1950 and quickly became a close friend. He remembers a campfire evening in the Virginia mountains during a fishing trip with von Braun in the summer of 1970 [2-37]. *"The last fishing story of the evening had been told,"* he wrote; *"the men were sitting around the flaming logs, each submerged in his own deep thoughts under an endless sky with myriads of stars. Finally, I broke the silence. 'Wernher, what do you think of the hereafter?' I asked. 'I believe in an immortal soul that can cherish the rewards or suffer the penalty decreed in the Last Judgment,' von Braun replied."*

An enchanted summer night on the banks of a rushing creek in the Shenandoah valley makes a beautiful setting for a talk about those questions which are so incessantly alive in every searching mind, and yet so inaccessible to any simplistic approach by rational thought alone. Von Braun, in his quest to see the world as one harmonious structure, must have spent many hours to find a synthesis between the sober, logical, cause-and-effect world of the natural sciences and that other world that begins in the innermost regions of the human mind and stretches out into the depth of space and time, and which will forever remain unfathomable for an earthling with his limited perception and understanding.

With this simple question, Bergaust had hit upon a well that gushed forth for hours during that night at the campfire.

"Our life does not have materialistic and intellectual aspects alone," von Braun said. *"This is as true today as it was centuries ago. We cannot live without ethical laws and some belief in a Last Judgment, where every one of us has to account for what he did with God's precious gift of life on Earth . . . More than ever, mankind's survival depends on adherence to some basic ethical principles. Our adherence to such principles alone will decide whether our new inventions in the field of atomic energy will provide mankind with an inexhaustible supply of energy and wealth, or whether mankind will perish by its abuse . . ."*

"Our present, sometimes seemingly hopeless political impasse, which is caused by warmongers and terrorists, shows us with a frightening clarity that all of man's scientific and engineering efforts are in vain unless they are performed and utilized within the framework of ethical standards commensurate with the power of the new tools provided by the technological revolution. The farther technology advances, the more fateful will be its impact on humanity. But if the world's ethical standards and moral laws fail to rise and to be adhered to with the advances of our technological revolution, we run the distinct risk that we shall all perish."

President George Bush, in his inaugural address on 20 January 1989, expressed the same thought in more concise form: *"America is never herself unless she is engaged in high moral principle."*

"Our knowledge and use of the laws of nature," von Braun continued, *"that enable us to fly to the Moon also enable us to destroy our home planet with the atom bomb. Science itself does not address the question whether we should use the power at our disposal for good or for evil. The guidelines of what we ought to do are furnished in the moral law of God. It is no longer enough that we pray that God may be with us on our side; we must learn again to pray that we may be on God's side,"* von Braun added, paraphrasing Abraham Lincoln's words, spoken more than a hundred years ago: *"I am not concerned that the Lord be on my side. I am concerned that I be on the Lord's side!"*

"It was late that night," Bergaust recalled, *"when we finally crept into our tent and sleeping bags, falling asleep with the calls of whippoorwills and owls in our ears."*

It had been a long talk, but it came from an abundance of thoughts that had accumulated in von Braun's mind over the previous ten or twenty years. Some of them had been expressed in speeches or writings [9-49]. In the summer of 1976, von Braun was invited by the Lutheran Church of America to give a presentation at a national church convention in Philadelphia on the subject of *"Responsible Scientific Investigation and Application."* He was happy to accept the invitation, and he wrote an essay consisting of five chapters [9-51]. The last chapter dealt with the subject *"Science and Religion."* When the symposium took place later that year, von Braun was already too ill to travel to Philadelphia and present his paper in person; it was read by the chairman of the session.

Walter A. McDougall, in an essay for the *American Review* in 1982 [9-52], wrote: *"The fallacy of the early space age was that the pursuit of power, especially through science and technology, could absolve modern man from his duty to examine, affirm, or alter his own values and behavior in the first place. The politicians climbed aboard. It was left to Wernher von Braun to admonish 'that man raise his ethical standards or perish'."*

Around 1975, when von Braun's advancing illness had begun to throw its shadow on his life, his mind turned more and more toward religious thoughts. His desire to see the world of science and technology in full harmony with the world of religion, particularly as it is manifested in Christian faith, grew even stronger. But he did not wish to argue about matters of personal creed. *"Finite man cannot begin to comprehend an omnipresent, omniscient, omnipotent, and infinite God . . . I find it best to accept God through faith, as an intelligent will, perfect in goodness and wisdom, revealing Himself through His creation . . ."*

It was surprising to some of von Braun's associates that in spiritual matters, he would reach so deeply into the realm of the irrational.

His entire work for space was solidly based on the exact laws of natural sciences. In his life as a human among humans, he advocated and tried to follow the rational, fundamental, time-honored rules of high morality and ethics. In his religious beliefs, it was different. He liked to talk about his beliefs, but although he would sometimes insert a brief *"don't you think so?"* or *"wouldn't you agree?"* He did not enter into discussions of the points he made. Obviously, he was not much interested in what others believed. *"Matters of faith are not really accessible to our rational thinking,"* he would say. *"I find it best not to ask any questions, but simply to believe . . ."*

This approach would not have been shared by all of von Braun's friends and admirers. However, it was typical of von Braun. He was so intent on understanding as much as possible of our physical and biological world, and he was proud of having contributed to this understanding through his life's work, but he did not wish to apply his capacity for creative thought to an area where he could not expect tangible results. So, he said: *"It is best not to think, but just to believe . . ."*

"The universe as revealed through scientific inquiry," he would add, *"is the living witness that God has indeed been at work."* He often quoted the immortal words spoken by Frank Borman who was asked, after his Christmas 1968 flight around the Moon with Apollo 8, whether he had seen God on his flight so far away from Earth. *"No,"* Borman said, *"I didn't see him, but I saw his evidence."*

10   A HUMAN PERSPECTIVE

Any attempt to see only one type of genius in von Braun would be futile. His personality had many facets, and each of them was deep-rooted and powerful. Many of those who met him only under one set of circumstances were inclined to see him primarily in the one field in which they just saw him: a presentation about high-precision rockets; or a speech describing a manned expedition to Mars; or a talk in which he pleaded for a better education in mathematics, physics, and English; or a top-secret report in the Pentagon about the military potential of long-range guided missiles. Had those observers been present when he landed his sailplane after a high-altitude flight above the Adirondack Mountains in New York, they would have taken him as an experienced gliderplane instructor, and a similar reaction would have occurred had they seen him in the Bahamas, returning in his diving gear from the magic world of an underwater coral reef.

Von Braun loved to talk and to share his experiences with others, and he relished being in a crowd that listened to him. His words always flowed easily, spiced with seldom-used, but colorful idioms, and in flawless diction. At such times it would have been unwise to interrupt him, or, even worse, to contradict him; von Braun would have responded with cynicism and ridicule. He did enjoy an occasional quip from a listener, provided that it came in a short, witty remark. He would respond with a burst of roaring laughter that quickly put him back into the center of action.

Successful projects always gave von Braun an opportunity to be magnanimous. At the end of a project, he praised all who had contributed to its success. He did this not only to stimulate continuing dedication and hard work in his co-workers; it was his keen desire to recognize devotion to the joint work, particularly when the effort was crowned by a brilliant success. His words of appreciation always were sincere, and they never failed to create happy feelings in those to whom they were addressed.

Sometimes, though, he went a little too far in his desire to be nice. One day, a young member of his team had *"invented"* a brand new machine that could produce electric power in space with an unbelievably high efficiency. He showed his plans to an older colleague who, being familiar with the laws of physics, advised him that his brainchild would be in conflict with Carnot's law of thermodynamics and therefore would not work at this high efficiency. *"You are just clinging to these old-fashioned formulae,"* the young genius said, *"we have much better techniques today. In fact, I have not used a formula at all, I did it on the computer. This gave me much better results, so I ignored the formula."* Undaunted, he went to the boss and complained that his research was being stifled by one of those antiquated senior scientists. Von Braun called his senior scientist in and said, without even looking at the details of the invention: *"Why don't you let this young chap have a little fun with his own research? You have so many honors and achievements to your credit; let him also enjoy some playing around with science and research! This will not do any harm to our real projects, and he will find out in his own good time that his ideas will not work!"*

With his proverbial ability to assess a situation with sober realism, von Braun knew very well that with this ruling he would assure the lasting good will of this young man and all his friends. The senior scientist, on the other hand, would swallow hard once or twice, but he would not waver a bit in his life-long loyalty to von Braun and all his *"real"* projects.

During the brief span from 1961 to 1969 von Braun not only accomplished almost all the technical tasks assigned to him within the preset limits of time and money; he also was at ease, unperturbed by a thousand competing pressures. He launched the first American astronaut into space, built the rocket for the Moon landing, started Skylab, gave many public speeches, wrote for journals, and traveled all over the Earth. He pursued his hobbies of flying, scuba diving, sailing, and hunting—in short, he enjoyed his life; he was happily on top of it!

"Wernher, how can you achieve all that, with only twenty-four hours a day at your disposal?" he was frequently asked.— *"For one thing,"* he used to answer, *"I do not waste time by grieving over things that I cannot change. When I see something I don't agree with, I try to do something about it. If there is no way, I don't spill my energy on futile attempts. I rather turn to something I can change!"*

There was another element in von Braun's makeup that helped him decisively in his achievements; that was his fabulous gift of persuasion. How much time do others have to spend, and to lose, on attempts to convince their opponents of their ideas? Von Braun worked like a magician. With his outstanding skill at articulating his thoughts, his firm, but beautifully modulated voice, his capability to make the other person feel that at this moment, he, or she, is the center of the universe to von Braun, and, of course, with his flawless logic, he convinced almost everybody in a very short time. If there was a partner with unusually strong views, von Braun would simply say, with his most charming smile: *"Be reasonable, see it my way!"* or: *"Don't be such a puritan; life becomes so much brighter when you allow yourself a little trespass once in a while!"* That did it in most cases.

This power of convincing was of use only when there was a well-defined objective to be promoted, and here lies another reason for von Braun's successes. For each idea, each proposal, each project he had done his homework. He had thought it through as far as possible; he knew the pros and cons, the questions to be answered, the pitfalls and dangers to be avoided. His mind was extremely efficient, and it must have been at work continuously at least during his waking hours.

Most decisive among the factors that made von Braun so outstanding as a leader in the world of technical projects, in the opinion of his co-workers, was his ability to see from the very beginning the essence of a project as a complete entity, as bold and novel as it was admissible under the limitations of the laws of physics and of technological feasibility, and yet realistic enough so that it could be accomplished within the unavoidable restrictions of time and money. Von Braun would have the basic concept of a new project ready when he discussed it for the first time with his technical staff, and he could describe it with all the technical and political reasoning needed to convince his co-workers. Where he found the time to do all the mental work needed to develop the concept—nobody knew. It came right out of his ingenious mind, nourished by a unique gift for technical vision, and by a lifelong self-imposed training in critical, productive, logical, no-nonsense thinking. This ability of von Braun, to do the analysis and the synthesis of a project during his leisure hours and to have the result ready for the first discussion of the project, stands in stark contrast to the way in which projects in other technical programs are usually begun. First, a lengthy period of costly contractor studies is initiated, resulting in a huge pile of papers that must be read, studied, understood, compared, and discussed by a host of experts and committees in endless meetings. At best, a compromise solution would gradually evolve, without spirit and guts, and without a sign of leadership.

Did von Braun gradually mature as a personality during his career?

Maturing, developing a distinct personality, getting wiser and more stable are common in many people whose lives are distinguished by unusual accomplishments. Von Braun did not follow this standard pattern. The basic characteristics of his personality were firmly established when the Peenemünde project began, probably even much earlier. They remained unchanged until his life came to its end.

Von Braun's way of conducting his rocket projects, too, followed an unchanging pattern ever since his early days in Kummersdorf. He always started with a penetrating analysis of all the technical intricacies, followed by a synthesis of the project. Although tasks and responsibilities were widely delegated, he continued to stay in close contact with the many facets of the project. The results of all the countless individual efforts finally converged in his hands and mind. In this pattern of leadership, von Braun did not change; he just remained true to himself.

The enduring nature of his unique talents was evident even in such mundane things as keeping his diary; he used the same format for his daily entries, the same markers for appointments, reminders, impressions, and decisions over a period of more than forty years.

Another conspicuous trait in von Braun's nature that did not change over the years was his firm belief in the basic goodness and honesty of people, and also in their intent to do something, to be creative in some way. *"All I am doing,"* he sometimes said, *"is lead others toward a goal they wanted to achieve anyway."*

The only area in which von Braun's long-time companions could observe a change was his religious belief, described earlier. Von Braun also adhered to some foibles as long as his oldest co-workers could remember. When two men, or a lady and a man, talked together and von Braun joined them, he immediately monopolized the discussion, without a word of excuse. When he held one opinion about a project today and found cogent reasons, in the interest of the project, to change it by tomorrow, he did so without remembering his previous opinion, and he considered everyone in error who held on to the old views. While his patience in all technical and managerial discussions was superhuman, he was quite impatient with discussions whose topics did not interest him. He would quickly take over and change the subject.

Von Braun had a strange predilection for pills. When he traveled, he always had a collection in his pocket. If he had to visit a military installation, he rarely missed the opportunity to make a quick call at the infirmary and ask for some pills that might help to subdue an upset stomach, a sore throat, a little sinus trouble, or some slight pain in the chest. When he took a trip to the South Pole in 1966, he asked the Navy doctor at the staging area in Christchurch, New Zealand, about some pills that his doctor at home had given him against common cold. *"Those pills are completely harmless,"* the Navy doctor said. *"In fact, they are almost a placebo. They would not make any difference if taken against a common cold. Besides, there is no common cold in Antarctica; there are no germs."*—*"I see,"* von Braun said, *"but would you think that they could do any harm?"*—*"Not at all, by no means."*—*"O.k.,"* replied von Braun with a happy smile, *"then I will take them,"* and he took one tablet every four hours, exactly as the label said.

All of those who met von Braun in private life would agree that he was thoroughly happy with his family. Being at home with Maria and the children, or going horseback riding, or boating on the Tennessee River, or enjoying a barbecue outing in the woods—it was always an experience that lifted his spirits. He loved to tell others about his daughters and his son; he carefully followed their development at school, and he complemented their education with innumerable talks about science, history, sports, books, and also about proper behavior. He was unhappy when they watched too much TV, and he was happy when they showed interest in science, technology, or history. Von Braun had the rare gift of clearly separating the various compartments of his action-filled daily schedules. When he was with the family, rocket projects, budget meetings, interservice problems, and launch schedules were moved out of sight. At least for an hour or two, he was only husband and father. *"Enjoy what you are doing,"* he often said. He wanted to be happy; in fact, he was most intent on being happy, and he found many ways to be so.

It must be emphasized, though, that Maria contributed decisively to this harmonious, active, and happy family life, not only by her natural gracefulness and affection, but also by an unusual—and wise—degree of generosity. *"Darling,"* Wernher might say, *"some of the fellows at our contractor's meeting today asked me to join them for a scuba diving trip to the Keys during the next weekend. I am sure that you agree that I should accept this invitation. Don't you feel that I should go? We will leave Saturday morning, and we will be back on Sunday. Can you do without me for this short period? I'm certain that you can, and that you will fully agree with me!"*—And Maria would answer: *"Yes, Wernher, of course. If you'd like to go, you should go, certainly."* Wernher would go and have a great time. Maria would stay home as a member of the *"solemn order of space widows,"* a collective term used among the families of the von Braun team members who had to spend many a weekend away from their loved ones, and not only on diving trips to Florida!

Von Braun was a hearty eater. He deeply enjoyed a good meal, particularly the vegetable course. When the vegetable dish at the dinner table reached him, he usually kept it there for a series of refills. His colleagues always considered it a pleasure and an honor to have Maria and Wernher as dinner guests at their homes. One of the housewives once revealed a little trick. *"When Dr. von Braun comes to dinner,"* she said, *"I always have two dishes with vegetable, one to make the rounds, and one to sit in front of Wernher!"*

At another occasion, a delicious casserole of beans was served with the dinner. Von

Braun helped himself generously, while giving an animated description of a recent sailboat trip. When a little pause developed before dessert was served, he turned to Maria: *"You know what I thought today when I came home from work? I was hungry, and I remembered the marvelous bean casseroles you have in your repertoire. I ate my last bean dish at least three months ago. Wouldn't you like to cook a dish of beans for us pretty soon?"* — *"But Wernher,"* Maria replied with some embarrassment, *"you just wiped the last vestiges of a superb bean casserole from your lips after having helped yourself three times!"* — *"Oh, really?"* was the answer. *"I am sorry. My mind must have wandered away. But the beans were out of this world, certainly!"*

Von Braun sometimes began his board meetings with a little story that was not directly linked to rockets or outer space. One morning, as he sat down with his board members, he had a distraught look on his face. *"You know,"* he began with a voice that faked concern, *"I am afraid I will have to see a psychiatrist soon. Something must be wrong with me."* While everybody looked at him in bewilderment, he continued: *"I have been married now for sixteen years, and I have not yet had a single fight with my wife. We are still getting along with each other as beautifully as we did on our first days together. I really do believe that something has gone wrong with me . . ."*

Looking for shady stories in von Braun's life would be an exercise in futility. There simply were none. He did not get involved in any scandal. All his many exciting activities were open, everybody would have been able to see what he was doing. He believed in the decency of man, and he included his own person in this quest for square deals. Any twilight operation would have run against his grain; he stayed away from all temptations.

It seemed that even the lure of big money left him cold. Friends and colleagues sometimes asked him why he did not accept one of the lucrative offers from industry that would enable him to draw a considerable income. *"I want to make rockets and spacecraft, not money,"* he always replied very promptly. *"Don't you see that as a member of an industrial company I would be obligated to produce dividends for the shareholders? I want to promote space projects, not consumer goods. Also, as a man from industry I would not be permitted to talk as freely to congressional leaders as I am now as a government employee. I would not sound convincing when I argued that spaceflight is a matter that concerns our entire nation, rather than a select interest group. I would like to propose what I believe is best for our country's continuing leadership in space, rather than having to take the standpoint 'right or wrong, my company!' And, besides, the money would not do me as much good as it might seem. Regardless of how much I make, I always spend it all and balance precariously between the black and the red. What I make is enough for my family and me to stay afloat, and to enjoy life. I have always tried to live by the rule that a man should acquire as much money as he needs, and as much knowledge as he possibly can."*

When von Braun spoke these words, he certainly meant what he said. However, there were times when he must have meant differently, and when it was obvious that he did appreciate the value of money. Realizing that a government salary would never allow him to build up—even at a slow rate—something like an estate for his family, he began to accept fees for consulting, for speeches, for articles and essays in journals, and for similar work as well as royalties from his book publishers. Some of his friends knew that he could become quite impatient if payments for these services did not arrive as promised. On the other hand, he was anxious to remain within the law with such outside activities, and he discussed them regularly with his superiors. Webb, during an interview many years after he had left NASA [9-53], mentioned that he defended von Braun against some critics, arguing that the work von Braun was doing for NASA, and for the country, would deserve a far higher salary than what he was being paid as a government employee. However, Webb did restrict von Braun's paid outside activities to a certain annual limit.

"Going public" with the idea of spaceflight, from the late 1940s on, resulted in a quick rise of von Braun's popularity. Wherever he went, he was spotted by somebody, and he had to give autographs. He liked to do that, just as an essential part of his campaign, but sometimes there was a sobering experience. A schoolgirl once asked him for two autographs. *"Do you plan to give one to your friend?"* von Braun asked. *"No,"* was the answer. *"You see, two of your autographs I can trade for one autograph from Elvis Presley!"*

Edward G. Uhl recalled how he, von Braun, and another friend traveled to Central America together on a hunting trip [9-54]. *"Seitz, Wernher, and I were down there in Yucatan in a Jeep,"* he said, *"driving from Campeche back into the jungles where Mexico and Guatemala and British Honduras come together. We reached a little Mayan Indian village with grass huts and chickens hanging from the front porch. And we stopped to buy a coke—the only thing we dared drink. And then all these little kids came out, and they recognized him! 'Wernher von Braun, Wernher von Braun!' they called and handed him little pieces of paper for his autograph. It is incredible to think that back there in the jungle there would be people looking for his autograph!"*

There were more stories like that. In December 1966 von Braun and Stuhlinger traveled together to Antarctica. They checked in at the White Heron Lodge in Christchurch, New Zealand, the staging area for the U.S.-sponsored South Pole activities. After a long day of traveling, briefings, and trying on Antarctic equipment, they finally enjoyed a late dinner and a quiet hour at the lodge. A band was playing on stage in the dining room, and a young lady with a microphone sang the newest hit songs. Von Braun remarked to his companion how relaxing it was to be at a place where nobody recognized him and asked for his autograph. At that time, the singer began to intone *"I want to go to the Moon with you,"* a song in vogue at that time. *"They seem to be pretty up-to-date even that far down under,"* von Braun said casually. When the lady had finished her song, she put the microphone down and made her way through the crowd straight to the two men from Huntsville. *"Dr. von Braun,"* she said, *"I sang this one just for you, and I mean it! Would you have a seat for me on your moon ship?"* For the rest of the evening, von Braun had to sign autographs. At another time, Stuhlinger drove in a little Volkswagen over the central highlands of Iceland toward Mount Herdubreid, a beautiful mountain in one of the loneliest areas in the northeast of the island. After half a day of driving, he met an old shepherd who tended his flock of sheep on a grassy patch. In his younger years, the man had been a sailor, so he spoke some English. *"What's your work?"* he wanted to know. *"I'm a kind of an engineer,"* was the reply. *"Electric?"*— *"No, not quite. Have you heard of those guys who build big rockets and want to fly to the Moon?"*— *"What?"*— *"Maybe you have seen a satellite in the night sky as it moved slowly between the stars?"*— *"What's that?"*— *"See, there is outer space, out there beyond the atmosphere, and we want to explore it . . ."*— *"Oh, you mean Wernher von Braun? I know who he is! Please, tell me more about him . . ."*

Some years later, Stuhlinger traveled through the Amboseli National Park in Kenya in Africa with his wife and a guide. Their car got a flat tire on the rough prairie road, so they had to stop at a little native village of thatched clay huts to have the tire fixed. Miraculously, even the most primitive-looking settlements in Kenya, and certainly in other African nations, too, are prepared to fix automobile tires. There was even a clay schoolhouse, and the children were just having a recess. They immediately surrounded *"the Americans,"* eager to practice the English they were learning at school. *"What do you do in America?"* they wanted to know. *"I am an engineer, and I help build rockets and space vehicles with which one can fly to the Moon. Have you ever seen a satellite at night, traveling across the sky between the stars?"*—*"Wernher von Braun?"* was the reply, as spontaneous as it was unexpected. *"Yes, exactly! And this man is even my boss!"*—*"He knows von Braun, he knows von Braun!"* the Amboseli boys and girls said to each other full of excitement, and they wanted to know more of him. *"Can you send us his picture, we want to hang it up in our classroom, please!"*—The picture was sent, of course, and the children responded with a most delightful thank-you letter.

When von Braun heard such stories, he reacted with a smile, but his smile had an uneasy undertone. *"People should focus their interest on the exploration of space,"* he would say, *"not on me personally. Space travel is not a one-man show, and not a one-time affair."* The volume of his fan mail was enormous. He tried to answer as many of the letters as possible—with the help of three full-time assistants—, and he always pointed out that our capability to explore outer space is the result of cooperation on a huge scale, and that spaceflight will be a firm part of human activities, and of man's destiny, from now on for all times in the future.

All these stories, while showing how much, in the perception of the public, von Braun personally was identified with the space program, convey an important message. It is the human element, the live person, on whom the public interest focuses first and foremost. People want to identify with another human being. They need the image of a person in order to respond with their thoughts, their interest, their hope, their trust, their faith. If there is no live person whom they know well from the papers, the news, the TV shows, or even his books, they remain cold toward a project, even if it has great merit as a potential benefactor of mankind.

After the first Moon landing in 1969, America again occupied place number one among the nations as far as the courage is concerned to tackle projects of huge dimensions, the ability to achieve success, and the determination to spend substantial funds just for human progress, but without military applications.

There was certainly no other event in human history that provided such a wealth of spiritual experience, such an abundant source of excitement to so many people at one time. The first lunar landing was observed on television screens by crowds around the globe estimated to one billion viewers.

"Spaceflight is now here to stay," von Braun had said in Peenemünde in 1942 after the first successful flight of an A-4 rocket. *"It was a good beginning,"* he said in 1970. *"Spaceflight did not happen because somebody thought that it would be an intriguing thing to do, but because it is part of our human destiny, and because its time had come. Let us continue to accept the challenge, and to respond with our best ability . . ."*

CHAPTER 10

FOOTPRINTS IN HUNTSVILLE

1 THE MAKING OF A UNIVERSITY

Shortly after the group of rocketeers from Texas had arrived in Huntsville in 1950, some of them were invited to an evening party where a distinguished lady, Dr. Frances C. Roberts, professor of history at the local extension of the University of Alabama in Tuscaloosa, gave a delightful lecture on Huntsville's colorful ante- and post-bellum history. After her presentation, she was asked: *"What impact will that influx of modern space technology have on the city of Huntsville?"* The professor paused for a while, then said with a deep sigh: *"Well, Huntsville survived that invasion of Yankees from the north; we may hope that it will also survive that invasion of rocketeers from the west."*

Almost forty years later, in 1988, after Huntsville's population had grown from 14,000 to about 170,000, after the little university extension had burgeoned into a fully autonomous university, and after Miss Roberts, now a highly honored Professor Emeritus, had become the most respected person ever connected with that university, the lady was asked the same question again.

"I'm presently writing a book on the history of Huntsville," she said. *"The city has grown in steps; first during the time before the Civil War, then after the war, then during the cotton era, then after World War II. By far the most decisive step came when von Braun and his crew moved here from Texas in 1950. Just everything began to grow in leaps and bounds! The population, stores, housing projects, schools, churches, streets, the cultural life, the symphony orchestra, the wealth of the city, and, of course, our university. It was just marvelous! That will be a very important chapter in my book . . ."*

Alabama achieved statehood in 1819, and a few years later its legislature created the University of Alabama in Tuscaloosa [10-1]. The university was destroyed by Union troops in 1865 because confederate cadets were trained on university grounds, but the campus was rebuilt in 1868.

As early as 1919, the university organized an extension service to make higher education available to people at other places in Alabama. In 1935, Huntsville was considered for an extension center, but community leaders were not interested.

During World War II, two young natives of Huntsville, Patrick Richardson and Macon Weaver, studied law at the University in Tuscaloosa. In 1947, they suggested to the Chamber of Commerce that an extension center be established in Huntsville. A committee was formed, and Richardson as chairman campaigned vigorously for the extension center, arguing that *"it is a matter vitally important to the future welfare of the boys and girls of our county . . ."* He met with full success, and on 6 January 1950 the University of Alabama Huntsville Extension Center opened its doors for evening classes in a high school building. The faculty of the fledgling center included Patrick Richardson (lawyer; political sciences and economics); Frances C. Roberts (school teacher; history); Mamie Steger (school teacher; mathematics); and a few others. A total of 137 students enrolled, each of them paying $2 registration fee, and $4 for each credit hour.

A few months later, von Braun and his co-workers arrived from Texas. The efforts of Huntsville's citizens to offer university extension services impressed him greatly. He pledged his help, and he persuaded several of his associates to teach classes at the extension. Gerhard Heller taught thermodynamics, Charles Bradshaw mathematics, Hans Tschinkel chemistry, Stuhlinger theoretical physics. The Army Ordnance Department also provided part-time teachers. Von Braun anticipated and convincingly predicted a rapid development of the city of Huntsville as a result of growing industrial activities and federal contracts. Trained individuals would be needed; employees would ask for opportunities to extend their own training, and also to provide their children with academic educations.

The urgent quest for educational opportunities in Huntsville increased in 1952 when the Army Missile Command was established. Philip Mason became director of the Huntsville Extension Center in 1953. He broadened the curriculum by adding courses in English, foreign languages, history, commerce, education, political sciences, sociology, psychology, engineering drawing, and business. However, almost all of these courses had to be taught by part-time teachers. The only full-time faculty member in 1956 was Miss Roberts, the history teacher! To earn a diploma, a student had to be a resident of Tuscaloosa for at least one year.

Huntsville citizens very quietly started to lay the foundation for future growth. In 1957, the City Board reserved eight acres of land as a first installment for a future university project. The following year, the city offered 83 acres of farmland for the same purpose.

Huntsville experienced a tremendous growth during those years. The Redstone and Jupiter missiles, the Explorer 1 satellite, and many new industrial enterprises had come to life in the city. For several years, Huntsville was the fastest-growing town of that size class in the United States. The need for educational opportunities was so obvious, but it was equally obvious that a decisive action would be needed to breathe life into a program that would lead to a full-size university.

General Medaris, commander of the Army Ordnance Missile Command, who fully shared von Braun's conviction that Huntsville needed a university, addressed the Alabama State Legislature in Montgomery on 23 June 1959 [10-2]. *". . . without a continuing supply of new knowledge, industry would stagnate, and the nation would face ruin,"* he said. *"We must educate for the future, not for the present or the past!"* As the population of Huntsville rapidly grew, von Braun's plea for opportunities of advanced education became stronger and stronger. He talked to the Chamber of Commerce and the City Council, to the heads of industrial companies, to officials in the City and State Governments, and to members of the university in Tuscaloosa. Frances Roberts remembers his untiring efforts [10-3]: *"Von Braun really understood academic needs. He knew how important a rounded education is, a proper balance between science, humanistic subjects, and technical courses. He also understood that our students would come from all age groups, and that a university education should not only prepare for a career in the natural sciences or in engineering. He could formulate his thoughts so beautifully, and he talked so that everybody would follow him and believe what he said. He could talk to all kinds of people and make them understand what he meant, even the politicians in the State Government. And he could convince people that the opportunity to provide Huntsville with a first class facility for academic teaching and scientific research was unique, and that the time to act was now. He was just tremendous!"*

Von Braun's efforts culminated in a speech to the state legislature in Montgomery on 20 June 1961 [10-1]. His impassioned plea for state of Alabama funding support met with immediate success; he asked for $3 million, and the legislature approved his request even without a debate! *"He could have asked for 5 million dollars, and he would have got it just as quickly,"* one of the state senators later remarked.

Von Braun's speech became a landmark in the history of Huntsville's university. He first reminded his audience of some of the exciting achievements of the space program, many of which had originated in Huntsville. Then he spoke of the decisive role that scientific research plays in all human endeavors that aim at a betterment of the quality of life on Earth. Describing some of the technical features of modern rockets and spacecraft, he pointed out how much the city of Huntsville could contribute to projects of this kind, provided that it accepts the challenge. One of the basic needs, he said, is *"the right climate . . . for the advancement of higher education and science . . . Opportunity is knocking at Alabama's door . . . just as opportunity knocked at California's door a few decades ago when the aircraft industry began to blossom . . . Shakespeare said: 'There is a tide in the affairs of men, which, taken at the flood, leads on to fortune.' For Alabama, the tide is at flood now . . ."* Huntsville, he continued, *"needs $3 million for buildings and equipment . . ."* and he expressed his confidence that the citizens of Alabama *"will accept this challenge with the gusto of Macbeth as he said: 'Lay on, Macduff, and damn'd be him that first cries, Hold, enough!'"*

Alabama's legislators did *"lay on."* The city of Huntsville and Madison County added $400,000 to their state's $3 million, a fine research institute was built, and Dr. Rudolf Hermann, developer of the large supersonic wind tunnel in Peenemünde during the 1930s, became its first director. Co-author Ordway worked for Hermann at the new institute for five years in the 1970s.

The full rank of an autonomous university was bestowed upon the Huntsville campus in the summer of 1969. As one of the youngest universities in the nation, it had an enrollment of approximately 8,000 students in 1993.

2   U.S. SPACE & ROCKET CENTER

As the Redstone and Jupiter missiles, and some of the smaller rocket weapons, came to life in Huntsville, the U.S. Army established a Missiles and Rockets Demonstration Laboratory at Redstone Arsenal where its own weapons were displayed along with German V-1s and V-2s. Being located within the Arsenal perimeter meant that the public had only limited access to the exhibit, and this concerned the local Chamber of Commerce. Therefore, a Space Museum Committee was formed under the chairmanship of Walter Linde with the objective to establish a rocket and space museum more accessible to the public than the Army exhibit.

Linde in 1959 briefed von Braun and others on plans for a 400-acre site on which a $10 million space and rocket museum might be erected. He tried to persuade the U.S. Army to donate a slice of land at the edge of Redstone Arsenal for this purpose, while von Braun asked his friend Walt Disney for some professional advice. Linde and von Braun then presented their plans to Alabama Senator John Sparkman in Washington, calling their project an *"exhibit"* rather than a museum.

Several years passed without much action. In 1960, von Braun and his team left the Army and joined NASA; subsequently, a new space exhibit was set up at the Marshall Center. Thus, by 1965 two Government space and rocket exhibits existed on the Redstone Arsenal premises, both of them offering only limited access to the public.

The time seemed ripe to move energetically toward a single exhibit, to be accessible to the public all the time. A statewide effort was begun to amend the Alabama constitution to authorize the sale of $1.9 million worth of long-term bonds. A committee was formed to push for the amendment, chaired by well-known University of Alabama football coach Paul *"Bear"* Bryant and James Record, chairman of the Madison County Board of Commissioners. The amendment was strongly endorsed by von Braun as well as by Major General John G. Zierdt, commander of Redstone Arsenal, and by Governor George Wallace.

House and Senate bills for the fund obligation bond passed in September 1965. Wallace appointed von Braun and other leading state citizens to serve on the Alabama Space Science Exhibit Commission; Lieutenant Governor James B. Allen of Montgomery was named chairman. Voters readily approved the amendment, and work could begin.

Von Braun promised that NASA-Marshall would continue *"to contribute fully to the educational, cultural, and financial soundness of the space science exhibit by procuring, constructing, operating, and maintaining the NASA Space Exhibit in the Center with artifacts, displays, models . . . that will indeed make our space exhibit The Space Exhibit."*

In December 1967, von Braun suggested that Edward O. Buckbee be appointed director of the exhibit center; until then, he had been assistant to the chief of the Public Affairs Office at NASA-Marshall.

The appointment of Lieutenant Governor Jim Allen as chairman of the Space Science Exhibit Commission gave the program continuous and strong political support. *"Allen was a real master of order and planning, and of bringing people together . . . He took care of administrative problems and politics, while von Braun looked after technical matters,"* Buckbee recalled [10-4]. *"A designer was hired, but when he proposed exhibits behind glass, protected by 'Do not touch' signs . . . it was totally wrong . . . Von Braun said: 'We want to show the story of the future . . . people should really feel space!' and that set the tone for what we have now, an involvement, a participatory experience. In fact, the Space Camp idea grew out of his early feelings. So, von Braun guided us on the proper track . . ."*

In 1968, the project went into high gear. Buildings were erected, components and parts were collected, scouts were sent out all over the country to the places where rockets and spacecraft were built and then retired or otherwise discarded. Redstone Arsenal contributed components of military systems. The exhibit rooms of the Center began to fill, and more and more co-workers were hired. Around that time, von Braun said to an associate: *"We are extremely fortunate to have Ed Buckbee. He turns out to be the ideal director for this project!"*

Von Braun wanted a Saturn V as the centerpiece of all exhibits. However, as Buckbee remembered, *"at that time NASA wanted to fly Saturn Vs, rather than put them in museums."* Individual Saturn stages and parts were scattered all over the country. The best way to obtain them for Huntsville, von Braun argued, was to put a mission requirement on the project. *"So,"* Buckbee continued, *"we sent a TWX down to the Cape, saying that we needed a Saturn V first stage for ground transportation tests. A Saturn third stage was in California; that one we needed 'to train crews in the handling of the stage during airlift operations.' After about 6 months, we had the entire Saturn V vehicle at the Marshall Center in Huntsville."*

But—how to legally transfer the complete Saturn V, after all ground transportation and loading tests had been completed, from the Marshall Center to the exhibit area? *"Von Braun came up with a solution,"* Buckbee recalled. *"He explained that we were going to train new crews in the loading and transportation of all the components on an overland route by shipping them from the Marshall Center to the museum site, about*

*2 miles (3 km) away. Then we would just leave them there for storage. The museum
would not charge NASA for the service! It was wonderful. So we got the Saturn stages
and parts to the museum, and they have been there ever since . . ."*

Eventually, NASA signed ownership of the Saturn V over to the Smithsonian
Institution. Later, there were talks that the huge Saturn launch vehicle should be moved
up north to a permanent exhibit proposed in the Washington area, and again later, the
Air Force expressed interest in it for the Air Force museum at Wright-Patterson Air Force
Base.

When the danger arose that the Alabama (later, U.S.) Space & Rocket Center might
lose its prize possession, someone had the splendid idea that the huge tanks of the giant
rocket, resting on some supports in a horizontal position, should be filled with
concrete. If this were done, the rocket simply would be too heavy to be moved. But
then, somebody offered an even better idea: The National Park Service should declare
the Saturn V a National Historic Landmark at its birthplace in Huntsville. The suggestion
worked: In 1978, Saturn V was listed in the National Register of Historic Places, and less
than a decade later (1987) it was named a National Historic Landmark. This secured for
all times Saturn V's presence in Huntsville.

The exhibit area was soon overflowing with rocket and space veterans including
the old V-1 and V-2, the Army's Hermes, Nike, Lacrosse, Corporal, Sergeant, Honest John,
Redstone, Jupiter, and Pershing; the famous space rockets Juno I (with America's first
satellite, Explorer 1, on top), Redstone-Mercury (that pioneered the U.S. manned
spaceflight program), the Air Force Atlas ICBM and Titan II launch vehicles, NASA's
Saturn I, Saturn V, and Space Shuttle with (empty) solid rocket boosters and external
tank; and the SR-71 and F-4C airplanes. Several models of lunar roving vehicles came on
display, as well as a lunar landing module within a simulated Moon crater. Also
exhibited at the center are several rocket motors, including the giant F-1 engine, and the
nuclear-powered Nerva engine. Mercury, Gemini, and Apollo capsules are on display
inside the exhibit halls, together with an original Saturn V instrument unit, and a full-
scale Skylab space station mock-up.

Besides these large objects, the visitors can see, and usually even touch, about 1,500
smaller rocket and spacecraft components, such as gyro platforms, rocket motors,
turbo pumps, and space-borne computers along with training equipment, and models
of the planets and the lunar surface. A number of spacesuit models are on display,
together with tools, equipment, and facilities used by the astronauts. Visitors can
experience the functioning of models of gyroscopes, optical instruments, and even live
rocket motors burning propane gas and oxygen.

One of the most exciting experiences for the visitors is a ride in the huge
centrifuge, holding forty-six *"space passengers,"* that provides the sensation of speed
and of an accelerating force up to about 2½ times the normal Earth gravity. A
Spacedome Theater with a modern 70 millimeter film projector and a 67 foot (20 m)
screen shows several films every day, among them the all-time classics *To Fly, Hail
Columbia, The Dream Is Alive*, and *Our Blue Planet*.

Visitors of the U.S. Space & Rocket Center also have the opportunity of a bus tour
through the nearby George C. Marshall Space Flight Center where they see mock-ups of
the space shuttle and the Space Station Freedom. They can view some of the development work going on at the Marshall Center, and observe simulated zero-gravity tests
going on in a large water tank in which components and operations are exposed to
neutral buoyancy conditions.

Since opening its gates in 1970, the U.S. Space & Rocket Center has enjoyed a
growing number of visitors: some 220,000 in 1970, 250,000 in 1980; and 500,000 in 1990.

Attached to the U.S. Space & Rocket Center are the U.S. Space Camp and the U.S. Space Academy, unique, exciting, and remarkably successful links between outer space and life on Earth. The story of its evolution is typical for von Braun. He recognized a need, and he did something about it.

After von Braun had left Huntsville, he still came to the Marshall Center occasionally. *"On his way back to the airport,"* Buckbee remembered, *"he would take about an hour and go through [the Space & Rocket Center]. He certainly worried about our education system . . . We were walking through the Rocket Park one day, and he began telling stories of the V-2, and how the fins kept coming off, and he was going to fire Eberhard Rees because he used screws instead of rivets. Eberhard would keep telling von Braun, 'these screws will hold, these screws will hold . . .' And they would fire the V-2 and the fins would fall off . . . And von Braun would ask Eberhard: 'Are you still of the opinion that the screws will hold?'—Rivets were then used to attach the fins, but von Braun did not fire Eberhard . . ."* On this particular day, a group of youngsters was going through with clipboards in their hands. Obviously, the teacher was having them take notes, or maybe giving them a test . . . As we watched them, von Braun remarked: *"You know, we have a lot of camps in this country. We have band camps, and cheerleader camps, and football camps. I wonder why we don't have a science camp?"* He then began to elaborate. *"With this place you have here, where people can get a hands-on experience, it would be great . . . if there could be a more involved experience . . ."*

The principles of rocketry and spaceflight would be taught for about five days, building up to some kind of climax. After the children have developed some knowledge, von Braun suggested, *"you conduct a mission, which will be the final examination of what the youngsters learned . . ."* This idea turned out to be very workable. *"In fact,"* Buckbee said, *"we are using the idea today . . . the seed was planted . . ."*

The Space Camp project began to take shape during the late 1970s and early 1980s. Von Braun was no longer alive at that time. The Camp opened in the summer of 1982 for an eight-week season. Still today, each *"course"* lasts five days; the children learn about rocket engines, guidance and control systems, gyroscopes, communication links, trajectories, aerodynamics, life under weightlessness, and life support systems for travel in the emptiness of outer space. They operate instruments, eat space food, experience reduced-gravity situations in spring-supported harnesses, figure out mission plans, analyze test reports, trouble-shoot failures, even test-fire small rocket engines. As the years went by, more and more hands-on activities were added, even simulated flights in the cockpit of a Shuttle. A 'Space Habitat' was built, simulating a space station in orbit, that can accommodate up to 440 persons for the five days they spend in the Camp.

"During the first summer," Buckbee noted, *"757 campers attended. That number grew steadily with every year. Young people come here from all fifty states, and from many foreign countries . . . In 1986, two grandsons of General Eisenhower enrolled in the Camp, also David Hartman's son, and Ernest Gallo's son from the wine country!"*

About 20,000 youngsters sign up each year for Space Camp and a related Space Academy for older children. Could there be a more impressive evidence of the fact that the American people—and people from many other nations as well—are still strongly in favor of a space program, and that modern youth, in particular, is fascinated by space? Through 1993, over 170,000 campers have enjoyed the experience.

Stimulated by the U.S. Space Camp's and U.S. Space Academy's success in Huntsville, similar Space Camp projects materialized in Titusville, Florida, close to the Kennedy Space Center; in Japan, where the largest steel manufacturing corporation on

Earth, Nippon Steel, entered into a license agreement with the U.S. Space Camp Foundation in Huntsville to establish a space camp; and in southern Belgium. Still others are under development elsewhere in the world—including Canada and Italy.

During the active summer season, about 700 people work at the center and camps, augmented by some Peenemünde oldtimers. Many of the helpers are students who work there during their long summer recess. In spite of its high degree of public involvement, visibility, and interaction with hundreds of thousands of visitors every year, the U.S. Space & Rocket Center is one of the few organizations of that magnitude in the United States that encounters no noticeable criticism—only enthusiasm and praise.

CHAPTER 11

THE MOVE TO WASHINGTON

1 *"AN EXCITING NEW PROJECT"*

Before the 1960s drew to a close, four astronauts had walked on the surface of the Moon and returned safely home to Earth. The Saturn-Apollo project had become a magnificent success. America's prestige as spacefaring nation number one was restored. The eyes of the world were focused on a technological and scientific accomplishment that moved the public attention away—at least temporarily—from the miseries of the Vietnam War; from racial unrest and student upheaval; from the staggering increase of crime rates and corruption in government; and from the dangers of population explosion, environmental degradation, and energy crises. Enthusiasm for space exploration was strong. *"There is a tide in the affairs of men which, taken at the flood, leads on to fortune,"* von Braun had quoted Marcus Brutus in Shakespeare's Julius Caesar at an earlier occasion (Chapter 10-1). Could this Apollo tide be taken at the flood?

Plans for follow-up projects had been started by NASA during the mid-1960s. There was the Orbital Workshop project that would use the hydrogen tank of the second stage of a two-stage Saturn IB rocket as a human habitat after burn-out; the tank would be transformed into a manned orbiting space station. This *"wet workshop,"* as it was called, would primarily serve as an observing station for solar astronomy. In addition, a number of medical, biological, and technological investigations would be made.

Gilruth's Manned Spacecraft Center, and von Braun's Marshall Center shared responsibilities for component development, integration, crew training, and preparation of the scientific projects, and for launching and operation of the system. Two days after the return of the Apollo 11 crew, while everybody was in high spirits, Mueller suggested to a congressional committee that instead of the *"wet"* workshop concept, one should plan for a *"dry"* workshop, also based on the second stage of a two-stage Saturn IB (which also served as third stage on a three-stage Saturn V), but to be launched as a completely equipped payload on top of a two-stage Saturn V. This scheme would be more expensive than the wet workshop scheme, but far more capable and useful as a pioneer station in space. In the favorable climate of the moment, Mueller's proposal was immediately accepted. This is how the dry workshop, which later was named Skylab, came to life. It was to be America's first manned station in orbit. *"Marshall did play a very strong role in the Skylab program,"* Mueller said in 1986 [11-1], *"and Wernher was one of the leaders in that project; many of the creative ideas there were due to him and to his team."*

Another prominent post-Apollo project in the making at that time was the reusable space shuttle. The guiding idea behind it was the desire to replace expendable *"throw-away"* rockets, useful for one flight only, by a kind of aerospaceplane capable of landing glider-fashion after returning from orbit.

Both the Skylab space station and the space shuttle were logical elements of a comprehensive spaceflight program as it has been envisioned by space enthusiasts over the past forty years. And yet, in spite of their indispensable role in the evolution of spaceflight, these projects would appear as anticlimactic in the shadow of the Apollo expeditions to the Moon.

Early in 1969, President Nixon had established a Space Task Group chaired by Vice President Spiro T. Agnew to advise him on potential *"exciting new projects"* in space that could be accomplished during the 1980s and 1990s, and that would be credited to him as the initiator. The Space Task Group published its report *"The Post-Apollo Space Program: Directions for the Future"* in September 1969 [11-2]. On the basis of this report, NASA, and also the President's Science Advisory Committee, urgently suggested that an aggressive post-Apollo space program be initiated.

This program was to utilize the experience and the hardware acquired during the Saturn-Apollo program. It was to include scientific projects, applications of satellites for purposes useful to people on Earth, and an exciting new initiative for space exploration.

Dr. Thomas O. Paine, who had succeeded Webb as NASA administrator in February 1969, and who was the main architect behind the Space Task Group's proposed program, was eager to aim for an exciting project that appeared to space-oriented people at that time as a natural follow-on to Apollo: a manned mission to the planet Mars.

Mueller enthusiastically supported this comprehensive and bold space program as a sequel to Apollo and Skylab. Both he and von Braun described the program in numerous speeches within NASA and to public audiences.

To some extent, the program as envisioned by the Space Task Group and Paine reflected von Braun's own thoughts that he had expressed while the Saturn-Apollo project neared its completion (Chapter 8-10). However, with his proverbial sixth sense to anticipate the future in space-related matters, he was convinced that this beautiful program—in spite of Mueller's and Paine's optimism—would need a tremendous effort of selling, first to the president, and then to Congress and the budget people, then to the scientists and other colleagues in NASA, and finally to the public.

There were enough signs to corroborate this feeling. President Nixon, after having asked for exciting new projects, including an expedition to Mars, early during his presidency, obviously lost interest in space later in 1969. The vice president, because of personal involvement in some questionable dealings, had lost credibility and subsequently had to resign. Congress at that time was largely preoccupied with burning problems that confronted the nation. The Office of Management and Budget had to cope with rising deficits. The mood of congressional leaders was a wait-and-see attitude, rather than a gung-ho enthusiasm for a great new adventure.

What was the will of the people? With this lack of leadership toward an active space program from the government, the people could not be expected to ask for bold space accomplishments. Had there been active leadership from the top for continuing American preeminence in space, voters would have rallied behind their government, and would have supported a well-planned, aggressive space program.

The need for a campaign was obvious. A brilliant opportunity existed for the United States to stay on top by utilizing the existing hardware, facilities, and experienced teams. The responsible planners in the government would have to be made aware of this unique opportunity. A crusader was needed to *"take the tide at the flood."*

Von Braun did not talk about it, but he knew that he would be the person, perhaps the only one available, to carry out this crusade. He also knew that he would be able to campaign far more convincingly from a position at NASA Headquarters than from a field center. There were at least two more people at NASA who held the same belief: Paine, and Mueller. Both of them approached von Braun with the suggestion that he move to Washington.

Paine even put his request in a somewhat wider context. Foreseeing a period of intense activity for NASA project planners and program managers, he expressed an urgent request for help to his field centers, particularly to the directors. *"You fellows are living like patriarchs in your kingdoms,"* von Braun quoted Paine, *"while I have to sweat it out in the crossfires of mission planners, budget cutters, public demands, congressional hearings, scientists, company representatives, and the president's advisers. Why don't you come up and help me in my daily chores?"*

During an interview in 1985 [11-3], Paine remembered some details of von Braun's move to Washington. *"My recollection is that it was my idea. I don't think Wernher broached the idea originally; when I brought [the move] up, he was somewhat on the fence . . . His first reaction was: 'Well, that is certainly something that will bear thinking about. I am delighted that you are interested, and just let me think about it. I really like my job here, but—well, let's think about it.'—But,"* Paine continued, *"I had a great ally, Maria. She wanted to come up to Washington. She had been down there long enough . . . I think Maria—and thinking also of the children—felt that the move to Washington would be in the family interest . . ."*

A candid analysis of Paine's reasons for wanting von Braun in headquarters was offered by Frank Williams [11-4], long-time associate of von Braun, and one of two of his team members who accompanied him to Washington in 1970: *"The 'advertised' job was planning, but what Paine had in mind was von Braun to be the master architect and creator of a really long-range view, and then use his expertise and charisma to 'market' the final product. Von Braun was, in fact, to orchestrate the selling of a grand plan for America's post-Apollo thrust into space. Paine recognized that von Braun was not only a great conceiver of ideas, but that he was equally able to articulate them in a very marketable fashion. So really his role was planning and marketing—expanding the future for NASA."*

Von Braun took Paine's plea to heart. Late in 1969, still unknown to his associates in Huntsville, he accepted Paine's request and decided to transfer to NASA Headquarters. That his wife Maria took a very positive attitude toward the prospect of moving to Washington certainly helped him make that decision; however, the decisive factor in his resolve was unquestionably that both Paine and he believed that a powerful campaign for the new space program was required, and that he would be the best choice to conduct that campaign. Thus, in the spring of 1970, he established his permanent place of work in NASA Headquarters as Paine's deputy associate administrator for planning, filled with high hopes that the American people would muster again the spirit that President Kennedy had aroused so wonderfully in 1961 when he brought Apollo to life.

A mission to Mars was certainly the most exciting project in the broad program that Paine envisioned in 1970, but there were also other impressive projects: several more Saturn-Apollo flights to the Moon; a number of science projects; Skylab I, to be launched in 1972 or 1973, and to be followed by Skylabs II and III; a space shuttle; and a large, permanently manned orbital station.

Each of these projects had been alive in von Braun's mind for years; for each of them, he maintained an up-to-date concept that he was always ready to describe and discuss in depth. It is only natural that these concepts were constantly in flux so that they could be kept in agreement with technical and scientific progress. For example, von Braun's original space station, presented in his *Collier's* essay in 1952, was a huge toroidal structure. The astronauts would observe the Earth's surface, global weather, storm formations, ocean states, agricultural crops, snow coverage, urban developments, and other worldwide phenomena. They would provide navigational help for ships and airplanes, and they would man the telescopes for astronomical observations; they would provide support functions for global communication systems; and they would assist in military activities by making strategic observations from points high above enemy territory. They would launch spacecraft to the Moon, and on deep space missions, and they would find out what other useful functions human crews in orbit could perform.

By 1970, it had been demonstrated that most of these functions can be carried out very well by unmanned systems, and that astronauts in orbit should concentrate on other activities. In planning and building a space station, von Braun said, *"we must proceed in an evolutionary way. First, we should build a habitat, preferably from an empty tank of a large upper stage in which a few astronauts can live and work for a couple of weeks, as we are planning it for Skylab. Then, we should cluster several of these empty tank modules together to form a more elaborate station. As we proceed through these stages, we will learn what man can do best on a station in orbit, and how well he can function and work under prolonged weightlessness . . ."*

What would von Braun's space station, model 1970, have looked like? *"A space station in orbit,"* he said at the time when he prepared to move to NASA Headquarters, *"should primarily be a 'home away from home,' a sort of house trailer, for astronauts. The station will give them a place to relax and rest in a comfortable environment, to eat, take a shower, and sleep in comfort after hours of extravehicular activities within the confinement of a spacesuit when they assembled a Moon ship, repaired a weather satellite, replenished attitude control propellant on a 'spy in the sky,' or made a deep space vehicle ready for a flight to Mars. They will also make materials processing experiments to find out which processes would be suitable on a manned platform with all its unavoidable mechanical disturbances, and which processes would require ultra-quiet free-flying substations, to be serviced at intervals from the station.*

Skylab, the first American station in orbit, was under construction when von Braun made these suggestions. *"Let's build and launch several of these in an evolutionary sequence,"* he proposed, *"each of them with the same basic structure of a third-stage Saturn V hydrogen tank, but with different equipment and work programs."*

"I bet you," von Braun sometimes said, *"one of the human activities that will make good and profitable use of an orbiting station in the future is tourism. Remember Robert Scott and Roald Amundsen who made the first daring trips to the South Pole? Less than seventy years later, the Lindblad cruise ships began taking tourists there on a routine basis!"*

There was an impressive assortment of potential projects for a comprehensive space program, and an obvious need for a coordinated planning effort. Also, there was hope—and Paine, von Braun, and others inside and outside NASA, strongly fostered that hope—that a signal from the White House would breathe life into America's space program at least to the extent that the country could maintain its leading position on the space frontier in the years to come.

This hope, combined with the desire to contribute his share to a future program worthy of the accomplishments of the past, was the driving force behind von Braun's decision to leave his team in Huntsville and to move to Washington.

2   GOOD-BYE TO THE TEAM

Before transferring to Washington, and even before announcing to his associates that he would leave the Marshall Center and his team, von Braun took a long-overdue leave of absence. He and his family traveled to the Bahamas for a seven-week vacation, *"the longest in my life,"* as he said. Indulging in one of his beloved hobbies, he taught his daughters Iris and Margrit scuba diving. *"They went down to 140 feet with me,"* he proudly told his friends afterwards.

While he was enjoying his Caribbean holidays, the *Huntsville Times* published a brief statement: *"Dr. von Braun will leave Huntsville for Washington, D.C."*

Then, Paine came to Huntsville and talked to the employees of the Marshall Center. *"Dr. von Braun has an unmatched record of looking to the future to choose the most promising arenas of technical advance. He brings to his new assignment sound vision, insight, and competence, and we are delighted he has agreed to accept this important post . . . He will look at all the NASA programs, and help us develop a total NASA program . . . His new duties will encompass technical, exploration, and overall NASA planning . . ."* [11-5].

After returning from the Bahamas, von Braun had to do some explaining. It must be said, though, that his associates were not totally surprised. His pending departure had been rumored for some time, and numerous signals had been picked up by his team members even without spoken words. When von Braun finally talked at a board meeting about his decision to leave the team and the city of Huntsville, and to join NASA Headquarters in Washington, one of his associates asked the simple question: *"Wernher, why are you going to leave?"*

He answered with a chuckle: *"Because I'm sick and tired of looking every day into the faces of the same old and tired businessmen!"* It was obvious that von Braun used this bit of wry humor only to help himself over the somber aspects of this fateful step. At that moment, everyone felt that this would now be the end of a supremely effective symbiosis that had begun for some of them in Peenemünde, for some even earlier in Kummersdorf, and for the others in Fort Bliss or Huntsville. This symbiosis had not only filled many years of joint work with a keen sense of purpose and accomplishment, it had also enriched beyond measure the life of everyone who had been privileged to share these years with von Braun.

"Now is the time," von Braun said, *"to consolidate and utilize the gains that our past successes in the space program have won for us . . . I am very, very grateful, and I approach my new job with tremendous enthusiasm . . . To help Dr. Paine and Dr. Low and other NASA leaders develop a space program worthy of the 1970s and 1980s is an immense opportunity . . ."*

"The agency now wants to address itself to planning, and I won't mind spending the rest of my useful years in this capacity . . . A marriage of science and engineering has become necessary, and it must come in space exploration, if the true benefits are to be found . . ." he said.

Von Braun's pending move to Washington caused a flood of news releases in papers all over the country, particularly in Huntsville. *"As early as September 1969,"* the *Huntsville Times* reported [11-6], *"von Braun told Paine that he was ready to move to Washington without hesitation if Dr. Paine believed his value was more important in Washington . . ."*—*"But,"* the paper said later, *"his touch will linger on in these North Alabama hills . . ."* The *New York Times* wrote [11-7]: *"Dr. von Braun has long been one of the most effective spokesmen in NASA, pleading the space program's cause before Congress . . . ,"* and the *Press* predicted [11-8]: *"Dr. von Braun is the one who can squeeze the most benefit out of reduced NASA expenditures . . ."*

There was no need to ask who would succeed von Braun as director of the Marshall Center. Eberhard Rees, his deputy of thirty years and also his closest confidant, would be the natural choice. The organization of the center would retain its firm and stable structure. Von Braun did not doubt that all the team members would be as loyal to Rees as they had been to him. The immediate work program would keep everybody busy; in fact, further Saturn-Apollo flights to the Moon, Skylab, and the beginning of space shuttle activities would provide more than a sufficient workload for the time being.

When Rees accepted his nomination as von Braun's successor, he said in his typical restrained way: *"Everyone should be aware that I cannot perform miracles. I'll just do my best . . . ,"* and *"Doing a good job is not enough; we'll have to do an excellent job."* The *Huntsville Times* commented [11-9]: *"His press clippings may be scanty . . . but he is a real pro when it comes to getting the job done . . ."*

"To become von Braun's successor is really tough," Rees said; however, when his nomination as the new Marshall Center director was announced to the employees by Paine, there was a spontaneous standing ovation for Rees. Surely, he and von Braun were two totally different personalities. However, he was by far the best choice to continue the tradition of the huge von Braun team, to preserve the spirit of openness, of mutual confidence and trust, to maintain the enormous momentum that was at work in the center, and to honor the principle of excellence that had been von Braun's guide throughout his life. In true von Braun fashion, Rees said: *"We have a job to do, let's roll up our sleeves and get to work."*

To the pleasant surprise of some members of the Marshall Center, Rees even began to address himself to matters of a scientific nature, an area from which he had shied away during previous years. A few months after taking over the reins of the center, Rees wisely expanded the center program by raising two projects, under study and detailed planning at Marshall for some time, to the level of active and approved development projects: the High Energy Astronomical Observatories [HEAO], and the Space Telescope [later named Hubble Space Telescope]. Mueller approved both projects for the Marshall Center. The HEAO project became an outstanding success with three astronomical satellites placed in orbit—for ultraviolet, X-ray, and cosmic ray research—during the late 1970s. The Hubble Space Telescope, ready for launch in 1986, had to wait for the availability of a shuttle; it was finally launched in May 1990. Also, Rees permitted the Space Sciences Laboratory to extend its in-house activities in several areas: infrared, X-ray, and gamma ray astronomy, superconductivity, solar physics, Sun-Earth interactions, aeronomy of the high atmosphere, and cosmic rays.

Five Saturn-Apollo flights to the Moon, number 13, 14, 15, 16, and 17, were accomplished while Rees was director of the Marshall Center; the manned Moon project came to its close late in 1972. Skylab was developed and prepared for a 1973 launch. Rees retired from government service in January of that year.

Early in 1970, Paine gave a press briefing in which he described the new space program that was left after President Nixon's drastic reductions. Valiantly, he made every effort to look at the approved, pared-down program with optimism, but it was obvious, at least to von Braun's team members, that without an exciting new project, von Braun's move to Washington would lose its most cogent justification. And yet, von Braun stuck to his decision and to his promise.

"I still see a very important task for me," von Braun said, *"and I plan to devote most of my time to it. Our space program, as it is laid out now, offers tremendous opportunities for science, as well as for technological research. Most of those who could profit tremendously from Skylab and shuttle, and from smaller unmanned satellites, are not fully aware of those golden opportunities. I will try to do some crusading there, and in the process I hope to learn much science for myself, something I had wanted to do for years. By the way,"* he said to his chief scientist at Marshall, *"could you please put together for me a list of the 'ten most wanted scientists' in the country who have a demonstrated interest, and even some previous practical experience, in some areas of space science, and whom I should contact first when I begin my work in Washington?*

That list would help me tremendously in my effort to stir up active interest in space science opportunities among the country's leading scientists."

Although this prospective work program was a far cry from that of a reigning king in an 8,000-man NASA field center, von Braun remained optimistic. He looked forward with great expectations to his work with Paine for whom he had always felt great respect and admiration. Also, his hope was still alive that a more aggressive space program, including an expedition to Mars, could be reconstituted during the forthcoming months.

"I will first go by myself," he remarked, *"and I will invite others from the team to join me as soon as an appropriate activity develops."* He went to Washington with only two young Marshall co-workers, Frank Williams of the Future Projects Office, and Jay N. Foster of the Executive Office. Ian Dodds from the Rockwell International Corporation in California, and William A. Fleming and James Scaggs at NASA Headquarters, joined them later.

Maria von Braun took the prospect of giving up the family's home of twenty years in stride, although it meant a decisive change in the life of the von Braun family. Having grown up in a world city, Berlin, she was looking forward to the opportunities offered by another world city, and she devoted herself with enthusiasm to the search for a new home, to the selection of schools for the children, and to the adoption of a new life-style in the capital. And, well known to the closer friends of the von Braun family, Maria fostered the hope that her husband, as a member of the planning staff at NASA Headquarters as contrasted to the director of a huge field center, might be a little less dominated by an over-demanding work program, and would have more time for the family.

When the time for von Braun to depart approached, the city of Huntsville honored its *"favorite son"* with a Wernher von Braun Day, in grateful remembrance of the fabulous rise that city had enjoyed since the summer of 1950 when *"those hordes from the western plains invaded our peaceful privacy."*

Their thriving community, in addition to thousands of new homes, included a new university, an industrial research park, and plans for a beautiful civic center which, upon completion in 1975, would bear von Braun's name. *"All this wonderful success here on Earth, and our flights to the Moon as well, would not have been possible without your steadfast and heartfelt support,"* von Braun said in his farewell speech to the citizens of this city in which he had lived longer, and had been happier, than in any other city. *"I spent here the finest days of my life,"* he said.

Mayor Joe Davis expressed his pride in Huntsville's *"first citizen"* in his own words: *"We understand that these people in Washington need you badly. Well, we are glad to help them out. But let it be understood that you are going to Washington strictly on a loan basis!"*

Von Braun began his work in Washington on 1 March 1970, three weeks before his fifty-eighth birthday.

3   A BRAVE NEW WORLD

Paine had become NASA administrator about one year before von Braun's arrival in Washington. He had chosen George M. Low, Apollo Spacecraft director at the Manned Spacecraft Center (later named Johnson Space Center) as his deputy administrator. Associate administrator was Homer E. Newell, NASA's chief scientist. Von Braun's position was to be deputy associate administrator for planning under Newell.

When Paine expressed his urgent desire for help in the fall of 1969, he expected that NASA would be working soon on an exciting new project—a manned mission to Mars—and he wanted von Braun as the master planner for this project. By the time von Braun arrived in Washington, a Mars mission was no longer on the president's agenda.

Planning was necessary in two areas: NASA's long-range plan, complete with documentation, brochures, and presentations; and NASA's space sciences program. Paine and von Braun frequently sat together to work on the long-range plan. *"They worked hard on the Mars project,"* as Frank Williams recalled [11-10].

Right from the beginning of his time at NASA Headquarters, von Braun found himself involved in a third major program: the shuttle. Each of these three activities proved to be more complex, and to demand more effort, than either Paine or von Braun had anticipated.

Long-range planning for NASA's future was mostly a personal effort between Paine and von Braun. Paine's enthusiasm for a bold space exploration program, combined with excellent personal relations between the two, gave von Braun the hope that his stay at NASA Headquarters might eventually lead to an exciting new project.

Paine made another attempt to obtain presidential support for a vigorous space program in June 1970. He, von Braun, and Robert Jastrow, director of the Institute for Space Studies under the NASA Goddard Space Flight Center, organized a conference on Wallops Island under the title *"Space Programs in the Year 2000."* Arthur C. Clarke, the prophet and international spokesman for spaceflight, was the keynote speaker. A number of high-ranking government officials were invited.

While the program reflected the recommendations of the Space Task Group of September 1969, it reached out much farther. Jay Foster [11-11] recalled that *"von Braun presented a paper on nuclear fusion propulsion, describing a vehicle with a pusher plate at the rear (Project Orion). With an apparatus similar to a machine gun, the vehicle ejects aspirin-size pellets that contain deuterium and tritium. Passing through a laser beam, the laser energy triggers a nuclear fusion reaction in each pellet several yards behind the pusher plate. The sequence of explosions propels the vehicle . . . Jastrow gave a paper that described an even more advanced propulsion scheme; it would utilize the energy of quarks—those very elusive and mysterious elementary particles, smaller than electrons, that seem to play a dominant role in holding atomic nuclei together."*

Fantastic as these prospects for future spaceflight sounded, it may be questioned whether this was the right approach to government representatives at a time when they had to struggle with the frugality guidelines from the president.

Nixon's response was disappointing. He was determined to reduce the alarming growth rate of the national budget, so he would only accept a *"quiet"* NASA program at a modest funding level which would, at best, keep the shuttle project and some unmanned science projects alive. Paine's effort for an exciting new post-Apollo space agenda did not meet with success.

Besides his work with Paine on NASA's long-range planning, von Braun worked with Newell on a broad plan for space science projects. Newell had joined NASA in 1958. By 1967 he had risen to the position of associate administrator and chief scientist. A description of his and NASA's efforts to develop a fruitful dialogue with scientists is presented in Newell's book *Beyond the Atmosphere*, a work of depth, detail, and considerable candor [4-10].

For Newell, the frugal New Englander, the purpose of spaceflight was primarily the collection, with small unmanned spacecraft, of scientific data that would increase man's knowledge of near as well as distant environments. *"All we need,"* he said in 1958, *"is a few thirty-pound satellites in Earth orbits. They will furnish enough observational data to keep our space scientists busy for decades to come."* While von Braun fully shared Newell's desire for a broad science program, space exploration was far more for him. It was a cutting edge for science as well as for technology, a stimulus for education, a catalyst for industrial endeavor, a doorway to high adventure, a means to provide direct benefits to many people on Earth, a way for man to expand the bounds of the world in which he lives, and an opportunity for enthusiastic involvement of the public.

After von Braun had become Newell's deputy, he often emphasized how much he enjoyed being close to a real scientist and how good their mutual relations were. And yet, there always remained a certain distance between the two. As a person of great restraint and personal modesty, Newell was convinced that scientists, solely by virtue of their noble pursuits, should receive all the support they need almost without asking for it. He was never a campaigner and crusader for the projects he wished to promote. Von Braun's approach was different. He believed that an endeavor as grandiose as space-flight would succeed only if the idea were taken to the public, and at the same time to the public's representatives in government, by a tireless and continuing campaign. He said, and he proved, that this approach could also provide superb opportunities for scientists to do their thing, even without the need to expose themselves to the rough environment of budget battles and public debate.

"Newell was an excellent scientist," Williams recalled [11-4], *"interested in a methodical growth of NASA's science program. Von Braun loved science, and he recognized science as one of the fundamental reasons for going into space. But he felt that science for science's sake alone was not marketable, that one had to present space to the public as a human adventure in order to gain and maintain support. However, this approach did not go down all that well with the scientific community . . ."*

Newell certainly admired von Braun for his accomplishments (Chapter 4-6). He even opted for a manned Mars mission in 1970 [11-12], but he never felt quite comfortable with von Braun's powerful promotion of spaceflight, although von Braun often made strong pleas for science. In August 1970 he gave a presentation to the Subcommittee on Science, Research, and Development in the House Science and Astronautics Committee concerning the need for a national science policy [11-13].

Our political leaders, he said, should view *"science and technology . . . as an investment from which returns are expected to the public welfare, to our national strength and security, to economic health and prosperity, to the arts, and to the improvement of the quality of life . . ."*, but a national science policy, he said, is not needed.

Von Braun's presentation was accepted with great interest, and also with enthusiastic applause, but he had no opportunity for action, neither did other members from NASA Headquarters try to influence the shaping of a national science policy.

Planning of a science policy within NASA had been the function of Newell personally, in cooperation with some of his associates. Proposing and executing specific projects was proceeding well under the experienced, active, and wise direction of John E. Naugle and his program managers in the Office of Space Science and Applications, particularly Jesse L. Mitchell who was responsible for projects in astrophysics. For them, planning of scientific projects, including countless meetings and negotiations with individual scientists, and also presentations, discussions, and disputes with panels and committees, had been their daily fare over the years. For von Braun and his few young associates, this many-splendored world of scientific projects was a new environment for which they were just not prepared. There was neither room nor need for von Braun and his group in the area of space science planning.

In spite of this fact, friendly personal contacts developed between von Braun and Naugle. *"Paine was a very good man, a visionary; I liked him,"* Naugle said during an interview in 1986 [9-30], *"and so was Wernher, whom I also liked very much. But the perception I had . . . was that Paine was pushing the system . . . far more than he should have. And he brought Wernher to headquarters to further that aim . . ."*

When Webb began to discuss long-range planning, Naugle said, *"Homer Newell and I recommended that the next step beyond Apollo be a manned mission to Mars. I was initially opposed to the shuttle . . . I felt that we should continue with the Apollo program and move on to a lunar colony, and then to Mars . . . By the late 60s, it had become clear that this view was no longer viable . . . Wernher and I shared some of the same concerns about Paine's policy. Wernher had a very good grasp of the public mood . . . he and I worked closely together to sell the 'Grand Tour' of the planets."*

"Grand Tour" refers to the fact that the outer planets sometimes happen to be in a position that would allow one spacecraft to visit several planets in sequence. Voyager spacecraft visited Jupiter, Saturn, Uranus, and Neptune during the twelve-year period from 1977 to 1989. Under the expert leadership of Dr. Edward C. Stone and the experienced project management of JPL, fortified by engineers from industry and scientists from universities and research institutes, the Voyager Grand Tour mission became one of the most impressive and successful projects in the space program.

"Wernher," Naugle said, *"did not have an easy job."* In the past, each of the associate administrators had been doing his own planning. *"Then Wernher came in with his group and set up a planning room and produced slick, fancy publications . . . His style was much different from what we were used to. Also, we were uneasy with the content, which became an issue. And the people who worked with him were not easy to get along with . . ."*

While there was no real need for von Braun in space science planning, there was an urgent need for him in the shuttle program.

Months after he had begun his work in Washington, he had not yet contacted a single scientist from the list his chief scientist in Huntsville had given him (Chapter 11-2). *"I am far too busy with something else,"* he said. *"These plans for the space shuttle, as conceived at present, are so hopelessly grandiose that there is no chance for a success, even if the $10 billion that presently are quoted were approved. In its present configuration, the shuttle will be far too complex, and far too expensive. All I am doing now here is crusading for a simpler shuttle. The first stage, presently a gigantic spaceplane with fly-back capability, should be reduced to an arrangement of droppable booster rockets, possibly even with solid propellants. The second stage, carrying the astronauts, must be returnable, of course, but it should be kept relatively small. Most of the liquid propellants needed for the ascent should be carried in an attached, droppable tank. And the payload bay in the returnable second stage, which will be the shuttle proper, must be large enough to accommodate all these instruments and facilities that we have been promising in order to justify the shuttle project two years ago. I am talking and talking, trying to keep the shuttle project alive."* After a brief pause, he added: *"I tell you, this is a thankless job. You don't make any friends being a Cassandra."*

From its beginning around 1968, the shuttle project had been largely in the hands of the Manned Spacecraft Center, with substantial support from the Marshall Center. From 1970 on, as Jay Foster remembered in 1989 [11-14], *"Wernher's office in Washington worked heavily on 'selling' the shuttle, particularly by conducting cost versus benefit analyses, and by putting the MSC and MSFC stories into context . . ."*

Von Braun had begun around 1966 to sell the idea of a shuttle-type spacecraft. *"As our manned operations in space gain momentum,"* he argued, *"we need a means to transport a small number of persons, or a limited load of freight, up and down quite frequently, sometimes, as in an emergency, even on very short notice. It would not be practical to mobilize a big rocket each time a few people have to go into or come back from orbit, and it would be even less practical to mobilize a naval task force each time a reentry capsule parachutes into the ocean. We need a small aerospaceplane that can meet these personnel transport requirements."*

When planning for a real shuttle project started in 1968, NASA envisioned a large vehicle with two stages, each of them capable of returning to Earth on wings.

A strong pitch for the space shuttle was made by George Mueller early in 1969. Projecting a modest cost for the development of a fully returnable, two-stage vehicle, and an extremely low price for a pound of payload in orbit, he quickly gained wide support for the big space shuttle, particularly with his contention that all other launch vehicles, civilian and military, would be superfluous after this shuttle had come into existence. Study contracts for the space shuttle, and also for an orbital space station, were let in 1969.

Mueller resigned from NASA in December 1969 and became chairman and chief executive officer of an industrial corporation in California.

A few months later, President Nixon, and congressional members, warned NASA not to engage in grandiose projects that would far exceed budgetary limits. Subsequently, plans for a Mars mission, for a space station, and for some other projects were dropped; only the space shuttle stayed alive. In the summer of 1970, NASA opted for the large shuttle, consisting of two fully recoverable stages. On 28 July 1970, five months after von Braun had moved to NASA Headquarters, Paine announced his resignation from NASA, and his intent to return to private industry.

Why did Paine leave at that time? *"I was a Democrat, appointed by a democratic president,"* Paine explained in 1985 [11-15]. *"I felt that President Nixon really ought to put his own man in. My fear was not so much that I was abandoning Wernher as it was the thought that if we could get a head of NASA to whom the president felt very close, we could improve NASA's strength—and, thereby, improve the prospects for Wernher's visions . . . So, I moved George Low, my deputy, in as acting administrator . . ."*

With Paine's departure, von Braun lost a strong and influential friend. He knew very well that a number of his colleagues at NASA Headquarters, and also at some field centers, resented his presence. Some wished him away for ethnic reasons, others disliked him because he had so much appeal to the public, or simply because of the undeniable successes of his projects. The fact that congressional committees always asked for him when hearings were to be held, and that he always drew so much applause and good will when he testified for NASA, was a source of irritation for some members of the hierarchy. Some program managers in headquarters felt that he stepped on their toes with his planning activities. Now, without strong backing by at least one powerful and prominent member of the NASA leadership, and without a large team of experienced co-workers, he found himself isolated, ill utilized, and not really wanted.

When von Braun was asked by former associates how he was doing, he always was quick to assure them that he was doing very well, and that he had the best personal relations with Newell, Low, and later with James C. Fletcher, the new NASA administrator appointed in 1971. Sometimes, he would add: *"I have enjoyed far more of the good life than my due share while I was at Marshall. It is only fair that I put in a few years of drudgery now. After all, NASA is confronted with a couple of very tough problems, and as a member of headquarters I may be able to help . . ."*

Low became Paine's successor as acting administrator on 16 September 1970. His first task was the establishment of a NASA program plan under the president's austerity directive. This included the need for the definition of a shuttle concept that would fit into the reduced budget.

Low was known to his colleagues as an excellent engineer of great natural talent. He had distinguished himself during the Saturn-Apollo project first in 1959 when he recommended a manned lunar mission as a goal for NASA, and again in 1967 when he directed the efforts to analyze the causes of the fire in the Apollo capsule that cost the lives of three astronauts. Also, he often succeeded in bringing the divergent views of the two centers together, under the simple motto: *"Let's put our emotional hang-ups aside, let's be reasonable, and let's work together toward our common goal . . ."*

Von Braun looked forward with confidence when he realized that he would be working for Low after Paine's departure.

The problems that Low faced now as acting administrator of NASA were quite different from those he had to deal with in the Apollo project, particularly at a time when existing program plans clashed with the president's desire to reduce government expenditures, and when congressional members were questioning the desirability of continuing an energetic national space program. Solving these problems would require a united stand of the best elements of the NASA leadership. It would call for a joint effort to plan and propose a program, and to promote it among members of the government as well as in public, a program tailored to the budget the president and the OMB would be willing to support, but also a program firmly supported by NASA Headquarters and field centers.

Paine had brought von Braun to Washington to guide the planning and the promotion of such a program. Von Braun would have been willing, and even eager, to do so, but he never had the chance to be NASA's strategic planner.

General Phillips said in 1988 [11-16]: *"Planning offices generally are not effective as such. They are effective only, if at all, if they are an arm of the boss . . . Wernher and Tom Paine spent a lot of time together. Now, if that situation had prevailed, it could have had a real impact. But Tom left, and I think at that point there was a disconnect . . . I suspect that with Tom Paine leaving and George Low remaining, and then Fletcher coming in, Wernher went adrift . . ."*

Low immersed himself fully in day-by-day work. As an interim caretaker administrator, he did not wish to preempt his successor as administrator, and Nixon was expected to nominate a new administrator almost any time. While Low was generally in favor of centralized planning, he did not address himself to the need for a real planning effort as long as he held his pro tem position. Besides, campaigning for a space project, talking to members of the government and to the public, establishing personal contacts with congressional committees, and interacting on a personal basis with those who felt responsible for the nation's space program, were not to his liking. But he did not want anyone else to do this for NASA either. Von Braun sought cooperation, Low did not [11-17]. *"I don't think George Low trusted anyone,"* Edward Z. Gray said [11-18]. *"He was an entirely different kind of a guy. George held everything close to his vest, and you never did know if you had his full agreement or not . . ."*

In his day-by-day management activities, Low really did not see any need for von Braun. It should not be surprising that Low did not wish to involve him in this short-term work.

The long-term program that von Braun envisioned for NASA in 1970 contained four major elements: (1) Skylab I, to be followed by Skylabs II and III with extended science and technology programs; (2) a reasonably small shuttle for quick Earth-orbit round-trip transportation; (3) retention of Saturn V production for heavy load transportation into orbit, including the Skylabs and spacecraft for the Moon and Mars, and (4) use of existing rockets, including Saturns, to launch science missions toward the Sun, to Mars, and on multiplanet missions. This program could be timed so that it would remain within the budget constraints. At the same time, it would prepare greater things to come later: A large shuttle; a large multipurpose orbiting space station; a lunar base for permanent occupancy; and a manned mission to Mars.

Von Braun could not find support for this planning strategy. Rather than being asked to help establish a program plan for the agency, he was told that he had to adjust to a number of existing project plans whose originators did not want to budge. He still received requests from congressional committees to testify, but he had to have his speech manuscripts *"reviewed for compatibility with NASA policy"* by staff members, and he was directed *"to speak only the party line"* [11-11].

Low, who had been such a brilliant *"man of the hour"* in the Saturn-Apollo program, did not wish to be the *"man of the decade"* during his brief term as acting administrator. He concentrated on the daily problem of keeping the agency afloat. William E. Lilly, comptroller general of NASA, had his hands full balancing the daily NASA budget. He preferred not to complicate the situation by committing to a program that would extend over several years. Besides, it appears that he never felt comfortable with von Braun's approach to space programming, and with his thoughts about the future of NASA [11-11].

When Fletcher arrived in 1971, he saw his first priority in the adjustment of all activities to the reduced budget ordered by the Nixon administration. Von Braun was not able to make any inroads with the new boss.

Still, von Braun tried to do as much as possible, almost singlehandedly, to find support for a broader space program. He and his few co-workers organized meetings with top level people inside and outside government to determine whether space activities might contribute to a solution of their problems. They talked also with the heads of the U.S. Maritime Administration, the IBM Corporation, the Military Sea Transport Administration, and others. There was definite interest at these organizations in communications and navigation satellites. However, von Braun had no budget of his own to fund even some modest studies that would define areas of interest and possible projects, and Lilly was not willing to give him any support or money. Being excluded from most meetings in which policies were discussed, he had no opportunity to suggest such projects before a decision-making forum [11-4].

All through 1970 and 1971, a rather frantic effort was underway to come up with an acceptable concept and design for the shuttle, an effort that involved not only NASA Headquarters and the field centers, but also a number of industries, government offices, military departments, the OMB, presidential advisers, and finally the president himself. From the beginning of that period, von Braun pleaded for the simpler version, with the argument that a full-size shuttle would be beyond affordable budgetary limits.

John M. Logsdon described this effort in a paper entitled *"The Space Shuttle Decision: Technology and Political Choice"* [11-19]. *"During the second half of 1971,"* he wrote, *"it was a chaotic exercise . . . Everyone was a Shuttle designer."*

Some members of the NASA Headquarters staff, under the initiative of the Manned Spacecraft Center, and supported by North American Rockwell and McDonnell-Douglas, stuck to the two-stage, fully returnable shuttle—*"not being economy-minded,"* as Logsdon said. Others, supported by Grumman, Lockheed, Boeing, and General Dynamics, tended toward the simplified design with one returnable stage, as recommended by von Braun.

OMB, in an unprecedented move, directed NASA to hire an outside firm for an economic analysis of the various proposed designs. The firm, Mathematica, Inc., of Princeton, New Jersey, was more inclined toward the simplified version, but that outcome left some headquarters personnel unhappy [11-11].

The Office of Science and Technology (OST), OMB, and the President's Scientific Advisory Committee (PSAC) participated in the debates; George Shultz, Caspar Weinberger, and Donald Rice from OMB, Edward David from OST, and Alexander Flax from the Department of Defense personally engaged in shuttle discussions. NASA finally proposed a two-phased approach: First, built the second stage of a two-stage, fully returnable shuttle, and launch it with a temporary booster stage. In parallel, develop and build the returnable first stage. Then, when it is completed, continue shuttle launchings with the returnable first stage.

While these debates and planning exercises were underway, President Nixon appointed Fletcher as the new administrator of NASA. He assumed his position on 26 April 1971. Low moved back into his former deputy position.

On 24 November 1971 Fletcher reported to the OST: *"a decision to proceed with the shuttle . . . is definitely in order. However, the selection of a specific configuration would still be somewhat premature"* [11-20]. The OMB kept prodding for more design studies, and even offered specific designs of its own which it requested to be analyzed, but NASA replied that designing shuttles was NASA's job, not OMB's [11-19].

Then, on 5 January 1972, President Nixon decided: *"The United States should proceed at once"* with this *"entirely new type of space transportation system . . ."* [11-21].

Eventually, the space shuttle came into existence, with one returnable stage, with droppable but returnable solid propellant boosters and a droppable nonrecoverable external tank, and with a payload bay sufficiently large to accept the majority of the payloads envisioned at that time.

4   LOST AND LONELY

In spite of his very good personal relations with most of his superiors and colleagues in Washington, von Braun found himself in an environment totally different from what he had been used to during the previous thirty-five years. One of his associates, touched by the turn his fortunes had taken, described the situation: *"Wernher is like a great conductor who has held the world in awe with his fabulous performances, and who suddenly finds himself without an orchestra, without players and their instruments, without a concert hall, and even without music-loving audiences. He still plays his own violin once in a while, but only few people listen to him . . ."*

Von Braun still had a small team, some former co-workers—Jay Foster, Frank Williams, William Fleming—and a few newcomers, including James Scaggs and Ian Dodds. Besides working on the shuttle concept, they tried their best to come up with space mission plans for the next decades. However, all those projects that had already reached some degree of acceptance were in the firm hands of the Offices of Science, Manned Space Flight, Technology, or Applications. There was little room, and almost no interest for new projects, but even for those few remaining planning activities there existed a number of people in NASA Headquarters, each of whom *"considered himself to be the chief planner, and resented everybody else as an intruder,"* as Williams noted [11-4]. Von Braun commented: *"We sometimes feel like moving into a vacuum."*

Von Braun's secretary, Julia (Julie) Kertes, saw another side of his life at headquarters. *"These two years were the busiest in my life,"* she wrote in 1985 [11-22]. At that time, von Braun tried to develop an interest in space at other agencies inside and outside the

Government. *"The phone rang constantly . . . there were calls from all over the world . . . For the first few months, only very little paperwork could be accomplished during the normal workday, consequently our days were long . . . von Braun received more mail than the other four executives together . . . He received so many requests for public appearances, and many from Congress, it was impossible for him to accept most of them . . . Bonnie Holmes, his former secretary in Huntsville, came up and helped me for a couple of weeks . . ."*

"Von Braun respected Dr. Newell very much; however, he had a special rapport with Dr. Paine, they were on the same wavelength . . . Dr. Low became acting administrator when Dr. Paine left . . ." Kertes continued. At the time when Low headed the Apollo program in Houston, he *"worked very closely with my boss at that time, General Sam Phillips. General Phillips had a very high regard for him, as did most of us. However, he became a changed person when Dr. Paine brought him to Washington as his deputy. There are many people in Washington who would agree with me . . ."* [11-23].

When Paine left, *"the one-to-one informal sessions with the administrator ended,"* Kertes went on, *"and appointments with the acting administrator to discuss our programs became more difficult to set up as time went by. Dr. von Braun was seldom invited to accompany other NASA officials when they went to the Hill to testify before the Congress . . . There was resentment and jealousy because Dr. von Braun was so well known and well liked . . . Even though Dr. von Braun never made a disparaging remark about anyone in my presence, this must have been a very frustrating period for him . . ."*

Casual visitors to von Braun's office in Washington during that time would not have observed much change in the personality they had known in previous years: warm-hearted, smiling, always ready to tell a little story or the newest joke. But to his closer friends, there were changes indeed. The luster in his eyes was losing radiance. His descriptions of pending space projects became less intense. Prospects for future space programs, evolving from past achievements, lacked his usual optimism. Quotes from encouraging discussions with high-ranking government officials became rare. Most surprising was the absence of any indication that he was participating in efforts to forge ahead with a national space program that would be a worthy successor to the accomplishments of the 1960s. It seemed sometimes that he was about to resign himself to a sort of *"internal emigration."*

Any attempt to find out where his apprehensions might originate, and whether his friends could share some specific burden with him, would be futile. *"I'm doing very well,"* he would say. *"All my colleagues are very nice, and my relations with my superiors are excellent. Of course, there is the usual budget crunch, but with a little common sense we will understand and learn to live with these problems . . . we must learn to be patient."* Very rarely, he would drop a few words that afforded a glimpse at his real thoughts: *"People are so totally unrealistic,"* he might say, or: *"We should focus on a definite goal,"* or: *"We are rapidly losing ground,"* or simply: *"There is so much talking and so little doing . . ."*

To complain would have been entirely uncharacteristic of von Braun. *"I don't want to waste my time by thinking of what is bad in this world"* was a frequent statement. Even those who were close to him over long periods of time can hardly remember that he ever spoke negatively about other people, least of all about his superiors. There was one person, though, who had a deeper insight into his own world: his wife Maria. Her memories of the years 1971 and 1972 show what must have occupied his mind at that time. *"On many evenings,"* she recalled, *"we walked around the block for hours and hours while he talked and poured out his soul . . . all I could do was just listen . . . he was so deeply depressed; for him, a world was falling apart . . . I felt that the only relief I could give him was just to encourage him to talk . . ."* [11-24].

After Paine left NASA, von Braun began to face growing isolation. He was no longer a regular participant in high-level meetings. His advice was rarely sought. Important decisions were discussed and made without him. While congressional committees still requested presentations and advice from him, his active role in NASA, for which he had come to Washington, diminished quickly. *"He walked through the corridors of head-quarters like a stranger,"* said one of his associates.

Disher, recalling those times in 1987 [8-32], said: *"There were plain human jealousies . . ."* One of von Braun's closest friends in industry, Samuel K. Hoffman, president of Rocketdyne where most of the nation's rocket motors were built, was even more outspoken [4-8]: *"There is a lot of politics going on in Washington . . . it seems that they just did not like him at NASA Headquarters. He had made such tremendous contributions to the space program, but he had no chances to contribute further at the time when he was at Headquarters . . ."*

This was a world quite different from that of the 1960s when the Saturn-Apollo project was underway. Webb, Seamans, Dryden, Mueller, Phillips, Holmes, Bisplinghoff, Silverstein had left the agency. The spirit had changed.

The reason for von Braun's deep concern was certainly not a wounded personal pride. For him, the brilliant successes of the past fifteen years were the fruit of a huge effort of the American people—of several hundred thousand engineers, scientists, technicians, planners, managers, and more than one hundred million taxpayers—who together built and paid for America's accomplishments in space. This effort established the nation's preeminence at the frontiers of technology and exploration; it had become a source of national pride and prestige.

Von Braun was aware that he personally had made decisive contributions to this development through his life's work. This knowledge may have given him some happy feelings, but it also created a profound sense of responsibility. At the time when the Moon project was at its climax, his primary concern was the question how the momentum in America's space program could be preserved for the future. The need to maintain the country's front place in space exploration, and particularly in space utilization, appeared mandatory to him. *"We have told the taxpayers that after the Moon, we will use Saturn vehicles to utilize space for benefits on Earth,"* he said.

The Saturn Applications Program, to be conducted with Saturn rockets and Skylab spacecraft after the Apollo project, was to serve this purpose. However, by 1971 the handwriting was on the wall that there was no prospect for a continuation of the Sky-lab program after Skylab I, and even of the Saturn V program after the last Apollo flight to the Moon.

Associate Administrator Dale Myers, during an interview in 1989 [11-25], recalled those days of change in the space program—depressing for all those who had hoped and worked for America's bright future in space. *"He was in a terrible down-hill situation at NASA Headquarters . . ."* Discontinuation of the Saturn V and the Skylab programs *"was a terrible blow . . . We fought for about a year until we realized that all we could do at the time was hold the shuttle. Von Braun and his people were very unhappy; there's no question about it. It was a tremendous blow to all of us . . ."*

Von Braun's progressing isolation in NASA had two aspects, a personal one, and another one that extended far beyond the limits of personal feelings.

The first aspect he would have been ready to accept. *"I had a wonderful life,"* he sometimes said. *"Really, I had my day in the sunshine. It is only right when others get to sit in the front seat now . . ."*

The other aspect of von Braun's demise from NASA concerns the echo it caused in the country.

A project as large as the space program has its life-sustaining roots not only in science and engineering, but, more decisively even, in the president and his cabinet, in the Congress, and in the people. To them, von Braun had been the spark that ignited the fire during the 1950s; the crusader who raised enthusiasm for the new ocean of space; the motivator who caused his country to become spacefaring nation number one. And now, it appeared that NASA did not want him any longer. No more testifying before Congress, no further opportunities to help forge ahead with exciting new projects, no longer speaking for the nation's space program in the name of NASA.

Adolf K. Thiel, senior vice president at the Thompson-Ramo-Wooldridge corporation, spoke about those times in 1988 [11-26]: *"Von Braun tried to focus NASA's thinking on long-range goals, but he received no help from the old headquarters bureaucrats, nor from the Johnson Space Center. After Paine had left, Fletcher, and particularly Low started to ignore von Braun . . . His effectiveness went to zero . . . It was a tremendous loss; he was the only visionary proponent of spaceflight left in the NASA hierarchy, the only communicator with Congress . . ."*

Von Braun's gradual exclusion from NASA's leadership circle gave a signal that was not lost on congressional members, on the news media, and on the people. The signal said that whoever was responsible for the space program at NASA and in the government did not want to continue the aggressive approach to space exploration that von Braun had preached and practiced for more than twenty years. Is it surprising, under these conditions, that the public support, which the space program had been enjoying through many years, began to wane? One of the media reporters who had followed and covered the space program through many of its highlights put his bewilderment in these words: *"What is happening here? They are killing the goose that laid their golden eggs!"*

To the surprise of many, nobody tried to put a halt to the growing alienation of von Braun in headquarters. Fletcher, who often expressed great admiration for von Braun's contributions to the space program, could have said to those who wished him away: *"Hold your horses, gentlemen, and swallow your pride! This man is a national asset, we need him!"* There were no such voices, neither from the administrator, nor the associate administrator, nor the office directors, nor the astronauts, nor the field centers, nor the Congress, nor the White House. There were no signs that anyone may have tried to retain von Braun for the good of the national space program, and of the country.

After von Braun had left NASA, Julie Kertes, his secretary, became Dr. Fletcher's secretary. Before she accepted the position, she asked von Braun for his advice. *"Dr. von Braun told me by all means to take the job . . . he said that Dr. Fletcher was a first-rate individual"* [11-22]. Kertes soon felt quite comfortable in her new position; one day, she told her boss that she blamed him for von Braun's resignation from NASA. *"Dr. Fletcher said that he could understand that all of us blamed him, but, he said, he was not the one who had the idea . . . Of course, he did admit that as administrator, he could have overruled [that person]."*

5   RETIREMENT FROM NASA

In May 1972, newspaper articles and TV news told of von Braun's impending retirement from NASA. He was quoted as saying that he wanted to use his remaining time to implement "some space projects I feel are of particular importance. I think I can do this best in industry where the tools of progress are made."

There was no great surprise among von Braun's countless friends who had followed his work and his fortunes through more than a quarter century, and who had realized how von Braun's shining star was moving behind a cloud while he worked at headquarters. They also felt that they knew quite well what his own answer would be if he were asked why he retired. *"Look,"* he would say, *"the space program is in good and stable condition, as far as present circumstances permit. The shuttle, reduced now to a size that is affordable, has been assigned to the Manned Spacecraft Center. Skylab nears completion at Marshall. Programs in space sciences enjoy the proven leadership of the Office of Space Sciences. Applications projects are underway to the extent the budget allows. A number of farther-out projects have been studied; they will not need further planning before they have moved closer to realization. I do not feel that I am needed at NASA Headquarters at this time. A man should do something constructive as long as he is mentally fit, shouldn't he? I hope I still have a couple of years to do some useful work. My life has given me such tremendous opportunities to learn; should I not try to make good use of what I have learned? I believe in the principle of returns on investments!"* These words would have been typical of von Braun—no complaints, no trace of disappointment or frustration, not the slightest hint of any personal tensions at his place of work, only the desire to continue to work in some productive fashion.

What would von Braun do next? Throughout his life, he was eager to have a powerful, strong-willed superior, a man who was ready to make a decision when needed, who was creative enough to formulate his own beliefs, and who had the courage to defend these beliefs. Von Braun himself had the same traits of character. While his basic nature was inclined toward technology and science, his best complement would be a boss who was at home on the complex battlefields of politics and budget fighting. On top of this, von Braun wanted and needed a boss with whom he could have a perfect man-to-man relationship in any discussion that might come up.

"My good fortunes have given me the best superiors I could ever have hoped for," von Braun used to say. *"General Becker in Kummersdorf, General Dornberger in Peenemünde, General Toftoy, General Medaris, Mr. Webb, Dr. Paine in the United States . . ."* With each of them, von Braun struck it rich. Except for Paine, whose leadership he could enjoy all too briefly, each of these men happened to be von Braun's superior during the times when von Braun achieved important technical breakthroughs.

When von Braun left NASA in 1972 to begin a new phase in his professional life, he looked for a boss with whom he would be able to establish again this very special relationship. He found the man in Edward G. Uhl, president of Fairchild Industries. Uhl and von Braun had known each other for a number of years (Chapters 9-3, 9-7, 9-10), not only from joint space projects, but also from exciting outdoors experiences. A brilliant business executive, a top-notch engineer, a distinguished gentleman, a man who stood at the peak of his life, and a company president who wanted to broaden the base of his aerospace firm by initiating satellite projects for the benefit of users on Earth—what more could von Braun hope for?

In June, there was a farewell party for von Braun in the executive dining room at NASA. Julie Kertes remembered some details [11-23]: *"Both Dr. Fletcher and Dr. Low spoke . . . There were members of Congress, two that I recall: 'Tiger' Teague and Don Fuqua . . . Quite a few came from Huntsville . . . To me, it was such a sad occasion . . . A lot of people, particularly those who worked for Dr. von Braun, commiserated with me . . ."*

There was another bit of recollection of that farewell party in 1972. Five years later,

Rees and Stuhlinger visited von Braun in his hospital room in Alexandria. It was to be the last time they saw their boss and friend. Von Braun's progressing illness had weakened him so much that he could not even sit up in his bed without assistance. He spoke slowly and with great effort, but his sentences were still as perfectly formed as they had ever been. He wanted to know about the projects at the Marshall Center, and he asked how his former associates were doing. The shuttle must have been very much at the center of his thinking; he wished to hear about many details. Then, although with difficulty, and obviously in pain, he said:

"When I left NASA in 1972, the people in headquarters gave me a nice farewell party. As we stood around with our martinis, George Low took me aside and said: 'Wernher, do you remember the time when you came up from Huntsville to join us in headquarters? When you realized what a grandiose concept we had for the shuttle, you were quite shocked, and you exhorted us to make it smaller and cheaper, just to keep it alive in the forthcoming budget fights. We were not pleased at all by your warning words, but finally we accepted your advice and built the shuttle smaller and simpler. Let me thank you today very sincerely, in the name of all of us at NASA, for what you did! If you had not raised the red flag at that time, I'm certain that the entire shuttle project would be dead by now. Thank you, Wernher!'"

"That," von Braun said as tears came to his eyes, *"was the happiest moment during my time at headquarters."*

CHAPTER 12

THE FAIRCHILD YEARS

1 VICE PRESIDENT FOR ENGINEERING

Von Braun's career at NASA ended on 30 June 1972. On 1 July, he began his work at Fairchild Industries in Germantown, Maryland, as corporate vice president for engineering and development. Edward G. Uhl, chairman of the board, president and chief executive officer, remembered von Braun's entrance into his company during an interview in September 1985 [12-1]: *"For many years, I had tried to get a strategic planning function established at Fairchild, and we had made some progress—but we really were not happy with what we were doing. So I gave that to him, as a main assignment, to put into place at Fairchild a strategic planning activity."*

That covered everything, aeronautical as well as space, and other work, *"and we still follow, fundamentally, everything that was established under Wernher's leadership. He made strategic planning an integral part of our operations, not something that resulted in a report to be filed away . . ."*

Thomas Turner, Fairchild's vice president for marketing, remembers von Braun [12-2] *"as a kindly man in a new jungle environment. Certainly, his technical background and astute mind well equipped him to meet all the technical prerequisites of handling liaison, whether on the A-10 aeroplane or advanced communications satellites. He could easily work his way through the jargon and the intricacies of the technology. From the people viewpoint, he never had a problem. From the public relations point of view, he was excellent—this was one of his greatest strengths. He looked well, he looked neat, he had a nice smile, and he was very gracious . . . People tripped all over themselves to have lunch with him in the executive dining room. No doubt the aura of his background went with him all the way . . .*

"All companies have to meet the outside world," Turner continued. *"Internationally, the doors to him were always wide open. For example, what would have been a normal marketing trip to the Spanish Air Force—when you traveled with Wernher they would roll out all the old aeroplanes, the old Heinkel 111s and the Messerschmitt 109s, and we would find ourselves sitting in the cockpits with the chief of staff. If Prince Juan Carlos knew we were in town, we would be invited to the palace for a private lunch with the princess—just the four of us. We would have very unusual discussions of worldwide interest . . . Or, you'd go to Iran. Normally, an industry guy would have great difficulty seeing the Shah; but when Wernher was there, you'd go to the palace and meet with the Shah of Iran. And the prime minister would loan you his private aircraft . . . There were trips to England where he talked to the Defence Establishment; and we had one particularly historic breakfast with Duncan Sandys who was Churchill's son-in-law. We had an interesting breakfast . . ."*

Von Braun got deeply involved in technical aspects of the company's products and developments. *"His role in marketing,"* Turner said, *". . . was very good. But it was not a large percentage of his working day. I would say that his working day consisted to 70 or 80 percent of engineering . . ."*

Von Braun's first secretary at Fairchild was Mrs. Patricia O. Webb. *"During our interview,"* Webb remembered later [12-3], *"I told Dr. von Braun that I heard [through office gossip] he was very demanding and dictatorial and hard to work for—in fact, a monster! He promised me he wasn't, and requested that I just try him out . . . Dr. von Braun was neither demanding nor was he at all dictatorial—quite the contrary, he was always asking me 'how do you suggest we handle this?' I don't think I have since met, and probably never will meet a boss who was so willing to please. We worked extremely hard, but he never once 'told' me to do something. He always 'requested' I do something, and he prefaced his request with a 'please'."*

"I think," she continued, *"he was extremely excited about [working for an industrial concern]. He wanted to know everything about Fairchild. His curiosity was insatiable. He pored over Fairchild information—took work home, had a light installed in the backseat of the car he was driven in so he could read when riding home after dark . . . I can remember a letter to Indira Gandhi for Dr. von Braun (regarding the Applications Technology Satellite); I had to redo it many times to get it letter perfect, and the way Dr. von Braun and Mr. Turner wanted it worded . . ."*

Next to his hard work, Webb has other memories of von Braun: *"I remember von Braun mostly as a father-type. He used to say to me: 'Maria and I are so concerned because Iris [who lived in India at that time] doesn't seem to have the time or inclination to write. How do you think we could get her to communicate with us on a more frequent basis?' I suggested that they buy her a tape recorder and send her tapes . . . He had three children, and he made every effort to be a good father . . ."*

When people learned that he would join Fairchild, *"everyone was so excited; everybody thought Mr. Uhl had pulled off a wonderful coup . . ."*

On the day of the last Apollo launch, von Braun had an interview with Walter Cronkite at the Cape. Patricia Webb, who drove von Braun from Orlando to the launch site, remembered [12-3]: *"He insisted that I go with him to the interview so that I could meet Cronkite since he thought Cronkite was such a wonderful person . . ."*

Webb's successor as von Braun's secretary was Miss Kayren Redman. *"On 24 March 1974,"* she remembered in 1989 [12-4], *"Pat introduced us. I said to him: 'Dr. von Braun, you have had such an interesting life.' He looked at me and said: 'Kayren, I'm still having it!' . . . We talked about my experience, and, believe it or not, my family, my roots, where I came from, my background . . . I was totally in awe of the gentleman . . . The biggest part of the job during the first couple of months was all the people who would call, and knowing who was who. That was where Pat, Bonnie [Holmes], and Julie [Kertes] [who often came to the office] were most helpful . . . He went to England [to speak] to the Royal Academy . . . it had to do with the training of English officers. It was quite an elite group, and he had a meeting with the Queen. He gave the speech on 26 May 1975—that was the day I got married. On the day he gave the speech and was meeting the queen he sent me a card, wishing me the best of everything . . ."*

Shortly after von Braun began his work at Fairchild, he asked Irvin Singer, at that time chief scientist and vice president of business development—later to be promoted to executive vice president—to be his deputy. *"This I did . . .",* Singer recalled in 1989 [12-5]. *"During a period of several years, Wernher and I interfaced on a daily basis. We traveled together extensively, and we became good friends."*

"Wernher, in some respects, was above it all," Singer said, *"a thinker and a long-range planner. But, of course, when . . . Ed Uhl wanted something done, Wernher was ready to do it . . . When he felt that the company was not backing him in foreign*

travels—this is, providing technical and marketing follow-through—he let the appro-priate people in the company know that he would stop our door-opening activities."

Von Braun made several trips to Alaska while he was at Fairchild. Singer remem-bered one trip in 1975: *"It was a fantastic experience. We hired Erik Bergaust to set up the Alaska trip. We were interested in Alaska from many different aspects. One, to see if we could challenge RCA in the communications area. Two, to determine if we could make any sales of some of our airplanes. Three, whether we should buy an airline. And four, to promote ATS [Applications Technology Satellite].*

"The first weekend we went hunting and fishing . . . out on a lake that had a cabin; we got in there on a seaplane . . . They even had a little, broken-down sauna. The first morning Wernher took a sauna, and then went dashing out and jumped into the lake with his arms flying. That was an interesting scene, a down-to-Earth Wernher!"

How did Singer remember von Braun over a decade after his death? *"He was a great guy. I miss him. This was something that certainly filled out my career, the experience of working with such a man . . ."*

2   SATELLITE TV PROGRAMS FOR APPALACHIA, ALASKA, INDIA, AND BRAZIL

"Eighteen months ago," von Braun said to a Senate Committee on Aeronautics and Space Science in 1973 [12-6], *"I left the National Aeronautics and Space Administration . . . Looking for a suitable spot in industry, I wanted to be helpful in expanding the tremendous potential of communications satellites, in particular their use for audio-visual education. It was for this reason that I joined Fairchild Industries which has long been a leader in this field . . ."*

Indeed, von Braun recognized the *"tremendous potential"* of communications from satellite orbit many years ago, and he used every opportunity to promote the idea of using orbiting spacecraft for that purpose. Others joined this campaign, most notably Arthur C. Clarke, who is credited with the original idea of putting a communications satellite into an equatorial geosynchronous orbit where it would remain above the same point of the equator indefinitely. NASA began in the 1960s to actively pursue the development of orbital receiving and transmitting systems. American industry quickly realized the promise of this gold mine in space, and private enterprise established a transoceanic communications satellite network that soon was to span the globe. Communications satellites in synchronous orbit quickly became a solid business—another example of the tremendous success that beckons to the pioneering spirit of free enterprise.

Soon after NASA and its industrial contractors had started to develop communica-tion links by satellite, the International Telecommunications Satellite (INTELSAT) system came into being. *"From 1966 till 1971,"* von Braun wrote in an essay *"The Promise of Space"* [12-7], the INTELSAT system grew *"from one small satellite and four ground terminals to five rather large satellites, plus two spares that can be activated, and fifty ground stations around the world . . ."*

Other countries were almost as quick in realizing the tremendous potential of communications satellites. *"The Soviet Union was the first, bridging the vast domestic distance between European Russia and Vladivostok with its Molniya satellites,"* von Braun said in a presentation to the American Institute of Aeronautics and Astronautics in 1972 [12-8], *"and the first country to acquire its own domestic synchronous satellite was Canada . . ."*

Fascinated and gratified by the rapid progress of communications through satellite, von Braun was even more interested in the impact satellites could have in providing a decent education to his fellow men—particularly in regions that are almost inaccessible by the usual ground communications means.

In his thinking, a better education would be the key to a better world. *"Give a hungry man a fish, and you will feed him for one day. Teach him how to catch a fish, and he will never go hungry again for the rest of his life,"* he said, quoting an ancient Chinese proverb.

In his preface to a book by L. B. Taylor, *For All Mankind* [12-9], von Braun wrote: *". . . it talks about powerful satellites beaming audio-visual television programs into remote hamlets to help break the stranglehold of illiteracy, which still retards the progress and well-being of a substantial part of mankind more than any other factor . . ."*

NASA, in addition to communications satellites, also developed a family of *"application technology satellites,"* ATS, to serve the specific needs of groups of people who, by geographic or other circumstances, encounter difficulties in catching up, or keeping pace, with the development of civilization in other countries. NASA selected Fairchild Industries as contractor to help develop and build the ATS satellites. ATS 1 and 3, launched in December 1966 and November 1967, demonstrated the ability of geosynchronous satellites to handle television projects for that purpose. An advanced telecommunications satellite in the ATS series, with a very large umbrella-shaped antenna to reach even small ground stations, was planned for launching in 1974. This satellite, named ATS-F before and ATS 6 after its launch, became a central element in von Braun's work program at Fairchild.

A few months after starting this work, he published a paper, *"ATS-F: TV Station in Outer Space"* [12-10], in which he emphasized the enormous benefits a country such as India could draw from a satellite for education in reading and writing, agricultural techniques, environmental protection, family planning, and many other activities that can improve the quality of life.

The big ATS satellite was launched into geosynchronous orbit in 1974. After some testing and subsequent use as a television relay station over the Western Hemisphere, including Appalachia and Alaska, it was moved within its geostationary orbit and placed over the Indian subcontinent. While NASA engineers kept the satellite in operational condition, the television programs over India were controlled solely by Indian authorities. ATS 6 remained over India during much of 1975 and 1976, broadcasting programs to some 2,400 remote villages. In each village, a 3-meter parabolic antenna and associated electronics received the programs. Indian participants in the project referred to it as *"the greatest communications experiment ever."*

Shortly after the satellite had begun broadcasting TV programs over India, von Braun gave a presentation to the Committee on Science and Technology in the House of Representatives [12-11], saying: *"ATS 6 . . . launched into geosynchronous orbit nearly 14 months ago . . . has performed virtually flawlessly ever since . . . It has proven the effectiveness of satellite television for education, and also for remote medical diagnosis and treatment . . . Thousands of teachers, school children, doctors, and nurses from the Appalachian hills to remote settlements in Alaska have not only seen it work, but have used it every day."*

Uhl shared von Braun's enthusiasm for using satellites to improve living conditions on Earth. *"The two of us,"* he said in 1985 [12-1], *"went up to Alaska when ATS 6 was on station . . . The thing that really impressed me, as it did Wernher, was seeing these little villages of maybe a hundred people, and they would have a paramedic and an ATS antenna and associated electronic equipment. You could take a television picture with a TV camera, feed it through the satellite, and get it to Fairbanks or Anchorage . . . you could get the doctors there to communicate through the return link, and instruct the paramedics or nurses on how to treat people, even to the extent of having one person do an appendectomy who had never done it before!"*

A state like Alaska really could have used a communication satellite, but, Uhl said, *"we could never get it all together,"* although he, von Braun, Turner, and Singer talked to the outgoing and the incoming governors of Alaska, and to other high officials of the state.

There was just nobody to pay for it! A massive allocation of funds would have been needed to build an operational system, complete with a maintenance and repair work force.

NASA, by its very charter, was not permitted to help in this situation beyond developing the basic system, training the potential users, and helping them to get started on their own operational system. Those people who would profit most from this satellite communications and broadcasting system were poor. They could not finance the build-up and maintenance of such a system.

The situation with COMSAT (Communications Satellite Corporation) or INTELSAT was different. Here, the participating members—the United States, Europe, Japan— were highly developed, well-organized, super-active, wealthy partners, and operation of a communications system would be a lucrative business from the beginning. Providing education, medical services, and an access to the news systems of countries with modern technologies for developing populations that are struggling for the basic necessities of life is a different story.

Turner described the ATS dilemma in 1989 [12-2]: *"The giant networks were not going to service poor markets; they had no interest in them."*

"Fairchild had gotten very much involved in India," Singer recalled [12-5]. *"We [Singer and von Braun] met with Mrs. Indira Gandhi and with the American ambassador, Senator Moynihan. Mrs. Gandhi appeared to be a very shy but sharp-witted individual, and the meeting was very reserved and formal . . . Wernher went in by himself while I chatted with the son . . ."*

The ATS project in India did not lead to any follow-up activities. *"That was more of a result of Indira Gandhi's taking over,"* Uhl said [12-1], *"and India beginning to tilt more towards Russia and away from the United States. Later, the Russians put up a satellite for India."*

"In Iran," Singer recalled, *"while the Shah was still in power, a group of Fairchild people came to discuss satellite communications . . . Dr. von Braun delivered a major speech at the university which was extremely well received with throngs of people trying to meet him personally. Of course, once the Shah was put down, we never touched Iran again . . ."*

3   MEANWHILE, BACK IN HUNTSVILLE . . .

While von Braun went through a process of increasing alienation at NASA Headquarters between 1970 and 1972, his team at the Marshall Center in Huntsville enjoyed a period of quiet and stability. Work proceeded well with the launching of Apollo flights number 13 through 17—the last one on 7 December 1972—under the balanced, solid leadership of von Braun's former deputy, Eberhard Rees. Skylab was built and prepared for launch; lunar Rovers were built and launched with each of the last three Apollo flights; and several other projects were started.

Work on the shuttle main engine, developed at Rockwell International under Marshall's auspices, was progressing, as well as work on the solid propellant boosters and on the external tank for the shuttle. A purely scientific space project, the Gravitational Redshift Experiment to verify predictions of Einstein's general relativity theory, was assigned to Marshall. Plans for a joint Soviet-American project, Apollo-Soyuz, and for a large, permanently occupied orbital space station were also underway there in close cooperation with colleagues in Houston.

Rees accepted the High Energy Astronomical Observatory [HEAO] project in April 1971, and the large Space Telescope project (Hubble Telescope), in May 1972 as active development projects for the center.

Life and work at the Marshall Center continued on the basis of the considerable momentum that had been built up in the von Braun team through many years.

Director Rees enjoyed the respect, confidence, and cooperative spirit of his employees, and of the center's many industrial contractors as well. Certainly, his management style, and also his personal engagement in space matters, differed from von Braun's. However, by his quiet, persistent, no-nonsense way of approaching his task, he succeeded in maintaining the traditional features of the von Braun team.

Then, in January 1973, Rees unexpectedly announced his resignation from NASA. For all his co-workers, it came too early.

His retirement had been expected within the next few years. A successor had even been picked and carefully prepared while von Braun was still at Marshall: William R. Lucas, a chemist, who had joined von Braun's group in the early 1950s and had worked his way up through the ranks; when von Braun left in 1970, Lucas became deputy director under Rees. When Rees left Marshall, Lucas seemed to be the natural choice as his successor.

However, NASA Headquarters decided that Lucas needed more experience, and named Rocco Petrone as Marshall's new director.

Petrone at that time was director of the Apollo program at headquarters. From 1952 until 1969, he had been a member of the Kennedy Space Center in Florida. Petrone was famous for his capacity for hard work, and for his almost limitless energy. He was a relentless driver for accomplishment, and a tough and demanding task master for his co-workers. As a graduate of the West Point Military Academy, any assignment for him was like a military order, it had to be carried out to the last minute detail. People who worked for him sometimes referred to Petrone as *"Il Duce."*

When it became known that Petrone would be the new boss at Marshall, people at the center took a cautious wait-and-see attitude. Von Braun, following his former center's fate and fortunes from up north, had words of encouragement. *"Rocco is an excellent man,"* he said, *"he knows the rocket business inside and out. He often told me how highly he values the work we have been doing at the Marshall Center. And besides,"* von Braun added, *"we German-Americans can certainly count on Rocco's intimate understanding of the problems which we as neo-citizens are still facing here and there. As the son of immigrant parents from Italy himself, Rocco will hold his protective hand over the former Germans in his center."*

Von Braun was correct with his first prediction. Petrone proved to be a go-getter of the first order.

Soon after his arrival, Skylab I was launched. As it ascended through the atmosphere and gained speed, differential aerodynamic forces developed at the meteoroid shield that surrounded much of the body of Skylab. These forces tore off part of the shield and of the heat-protecting cover of Skylab, and also one of the two large solar arrays that would provide electric power for Skylab. This accident was even more tragic because several members of the center had warned of the danger-prone design of the meteoroid shield; Ernst Geissler, head of the Aerodynamics Laboratory, had pointed out that differential air forces might arise at the shield and cause trouble—but his warnings were brushed aside (Chapter 8-5).

Petrone immediately organized a massive effort at Marshall, at the Manned Space-craft Center (from 1973, Johnson Space Center), and at some contractor plants to repair the wounded space station, and to restore its functional capabilities as far as possible. This effort was successful, and Petrone was admired greatly for his efficiency in dealing with this emergency. The Skylab project became an outstanding accomplishment with three shifts of astronauts, each shift with three members, who together spent a total of 177 days of three-man occupation in orbit, conducting a rich program of experiments and observations. Skylab was the first American space station in orbit—a proud achievement for all who contributed to its success, particularly for its project manager at MSFC, Leland F. Belew, and its program director at NASA Headquarters, William C. Schneider.

Von Braun's second prediction, to the effect that Petrone would have a true understanding for the specific problems that confronted the Marshall Center with its nucleus of former German nationals, did not bear out.

"We were just ending Apollo, and getting ready to fly Skylab," Petrone recalled in 1989 [8-39]. *"Behind these events was the planning going on in Washington to downsize Marshall to a smaller center. I did not know this at the time I became director of Marshall. Our first business was to successfully fly Skylab, and to make plans for some future programs such as space shuttle and HEAO* [High Energy Astronomical Observatory]. . . . *But, Washington had made plans to cut back MSFC by over one thousand civil service, and two thousand in-house contractors . . ."*

It soon became obvious that in this reduction, most of the former Germans would lose their jobs or be given the choice between retirement and substantial reduction in grade. The impression arose that Petrone had received strict orders from NASA Headquarters to *"Americanize"* the Marshall Center. He carried out this assignment like a brave soldier. When Petrone left Marshall less than one year after he had taken over its directorship, only very few of the former Germans were still at work there; and the few, with one or two exceptions, did not occupy positions of mainline responsibility.

Reduction procedures involved more than the downsizing of personnel strength; they resulted also in a profound change in the management philosophy at the Marshall Center.

Von Braun had always taken the position that a government organization—in this case his team—should establish and maintain the capability to formulate exactly the technical details of a desired product, and then to advise, support, and monitor the contractor who was building the product, to provide help when needed, to verify the quality of completed products, and to judge and control cost figures. In some cases, development work on novel technologies should be conducted in-house, such as the welding and X-ray testing of huge aluminum tanks, or the ablation method to protect reentering warheads and space capsules. Under the new ruling, Marshall's in-house capability was all but eliminated. Shops, test areas, laboratories soon became empty and lifeless.

The impression was unavoidable that Washington, in selecting a new director for the Marshall Center, was not looking for experience in center leadership, but only for faithful execution of an order that seemed appropriate to headquarters. For Petrone, leading a center of Marshall's size and complexity was an entirely new situation. There would have been plenty of experience available among the laboratory and office directors to provide advice and assistance, but rather than having policy discussions and debates first with his associates at MSFC, and then with his superiors in Washington, he chose to strictly carry out the orders given to him.

If a reduction of operating cost of NASA was necessary, and the president obviously was asking for it, this could have been accomplished on the basis of discussions, careful planning, and wise decisions between NASA Headquarters, center directors, and leading managers, engineers, and scientists. The basic capabilities of the team could then have been saved. As it happened, the very fiber of the Marshall team, its proven capability for technical achievement, faded away. The Marshall Center became a different place in 1973. Petrone's isolation from the people he had come to lead was unavoidable.

Feelings of Marshall members toward Petrone were compassionate, rather than hostile. After a brilliant career at the Cape, during which he had come into close contact with the Marshall Center and had often praised the center and its director for their excellent work, he had now become its director. But rather than helping it continue its line of accomplishments, he had to force it to cut back. Rather than making it *"his"* center, and giving it all the protection and leadership it deserved, he saw no other way than to obey his orders from Washington—regardless. To help change and downsize the Marshall team that had developed the Saturn which in turn gave him, as Saturn manager at the Kennedy Space Center, the opportunity for splendid personal accomplishments, must have been an excruciating task for him.

It was obvious that Petrone himself was not happy at the Marshall Center. He was very tense; people tried to avoid crossing his path. One of Marshall's program managers at that time remembers: *"Sometimes, Petrone was really tough. Poor Hermann Weidner! He had worked on the development and testing of rocket engines for more than thirty years, and he had contributed to a number of very successful projects, and yet Petrone poured his relentless criticism over him . . . You could hardly say anything without incurring his rebuke . . . The center surely became a different place during that year . . ."*

At about the same time, two other events occurred that cast deep shadows over the space program: NASA decided that Skylab should be terminated after the highly successful Skylab I flight, even though two more advanced Skylabs were in preparation. NASA also decided that no further Saturn Vs should be built or planned for future projects. Production of Saturn's famous engine, the F-1, was also terminated. *"The entire tooling for the engine . . . is no longer in existence . . . it was absolutely foolish . . ."* said Samuel K. Hoffman of Rocketdyne in 1988 [4-8].

Lucas, Petrone's successor, faced a difficult task. How long would it take before a mutual trust between front office and work force, so characteristic of von Braun's leadership, would be restored? How long would it take before a technical in-house capability could be rebuilt? The team, once a well-integrated, organically grown group of several thousand people, had changed. Openness, mutual confidence, easy flow of communications had given way to tension, alienation, and lack of trust. Workshops, laboratories, test stands, design rooms were almost empty.

Sometimes, one of the Marshall people would mention to von Braun at Fairchild Industries that things were changing at his former center. True to his principle not to criticize any superior, he would not commiserate. *"This world is not a bed of roses,"* he would say. *"We had a number of excellent years, didn't we? Nobody could expect that this would go on like that forever. When a new boss comes to an organization, he will always bring his own rules of operation, and you have to allow him to do this . . ."*

These were brave words, but they were not von Braun's only reaction to the events in Huntsville. In rare moments, he would show how deeply concerned he was about those changes. It was not so much the personal grief of those who were directly affected, but rather the fact that a brilliant ability of the nation, acquired through the effort, dedication, and trust of several hundred thousand of its citizens, and many millions of taxpayers, and ready to keep the United States in the front line of technical and scientific accomplishments, was being degraded, and perhaps even lost.

In all fairness, it must not be overlooked that a contributing factor to this change in the fortunes of the von Braun team perhaps may be found within the von Braun team itself.

During the early 1950s, when von Braun—on short notice—had to organize a team that could develop, and help build, test, and launch a guided missile for the Army, the Redstone, it was natural that he placed his experienced members of the former Peenemünde establishment in those positions that they had held in a similar project before: design, testing, guidance and control, aerodynamics, trajectories, measuring systems, rocket engine development, computer simulation, machine shop, and assembly work for the V-2 missile. Each of these men, during the years following their arrival in Huntsville, developed his laboratory or shop as required by the new project assignments.

At the peak of activities in Huntsville during the Saturn-Apollo project, the in-house team had grown to almost 8,000 people. This was a tremendous growth from the size of the original group, and there were a large number of excellent young people who had joined the bandwagon, as von Braun sometimes said. He also said—and his Peenemünde oldtimers would heartily agree—that the quality of the young men and women who became team members during the 1950s and 1960s was in every way equivalent to the quality of those people who had developed and built the V-2 in Peenemünde; the only difference may be seen in the fact that *"we oldtimers had twelve more years to make mistakes, and to learn from them,"* a difference that certainly had washed out during the years when the Redstone, the Jupiter, the Pershing, Explorer 1, the Saturns, and Skylab were developed and built in Huntsville.

And yet, it appeared to some observers that von Braun was hesitant to give American-born co-workers the opportunity to grow into top technical positions of his organization. The impression arose that there was little intent on the part of his directors, and no encouragement on his part, to actively prepare younger colleagues for top positions.

When the Saturn program began around 1961, every one of von Braun's thirteen technical divisions was headed by an individual that had carried out similar work in Peenemünde; only positions with administrative and coordination functions were occupied by American-born persons. Many observers retained that image of von Braun's organization, although a number of American-born colleagues entered into prominent technical positions as the years went by, among others William Lucas, James Farrior, Lee James, Brooks Moore, Leland Belew, James Murphy, Robert Lindstrom, Jack Balch, George Constan, Charles Bradshaw, James Shepherd, James Bramlet, Bill Sneed, Stanley Reinartz, William Tier, George Bucher, Frank Williams, Ludie Richard, George Hardy, James Kingsbury, O. C. Jean, Fletcher Kurtz, Robert Marshall, William Huber, James Downey, Robert Schwinghamer, and many others. Still, there was occasional criticism because this turnover did not proceed at a faster pace. Actually, there were several among the oldtimers who advised von Braun to do this, pointing out that if such transitions were planned over a few years, the changing of the guard could be made in a natural, pleasant way. This process would contribute decisively to a continuing stability of the team.

Von Braun professed full agreement with such proposals, but he wished to proceed slowly with changes before the Saturn project was over the hump. When that time came, von Braun left his team, and the impression remained with some that he was not really determined to offer top technical positions to American-born co-workers. That impression was unjustified. Whenever von Braun had to arbitrate between an American-born and a foreign-born team member who had different opinions, he always was strongly inclined to give the nod to the American-born. However, the image and the perception were stronger than the facts. Had proper actions been taken in due time, perhaps some of the tragic events of the early 1970s might have been avoided or at least alleviated.

Petrone returned to NASA Headquarters in December 1973 as associate administrator for Manned Space Flight. Lucas followed him as director of the Marshall Center. In 1975, Petrone left NASA and became chief executive of an industrial firm, the National Center for Resource Recovery. A few years later, in 1981, he joined Rockwell International as director of the Shuttle Division.

4   NATIONAL SPACE INSTITUTE

Fletcher, NASA administrator since April 1971, recalled many years later how public interest in the Nation's space program had begun to decrease even before the last Moon landing. *"I began to get concerned,"* he said [12-12], *"about the growing disillusionment about space. Magazine articles appeared asking . . . 'Why are we spending so much money in space?' and 'If we can land somebody on the Moon, why can't we solve this or that problem on Earth?' I happened to notice that there were many well-known people—not involved with space—who thought it was the greatest thing that could happen to the world. And they were from all walks of life, from the media, from the entertainment world, and from the business community. 'There must be some way,' I said to myself, 'to bring all these people together, and get them to say their piece.' After all, space was not of interest just to the federal sector . . ."*

That's when the idea of a National Space Institute (NSI) got started.

"I brought E. Z. [Edward Z.] Gray into the picture," Fletcher continued. *"And George Low was interested, too . . . we contacted Ed Uhl to ask if we could borrow Tom Turner . . . He let Tom work on the project for six months or so; Ed really went that extra mile . . . Later, he hired Chuck [Charles C.] Hewitt and put him on the Fairchild payroll. We next proceeded to twist the arms of some aerospace people to put some money into the Space Institute. (About $500,000 was contributed.) Meanwhile, Ed—bless his heart—volunteered Wernher's time, and we were on the road . . . We asked E. Z. Gray to do a lot of the promotion. I don't drink, so I cannot socialize at bars the way others can, and drum up support. And Tom Turner did a lot of promotion, too . . ."*

Turner confirmed Fletcher's recollections. *"We chose Wernher to head it because of his stature . . . from the very initial concept Wernher was to be the figurehead . . ."* [12-2].

"We obtained financial support from Boeing and McDonnell Douglas, as well as from Fairchild," Gray recalled.

Interestingly, von Braun at first was hesitant, even negative toward the idea of a National Space Institute. *"Another talking club,"* was his spontaneous reaction. Then, he found himself at the receiving end of a campaign of persuasion, led by Gray, Fletcher, Turner, and others, and he became the most active, persuasive, and successful promoter the Space Institute ever had.

"Later," Gray continued, *"we got a good chunk of money. We received a lot from United Technologies (UT) . . ."*

The National Space Institute was incorporated on 13 June 1974. von Braun was elected president, and Charles Hewitt was appointed executive director. Hewitt later remembered his conversations with von Braun [12-13]: *"I felt in awe before this man . . . thinking of the tremendous accomplishments he had made, and feeling that he was one step above all of us . . . But one of the things I vividly recall was his sense of humor, and his way of putting one completely at ease . . . I had that good feeling of warmth from the first moment we spoke . . . His goals and objectives—presenting space as a tool to solve mankind's problems—coincided with my beliefs . . . He focused on the thought that somehow we must make the American people understand that space is a resource . . . First, we had to determine how we would get the funding . . . This meant primarily going after the manufacturers . . . they did help us largely out of respect for Wernher and indebtedness to him, but also because they believed that it was worth giving it a try."*

Many celebrities were attracted to the NSI. As Fletcher recalled [12-12], *"There were people who were not space experts, but well known by our generation. John Denver and Ethel Merman, for example. She came to me one day*—Annie Get Your Gun *was her thing—and asked: 'What can I do to help?' And there was Johnny Carson who was a space buff long before Carl Sagan got to him. And Bob Hope . . . as well as several corporate executives . . ."* Others involved with the Institute were actor Hugh O'Brian; Reverend Fulton J. Sheen; space scientist James A. Van Allen; oceanographer Captain Jacques Cousteau; astronaut Alan B. Shepard; writers Isaac Asimov and Arthur C. Clarke; and artist James Wyeth. We got them all together at a big bash in Dallas [May 1977]. Bob Hope was master of ceremonies."

In July 1975, von Braun addressed the NSI Board of Directors and the Board of Governors at the first annual meeting [12-14]. Congressman Olin E. Teague from Texas, a member of the NSI Board of Governors and a very enthusiastic supporter of the space program for many years, had von Braun's address read into the Congressional Record. *"A new organization is needed,"* von Braun said, *"to communicate the benefits of our national space program to the American public. The National Space Institute, which we are formally launching today, shall perform that function . . . In order to keep our country advancing as a world leader, we must maintain our efforts in the advancement of space technology. There is a need for the American public to know and understand the value and benefits resulting from our national space program . . . Benefits from space technology have entered into our daily lives to a far greater extent than most people realize. Advances in medicine, communications, Earth resources, environmental monitoring, and thousands of new products and materials have given the United States technological leadership in the world today. The space program is essential to retaining that leadership . . ."*

The Institute became isolated when it did not succeed in having its efforts integrated into a greater NASA effort for a vigorous promotion of the national space program.

Another damaging situation arose in the fall of 1975, described by Hewitt: *"Wernher went into the hospital in November . . . From that time on, we started losing his energy and his leadership . . . We were on a ship without a captain, or, indeed, on a ship without an engine. It was an awful situation . . ."*

Despite his health problems, von Braun took once more the opportunity to extol all the prospective benefits of spaceflight, and to make a pitch for the NSI and its objectives to convey to the public an awareness of these golden opportunities. In an interview with *Washington Star* staff writer Vernon A. Guidry, Jr., he said [12-15]:

"I'm fully aware that public interest is a very fickle thing. One day, the word is 'Moon or bust,' and the next day it is 'let's clean up the rivers.' And people get so much information today that the priorities in their minds swing back and forth. The Apollo flights to the Moon were demonstrations of immense capabilities and potential, but in some respect they may be compared with Lindbergh's flight across the ocean. I think space is now entering a maturing period where it will be less 'gee-whiz,' less sensational, but it will become more a part of everyday life—just like the airlines . . . The problem is that very often, the potential benefits of these efforts . . . are not even known to the potential beneficiaries. So one of our functions at the National Space Institute will be to improve the discussion between NASA, the academic community, and the potential users . . . We are interested first of all in the public at large, in people who are not necessarily identified with the space program as such, but with other areas . . . one of the members of our board is Captain Cousteau, the oceanographic pioneer. We have Bob Hope on our board because he is also convinced that space is a very good thing for America. He has an excellent instinct for what's good for the country, and he is also a man people listen to. We have the head of the Boy Scouts on our board; he is convinced that the youth interest is alive . . . So it is through these men and their media, and the groups they represent, that we hope to reach large numbers of people . . . As you get older, somebody else picks up from where you leave off. We want to make sure that this legacy can now be passed on to the next generation, the people who will really pick the fruits of the trees we have planted. I think the silliest part of the decay of the public interest in space is that they are taking a position like, 'All right, we planted this orchard, and we nourished and fertilized it and watered it and gave it all our tender loving care . . .' And now, as the time comes when the fruits can be picked, they don't want to pay the fruit pickers! That is where the young generation can make the greatest contribution—pick the fruits."

In February 1976, von Braun, Downs, and Hewitt went to see Vice President Nelson Rockefeller to tell him about NSI activities. *"We were trying to have established at the White House some stated policy goals that would lead to the strengthening of the space program,"* Hewitt recalled, *"but nothing really happened . . . At the same time, we were faced with lessened support for our activities by executives in the aerospace industry . . . Also, NASA was becoming even less interested in what we were doing . . ."*

When von Braun died in June 1977, Downs became chairman of the board. Ben Bova assumed the presidency, and Fletcher, after leaving NASA in May 1977, became vice president. By this time, Ed Uhl was no longer actively involved in the Institute. *"Ed told me very clearly,"* Hewitt remembered, *"that without NASA support we could simply not survive. He had lost confidence in the whole project."*

The Institute did survive. After Hewitt departed in 1980, Courtney Stadd served for a period as general manager. During an interview in 1989 [12-16], he stressed the *"enormous void"* left by von Braun. In Stadd's words, *"no one has ever approached the effectiveness of von Braun, whose intelligence, drive, and personality were simply unmatched in the space field."*

Stadd was succeeded later by executive directors Mark R. Chartrand (to 1984) and Glen P. Wilson. Under the guiding influences of Wilson and NSI president Ben Bova, NSI merged with the L-5 Society in March 1987. The result was the National Space Society, NSS. The new organization immediately began to strengthen the approximately ninety former L-5 chapters, and to expand grassroots support for a vigorous space program.

In looking back at the early days of the National Space Institute, Wilson observed [12-17] that *"von Braun, and the other NSI leaders in the 1970s, understood the importance of broad public support . . . The space program does not only need supporters who are knowledgeable about space, it needs people who want to be engaged in the political process . . ."*

Today, many of the National Space Society's members are associated with some 120 sections located throughout the United States, and in a number of foreign countries. Among the distinguished leaders of the merged organization are former space shuttle astronaut Charles Walker, president; Apollo 11 astronaut Edwin ("Buzz") Aldrin, chairman, board of directors; television and radio personality Hugh Downs, chairman, board of governors; and Lori B. Garver, Wilson's immediate successor as executive director.

Garver, representing today's generation of young space enthusiasts, emphasized [12-18] that *"Wernher von Braun continues to be a driving force behind our Society . . . His ideas for both the space program and the Space Society continue to show incredible vision and foresight . . ."*

Most of NASA's means and energies during the recent past were spent on two major projects, the space shuttle and the space station. Both are facilities. What will really count in the long run is the efficient use of these facilities for the benefit of the inhabitants of planet Earth—material, scientific, educational, and spiritual. To bring about an awareness of the potential uses of these facilities has been the motivation behind the National Space Institute; it continues to guide its successor, the National Space Society.

5 MAN'S FUTURE IN SPACE AND ON EARTH

"Man's reach into space can be compared with the daring steps of those Devonian salamanders which, 400 million years ago, left their aquatic environment and moved onto dry land. Like them, we will never give up our new high ground again . . ." von Braun would often remark.

The major steps in von Braun's visionary evolution, described for the first time in the 1940s, remained the same over the years: large precision rockets, satellites in orbit, probes to the Moon and the planets, man in orbit, man on the Moon, permanent orbital stations, permanent lunar bases, man on Mars. This will be the first phase of man's move into space. Then, in the further future, perhaps a permanent base on Mars; perhaps voyages to other planets and their moons; perhaps changes of the atmospheres of Mars and Venus, with the help of some huge, planet-wide atmospheric chain reactions, to make these planets livable for humans.

Asked why we should do all this, he simply answered: *"Because it's human destiny."*

J. Robert Oppenheimer, contemplating the atomic bomb, expressed his thoughts about the reason for scientific research [12-19]: *"None of the great discoveries in science was made because it was needed. It was made because it had become possible to make it."* Paraphrasing his words, one could say: None of the great explorations on Earth and in space were made in response to a human need; they were made because it had become possible to make them.

Others have answered the same fundamental question in their own words. Hugh Sidey, in his Goddard Dinner speech in 1989 [12-20], said: *"If we fail in space now, we fail, period,"* and James A. Michener wrote in 1979 [12-21]: *"If a nation misses the great movements of its time, it misses the foundations on which it can build for the future . . . The life of any nation since the beginning of history has been a record of how it confronted the great challenges that inevitably came its way . . ."*

"I believe that the discoveries, the advances in technology, and the applications of knowledge that will be within our reach during the post-Apollo period of space exploration will far exceed the achievements of our first decade in space, if we but resolve to use the space capability now on hand in a continuing evolutionary manner," von Braun said in July 1969 [12-22]. However, this belief—and hope—was not to be fulfilled.

After joining Fairchild Industries in 1972, he had to let plans for large orbiting stations, bases on the Moon, and expeditions to Mars slip back into the realm of dreams. Instead, he immersed himself in space projects that would serve some of the most pressing human needs on Earth.

Von Braun often pointed out that there is impressive proof of the great public interest in and support for our national space program. One indication is the huge volume of mail—hundreds of thousands of letters—that arrive year after year at NASA Headquarters, and at its field centers, from people who ask for more information on space matters. Another indication is the hundreds of thousands of visitors who travel each year to NASA's many visitor centers and the U.S. Space Rocket Center, plus the millions who visit the Smithsonian Institution's National Air and Space Museum in Washington, D.C.

Also, he never missed an opportunity to emphasize the ability of space projects, present and future, to help alleviate many of the pressing and growing problems that confront us on Earth today: energy, food, environment, education, economy. What is needed here, he said, is the proper direction and support of the effort, and, perhaps the most important requirement, the resolve to use our space technologies for the benefit of people on Earth. *"A hundred years from now,"* he would say, *"people will look back and wonder how man could ever have managed his affairs on his planet without the tools provided by the space program. That there ever could have been a world without spacecraft will be just as difficult for them to perceive as for us to imagine living in a world without telephones and airliners . . ."*

Von Braun's primary concern during the last years of his life was the use of space technology to reach out to wherever there is a human need. However, his urge to reach out also to the unknown, into the unfathomed depth of outer space, remained as strong as it had ever been. Addressing the National Space Institute in July 1975 [12-14], he said:

"I would like to conclude with a short comment on what I believe is the future of space exploration. It is man's nature that he always wants to explore—to move on, to develop, and to advance. If we stop doing that, we will no longer be human. I am convinced that man will be back on the Moon, and whether we find very low forms of life on Mars or not, man will be on Mars, maybe by the turn of the century, maybe ten or twenty years thereafter. And should we have lost our resolve as a nation to do it, somebody else will."

Did the space program fail to retain its impetus after Apollo because the people lost interest in it? Whenever von Braun heard this question, he answered with an impassioned reply: The American people do not represent a well-structured, well-organized entity that would develop a carefully thought-out, uniform opinion about a major public issue such as the space program. Do the people offer uniform opinions and initiatives about nuclear energy, or defense matters, or education, or foreign policy? The people are exposed to a multitude of signals that come from the White House, from congressional leaders, from the news media, from election campaigners, from charismatic personalities, from their own fears and hopes, from imminent dangers, and from crusaders.

When signals for a strong national space program, offering technical preeminence, material benefits, national prestige, economic gains, scientific discovery, and a spirit of exploration and adventure, are coming through loud and clear, the people are quick to tune in and to share the enthusiasm. When such signals begin to subside, the people tune their receivers to other signals.

In 1952, there was a first wave of spaceflight signals: Man must explore space. The signals came from a popular magazine, the press, Walt Disney, radio and television, and from an exciting crusader—and the people responded with enthusiasm to the challenge of space.

Then, in 1957, there was another signal. It was sent as a persistent beep-beep from a little red star in orbit, and its effect on the people was tremendous. The reaction was spontaneous: total surprise, shock, anguish, and calls for better education, more determined effort, more purpose and resolve, more leadership toward national preeminence.

Four years later, there was another tidal wave of signals: Let's travel to the Moon! This time, the signals came from President Kennedy, Vice President Johnson, congressional leaders, NASA, industrial leaders, scientists, the news media, and again from the crusader—and the people's response was overwhelming, all over the globe!

Memories of this outburst of enthusiasm may have been on the mind of NASA Administrator Richard H. Truly when he said in 1989 [12-23]: *"A program for manned exploration will never bubble up from the bottom. It will never result from a series of cost/benefit analyses. It must come from the top down, and that means the President and the Congress."*

In 1970, while America was riding on the crest of its brilliant success with the Moon project, enthusiasm began to subside. The president lost interest; Congress became lukewarm; NASA was looking for a new identity; the crusader was subdued; the news media searched for clues and asked penetrating questions. The people looked for signs of leadership, for signals that would have given new substance and direction to the former enthusiasm—and did not see or hear them. Would it be fair to expect that the people would provide now the signals, the substance and direction, the leadership, and the spirit of a crusader?

"The problem is," von Braun said in 1971, *"that we have run out of Moons."* Actually, by that time, we had also run out of Kennedys, out of Webbs, out of Johnsons, and out of von Brauns.

CHAPTER 13

THE CURTAIN FALLS . . .

"Shortly after von Braun arrived at Fairchild," Ed Uhl recalled [13-1], *"I told him, 'Wernher, you know, we encourage our top executives to take physical examinations at regular intervals.'—'O.k.,' he said, and he decided to go down to Houston to the clinic of Dr. James R. Maxfield, Jr., a close friend of his. After his physical, he came back and said that they had found some kind of shadow around one of his kidneys, and he did not know just what to do. He said he had just come to the company and did not want to take a lot of time off. I told him that number one, he should do exactly what the doctor says, and if he had to take off six months, so be it. He then had his operation at Johns Hopkins, and it turned out that there was a tumor that was malignant. The doctors said they thought they got everything, and he felt pretty good about it. He seemed to be in quite fine shape for a while . . ."*

Von Braun's health became a matter of growing concern to his family and his friends. Radiation treatments followed. Then, von Braun felt fairly healthy for almost two years. His secretary at Fairchild, Kayren, remembered that during that time *"he was not sick; in fact, he was in excellent shape . . ."* [13-2]. It was the time when he put much work into the Applications Technology Satellite projects in Alaska, India, and Brazil; into some other Fairchild projects; and into the National Space Institute. It was also the time when he received the coveted Silver C badge for soaring with his sailplane up to an altitude of 11,000 feet (3,300 meters) in a wavewind pattern above the Adirondack Mountains in upstate New York, and when he earned, during one action-packed weekend in Alaska, the private pilot's license for seaplanes.

Then, in August 1975, while enjoying a family vacation in the wilderness of Canada's North Bay area, he noticed internal bleeding. He pushed it out of his mind, but it recurred a few weeks later during a business trip to Alaska together with Ed Uhl. *"As soon as we got back to Washington,"* Uhl recalled, *"he went over to Johns Hopkins in Baltimore where a tumor of the colon was found that had advanced rather far."* A colon resection was performed, and Uhl remembered that *"after this, he never really regained his total strength; he was always somewhat weakened."* In May 1976, he went back to the hospital in Alexandria for more treatment.

"Von Braun did maintain his optimistic attitude," Uhl continued. *"But as time went on, he got sicker. He would come to the office less and less frequently, and finally he had to stay in the hospital, or at home. From time to time, he would call, and we would talk. Or I would go and see him . . . I felt I would be there for perhaps fifteen minutes, but I would end up staying for an hour or two."*

Old friends from Huntsville would sometimes come and visit him at home or in the hospital. While his body was withering away, his mind stayed as sharp and active as it had ever been. On his sixty-fourth birthday, 23 March 1976, Ordway and Werner Buedeler, a friend from Munich, lunched together with him at the Rotunda restaurant in Washington. Von Braun and Ordway were working at that time on their *New Worlds* book [13-3], and on National Space Institute matters. *"On 31 July,"* Ordway remembers, *"he called from the hospital, saying he was feeling better and was working on the book . . ."*

During the winter of 1976–1977, he was in and out of the hospital; several times, he even went to his office at Fairchild for a few hours. As spring came, he grew weaker and weaker, and pain became almost continuous. His three children came home and stayed with him.

"All this misery," he would say, *"has at least one positive aspect, too. I have my wife and our children around me, and they are absolutely wonderful! They take such a perfect care of me. I can't tell you how much I relish this. Only now do I realize what price I had to pay during all these years when my work kept me away from my home and family most of the time. This heartwarming experience really makes it so much easier for me to accept that miserable state in which I find myself . . ."*

Having his family around him all day long, without the need to rush off in the next minute to the office, or the airport, or at least to the telephone, was indeed a new experience for von Braun. There were Maria, his wife of thirty years; Iris, 28; Margrit, 24; and Peter, 16—and there were many fond memories of those thirty years.

All the von Braun children had shown some common features at an early age. They were alert, quick-witted, eager to learn, intent on having and expressing their own opinions, and clinging to the family. All were exceptionally gifted in a broad sense, and all liked to argue with their father (although with that father, chances to win were minimal!). Von Braun was very proud of each of them, and he often made this known to his friends. In fact, von Braun's closer associates were always well informed about the progress of his children. *"Iris plays the piano very nicely, I particularly like her Mozarts and Schuberts,"* he might say. Margrit received a real horse, Susie, on her seventh birthday. *"She is becoming a little horsewoman very quickly,"* her father said. *"As young as she is, she knows already more about horses than I will ever know!"* Back in the 1950s, as a little girl, Margrit once said: *"I wish daddy would buy a drugstore and stay home with us, he is so much fun . . ."*

"Little Peter," von Braun said, *"is the engineering type. He always hangs around with the construction workers in our street. His mother has to fix him a lunch in a lunch box, and he sits around with the masons and carpenters and speaks their language . . ."*

When the children grew older, they became avid water skiers and scuba divers, following in their father's footsteps. Maria learned flying at the Huntsville airport and received her private license, much to her husband's delight. On the other hand, von Braun was not spared some of the usual fatherly concerns. *"I wish I could find a way,"* he sometimes confided to a friend, *"to keep them away from the television tube. It's such a waste of time. They really should make a better use of their lives . . ."*

Now, in 1977, all this was a glimpse at the remote past. Von Braun had to accept a state of complete physical inactivity, while his family did its best to make his plight as bearable as possible. However, his thoughts could roam freely over these past thirty years—and they did.

Iris Careen attended the National Cathedral School in Washington during her three high school years, and then entered Oberlin College in Cleveland, Ohio, to study music and history. After graduating in 1971, she went to India where she taught German at the Goethe Institute in New Delhi. In 1974, she married Rajiv Khanna, partner and heir of his father's textile business in New Delhi and other Indian cities. When Iris's father had to go to the hospital in 1975, she came back to stay with him and her mother for four months. One year later, when von Braun had to be hospitalized again, she returned to Alexandria to be with her parents for several months. In May 1977, her father's condition worsened and once again she returned to continue to comfort him.

Margrit Cecile, at age sixteen in 1968, switched from the high school in Huntsville to Westminster Boarding School in Atlanta, Georgia, where she graduated in 1970. Her academic career began with a freshman year at Oberlin College in Cleveland; she then transferred to the University of California in Los Angeles to study civil engineering from 1972 to 1974. She moved back to Atlanta in 1974 to continue her studies as a civil engineer at the Georgia Institute of Technology. In the same year, she married John Adams, a composer by profession. After graduating in 1976, she and her husband moved to Idaho where Margrit joined the university at Moscow as a civil engineer. Margrit, too, returned to her parent's home in Alexandria in the spring of 1977 to be with her father during the final phase of his illness.

Peter Constantine, born on 2 June 1960 in Huntsville, spent his high school years in Alexandria where his parents had moved in 1970. At an early age, he developed a great love for trains. *"He spends most of his free time down at the railroad switchyard, watching the locomotives moving the cars around. It is unbelievable how many technical details he knows about the engines,"* his father said. Peter had his own way of describing his predilection for railroading. *"My old man,"* he said, *"is taking care of all these rockets and spacecraft and airplanes and related stuff. He has really covered the entire waterfront. All that is left for me is railroads and locomotives. That's what I want to be the centerpiece of my life."* Von Braun was happy with Peter's decision. After all, it kept in line with a maxim von Braun sometimes gave to a co-worker: *"No matter what you do—but, for heaven's sake, do something! Don't sit around idle!"*

Transportation engineering was Peter's chosen field. However, when he was about fifteen, he asked his father whether he might be allowed to first study history for three semesters, before switching to engineering. Of course, father happily approved of this plan.

Peter graduated from high school after his father's death. As planned, he enrolled at Johns Hopkins, and he graduated with a B.A. in history in 1981.

For von Braun's family, his long suffering at home and in the hospital must have been a most depressing experience, particularly after having known him for so many years as a man of seemingly unlimited strength, ability and exuberance. For the children, he had always been the ultimate source of advice, help, and support. To see him waste away must have left a deep scar in their minds. Later in their lives, they were not spared the harsh realities of life. If von Braun could observe how bravely they coped with adversities, he would be proud—as he always was during the thirty-odd years he found delight in being their father.

Besides his immediate family, close friends were allowed to see von Braun on brief visits. Longer visits were still possible in 1976 when he was in the hospital in Alexandria. When friends from Huntsville came, he often asked them to stay longer than the doctor would have permitted. He wished to know all about the Marshall Center; but sometimes, he would ask: *"Do you think that was right what we were doing all these years? I spent my life in an effort to develop spaceflight, and I have induced thousands to do the same. We spent huge sums of money. There is so much misery in the world which needs immediate help. Did we really do the right thing?"*

Of course, von Braun, as well as his friends, knew that this was a purely rhetorical question. Von Braun's course had been set and directed by the force of destiny, a force deep within his subconscious control center, far stronger than any willful intents and decisions.

The friends brought up many rational arguments: The money was not thrown out into space; it was all spent and used right here on Earth. Think of the many thousands, perhaps millions of families who have lived on space-related salaries, and who have had a better life because there was a space program! Think of the innumerable buildings and constructions which, at least indirectly, owe their existence to space activities: houses, hospitals, schools, churches, libraries, shopping centers, streets, bridges, factories, railroads, airlines.

Think of the countless technical innovations that had their origins in studies for space projects; they include, at least to a large part, such technical giants as computers and microelectronics. Think of the network of communication satellites that has brought the countries of the Earth closer together. Think of the tremendous boost that science and research have received through our work on space projects. Think of the applications technology satellites that can bring education and medical aid to millions of needy people. Think of the possibilities of producing more food, and of distributing it more justly, because of global survey possibilities. Think of the spiritual elation that several hundred million people experienced when they watched man's fabulous voyages to the Moon. And don't forget the many bridges of goodwill and joint endeavor that space technology and research have built to other countries, to Europe and Japan, even to the Soviet Union and China.

The United States spends, year after year, about twenty times as much money on misery all over the world as it spends on the space program. If all space projects were canceled, and if all the money spent now for salaries and industry support were added to stem-the-misery programs, the budgets of those programs would be increased by a mere five percent. But, in that case, the number of the needy would jump up by several millions because of those who had lost their space-related subsistence as a result of the space program being abolished. Also, one should not forget that Chinese proverb—how many people did the space program teach how to catch a fish?

Von Braun would listen, and would say: *"Well, that is what I have believed and said all the time. Do you think it is true?"*—*"Yes, absolutely . . ."*

Doubts like this would overcome von Braun from time to time, but his profound optimism for everything related to space, and for life quite generally, would quickly return. Then, he would repeat what he had said in 1972, when the last Apollo crew returned from the Moon: *"Life has been so beautiful. It surpassed even my wildest dreams. I will be forever grateful for all that was given to me . . ."*

Despite his sad condition, he did not lose his sense of humor. Charles Hewitt, his friend and associate from the National Space Institute, after visiting von Braun in the hospital in Alexandria, remembered [12-13]: *"Here was this man whom I admired so much, telling me that he was now almost as American as I was, for he had more than 400 pints of American blood running through his veins! He was so proud to be an American . . ."*

At another time, Astronaut Neil Armstrong visited him in the hospital. *"Statistically,"* von Braun said, *"my prospects are very poor. But, you know how false statistics can be. By the prognosis of statisticians, you should be dead in space, and I should be in jail on Earth!"*

During the 1976–1977 winter, von Braun's health deteriorated more and more. *"When Gerald Ford was president,"* Uhl recalled, *"Wernher was awarded the National Science Medal. The doctor would not let the White House people go to see him, and asked me if I would make the presentation. So I talked to Maria and to the doctors, and they said they would let me know when a satisfactory time arrived. Wernher was very, very ill . . . Well, one day they thought I could go and make the presentation. It was very sad, for Wernher was completely wasted . . . I told him that I was going to present him with the medal . . . and Wernher began to cry a little bit and turned to Maria and said, 'Isn't this a great country! Here I come in from another country and they give me this great honor. Isn't this a wonderful country!' As I got ready to leave, he said: 'No, please stay. I want to talk to you.' And I was there for almost two hours. That was the last time . . ."*

Two of von Braun's old friends in Huntsville, Rees and Stuhlinger, visited him shortly thereafter. He told them how deeply honored he felt by the award of the medal, and then he remembered his farewell party at NASA five years ago, and how George Low had praised him for his shuttle work (Chapter 11-5).

Almost the whole world had witnessed the gigantic strides of von Braun's life and work. He relished the incredible popularity of his space achievements. The final phase of his fabulous life in the sick room of Alexandria Hospital was marked by seclusion and silence. *"Thy will be done"* was his last credo. Wernher von Braun ended his earthly voyage on 16 June 1977.

He was buried in a small church yard in the Washington area before the world learned of his death, as he had wished. Only his family and a few friends were present. Six days later, a memorial service was held in the Washington National Cathedral conducted by its dean, the Very Reverend Francis B. Sayre, Jr. It had been arranged by the National Space Institute.

Dean Sayre had been a long-time friend of von Braun, and also of everything related to the exploration of space. Several years earlier, he had a rock sample from the Moon set high in one of the cathedral's windows, with appropriate dedication ceremony. He also had served on the National Space Institute's Executive Committee.

Under the somber, and yet so powerful organ sounds of Brahms and Bach, about five hundred people attended the simple, but dignified service. The West German Ambassador to the United States, Berndt von Staden, honored the son of his country with a wreath from the president of the Federal Republic of Germany, Walter Scheel. Eulogies were delivered by three of von Braun's former colleagues, James Fletcher; Michael Collins, Apollo 11 astronaut, and at the time director of the National Air and Space Museum; and Ernst Stuhlinger. Fred Ordway was traveling for the Energy Research and Development Administration in South America at that time; he could not attend the service.

"In the words of the prophet Joel," Fletcher said, *"'your young men shall see visions, and your old men shall see dreams.' Fortunately for the human race, a few men arise in each century who 'see visions' and 'dream dreams' that give hope and spiritual nourishment to us all . . . Wernher von Braun was such a man . . . He clung to what seemed an impossible dream for his entire life, despite pressures of politics, bureaucratic entanglements, war, loss of fortune, and even, especially, personal criticism. Nearly all of our major technical accomplishments today, on Earth as well as in space, were foreseen by him at one time or another during his lifetime. The manned voyage to the Moon, the unmanned exploration of the solar system, and, by observing platforms, the entire universe were all part of his vision. They are now reality, and an integral part of our consciousness. Television satellites, weather satellites, Earth resources satellites, and many more 'down-to-Earth' programs were not only predicted by him, but he and his associates—many of whom are here today—brought many of these projects to fruition. And his dreams carried well into the future . . . Those of us who remain must transform those dreams of the future into reality, and pass on to the next generation what can be and should be their own dreams . . . I sincerely hope that Wernher von Braun's passing shall be a reminder for all of us of what one person can do to show the world the magnificent future which is in store for it, and the wonders that man is capable of performing."*

Collins spoke with affection of the man to whom he owed his journey to the Moon. *"Wernher was a leader,"* he said, *"with the versatility that leaders of genius must possess*

. . . He was a master of the intricacies of his machines . . . , but he realized that rockets could be only as successful as the people who built them, and he assembled an extraordinarily talented team, people who worked well with each other, and who were totally devoted to Wernher . . . Thirty-three Saturn flights, all successful, all without loss of life, all without weapons . . . Saturns sent twenty-seven Americans to the Moon, twelve of them to walk on it. Saturns sent nine astronauts up to Skylab, which itself was a converted Saturn upper stage. And, finally, the last Saturn sent an American crew up to join a Russian spacecraft in Earth orbit . . . Von Braun was, at the same time, a visionary and a pragmatist, a technologist and a humanist. From his youth he had dreamed of flying to the far corners of the solar system, yet it was always the next flight that seemed the most important one to him . . . Because he worked with rockets, I would call him a rocket man—but that is a cold term, and he was anything but cold. He was a warm and friendly man, interested in everyone around him . . . Wernher von Braun believed that the desire to explore was a fundamental part of mankind's nature . . . Although he is no longer with us, I like to think that he is around us, exploring, traveling through the far reaches of the universe, traveling paths of which he long dreamed, and which, more than any other man, he has brought closer to reality . . ."

Stuhlinger said about his long-time boss and friend: *"Scientists, poets, and prophets have known for a long time that one day man will travel to the Moon. Von Braun made this dream come true . . . How can we fathom this life full of prophetic vision and supreme accomplishment, of human warmth and engineering marvels, of romantic poetry and clockwork precision, of grandiose space exploration and minute technical detail? 'When a man dies,' Anne Morrow Lindbergh said, 'it is like a tree falling: every part and phase of his life becomes visible at one time.' Wernher's life, from its very beginning, was distinguished by an obsession to give only the best. As a youthful astronomer, as a volunteer-helper of rocket pioneer Hermann Oberth, as a student of physics, and particularly as a rocket engineer first in Germany and then in the United States—he always wanted to give his very best . . . He had the rare and precious gift of instilling in his many co-workers his own enthusiasm for hard work and high quality. But he was not only a tough and demanding task master; he was a path finder and problem solver, and he always overflowed with an exuberant joy of life that lighted up many dark chasms on the road to the stars.*

Von Braun took space exploration as a way for man to find his place and destiny in the universe. As a young boy, he decided that this exploration could be accomplished with rockets, so he devoted his life to the development of powerful high precision rockets. Mathematics, physics, and engineering are only part of the ingredients needed for such a gigantic program. When he was asked in later years what it takes to send men to the Moon, he answered: 'The will to do it!' He certainly had the will to do it, but he possessed even more: an irresistible personal charm, coupled with almost magic powers of persuasion, which helped him conquer many hesitant or doubtful minds.

Wernher has always felt deeply grateful to this country which became his second home. More than thirty years ago, it was his 'haven of promise'; later, he often remarked how wonderful America had been to him and his family, and to all his friends who immigrated with him. However, he never failed to add that his team really consisted of all the thousands and thousands of men and women in government, industry, universities, and the armed forces who gave him their talents and their confidence, and who all share credit for the success of the space adventure.

With a deep-rooted interest in philosophy and religion, he saw no conflict between scientific knowledge and religious faith. 'The natural sciences,' he said, 'deal with creation; religion deals with the creator. The two are really complementing each other perfectly . . .'

'When my journey comes to an end,' he once remarked, 'I hope that I can retain my clear mind and perceive not only those precious last moments of my life, but also the transition to whatever will come then. A human being is so much more than a physical body that withers and vanishes after it has been around for a number of years. It is inconceivable to me that there should not be something else for us after we have finished our earthly voyage. I hope that I can observe and learn, and finally know what comes after all those beautiful things we experience during our lives on Earth.'"

Reverend Sayre expressed the feelings of those present in the cathedral, and of millions all over the world: *"We thank Thee, God of the Heavens, for a man of new beginnings . . ."*

There were many good words, spoken or written by innumerable friends all over the world, whose minds and hearts von Braun had touched, and who wished to share their deep feelings at this time of mourning.

President Jimmy Carter wrote: *"To millions of Americans, Wernher von Braun's name was inextricably linked to our exploration of space, and to the creative application of technology. He was not only a skillful engineer, but also a man of bold vision; his inspirational leadership helped mobilize and maintain the effort we needed to reach to the Moon and beyond . . . Not just the people of our nation, but all the people of the world have profited from his work. We will continue to profit from his example."*

Alan Lovelace, Acting Administrator of NASA, said: *"In the tradition of Newton and Einstein, he was a dreamer pursuing visions, and at the same time a creative genius. He was a twentieth century Columbus who pushed back the new frontiers of outer space with efforts that enabled his adopted country to achieve a preeminence in space exploration."*

Don Fuqua, U.S. Congressman from Florida, wrote: *"He was such an outgoing person, full of vim and vigor . . . To see him as he was beginning to wither was a very, very sad experience . . ."*

Father (formerly Major General) John Bruce Medaris wrote: *"His imagination strolled easily among the stars, yet the farther out into the unknown and unknowable vastness of Creation his thoughts went, the more he was certain that the universe, and this small garden spot within it, came from no cosmic accident, but from the thought and purpose of an all-knowing God . . ."*

William R. Lucas, Director, NASA Marshall Space Flight Center, said: *"Wernher von Braun was a man whose eyes were steadfastly fixed on the future. He had the mind of a scientist, the hands of an engineer, the soul of a poet, and the vision of a prophet."*

Arthur C. Clarke, the *"Prophet of Space,"* wrote: *"There are few in the whole of history who have left such a record of achievement as Wernher, or who have seen, in their own lifetime, so triumphant a vindication of their ideals and dreams. He will be an inspiration for generations to come. I count it as one of the greatest privileges of my life to have known him as a friend."*

Frederick C. Durant III said: *"I feel that Wernher von Braun was one of the greatest men I have ever met . . . His greatness was pointing out the feasibility of spaceflight, and the way to achieve it . . . And his greatness was the ability to communicate these facts, and his ability to lead the design of the vehicles that would make spaceflight possible, and to go ahead and build these vehicles . . ."*

Joachim Kuettner, a longtime friend and co-worker, wrote: *"There can be no doubt that it was only his genius which succeeded in overcoming the countless difficulties and problems in the Saturn V program. He never complained about obstacles or setbacks; he only invented new ways and solutions that gave directions to his co-workers. His presence always had an electrifying effect. Boring conferences became interesting and stimulating when he entered the room . . . It was always a pleasure to be near him . . . He filled his life to the breaking point with activity, as if he had known that his time on Earth would be limited . . ."*

Riccardo Giacconi, scientific director of the great Hubble Space Telescope project, expressed his own feelings—but they are certainly shared by thousands of those who had known Wernher von Braun:

"He had a nobility around him that set him apart from all other people in the space program . . . He believed in the decency of man . . ." [13-4].

EPILOGUE

VON BRAUN'S FINEST HOUR

"Wernher, what was your finest hour?" That question was often posed to him, and he always relished answering it.

"Life has been extremely good to me," he would say. *"In fact, it gave me several finest hours! I remember how I fell into a state of supreme elation when, at the age of fourteen, inspired by Hermann Oberth's book* The Rocket into Planetary Space, *and reassured by my own youthful calculations, I realized that human travel to the Moon and to some of the planets with the help of rockets is a distinct possibility, and that I may be able to contribute to man's venture into space if I only worked hard enough, and if I put forth sufficient will power to do so."*

Von Braun's next finest hour came on 3 October 1942, after his A-4 rocket in Peenemünde had made its first long-range test flight. Colonel Dornberger arranged for a little celebration, and he said: *"Ladies and gentlemen, today the spaceship has been born. We have opened with our work the gateway to space for mankind . . ."*

Then came the hour, on 31 January 1958, when the free world's first satellite, Explorer 1, reached its orbit. *"That success made me particularly happy,"* von Braun said, *"because it allowed me to show my deep gratitude to the American people who had so generously given my co-workers and me the opportunity to carry on our work for the exploration of space."*

And then, on 27 July 1969, three live and healthy astronauts returned to Earth after they had walked on the Moon. *"That was an hour of exuberant joy,"* von Braun recalled, *"and, I admit, also of a tremendous relief!"*

VON BRAUN'S DARKEST HOUR

Did von Braun also have a darkest hour? Here is his reply:

"I most certainly did, and I will remember it all my life. It began in the fall of 1943 when Himmler and his SS men wrenched control over the A-4 program out of our hands in order to enforce mass production and military deployment of the rocket, long before its development and testing were completed." Von Braun had always hoped and expected that the war would be over before the A-4 could be used as a weapon. *"The most depressing fact was that I had absolutely no influence over this course of events. Even if I personally had withdrawn completely from the project, production and deployment would have continued, enforced by SS orders."* By staying with the project and keeping the development and test program going, von Braun could at least hope that the war would come to its end before completion of the rocket, but that the team's experience in rocketry could be preserved for later times (Chapter 1-3). *"The darkest hour,"* von Braun said, *"came on 8 September 1944, when I learned that A-4 rockets, named V-2 by Dr. Goebbels, had been launched against Paris. We wanted our rockets to travel to the Moon and Mars, but not to hit our own planet . . ."*

Von Braun's strong emotional reaction to the use of his A-4 dubbed V-2 as a weapon of aggression may appear contradictory to his voluntary acceptance of the German

Army's invitation to develop military rockets in 1932, and much later the American Army's invitation to develop military rockets beginning in 1945.

He did agree to develop such rockets for defense, and as a deterrent; building a defensive and deterrent capability has long been considered the responsibility of every sovereign nation. Millions of scientists and engineers worldwide are involved in the development of everything from small arms to super aircraft carriers, from fighter planes to spy and nuclear detection satellites, hoping they will only be used as a deterrent to would-be aggressors. Von Braun found himself in a similar situation in Germany and again in the United States.

Following World War II, industrialized nations mated nuclear warheads to long-range ballistic missiles in the belief that only that awesome combination would deter would-be aggressors. That World War III has never occurred is striking testimony to the peacekeeping role of the precision rocket whose origin was von Braun's A-4.

NAME CHANGES

TECHNICAL NOTATION: A-4 OR V-2?

The name A-4 was given to the Peenemünde rocket in the summer of 1937. A-4 was the fourth member, or *"Aggregat 4,"* of an evolving family of rockets developed by von Braun and his co-workers first in Reinickendorf and Kummersdorf, and then, from 1937 on, in Peenemünde.

The name V-2 was introduced by Hitler's propaganda minister Joseph Goebbels in September 1944 when A-4s were launched for the first time at military targets (Paris and London). *"V"* means Vergeltungswaffe or vengeance weapon. The V-1 was the buzz bomb or flying bomb, developed by the German Air Force at Peenemünde West (von Braun's group worked at Peenemünde East).

Although the designation V-2 became the official name after September 1944, the Peenemünders continued to call their rocket A-4. In the present book, A-4 is generally used in describing events before, and V-2 in describing events after September 1944. However, both names are used interchangeably throughout the book.

The designations *"A-4"* and *"V-2"* are technically identical.

* * * *

During the years that von Braun and his team worked in the United States, a number of name changes occurred to federal facilities in which they carried out their activities or with which they were regularly involved. The following paragraphs are designed to help the reader identify installations affected by name changes over the years.

* * * *

FORT BLISS, TEXAS

The German team was integrated into the Ordnance Research & Development Division Suboffice (Rocket), sometimes referred to as the Research & Development Service Suboffice (Rocket). Within that structure, von Braun served as project director, chairman of the Development Board, and chairman of the Ramjet Committee.

HUNTSVILLE, ALABAMA

Two adjacent arsenals were established during World War II, the Chemical Corps Huntsville Arsenal and the Ordnance Corps Redstone Arsenal, both of which were deactivated following the end of hostilities. When von Braun arrived in Huntsville from Texas in 1950, they had been reactivated and integrated into Redstone Arsenal under the authority of U.S. Army Ordnance. Von Braun successively held titles as technical director, U.S. Army Ordnance Missile Group; chief, Guided Missiles Development Group; and chief, Guided Missiles Development Division. Later, with the establishment of the Army Ballistic Missile Agency on 1 February 1956, he became director of its Development Operations Division; ABMA had absorbed Redstone's Guided Missile

Development Division, the Redstone missile program office, and the Missile Firing Laboratory at Cape Canaveral. On 31 March 1958, the Army Ordnance Missile Command was established incorporating ABMA, the Army Rocket and Guided Missile Agency, the White Sands Missile Range in New Mexico, and the Jet Propulsion Laboratory in Pasadena, California. A couple of years later, on 14 March 1960, NASA established what it called the NASA Huntsville Facility largely made up of ABMA's Development Operations Division personnel. Then, on 1 July, a mass personnel transfer from ABMA took place as the NASA-George C. Marshall Space Flight Center officially came into being.

LANGLEY FIELD, HAMPTON, VIRGINIA

Construction started in 1917 of the National Advisory Committee for Aeronautics' Langley Memorial Aeronautical Laboratory, which was dedicated on 11 July 1920. On 1 October 1958, it and other NACA facilities were transferred to the newly created NASA. In November 1960, Langley's Space Task Group was redesignated Manned Spacecraft Center; and, on 3 January 1961, became an independent NASA field installation.

HOUSTON, TEXAS

With the redesignation of the Space Task Group as the Manned Spacecraft Center in November 1960 and its transfer from Virginia to Clear Lake near Houston, Texas in the summer of 1962, a major buildup began to accommodate the blossoming Apollo program. The Manned Spacecraft Center designation lasted until 17 February 1973 when it was changed to the Lyndon B. Johnson Space Center.

CAPE CANAVERAL, FLORIDA

The original military installation at the Cape was the Banana River Naval Air Station. On 1 October 1949, the Air Force established there the Long Range Proving Ground which evolved over the years to the Atlantic Missile Range and later the Eastern Test Range. Meanwhile, in 1951 Huntsville established its Experimental Missiles Firing Branch at the Cape. In January 1953, this became the Army's Missile Firing Laboratory; on 1 July 1960, the NASA Launch Operations Directorate; and, on 1 July 1962, the NASA Launch Operations Center. Finally, on 29 November 1963 following the death of President Kennedy, the name was changed to the John F. Kennedy Space Center. (Cape Canaveral itself was known as Cape Kennedy for the ten-year period 29 November 1963 to 9 October 1973.)

PASADENA, CALIFORNIA

In 1936, the GALCIT project was established by the Guggenheim Aeronautical Laboratory of the California Institute of Technology. In November 1944, GALCIT's name was changed to the Jet Propulsion Laboratory; it occupied facilities owned by U.S. Army Ordnance and reporting to Huntsville. Later, on 3 December 1958—following the establishment of NASA—JPL was transferred from the Army to the space agency at which time it became independent of Huntsville.

WHITE SANDS, NEW MEXICO

At the Army's White Sands Proving Ground, von Braun and his team fired V-2 rockets during the post-World War II years and continued their involvement there to a lesser extent after the transfer to Huntsville. Later, the Army changed the name to White Sands Missile Range. NASA involvement began in June 1962 when the Houston-based Manned Spacecraft Center established its White Sands Operations at the Army range; subsequently, on 25 June 1965, the NASA element became the White Sands Test Facility.

MICHOUD, LOUISIANA

On 7 September 1961, the Michoud Ordnance Plant became Michoud Operations, reporting to NASA-Marshall in Huntsville. It was redesignated Michoud Assembly Facility on 1 July 1965 and became famous as the site where Saturn IB and Saturn V final assembly took place.

BAY SAINT LOUIS, MISSISSIPPI

The Mississippi Test Facility was established by NASA-Marshall on 25 October 1961 to test Saturn V first and second stages. Two months later, the name Mississippi Test Operations was assigned; but, it never stuck so, on 1 July 1965, the site officially reverted to its original name. On 9 November 1970, MTF was placed in standby status and then, on 14 June 1974, was reactivated as the National Space Technology Laboratories. Most recently, on 28 May 1988, it underwent still another name change to become the John C. Stennis Space Center.

CLEVELAND, OHIO

The NACA Aircraft Engine Research Laboratory started operations in 1942; and, on 28 September 1948, was renamed the Lewis Flight Propulsion Laboratory. With the creation of NASA on 1 October 1958, it became the Lewis Research Center.

REFERENCES

Preface

1. Dornberger, Walter, *V-2—Der Schuss ins Weltall*, Bechtle Verlag, Esslingen, Germany, 1952; *V-2*, Viking Press, New York, 1954; *Peenemünde, Die Geschichte der V-Waffen*, Bechtle Verlag, Esslingen, Germany, 1981.

2. Irving, David, *The Mare's Nest*, William Kimber, London, 1964.

3. Huzel, Dieter K., *Peenemünde to Canaveral*, Prentice-Hall, Inc., Englewood Cliffs, New Jersey, 1962.

4. Ruland, Bernd, *Wernher von Braun, Mein Leben für die Raumfahrt*, Burda Verlag, Offenburg, Germany, 1969.

5. Bergaust, Erik, *Reaching for the Stars*, Doubleday & Co., Inc., New York, 1960; *Wernher von Braun, Ein Unglaubliches Leben*, Econ Verlag, Düsseldorf, Wien, 1976; *Wernher von Braun*, National Space Institute, Washington, D.C., 1976.

6. Adams, Carsbie C., et al., *Space Flight*, McGraw-Hill Book Company, Inc., New York, 1958.

7. Goodrum, John C., *Wernher von Braun, Space Pioneer*, Strode Publishers, Huntsville, Alabama, 1969.

8. Gartmann, Heinz, *The Man Behind The Space Rockets*, David McKay, New York, 1956.

9. Walters, Helen B., *Wernher von Braun, Rocket Engineer*, Macmillan, New York, 1964.

10. David, Heather M., *Wernher von Braun*, Putnam, New York, 1967.

11. Ordway, Frederick I., III, and Mitchell R. Sharpe, *The Rocket Team*, Thomas Y. Crowell, New York, 1979; William Heinemann, London, 1979; MIT Press, Cambridge, Massachusetts, 1982; Aircraft Designs, Monterey, California, 1992.

Chapter 1

1-1. Needham, Joseph, *Science and Civilization in China, Vol. V, Military Technology; The Gunpowder Epic*. Cambridge University Press, London, 1986.

1-2. Von Braun, Wernher, and Frederick I. Ordway III, *History of Rocketry and Space Travel*, Thomas Y. Crowell Company, New York, 1966, 1969, and 1975; von Braun, Wernher, Frederick I. Ordway III, and Dave Dooling, *"Space Travel, a History*, Harper and Row, New York, 1985; Büdeler, Werner, *Die Geschichte der Raumfahrt*, Sigloch Edition, Künzelsau, Germany, 1979.

1-3. Goddard, Esther C., and G. Edward Pendray, eds., *The Papers of Robert H. Goddard*, 3 vols., McGraw-Hill, New York, 1968.

1-4. Newell, Homer E., *Beyond the Atmosphere*, National Aeronautics and Space Administration, NASA SP-4211, Washington, D.C., 1980. See also *High Altitude Rocket Research*, Academic Press, New York, 1953.

1-5. Von Braun, Wernher, *"Vom Beginn der Raumfahrt,"* Keynote Speech at the Fiftieth Anniversary of the First International Air Show and Exhibit, Paul's Cathedral in Frankfurt/Main, Germany, on September 6, 1959. Excerpts translated by Ernst Stuhlinger.

1-6. Carter, Leonard J., Interview by Frederick I. Ordway III, Stockholm, Sweden, October 10, 1985.

1-7. Churchill, Winston S., *Triumph and Tragedy*, Houghton Mifflin, Boston, 1953.

1-8. Glennan, T. Keith, Interview by Frederick I. Ordway III, Reston, Virginia, April 7, 1986.

1-9. Schriever, Bernard A., Interview by Frederick I. Ordway III, Washington, D.C., February 8 and May 7, 1988.

1-10. Teller, Edward, see Richard Rhodes, *The Making of the Atomic Bomb*, Simon and Schuster, New York, 1986.

1-11. Einstein, Albert, see Smyth, Henry DeWolf, *Atomic Energy for Military Purposes*, Princeton University Press, Princeton New Jersey, 1946, and Rhodes, Richard, loc. cit. [1-10]. Also Clark, Ronald W., *Einstein—The Life and Times*, Avon Books, Hearst Corporation, New York, 1971.

Chapter 2

2-1. Von Braun, Magnus Freiherr, *Von Ostpreussen bis Texas*, Helmut Rauschenbusch Verlag, Stollhamm (Oldenburg), Germany, 1955.

2-2. Engel, Rolf, Interview by Frederick I. Ordway III, Innsbruck, Austria, October 8, 1986.

2-3. Bergaust, Erik, *Reaching for the Stars*, Doubleday, Garden City, New York, 1960; *Wernher von Braun*, National Space Institute, Washington, D.C., 1975; *Wernher von Braun—Ein Unglaubliches Leben*, translated by Guy Montag, Econ Verlag GmbH, Düsseldorf und Wien, 1976.

2-4. Generales, Constantine D. J., Jr., *"Recollections of Early Biomedical Moon-Mice Investigations,"* Proceedings of the First and Second History Symposia of the International Academy of Astronautics at Belgrade, Yugoslavia, September 26, 1967, published in Durant, Frederick C., III, and George S. James, editors, *First Steps Toward Space*, Univelt, San Diego, 1985 (republished from the 1979 edition published by the Smithsonian Institution Press, Washington, D.C.).

2-5. Generales, Constantine D. J., Jr., loc. cit. [2-4]; also personal communication to Ernst Stuhlinger, 1979.

2-6. Pendray, G. Edward, *The Coming Age of Rocket Power*, Harper and Brothers, New York, 1945; see also Von Braun, Wernher, and Frederick I. Ordway III, loc. cit. [1-2]; also: Büdeler, Werner, loc. cit. [1-2].

2-7. Pendray, G. Edward, see Ruland, Bernd, *Wernher von Braun, Mein Leben für die Raumfahrt*, Burda Verlag, Offenburg, Germany, 1969.

Chapter 3

3-1. Dornberger, Doris, Personal Communication to Ernst Stuhlinger, Huntsville, Alabama, 1987.

3-2. Von Braun, Wernher, *"Reminiscences of German Rocketry,"* Journal of the British Interplanetary Society, Vol. 15, No. 3, May-June, 1956.

3-3. Dornberger, Walter, V-2, loc. cit. [1].

3-4. Speer, Albert, *Inside the Third Reich—Memoirs*; translated from the German *Erinnerungen* (1969) by Richard and Clara Winston. Macmillan, New York, 1970.

3-5. Speer, Albert, *Infiltration*; translated from the German *Der Sklavenstaat*, Ullsteinbuch No. 33041, Ullstein GMBH, Frankfurt/Main-Berlin-Wien, 1981, by Joachim Neugroschel. Macmillan, New York, 1981.

3-6. Thiel, Adolf K., Personal Communication to Ernst Stuhlinger, Huntsville, Alabama, 1988.

3-7. Reisig, Gerhard H. R., Personal Communication to Ernst Stuhlinger, Huntsville, Alabama, 1989.

3-8. Hermann, Rudolf, Interview by Ernst Stuhlinger, Huntsville, Alabama, 1983.

3-9. Berthold, Will, *Die 42 Attentate auf Adolf Hitler* (*The 42 Attempts on Adolf Hitler's Life*), Wilhelm Goldman Verlag, München, 1981.

3-10. Stuhlinger, Ernst, Rocket Center Peenemünde, Personal Memories, 1985. Stuhlinger Archives, Huntsville, Alabama.

3-11. Reisig, Gerhard H. R., Von den Peenemünder 'Aggregaten' zur Amerikanischen 'Mondrakete' [From the Peenemünde Rockets to the American Moon Rocket], *Astronautik—Hermann Oberth Society*, #1, Bremen, Germany, 1986.

3-12. Michel, Jean, *Dora*, Editions J.-C. Lattès (in French), Paris, 1975. English translation by George Weidenfeld and Nicolson, London, 1979, and Holt, Rinehart and Winston, New York, 1980.

3-13. Air Materiel Command, Staff Study; see Ordway, Frederick I., III, and Mitchell R. Sharpe, *The Rocket Team*, loc. cit. [11].

3-14. Davidson, Eugene, *The Trial of the Germans*. Macmillan, New York, 1966.

3-15. Bornemann, Manfred, *Geheimprojekt Mittelbau: Die Geschichte der Deutschen V-Waffen Werke*. L. F. Lehmann Verlag, München, 1971.

3-16. Bornemann, Manfred, and Martin Broszat, *"Studien zur Geschichte der Konzentrationslager,"* Vierteljahreshefte für Zeitgeschichte, No. 21, H. Rothfels and T. Eschenburg, ed. Deutsche Verlags-Anstalt, Stuttgart, 1970.

3-17. Tusa, Ann, and John Tusa, *"The Nuremberg Trial,"* entries under Sauckel and Speer. Atheneum, New York, 1986.

3-18. Kersten, Dorette (Mrs. Rudolf Schlidt), Huntsville, Alabama; personal communication to Ernst Stuhlinger, 1987.

3-19. Churchill, Winston S., *"'Absolute silence' toward any peace inquiries, particularly those by German dissidents, [was] decreed by Churchill in 1941,"* quoted from Klemens von Klemperer, *"The Legacy of the Plot to Kill Hitler"*, *The New York Times*, July 21, 1990. Richard Rhodes, in *The Making of the Atomic Bomb*, Simon and Schuster, New York, 1986, describes how Roosevelt and Churchill arrived at the decision to demand *"unconditional surrender,"* and how this demand became official Allied policy.

3-20. Markovna, Nina, *Nina's Journey, A Memoir of Stalin's Russia and the Second World War*, Regnery Gateway, New York, 1990.

3-21. Von Braun, Wernher, *Survey of Past Liquid Propellant Rocket Development in Germany, and of Future Prospects* (Übersicht über die bisherige Entwicklung der Flüssigkeitsrakete in Deutschland, und deren Zukunftsaussichten), Report written for Army Ordnance in 1945. The essence of that report was published by the *British Interplanetary Society (BIS)* under the title *"Reminiscences of German Rocketry"* in 1956, see [3-2].

3-22. Staver, Major Robert B., *"The Liquid Jet Propulsion Program of the German Ordnance Department,"* December 17, 1945. This paper was never published. Private collection of manuscripts, Mitchell R. Sharpe, Huntsville, Alabama. See also Staver, R. B., *"The Future of Ordnance in Jet Propulsion."* War Department, Office of the Chief of Ordnance, Washington, D.C., December 17, 1945.

3-23. Porter, Richard W., Interview by Frederick I. Ordway III, Arlington, Virginia, May 4, 1989; also Hamill, James P., personal communication to Ernst Stuhlinger, Fort Bliss, Texas, 1946; also Ordway, Frederick I., III, and Mitchell R. Sharpe, loc. cit. [11].

Chapter 4

4-1. Winterstein, Colonel William E., Interview by Frederick I. Ordway III in Huntsville, Alabama, April 18, 1986 and follow up correspondence dated June 9, July 29, October 27, and December 1, 1986 plus numerous telephone conversations.

4-2. Porter, Richard W., loc. cit. [3-23]; also Hamill, James P., personal communication to Ernst Stuhlinger, Fort Bliss, Texas, 1946; also Ordway, Frederick I., III, and Mitchell R. Sharpe, loc. cit. [11].

4-3. Fagan, James J., Interview by Ernst Stuhlinger, Huntsville, Alabama, July 25, 1988.

4-4. Wernher von Braun, *Das Marsprojekt*, Bechtle Verlag, Esslingen, Germany, 1952; English version: *The Mars Project*, University of Illinois, Urbana, Illinois. Translated by Henry J. White; 1953; 1965; 1991.

4-5. Rosen, Milton W., Interview by Frederick I. Ordway III, Bethesda, Maryland, October 7, 1988.

4-6. Friedman, Herbert, Interview by Frederick I. Ordway III, Arlington, Virginia, February 23, 1990.

4-7. Atwood, J. Leland, written responses to questions posed by Ernst Stuhlinger, El Segundo, California, August 12, 1988.

4-8. Hoffman, Samuel K., written responses to questions posed by Ernst Stuhlinger, Pacific Grove, California, July 29, 1988.

4-9. Von Braun, Wernher, *"The Future Development of the Rocket,"* Presentation to the Rotary Club in El Paso, Texas, January 16, 1947.

4-10. Newell, Homer E., *High Altitude Rocket Research*, Academic Press, Inc. Publishers, New York, 1953; also *Sounding Rockets*, McGraw Hill, New York, Toronto, London, 1959; *Express to the Stars*, McGraw Hill, New York, Toronto, London, 1962.

4-11. Goldberg, Leo, letter to Dr. Menzel, Harvard University, Cambridge, Massachusetts (Menzel Papers). September 28, 1945.

4-12. Krause, Ernst H., see *Beyond the Atmosphere* by Homer E. Newell, National Aeronautics and Space Administration, Washington, D.C., 1980, [1-4].

4-13. Von Braun, Wernher, *"Investigations of the Upper Atmosphere with the A-4 (V-2) Rocket Missile,"* Naval Research Laboratory Records, Acc #11704, Folder 2, NARS, April 1946.

4-14. Zwicky, Fritz, *"Report on Certain Phases of War Research in Germany,"* Air Materiel Command, Rep. F-SU-3-RE. October 1, 1945. Released in January 1947.

4-15. Von Braun, Wernher, *"A Large Multi-stage Booster Rocket,"* Department of the Army, Ordnance Research and Development Division Suboffice (Rocket), Fort Bliss, Texas, April 1949.

4-16. Von Braun, Wernher, *"Space Superiority as a Means for Achieving World Peace,"* written in 1949, Ordnance, Vol. 37, No. 197, p. 770, March-April 1953.

4-17. Thiel, Adolf K., personal communication to Ernst Stuhlinger, 1985.

4-18. Goldberg Leo, Address at the National Academy of Sciences Symposium on *"Space Science—Past and Prologue"*, May 24, 1976. NRL Report 8113.

Chapter 5

5-1. Smith, Wilson D., Jr., personal communication to Ernst Stuhlinger, Huntsville, Alabama, 1986.

5-2. Von Braun, Wernher, *"Why I Chose America,"* The American Magazine, New York, July 1952.

5-3. Medaris, Maj. Gen. John Bruce, *Countdown for Decision*, G. P. Putnam's Sons, New York, 1960.

5-4. Von Braun, Wernher, *"Space Travel: Its Dependence upon International Scientific Cooperation,"* Paper presented at Third International Astronautical Congress in Stuttgart, Germany, translated by Henry J. White, and published in Kölle, H. H., editor, *"Probleme aus der Astronautischen Grundlagenforschung,"* Stuttgart, 1952.

5-5. Von Braun, Wernher, *"Why Guided Missiles?"* Paper written in 1951. Wernher von Braun Archives, U.S. Space & Rocket Center, Huntsville, Alabama.

5-6. Hale, Edward Everett, *"The Brick Moon,"* in *"His Level Best and Other Stories*, Robert Brothers, Boston, 1873; also original in *Atlantic Monthly* Vols. 24–25, 1869–70 (four parts).

5-7. Tsiolkovskii, Konstantin Eduardovitch, Collected Works. Izd. Akademii Nauk, Moscow, USSR, 1951, 1954, 1959. Translated and released by the National Aeronautics and Space Administration, Washington, D.C., F 236, 237, 238, 1965.

5-8. Oberth, Hermann, *Die Rakete zu den Planetenräumen*, R. Oldenbourg, München, 1923. Reprinted by Uni Verlag, Feucht/Nürnberg, Germany, 1960, 1964, 1984.

5-9. Esnault-Pelterie, Robert, *L'Astronautique*. A. Lahure, Paris, France, 1930.

5-10. Von Pirquet, Guido, *"Fahrtrouten,"* Die Rakete, Vol. 2, 1928, and Vol. 3, 1929, Breslau, Germany.

5-11. Ley, Willy, *Die Möglichkeit der Weltraumfahrt*, Hachmeister und Thal, Leipzig, Germany, 1928.

5-12. Noordung, Hermann, *Das Problem der Befahrung des Weltraums*, Richard Carl Schmidt, Berlin, 1929.

5-13. Bernal, J. D., *The World, the Flesh, and the Devil*, Kegan Paul, Trench and Trubner, London, 1929.

5-14. Ross, H. E., *"Orbital Bases,"* Journal of the British Interplanetary Society, Vol. 8, London, January, 1949.

5-15. Armstrong, Major General Harry G., *"Space Medicine in the United States Air Force,"* in *Space Medicine: The Human Factor in Flights beyond the Earth*, edited by John P. Marbarger, University of Illinois Press, Urbana, Illinois, 1951.

5-16. Von Braun, Wernher, *"Multi-stage Rockets and Artificial Satellites,"* in *Space Medicine: The Human Factor in Flights beyond the Earth*, edited by John P. Marbarger, University of Illinois Press, Urbana, Illinois, 1951.

5-17. Von Braun, Wernher, *"The Importance of Satellite Vehicles in Interplanetary Flight,"* Second International Astronautical Congress, London, September 3–8, 1951, and abstracted in Carter, L. J., editor, *"The Artificial Satellite,"* British Interplanetary Society, London, 1951.

5-18. Durant, Frederick C., III, Interview by Frederick I. Ordway III, Boston, July 13, 1988.

5-19. Von Braun, Wernher, *"We Need a Coordinated Space Program,"* Fourth International Astronautical Congress in Zurich, Switzerland, August, 1953, and published in *Space Flight Problems*, Druck und Verlag Biel-Bienne, Switzerland, 1953.

5-20. Schachter, Oscar, Interview by Frederick I. Ordway III, New York City, New York, February 21, 1986.

5-21. Whipple, Fred L., Interview by Frederick I. Ordway III, Cambridge, Massachusetts, February 24, 1986.

5-22. Ryan, Kathryn Morgan, Interview by Frederick I. Ordway III, Ridgefield, Connecticut, April 26, 1986.

5-23. Manning, Gordon, Interview by Frederick I. Ordway III, New York, New York, December 12, 1986.

5-24. Kimball, Ward, Interview by Frederick I. Ordway III, San Gabriel, California, May 27, 1990; letters dated April 15 and June 9, 1986, and numerous telephone discussions from May to November 1990.

5-25. Von Braun, Wernher, *"The Selling of an Idea,"* American Astronautical Society, first annual dinner, New York City, New York, December, 1954. Wernher von Braun Archives at the U.S. Space & Rocket Center, Huntsville, Alabama.

Chapter 6

6-1. Rand Report of the Douglas Aircraft Company, Inc., *"Preliminary Design of an Experimental World-circling Spaceship,"* Report No. SM-11827, Contract W33-038 ac-14105, Santa Monica, California, May 2, 1946. Also Von Braun, Wernher, and Frederick I. Ordway III, *History of Rocketry and Space Travel,* loc. cit. [1-2].

6-2. Glenn L. Martin Company, *"Orbiter Project,"* Martin Engineering Report 2666, Contract 8376, Baltimore, Maryland, September 15, 1946.

6-3. Millikan, Clark B., 1947. See Von Braun, Wernher, and Frederick I. Ordway III, *History of Rocketry and Space Travel,* loc. cit. [1-2].

6-4. Forrestal, James V., December 1949. See Von Braun, Wernher, and Frederick I. Ordway III, *History of Rocketry and Space Travel,* ibid.

6-5. Rosen, Milton W., *"On the Utility of an Unmanned Earth Satellite"* (Report of the Rosen Committee). American Rocket Society, November 24, 1954.

6-6. Durant, Frederick C., III, Interview by Frederick I. Ordway III, Boston, July 13, 1988. See also George W. Hoover, *"Why an Earth Satellite?"* Office of Naval Research, Washington, D.C., February 22, 1956.

6-7. Von Braun, Wernher, *"A Minimum Satellite Vehicle Based on Components Available from Missile Development of the Army Ordnance Corps."* Guided Missile Development Division, Ordnance Missile Laboratories, Redstone Arsenal, Huntsville, Alabama, September 15, 1954. See also Von Braun, Wernher, *"Importance of Satellite Vehicles in Interplanetary Flight," Journal of the British Interplanetary Society,* Vol. 10, No. 5, September 1951; Shepherd, Leslie R., ibid., No. 6, November 1951; Spitzer, Lyman, Jr., ibid.; and Von Braun, Wernher, *"Early Steps in the Realization of the Space Station,"* ibid., Vol. 12, No. 1, January 1953.

6-8. Von Braun, Wernher, *"Presentation to the Association of the U.S. Army,"* Washington, D.C., October 29, 1957. Also Stuhlinger, Ernst, *"Possibilities of Satellite Launching with Modified Redstone Rocket,"* presentations to Army Ordnance and Office of Naval Research, August 1957. Wernher von Braun Archives, U.S. Space & Rocket Center, Huntsville, Alabama.

6-9. Bardin, I., Statement at the IGY Planning Meeting in Barcelona, Spain, September 11, 1956, reported by Homer E. Newell, *Beyond the Atmosphere,* loc. cit. [1-4].

6-10. Lloyd Berkner, Information received at an IGY Committee Meeting in June 1957 about Soviet plans to launch a satellite. Reported by von Braun, Wernher, and Frederick I. Ordway III, *History of Rocketry and Space Travel,* Thomas Y. Crowell Company, New York, 1966, 1969, and 1975.

6-11. Glennan, T. Keith, reported by Homer E. Newell, *Beyond the Atmosphere,* loc. cit. [1-4]. See also Koppes, Clayton R., *"JPL and the American Space Program,"* Yale University Press, New Haven, Connecticut, 1982.

6-12. Pickering, William H., Interview by Frederick I. Ordway III, Innsbruck, Austria, October 10, 1986 and follow-up telephone conversations.

Chapter 7

7-1. Von Braun, Wernher, *"The Explorers," Astronautica Acta* 5, 1959.

7-2. Von Braun, Wernher, *"Present and Future Space Vehicles and their Capabilities,"* Army Ballistic Missile Agency (ABMA) Report No. D-TN-1-59, Huntsville, Alabama, December 15, 1958.

7-3. Shepherd, Leslie R., and A. Val Cleaver, *"The Atomic Rocket," Journal of the British Interplanetary Society,* Vol. 7, 1948, Vol. 8, 1949.

7-4. Hoffman, Samuel K., personal communication to Ernst Stuhlinger, July 1988.

7-5. Von Braun, Wernher, *"The Acid Test," Chemical and Engineering News"*, Vol. 36, No. 9, March 3, 1958.

7-6. Von Braun, Wernher, *"Education in the Space Age,"* presented to the Elliott Committee on Education and Labor, House of Representatives, Washington, D.C., published in *Science Newsletter*, Vol. 3, No. 2, Spring 1958.

7-7. NACA study on *"Problems Associated with Unmanned and Manned Flight at Altitudes from 50 Miles to Infinity,"* 1952. See John M. Logsdon, *The Decision to Go to the Moon*, MIT Press, Cambridge, Massachusetts, 1970.

7-8. Air Force Committee (Chaired by H. Guyford Stever) Report: *"Military Implications of Space Technologies,"* October 9, 1957. See Sturm, Thomas A., *"The USAF Scientific Advisory Board,"* Government Printing Office, Washington, D.C., 1967.

7-9. Air Force Committee (Chaired by Edward Teller) Report on recommended Air Force actions, October 28, 1957. See Swenson, Lloyd S., James M. Grimwood, and Charles C. Alexander, *This New Ocean: A History of Project Mercury*, National Aeronautics and Space Administration, Washington, D.C., 1966.

7-10. Logsdon, John M., *The Decision to Go to the Moon*, loc. cit. [7-7].

7-11. *Introduction to Outer Space* ('Killian Report') by the President's Science Advisory Committee. Washington, D.C., The White House, 1958.

7-12. President Eisenhower as quoted in *The Decision to Go to the Moon, Project Apollo and the National Interest* by John M. Logsdon, loc. cit. [7-7].

7-13. Von Braun, Wernher, *"Proposal for a National Integrated Missile and Space Vehicle Development Program."* Army Ballistic Missile Agency Report, Huntsville, Alabama, 1958.

7-14. *"Project Horizon: A U.S. Army Study for the Establishment of a Lunar Outpost,"* Army Ordnance Missile Command, Huntsville, Alabama, 1959. See also Frederick I. Ordway III, Mitchell R. Sharpe, and Ronald C. Wakeford, *"Project Horizon: An Early Study of a Lunar Outpost,"* *Acta Astronautica*, Vol. 17, 1988.

7-15. Glennan, T. Keith, Interview by Frederick I. Ordway III, Reston, Virginia, April 7, 1986.

7-16. Schriever, Bernard A., Interview by Frederick I. Ordway III, Washington, D.C., May 7, 1988.

7-17. York, Herbert F., Department of Defense Memorandum, Washington, D.C., June 9, 1959.

7-18. York, Herbert F., *Race to Oblivion*, Simon and Schuster, New York, New York, 1971.

7-19. Medaris, Major General John Bruce, with Arthur Gordon, *Countdown for Decision*, G. P. Putnam's Sons, New York, 1960.

7-20. Eisenhower, Dwight D., Transfer of the Army's space team to NASA, see Robert Rosholt *An Administrative History of NASA*, 1958–1963, National Aeronautics and Space Administration, Washington, D.C., 1966.

7-21. Goddard, Robert H., see [1-3]. The two papers published by Goddard: *"A Method of Attaining Extreme Altitude,"* 1919, and *"Liquid Propellant Rocket Development,"* 1936, Smithsonian Institution, Washington, D.C., were reprinted by the American Rocket Society, New York, 1946. A third paper, *"Rocket Development: Liquid-Fuel Rocket Research, 1929–1941"* was published posthumously by Prentice-Hall, New York, 1948. Another short note was published by Goddard under the title *"That Moon Rocket Proposition (Its proponent says a few words in refutation of some popular fallacies),"* *Scientific American*, February 26, 1923. See also *"The Rocket Marshal,"* *The Journal of the Worcester Polytechnic Institute*, Vol. XXIII, No. 3, April 1920.

7-22. Pendray, G. Edward, *The Coming Age of Rocket Power*, Harper, New York, 1945.

7-23. Newell, Homer E., *Beyond the Atmosphere*, loc. cit. [1-4]. See also Newell, Homer E., *Guide to Rockets, Missiles, and Satellites*, McGraw-Hill Book Co., New York, 1958.

7-24. Von Braun, Wernher, *"Dear John,"* letter to a student about Goddard's patents. Von Braun Archives, U.S. Space & Rocket Center, Huntsville, Alabama.

7-25. Von Braun, Wernher, Banquet speech on the 40th anniversary of the world's first liquid fueled rocket in Worcester, Massachusetts, *Worcester Sunday Telegram*, March 13, 1966.

7-26. Boushey, Homer A. (paper about R. H. Goddard). Also: Ordway, Frederick I. III, *"Robert Hutchings Goddard,"* in *The Cambridge Encyclopedia of Space*, edited by Michael Rycroft. Cambridge University Press, Cambridge, England, 1990.

7-27. Durant, Frederick C., III, and George C. James, eds., *First Steps toward Space*, Smithsonian Annals of Flight No. 10, Smithsonian Institution Press, Washington, D.C., 1974; republished by Univelt, San Diego, California, 1985.

7-28. Lehman, Milton, *This High Man* (Goddard biography). Farrar, Straus, and Giroux, Inc., New York, 1963.

7-29. Sharpe, Mitchell R., *"The Centenary of Robert H. Goddard, 1882–1982,"* Journal of the British *Interplanetary Society*, Vol. 35, 12, p. 539, December 1982.

7-30. Von Braun, Wernher, remarks at dedication of the Robert Hutchings Goddard Rocket Collection and the Paul Horgan Gallery of the Roswell Museum and Art Center, Roswell, New Mexico, 25 April 1959 (Ordway files).

7-31. For further reading: Winter, Frank H., *Rockets into Space*, Harvard University Press, Cambridge, Massachusetts, 1990, and *"Planning in Space Flight,"* in *Blueprint for Space*, edited by Frederick I. Ordway III and Randy Liebermann, Smithsonian Institution Press, Washington, D.C., 1992.

Chapter 8

8-1. Zwicky, Fritz, *"Report on Certain Phases of War Research in Germany,"* Air and Material Command, Report F-SU-3-RE, October 1, 1945. Wright Field, Ohio, Headquarter Air Material Command, 1946.

8-2. Ross, H. E., *"Orbital Bases," Journal of the British Interplanetary Society*, Vol. VIII, London, January 1949.

8-3. Logsdon, John M., *The Decision to Go to the Moon*. Project Apollo and the National Interest. MIT Press, Cambridge, Massachusetts, 1970.

8-4. Bilstein, Roger E., *Stages to Saturn. A Technological History of the Apollo/Saturn Launch Vehicles*. National Aeronautics and Space Administration, Washington, D.C., 1980.

8-5. Van Dyke, Vernon, *Pride and Power*: The Rationale of the Space Program. University of Illinois Press, Urbana, 1964.

8-6. This remark by President Eisenhower was reported by Logsdon [8-3], who quoted a *"privileged source."*

8-7. Baldwin, Hanson, *The New York Times*, April 17, 1961.

8-8. Sidey, Hugh, *John F. Kennedy, President*, Atheneum Press, New York, 1964.

8-9. Wiesner, Jerome B., *Where Science and Politics Meet*, McGraw-Hill, New York, 1964.

8-10. Memorandum from John F. Kennedy to Vice President Lyndon B. Johnson, April 20, 1961. NASA Historical Archives.

8-11. Johnson, Lyndon B., Interview by Walter Cronkite. CBS Television, July 5, 1969.

8-12. Evans, Rowland, and Robert Novak, *Lyndon B. Johnson, The Exercise of Power*, New American Library, New York, 1966.

8-13. Von Braun, Wernher, Memorandum to Vice President Lyndon B. Johnson, April 1961. NASA Historical Archives.

8-14. Johnson, Vice President Lyndon B., Memorandum to President Kennedy, April 29, 1961. NASA Historical Archives, Washington, D.C.

8-15. Webb, James E., Letter to Jerome B. Wiesner, May 2, 1961. NASA Historical Archives, Washington, D.C.

8-16. Webb, James E., and Robert McNamara, Joint Memorandum to Vice President Johnson: *"Recommendations for Our National Space Program: Changes, Policies, Goals."* See Young, Hugo; Bryan Silcock; and Peter Dunn, *"Why we Went to the Moon," The Washington Monthly*, April, 1970.

8-17. Kerr, Robert. See Holmes, Jay, *America on the Moon: The Enterprise of the Sixties*. J. P. Lippincott Company, Philadelphia, Pennsylvania, 1962.

8-18. Kondratyuk, Yuri V., see *Pioneers of Rocket Technology: Selected Works*. National Aeronautics and Space Administration, Technical Translation F-9285, Washington, D.C., November 1965.

8-19. Kondratyuk, Yuri V., ibid. See also Werner Büdeler, *Die Geschichte der Raumfahrt*, loc. cit. [1-2].

8-20. Dolan, Thomas E., and Edward Marshall, *"Manned, Modular, Multi-Purpose Space Vehicle,"* Vought Astronautics Company Report, Dallas, Texas, January 1960.

8-21. Michael, William, *"Weight Advantages of Use of a Parking Orbit for Lunar Soft Landing Mission,"* National Aeronautics and Space Administration, Langley Research Center, Virginia, May 26, 1960.

8-22. Houbolt, John C., Letters to Robert C. Seamans, Jr. of May 19, September 9, and November 15, 1961. NASA Archives, Washington , D.C.; Johnson Space Center Archives, Houston, Texas.

8-23. Seamans, Robert C., Jr., *"Establishment of Ad Hoc Task Group for Manned Lunar Landing Study"* (Fleming Committee). NASA Archives, Washington, D.C., May 2, 1961.

8-24. Seamans, Robert C., Jr., *"Organization of a Broad Study of Various Ways for Accomplishing Manned Lunar Landing Missions"* (Lundin Committee). NASA Archives, Washington, D.C., May 25, 1961.

8-25. Logsdon, John M., *"Selecting the Way to the Moon: The Choice of the Lunar Orbital Rendezvous Mode,"* *Aerospace Historian*, Washington, D.C., June 1971.

8-26. Lundin, Bruce: *"A Survey of Various Vehicle Systems for the Manned Lunar Landing Mission,"* NASA Archives, Washington, D.C., June 10, 1961.

8-27. Seamans, Robert C., Jr., *"Establishment of an Ad Hoc Group for Manned Lunar Landing by Earth Orbital Rendezvous Techniques"* (Heaton Committee). NASA Archives, Washington, D.C., June 20, 1961.

8-28. Von Braun, Wernher, Interview by Robert Sherrod, NASA Headquarters, Washington, D.C., August 25, 1970.

8-29. Gilruth, Robert R., see Bilstein, Roger E., loc. cit. [8-4].

8-30. Seamans, Robert C., Jr., Interview by Frederick I. Ordway III, Cambridge, Massachusetts, February 24, 1986.

8-31. Rosen, Milton W., *"Recommendations for NASA Manned Space Vehicle Program,"* NASA Archives, Washington, D.C., November 20, 1961. Also Logsdon, John M., loc. cit. [8-25].

8-32. Disher, John H., Interview by Frederick I. Ordway III. Washington, D.C., June 29, 1987.

8-33. Houbolt, John C., Letter to Robert C. Seamans, Jr., November 15, 1961. NASA Archives, Washington, D.C.; Johnson Space Center, Houston, Texas.

8-34. Shea, Joseph F., Interview by Frederick I. Ordway III, Washington, D.C., February 11, 1988. Also Bilstein, Roger E., loc. cit. [8-4].

8-35. Gilruth, Robert R., Interview by Frederick I. Ordway III, Kilmarnock, Virginia, April 29, 1988.

8-36. Von Braun, Wernher, quoted by Joseph F. Shea, Interview by Frederick I. Ordway III, Washington, D.C., February 11, 1988. Also personal communication to Ernst Stuhlinger by Frank Williams, Huntsville, Alabama, 1984.

8-37. Rosen, Milton W., loc. cit. [8-31].

8-38. Petrone, Rocco A., Chapter 6 in *Apollo Expeditions to the Moon*, ed. Edgar M. Cortright, National Aeronautics and Space Administration, Washington, D.C., 1975.

8-39. Petrone, Rocco A., written responses to questions posed by Ernst Stuhlinger, October 20, 1989.

8-40. Seamans, Robert C., Jr., and Frederick I. Ordway III, *"The Apollo Tradition: An Object Lesson for the Management of Large-scale Technical Endeavors,"* *Interdisciplinary Science Reviews*, Vol. 2, No. 4, 1977, Heyden and Son, Ltd., London. Republished in *Between Sputnik and the Shuttle* edited by Frederick C. Durant III. Univelt, San Diego, 1981; and, in *Macro-Engineering and the Future* edited by Frank P. Davidson and C. Lawrence Meador, Westview Press, Boulder, Colorado, 1982. Also Hoffman, Samuel K., personal communication to Ernst Stuhlinger, 1988.

8-41. Rosen, Milton W., Memorandum from Rosen to D. Brainerd Holmes, *"Large Launch Vehicle Program,"* National Aeronautics and Space Administration, Washington, D.C., November 6, 1961.

8-42. *Huntsville Times*. Huntsville, Alabama. A series of articles about this subject was published on August 15, 16, 17, 24, and 26, 1962.

8-43. Report by the Association of Huntsville Area Contractors, July 5, 1963. NASA-George C. Marshall Space Flight Center, Director's File, National Archives Depository, Atlanta, Georgia.

8-44. Von Braun, Wernher, *"Huntsville in the Space Age,"* Presentation to the Huntsville Chamber of Commerce, December 8, 1964. Von Braun Archives, U.S. Space & Rocket Center, Huntsville, Alabama.

8-45. Franklin, Ben A., *San Francisco Chronicle*, June 16, 1965.

8-46. Webb, James E., Address to Alabama Governor George C. Wallace and Huntsville Chamber of Commerce in Huntsville, Alabama, on June 8, 1965. NASA Archives, Washington, D.C.

8-47. McDivitt, James A., quoted by George M. Low, *Apollo Expeditions to the Moon*, National Aeronautics and Space Administration, Washington, D.C., 1975.

8-48. Mueller, George E., Interview by Frederick I. Ordway III, Arlington, Virginia, May 1, 1986.

8-49. Lucas, William R., see Bilstein, Roger E., loc. cit. [8-4].

8-50. Von Braun, Wernher, *Apollo Expeditions to the Moon*, loc. cit. [8-47].

8-51. Low, George M., ibid.

8-52. Holmes, D. Brainerd, Interview by Frederick I. Ordway III, South Natick, Massachusetts, July 12, 1988.

8-53. Von Braun, Wernher, *Management Policy Statement #1, NASA-George C. Marshall Space Flight Center, Huntsville, Alabama."* MSFC Archives, August 16, 1962.

8-54. Sneed, Bill H., Interview by Ernst Stuhlinger, Huntsville, Alabama, June 1986.

8-55. Seamans, Robert C., Jr., Interview by Frederick I. Ordway III, Cambridge, Massachusetts, February 24, 1986.

8-56. Webb, James E., see Bilstein, Roger E., loc. cit. [8-4].

8-57. Webb, James E., quoted by von Braun in *Apollo Expeditions to the Moon*, loc. cit. [8-47].

8-58. Mueller, George E., loc. cit. [8-48].

8-59. Disher, John H., loc. cit. [8-32].

8-60. Shea, Joseph F., loc. cit. [8-34].

8-61. Phillips, Samuel C., Interview by Frederick I. Ordway III, Washington, D.C., January 29, 1988. Also *"Destination Space: Managing the U.S. Space Program,"* Wernher von Braun Memorial Lecture, Smithsonian Institution, National Air and Space Museum, Washington, D.C., January 28, 1988.

8-62. Durant, Frederick C., III, Foreword of this book.

8-63. Rees, Eberhard, personal communication to Ernst Stuhlinger, Huntsville, Alabama, 1986.

8-64. Stuhlinger, Ernst, et al., eds. *Astronautical Engineering and Science: From Peenemünde to Planetary Space.* (A collection of papers dedicated to Wernher von Braun on his fiftieth birthday.) McGraw-Hill, New York, 1963.

8-65. Webb, James E., quoted by Robert C. Seamans, Jr., and Frederick I. Ordway III, *"The Apollo Tradition,"* loc. cit. [8-40].

8-66. Webb, James E., *Apollo Expeditions to the Moon*, loc. cit. [8-47].

8-67. Fletcher, James C., Foreword to *Apollo Expeditions to the Moon*, loc. cit. [8-47].

8-68. Edgar M. Cortright, ed., ibid.

8-69. Lovell, James A. (Jim), ibid.

8-70. Lowman, Paul D., Jr., *"The Apollo Program, Was It Worth It?"* World Resources: *The Forensic Quarterly*, Vol. 49, August, 1975.

8-71. Paine, Thomas O., Interview by Frederick I. Ordway III, Washington, D.C., August 6, 1985.

8-72. Space Task Group: See Bilstein, Roger E., loc. cit. [8-4], *"America's Next Decades in Space: A Report to the Space Task Group,"* National Aeronautics and Space Administration, Washington, D.C., September 1969; and *"The Post-Apollo Space Program: Directions for the Future,"* Space Task Group Report to the President, The White House, Washington, D.C., September 1969.

Chapter 9

9-1. Ruland, Bernd, *Wernher von Braun, Mein Leben für die Raumfahrt*, Burda Verlag, Offenburg, Germany, 1969.

9-2. Bergaust, Erik, *Reaching for the Stars*, Doubleday, New York, 1960.

9-3. Bergaust, Erik, *Wernher von Braun*, National Space Institute, Washington, D.C., 1976; *Wernher von Braun, Ein Unglaubliches Leben*, Econ Verlag, Düsseldorf und Wien, 1976.

9-4. Pet, Saul (AP Special Correspondent): *"FDR at 100," Huntsville Times*, Huntsville, Alabama, January 24, 1982.

9-5. Friedman, Herbert, Interview by Frederick I. Ordway III, Arlington, Virginia, February 23, 1990.

9-6. Williams, Frank, Interview by Frederick I. Ordway III, Slidell, Louisiana, June 22, 1985 and Washington, D.C., August 21, 1985. Also Interview by Roger E. Bilstein (Stages of Saturn), MSFC, December 3, 1971.

9-7.   Dannenberg, Konrad, Interview at NASA-Marshall Space Flight Center on July 30, 1975, quoted in Bilstein, Roger E., *Stages of Saturn, A Technological History of the Apollo/Saturn Launch Vehicles*, National Aeronautics and Space Administration, Washington, D.C., 1980.

9-8.   James, Lee B., Interview by Ernst Stuhlinger, Huntsville, Alabama, June 20, 1988.

9-9.   Von Horstig, Lt. Col. Wolfram Ritter, Reference on young von Braun, 1936. (Stuhlinger files.)

9-10.   Dornberger, Walter, loc. cit. [1]. See also Dornberger, Walter in Ernst Stuhlinger, et al., eds., *Astronautical Engineering and Science—From Peenemünde to Planetary Space*. McGraw-Hill, New York, 1963.

9-11.   Toftoy, Holger N., quoted by Erik Bergaust, *"Wernher von Braun,"* National Space Institute, Washington, D.C., 1976.

9-12.   Toftoy, Holger N., Speech on April 14, 1955 when von Braun and most of his team members received United States citizenship; Huntsville, Alabama, 1955.

9-13.   Hamill, James P., Interview by Vince Hackett, Washington, D.C., 1959.

9-14.   Medaris, Father John Bruce (former Major General), Interview by Frederick I. Ordway III, Washington, D.C., March 10, 1989.

9-15.   Glennan, T. Keith, Interview by Frederick I. Ordway III, Reston, Virginia, April 7, 1986.

9-16.   Tatarewicz, Joseph N., David H. DeVorkin, Martin Collins, and Allan Needell, Webb Oral History Program, National Air and Space Museum, Smithsonian Institution, Washington, D.C., 1985.

9-17.   Seamans, Robert C., Jr., Interview by Frederick I. Ordway III, Cambridge, Massachusetts, February 24, 1986.

9-18.   Holmes, D. Brainerd, Interview by Frederick I. Ordway III, South Natick, Massachusetts, July 12, 1988.

9-19.   Mueller, George M., Interview by Frederick I. Ordway III, Arlington, Virginia, May 1, 1986.

9-20.   Phillips, Samuel C., Interview by Frederick I. Ordway III, Washington, D.C., January 29, 1988.

9-21.   Phillips, Samuel C., *"Destination Space: Managing the U.S. Space Program,"* Wernher von Braun Memorial Lecture, National Air and Space Museum, Washington, D.C., January 28, 1988.

9-22.   Paine, Thomas O., Interview by Frederick I. Ordway III, Washington, D.C., August 6, 1985.

9-23.   Myers, Dale D., Telephone interview by Frederick I. Ordway III, Leucadia, California, December 3, 1989.

9-24.   Fletcher, James C., Interview by Frederick I. Ordway III, Washington, D.C., November 8, 1985.

9-25.   Uhl, Edward G., Interview by Frederick I. Ordway III, Chantilly, Virginia, September 18, 1985.

9-26.   Pickering, William H., Interview by Frederick I. Ordway III, Innsbruck, Austria, October 10, 1986.

9-27.   Cortright, Edgar M., Interview by Frederick I. Ordway III, Yorktown, Virginia, April 30, 1988.

9-28.   Rees, Eberhard, personal communication to Ernst Stuhlinger, April, 1988.

9-29.   Silverstein, Abe, Telephone interview by Frederick I. Ordway III. Fairview Park, Ohio, September 20, 1989.

9-30.   Naugle, John E., Interview by Frederick I. Ordway III, Washington, D.C., March 10, 1986.

9-31.   Collins, Michael, Interview by Frederick I. Ordway III, Washington, D.C., March 5, 1987.

9-32.   Porter, Richard W., Interview by Frederick I. Ordway III, Arlington, Virginia, May 4, 1989.

9-33.   Wilson, Glen P., Interview by Frederick I. Ordway III, Washington, D.C., December 7, 1989.

9-34.   Fuqua, Don, Interview by Frederick I. Ordway III, Washington, D.C., September 3, 1987.

9-35.   Rosen, Milton W., *"A Down-to-Earth View of Space Flight,"* Journal of the British Interplanetary Society, London, Vol. 12, 1953.

9-36.   Clarke, Arthur C., Letter to Frederick I. Ordway III, dated November 5, 1952. (Ordway files.)

9-37.   Sagan, Carl, Letter and essay to Frederick I. Ordway III, dated November 30, 1989. (Ordway files.)

9-38.   James, Lee B., written response to questions posed by Ernst Stuhlinger, Huntsville, Alabama, June 20, 1988.

9-39.   Holmes, Emern Bonnie, Letter to Ernst Stuhlinger, Vinemont, Alabama, February 12, 1986 (Stuhlinger files).

9-40. Wernher von Braun, in *"From Dreams to Reality,"* a collection of congratulatory letters honoring Hermann Oberth on his seventieth birthday, NASA-George C. Marshall Space Flight Center, Huntsville, Alabama, June 25, 1964.

9-41. Wernher von Braun, congratulating Hermann Oberth on his seventy-fifth birthday, Von Braun Archives, U.S. Space & Rocket Center, Huntsville, Alabama, June 25, 1969; also "Briefwechsel" (Letters), collected and edited by Hans Barth, Vol. 1, Kriterion Verlag, Bukarest, 1979.

9-42. Oberth, Hermann, addressing von Braun on the occasion of the first successful Saturn-Apollo flight to the Moon, July 1969; also "Briefwechsel" (Letters), collected and edited by Hans Baith, in Vol. 1 Kriterion Verlag, Bukarest, 1979.

9-43. Adams, Carsbie C., Interview by Frederick I. Ordway III, Spotsylvania, Virginia, September 24, 1989.

9-44. Bergaust, Erik, loc. cit. [9-2]; [9-3].

9-45. Von Braun, Wernher, and Frederick I. Ordway III, jointly authored the following books: *History of Rocketry and Space Travel*, Thomas Y. Crowell, New York, 1966, 1969, 1975; *Careers in Astronautics and Rocketry* (with C. C. Adams), McGraw-Hill, New York, 1962; *The Rockets' Red Glare*, Anchor Press/Doubleday, New York, 1976; *New Worlds: Discoveries from our Solar System*, Anchor/Doubleday, Garden City, New York, 1979; *Space Travel, A History* (with Dave Dooling), Harper and Row, New York, 1985.

9-46. Clarke, Arthur C., Interview by Frederick I. Ordway III, Washington, D.C., July 31, 1988.

9-47. Whipple, Fred L., Interview by Frederick I. Ordway III. Cambridge, Massachusetts, February 24, 1986.

9-48. Von Braun, Wernher, *"Space Man's Look at Antarctica," Popular Science*, Vol. 190, No. 5, May 1967.

9-49. Von Braun, Wernher, *"Immortality," This Week Magazine*, January 24, 1960; *"Why I believe in Immortality," The Third Book Of Words To Live By*, ed. W. Nichols, Simon and Schuster, New York, 1962; *"What I Believe," Space World*, Vol. 4, November, 1960; *"Why I Believe," This Week Magazine*, July 18, 1965.

9-50. Lovell, Sir Bernard, *Astronomer by Choice*, Basic Books, Alfred P. Sloan Foundation Series, New York, 1990.

9-51. Von Braun, Wernher, *"Responsible Scientific Investigation and Application,"* presentation at a symposium of the Lutheran Church of America, Philadelphia, Pennsylvania, October 29, 1976, published in H. Ober Hess, ed., *"The Nature of a Humane Society,"* Philadelphia, 1976.

9-52. McDougall, Walter A., *"Technocracy and Statecraft in the Space Age—Toward the History of a Saltation," American Historical Review*, Vol 87, No. 4. October, 1982.

9-53. Webb, James E., Webb Oral History Program, loc. cit. [9-16]; also: Robert C. Seamans, Jr., Interview by Frederick I. Ordway III, loc. cit. [9-17].

9-54. Uhl, Edward G., Interview by Frederick I. Ordway III, Chantilly, Virginia, September 18, 1985.

Chapter 10

10-1. Ferguson, James E. III, *A History of the University of Alabama in Huntsville*, The University of Alabama in Huntsville (UAH), 1975.

10-2. Medaris, John Bruce, *"The Redstone Story,"* Redstone Arsenal Archives, Huntsville, Alabama, June 23, 1959.

10-3. Roberts, Frances C., personal communication to Ernst Stuhlinger, 1988.

10-4. Buckbee, Edward O., Interview by Frederick I. Ordway III, Huntsville, Alabama, July 10, 1986.

Chapter 11

11-1. Mueller, George E., Interview by Frederick I. Ordway III, Arlington, Virginia, May 1, 1986.

11-2. *"The Post-Apollo Space Program: Directions for the Future,"* Report of the Space Task Group, National Aeronautics and Space Administration, Washington, D.C., 1969.

11-3. Paine, Thomas O., Interview by Frederick I. Ordway III, Washington, D.C., August 6, 1985.

11-4. Williams, Frank, Interview by Frederick I. Ordway III, Slidell, Louisiana, June 22, 1985.

11-5. Paine, Thomas O., Address at George C. Marshall Space Flight Center, NASA-MSFC Public Affairs Office, Huntsville, Alabama, January 27, 1970.

11-6. *Huntsville News*, Phil Smith; Bill Sloat; January 28, 1970.

11-7. *The New York Times*, Harold M. Schmeck, Jr.; January 27, 1970.

11-8. *The Press*, quoting Dr. T. O. Paine's address of January 27. February 10, 1970.

11-9. *Huntsville Times*, Bob Ward, February 1, 1970; also Jack Hartsfield, February 3, 1970.

11-10. Williams, Frank, loc. cit. [11-4].

11-11. Foster, Jay N., Interview by Ernst Stuhlinger, Huntsville, Alabama, 1987.

11-12. Newell, Homer E., see Interview of John E. Naugle by Frederick I. Ordway III, Washington, D.C., March 10, 1986, loc. cit. [9-30].

11-13. Von Braun, Wernher, Presentation to the Subcommittee on Science, Research, and Development in the House Committee on Science and Astronautics, House of Representatives, August 18, 1970.

11-14. Foster, Jay N., loc. cit. [11-11].

11-15. Paine, Thomas O., Interview by Frederick I. Ordway III, Washington, D.C., August 6, 1985.

11-16. Phillips, Samuel C., Interview by Frederick I. Ordway III, Washington, D.C., January 29, 1988.

11-17. Foster, Jay N., personal communication to Ernst Stuhlinger, 1987.

11-18. Gray, Edward Z., Interview by Frederick I. Ordway III, Cobbs Creek, Virginia, May 1, 1989.

11-19. Logsdon, John M., *"The Space Shuttle Decision: Technology and Political Choice." Journal of Contemporary Business*, Vol. 7, No. 3, 1978.

11-20. Fletcher, James, quoted in Logsdon, John M., loc. cit. [11-19].

11-21. Nixon, President Richard M., quoted in Logsdon, John M., ibid.

11-22. Kertes, Julie, Letters to Frederick I. Ordway III of July 21 and August 16, 1985, and numerous telephone conversations.

11-23. Kertes, Julie, Letter to Frederick I. Ordway III, September 15, 1985.

11-24. Von Braun, Maria, personal communication to Ernst Stuhlinger, 1985.

11-25. Myers, Dale D., Telephone interview by Frederick I. Ordway III, Leucadia, California, December 3, 1989.

11-26. Thiel, Adolf K., Interview by Frederick I. Ordway III, Washington, D.C., February 11, 1988.

Chapter 12

12-1. Uhl, Edward G., Interview by Frederick I. Ordway III, Chantilly, Virginia, September 18, 1985.

12-2. Turner, Thomas, Telephone interview by Frederick I. Ordway III, San Antonio, Texas, May 21, 1989; and in person, San Antonio, May 25, 1991.

12-3. Webb, Patricia O., Telephone interview by Frederick I. Ordway III, Hurst, Texas, June 26, 1989.

12-4. Redman, Kayren (formerly Kayren Governale), Interview by Frederick I. Ordway III, Phoenix, Maryland, August 31, 1989.

12-5. Singer, Irvin, Interview by Frederick I. Ordway III, Fairchild Space Company, Germantown, Maryland, May 23, 1989.

12-6. Von Braun, Wernher, Address to the Senate Committee on Aeronautics and Space Science, Washington, D.C., September 27, 1973.

12-7. Von Braun, Wernher, *"The Promise of Space,"* ENO Foundation for Transportation, published in *Traffic Quarterly*, October 19, 1971.

12-8. Von Braun, Wernher, *"Expanding Goals of Space Applications,"* Presentation to the American Institute of Aeronautics and Astronautics, AIAA-NABE Meeting, Los Angeles, California, December 8, 1972.

12-9. Von Braun, Wernher, Foreword to the book *For All Mankind* by L. B. Taylor, E. P. Dutton, New York, 1975.

12-10. Von Braun, Wernher, *"ATS-F: TV Station in Outer Space,"* *Environmental Quality Magazine*, September 10, 1973.

12-11. Von Braun, Wernher, Presentation on the Advanced Technology Satellite (ATS) at the House Committee on Science and Technology, Washington, D.C., July 22, 1975.

12-12. Fletcher, James C., Interview by Frederick I. Ordway III, Washington, D.C., November 8, 1985.

12-13. Hewitt, Charles C., Interview by Frederick I. Ordway III, Alexandria, Virginia, September 30, 1985.

12-14. Von Braun, Wernher, *"Institutional Developments,"* Address to the Board of Directors and the Board of Governors, National Space Institute, July 15, 1975.

12-15. Guidry, Vernon A., Jr., *"Von Braun on the Future of Space,"* Von Braun Interview, *Washington Star*, January 20, 1976.

12-16. Stadd, Courtney, Interview by Frederick I. Ordway III, Washington, D.C., December 5, 1989.

12-17. Wilson, Glen P., Interview by Frederick I. Ordway III, Arlington, Virginia, December 7, 1989.

12-18. Garver, Lori B., Interview by Frederick I. Ordway III, Washington, D.C., December 9, 1989.

12-19. Oppenheimer, J. Robert, quoted in Richard Rhodes, *The Making of the Atomic Bomb*, loc. cit. [1-10].

12-20. Sidey, Hugh, Keynote speech at Goddard Memorial Dinner, NASA Goddard Space Flight Center, Greenbelt, Maryland, 1989.

12-21. Michener, James A., Statement before the Subcommittee on Science, Technology, and Space, Committee on Commerce, Science, and Transportation, U.S. Senate, February 1, 1979.

12-22. Von Braun, Wernher, *"The Saturn/Apollo Transportation System,"* Presentation to Life Industrial Group, Titusville, Florida, July 15, 1969.

12-23. Truly, Richard H., Editorial in *Aviation Week and Space Technology*, July 17, 1989.

Chapter 13

13-1. Uhl, Edward G., Interview by Frederick I. Ordway III, Chantilly, Virginia, September 18, 1985.

13-2. Redman, Kayren (formerly Kayren Governale), Interview by Frederick I. Ordway III, Phoenix, Maryland, August 31, 1989.

13-3. Von Braun, Wernher, and Frederick I. Ordway III, *New Worlds: Discoveries from Our Solar System*. Anchor/Doubleday, Garden City, New York, 1979. See also [9-45].

13-4. Hewitt, Charles C., Interview by Frederick I. Ordway III, Alexandria, Virginia, September 30, 1985.

13-5. Giacconi, Riccardo, personal communication to Ernst Stuhlinger, May 7, 1984.

ACRONYMS

AAS	American Astronomical Society; American Astronautical Society
ABMA	Army Ballistic Missile Agency
AEC	Atomic Energy Commission
AF	Air Force
AIAA	American Institute of Aeronautics and Astronautics
ALSEP	Apollo Lunar Surface Experiments Package
ALSOS	(Greek for 'grove') A task force established by Brig. Gen. Leslie R. Groves in 1943 and headed by Lt. Col. Boris Pash to retrieve information, materials, instrumentation, and members of the German atomic energy project immediately after termination of military activities at the end of WW II.
AOMC	Army Ordnance Missile Command
ARDC	Air Research and Development Command
ARPA	Advanced Research Projects Agency
ARS	American Rocket Society
ASTP	Apollo-Soyuz Test Project
ATM	Apollo Telescope Mount
ATS	Application Technology Satellite
B.A.	Bachelor of Arts
BMC	Ballistic Missile Command
BIS	British Interplanetary Society
BOB	Bureau of the Budget
CalTech	California Institute of Technology
CSAGI	Comité spécial de l'année géophysique internationale
CEFSR	Committee for Evaluating the Feasibility of Space Rocketry
CG	Commanding General; Center of Gravity
CIA	Central Intelligence Agency
CIC	Counter Intelligence Corps
COMSAT	Communications Satellite Corporation
CSM	Command and Service Module
CIOS	Combined Intelligence Operations Subcommittee
CM	Command Module
DA	Department of the Army
DAF	Department of the Air Force
DOD	Department of Defense; Development Operations Division
DOE	Department of Energy
EOR	Earth Orbit Rendezvous Mode
ERTS	Earth Resources Technology Satellite
ESP	Electric Space Propulsion
EVA	Extra-vehicular Activities

FAA	Federal Aviation Agency
FBI	Federal Bureau of Investigation
F-1	Rocket Engine of Saturn V First Stage
Galcit	Guggenheim Aeronautical Laboratory, California Institute of Technology
G&C	Guidance and Control
GEO	Geosynchronous Earth Orbit
GESTAPO	Geheime Staatspolizei (Secret National Police)
GMBH	Gesellschaft mit Beschränkter Haft ('Limited')
GMDD	Guided Missile Development Division
GMDG	Guided Missile Development Group
GNP	Gross National Product
GSFC	Goddard Space Flight Center
HAP	Heeres-Anstalt Peenemünde (Army Station Peenemünde)
HEAO	High Energy Astronomical Observatory
HEW	Department of Health, Education, and Welfare
HLV	Heavy Lift Vehicle
HVP	Heeres-Versuchsstelle Peenemünde (Army Test Station Peenemünde)
IAF	International Astronautical Federation
IBM	International Business Machines Corporation
ICBM	Intercontinental Ballistic Missile
ICSU	International Council of Scientific Unions
IGY	International Geophysical Year
IMLEO	Initial Mass in Low-Earth Orbit
INTELSAT	International Telecommunications Satellite Consortium
IOD	Industrial Operations Division
IRBM	Intermediate Range Ballistic Missile
IU	Instrument Unit (of Saturn V)
JATO	Jet-assisted Take-off
JBIS	Journal of the British Interplanetary Society
JP	Jet Propellant
JPL	Jet Propulsion Laboratory
JSC	Johnson Space Center
J-2	Rocket Engine of Saturn V Second and Third Stages
KSC	Kennedy Space Center
KZ	Konzentrationslager (Concentration Camp)
LAGEOS	Laser Geodetic Satellite
LaRC	Langley Research Center
LEM	Lunar Excursion Module
LeRC	Lewis Research Center
LM	Lunar Module
LOC	Launch Operations Center
LOD	Launch Operations Directorate
LOR	Lunar Orbit Rendezvous Mode

LOX	Liquid Oxygen
L-5	Fifth Lagrangean Point of Neutral Gravitational Forces
MAF	Michoud Assembly Facility
MIT	Massachusetts Institute of Technology
MOL	Manned Orbital Laboratory
MOUSE	Minimum Orbital Unmanned Satellite of the Earth
MSC	Manned Spacecraft Center
MSFC	George C. Marshall Space Flight Center
MTF	Mississippi Test Facility
NACA	National Advisory Committee for Aeronautics
NAS	National Academy of Sciences
NASA	National Aeronautics and Space Administration
NCO	Non-commissioned Officer
NEP	Nuclear-electric Propulsion
NERVA	Nuclear Engine for Rocket Vehicle Application
NLS	National Launch System
NRC	National Research Council
NRL	Naval Research Laboratory
NTP	Nuclear-thermal Propulsion
NSB	National Science Board
NSF	National Science Foundation
NSI	National Space Institute
NSS	National Space Society
OART	Office of Advanced Research and Technology
OMB	Office of Management and Budget
OMSF	Office of Manned Space Flight
ONR	Office of Naval Research
OSSA	Office of Space Sciences and Applications
OST	Office of Science and Technology (President's)
PERT	Performance Evaluation and Review Technique
Pfc.	Private First Class
PoP	Prisoner of Peace
PoW	Prisoner of War
PSAC	President's Scientific Advisory Committee
R&D	Research and Development
RL-10	Hydrogen-Oxygen Rocket Engine
RP	Rocket Propellant
RfP	Request for Proposal
RfQ	Request for Quotation
SAC	Strategic Air Command
SEPS	Solar-electric Propulsion System
SINS	Shipboard Inertial Navigation System
SM	Service Module
SRB	Solid Rocket Booster

SRI	Stanford Research Institute
SRM	Solid Rocket Motor
SS	Schutz Staffel (Elite Military Unit of the Nazi Party)
SSME	Space Shuttle Main Engine
SST	Supersonic Transport
STG	Space Task Group
S IC	Stage one of Saturn V
S II	Stage two of Saturn V
S IVB	Stage three of Saturn V
USSR	Union of Soviet Socialist Republics
UT	United Technologies
VAB	Vertical (later, Vehicle) Assembly Building
VE	Victory in Europe
VJ	Victory over Japan
VfR	Verein für Raumschiffahrt (Society for Space Travel)
VKN	Versuchs-Kommando Nord (Test Command North)
WIFO	Wirtschaftliche Forschungsgesellschaft (Economic Research Organization or Council)
WSPG	White Sands Proving Ground

TIMETABLES

TIMETABLE (GERMANY)

	11	12	13	14	15	16	17	18	19	20	21	22	23	24	25	26	27	28	29	30	31	32	33	34	35	36	37	38	39	40	41	42	43	44	45
Head of State	Emperor Wilhelm II							President Ebert							President von Hindenburg								Hitler												
In Charge of Programs																						Army Becker, Dornberger											SS Him Kam	
Von Braun's Superior																											Dornberger			Zanssen					
Von Braun's Position							Student (School)													Stu-dent (Univ.)		Technical Director Rocket Develop. Center													
Von Braun's Residence and Place of Work	Wirsitz								Gumb	Berlin						Ettersburg		Spie		Zu Berlin Rei		Kummersdorf					Peenemünde								

Him: Himmler; Kam: Kammler; Gumb: Gumbinnen; Spie: Spiekeroog; Zu: Zurich (Switzerland); Rei: Reinickendorf

TIMETABLE (USA)

	45	46	47	48	49	50	51	52	53	54	55	56	57	58	59	60	61	62	63	64	65	66	67	68	69	70	71	72	73	74	75	76	77	78
U.S. President	Truman								Eisenhower								Kennedy			Johnson					Nixon						Ford		Carter	
Vice President					Barkley				Nixon								Johnson			Humphrey					Agnew				Ford	Rockefeller			Mondale	
NASA Administrator														Glennan			Webb								Pai		Fletcher						Frosch	
Deputy Administrator														Dryden								Sea-mans		Pai	Low								Lovelace	
Von Braun's Superior			Hamill			Toftoy		Attaya		Chatf		Medaris				Webb				Sea	Holm	Mueller				Newell			Uhl					
Von Braun's Position			Tec. Dir. RDDSR					Tec. Dir. GMDG		Chief GMDD		Director DOD-ABMA				Director Marshall Space Flight Center										Dep. Assoc. Admin.				V.P. Eng. and Develop.				
Von Braun's Place of Work	Fort Bliss, Texas					Huntsville, Alabama																				NASA, Wash.			Fairchild, Germantown					
Director of MSFC																Von Braun										Rees			Petr		Lucas			

Chatf: Chatfield; Sea: Seamans; Holm: Holmes; Pai: Paine; Petr: Petrone.
RDDSR: Army Ordnance Research and Development Division, Suboffice Rocket
GMDG: Guided Missile Development Group
GMDD: Guided Missile Development Division
DOD-ABMA: Development Operations Division, Army Ballistic Missile Agency
MSFC: George C. Marshall Space Flight Center, Huntsville, Alabama

NAME INDEX

SUBJECT INDEX

10

11

14

17